An Introduction
to Measure and
Integration

An Introduction to Measure and Integration

SECOND EDITION

Inder K. Rana

Graduate Studies
in Mathematics

Volume 45

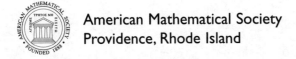

American Mathematical Society
Providence, Rhode Island

2000 *Mathematics Subject Classification.* Primary 28–01;
Secondary 28A05, 28A10, 28A12, 28A15, 28A20, 28A25,
28A33, 28A35, 26A30, 26A42, 26A45, 26A46.

ABSTRACT. This text presents a motivated introduction to the theory of measure and integration. Starting with an historical introduction to the notion of integral and a preview of the Riemann integral, the reader is motivated for the need to study the Lebesgue measure and Lebesgue integral. The abstract integration theory is developed via measure. Other basic topics discussed in the text are Fubini's Theorem, L_p-spaces, Radon-Nikodym Theorem, change of variables formulas, signed and complex measures.

Library of Congress Cataloging-in-Publication Data

Rana, Inder K.

    An introduction to measure and integration / Inder K. Rana.—2nd ed.

      p. cm. — (Graduate texts in mathematics, ISSN 1065-7339 ; v. 45)

    Includes bibliographical references and index.

    ISBN 0-8218-2974-2 (alk. paper)

    1. Lebesgue integral. 2. Measure theory. I. Title. II. Graduate texts in mathematics ; 45.

QA312 .R28   2002

515′.42—dc21

2002018244

Contents

Preface

> *"Mathematics presented as a closed, linearly ordered, system of truths without reference to origin and purpose has its charm and satisfies a philosophical need. But the attitude of introverted science is unsuitable for students who seek intellectual independence rather than indoctrination; disregard for applications and intuition leads to isolation and atrophy of mathematics. It seems extremely important that students and instructors should be protected from smug purism."*

> —— **Richard Courant** and **Fritz John**
> (Introduction to Calculus and Analysis)

This text presents a motivated introduction to the subject which goes under various headings such as Real Analysis, Lebesgue Measure and Integration, Measure Theory, Modern Analysis, Advanced Analysis, and so on.

The subject originated with the doctoral dissertation of the French mathematician Henri Lebesgue and was published in 1902 under the title *Intégrable, Longueur, Aire*. The books of C. Carathéodory [8] and [9], S. Saks [35], I.P. Natanson [27] and P.R. Halmos [14] presented these ideas in a unified way to make them accessible to mathematicians. Because of its fundamental importance and its applications in diverse branches of mathematics, the subject has become a part of the graduate level curriculum.

Historically, the theory of Lebesgue integration evolved in an effort to remove some of the drawbacks of the Riemann integral (see Chapter 1). However, most of the time in a course on Lebesgue measure and integration, the connection between the two notions of integrals comes up only

after about half the course is over (assuming that the course is of one se-
mester). In this text, after a review of the Riemann integral, the reader is
acquainted with the need to extend it. Possible methods to carry out this
extension are sketched before the actual theory is presented. This approach
has given satisfying results to the author in teaching this subject over the
years and hence the urge to write this text. The nucleus for the text was
provided by the lecture notes of the courses I taught at Kurukshetra University (India), University of Khartoum (Sudan), South Gujarat University
(India) and the Indian Institute of Technology Bombay (India). These notes
were slowly augmented with additional material so as to cover topics which
have applications in other branches of mathematics. The end product is a
text which includes many informal comments and is written in a lecture-note
style. Any new concept is introduced only when it is needed in the logical
development of the subject and it is discussed informally before the exact
definition appears. The subject matter is developed by motivating examples
and probing questions, as is normally done while teaching. I have tried to
avoid slick proofs. Often a proof is either divided into steps or is presented
in such a way that the main ideas of the proof emerge before the details
follow.

Summary of the text

The text opens with a **Prologue** on the length function and its properties
which are basic for the development of the subject.

  Chapter 1 begins with a detailed review of the Riemann integral and its
properties. This includes Lebesgue's characterization of Riemann integrable
functions. It is followed by a brief discussion on the historical development of
the integral from antiquity (around 300 B.C.) to the times of Riemann (1850
A.D.). For a detailed account the reader may refer to Bourbaki [6], Hawkins
[16] and Kline [20]. The main aim of the historical notes is to make young
readers aware of the fact that mathematical concepts arise out of physical
problems and that it can take centuries for a concept to evolve. This section
also includes Riemann's example of an integrable function having an infinite
number of discontinuities and a proof of the fundamental theorem of calculus
due to G. Darboux. The next section of Chapter 1 has a discussion about
the drawbacks of the Riemann integral, including the example due to Vito
Volterra (1881) of a differentiable function $f : [0, 1] \longrightarrow \mathbb{R}$ whose derivative
function is bounded but is not Riemann integrable. These considerations
made mathematicians look for an extension of the Riemann integral and
eventually led to the construction of the Lebesgue integral.

  Chapter 2 discusses two significantly different approaches for extending
the notion of the Riemann integral. The one due to H. Lebesgue is sketched

in this chapter and is discussed in detail in the rest of the book. The second is due to P.J. Daniel [10] and F. Riesz [32], an outline of which is given. These discussions motivate the reader to consider an extension of the length function from the class of intervals to a larger class of subsets of $\mathbb{R}$.

Chapters 3, 4 and 5 form the core of the subject: extension of measures and the construction of the integral in the general setting with the Lebesgue measure and the Lebesgue integral being the motivating example. The process of extension of additive set functions (known as the Carathéodory extension theory) is discussed in the abstract setting in **Chapter 3.** This chapter also includes a result due to S.M. Ulam [41] which rules out the possibility of extending (in a meaningful way) the length function to all subsets of $\mathbb{R}$, under the assumption of the Continuum Hypothesis.

The outcomes of the general extension theory, as developed in Chapter 3, are harvested for the particular case of the real line and the length function in **Chapter 4**. This gives the required extension of the length function, namely, the Lebesgue measure. Special properties of the Lebesgue measure and Lebesgue measurable sets (the collection of sets on which the Lebesgue measure is defined by the extension theory) with respect to the topology and the group structure on the real line are discussed in detail. The final section of the chapter includes a discussion about the impossibility of extending the length function to all subsets of $\mathbb{R}$ under the assumption of the Axiom of Choice.

In **Chapter 5,** the construction of the extended notion of integral is discussed. Once again, the motivation comes from the particular case of functions on the real line. Lebesgue's recipe, as outlined in Chapter 2, is carried out for the abstract setting. The particular case gives the required integral, namely, the Lebesgue integral. The space $L_1[a, b]$ of Lebesgue integrable function on an interval $[a, b]$ is shown to include $\mathcal{R}[a, b]$, the space of Riemann integrable functions, the Lebesgue integral agreeing with the Riemann integral on $\mathcal{R}[a, b]$. Also, it is shown that $L_1[a, b]$ is the completion of $\mathcal{R}[a, b]$ under the L_1-metric. The final section of the chapter discusses the relation between the Lebesgue integral and the improper Riemann integral.

Chapter 6 gives a complete proof of the fundamental theorem of calculus for the Lebesgue integral. (This theorem characterizes the pair of functions F, f such that F is the indefinite integral of f. This removes one of the main drawbacks of Riemann integration.) As applications of the fundamental theorem of calculus, the chain-rule and integration by substitution for the Lebesgue integral are discussed.

The remaining chapters of the book include special topics. **Chapter 7** deals with the topic of measure and integration on product spaces, with

Fubini's theorem occupying the central position. The particular case of Lebesgue measure on $\mathbb{R}^2$ and its properties are discussed in detail.

Chapter 8 starts with extending the concept of integral to complex valued functions. The remaining sections discuss various methods of analyzing the convergence of sequences of measurable functions. The L_p-spaces and discussion of some of their dense subspaces in the special case of the Lebesgue measure space are also included in this chapter. The last section of the chapter includes a brief discussion on the application of Lebesgue integration to Fourier series.

Chapter 9 includes a discussion of the Radon-Nikodym theorem. As an application, the change of variable formulas for Lebesgue integration on $\mathbb{R}^n$ are derived.

In **Chapter 10,** the additive set functions, which are not necessarily nonnegative or even real-valued, are discussed. The main aim is to prove the Hahn decomposition theorem and the Lebesgue decomposition theorem. As a consequence, an alternative proof of the Radon-Nikodym theorem is given. This chapter also includes a discussion of complex measures.

The text has three appendices. **Appendix E** gives a proof of the singular value decomposition of matrices, needed in sections 7.4 and 9.3. In **Appendix F**, functions of bounded variation (needed in section 6.1) are discussed. **Appendix G** includes a discussion of differentiable transformation and a proof of the inverse function theorem, needed in section 9.3. (In the present edition four more appendices, A,B,C and D, have been added.)

The text is sprinkled with 200 exercises, most of which either include a hint or are broken into doable steps. Exercises marked with • are needed in later discussions. The sections and exercises marked with * can be omitted on first reading. Some of the results in the text are credited to the discoverer, but no effort is made to trace the origin of each result. In any case, no originality is claimed.

Prerequisites and course plans

The text assumes that the reader has undergone a first course in mathematical analysis (roughly equivalent to that of first five chapters of Apostol [2]). The text as such can be used for a one-year course. A recipe for a one-semester course (approximately 40 lecture hours and 10 problem discussion hours) on Lebesgue measure and integration is given after the preface. Since the text is in a lecture-note style, it is also suitable for an individual self-study program. For such readers, the chart depicting the logical interdependence of the chapters will be useful.

Acknowledgments

It is difficult to list all the individuals and authors who have influenced and helped me in preparing this text, directly or indirectly. First of all I would like to thank my teacher and doctoral thesis advisor, Prof. K.R. Parthasarathy (Indian Statistical Institute, Delhi), whose lectures at the University of Bombay (Mumbai) and the Indian Statistical Institute (Delhi), clarified many concepts and kindled my interest in the subject. I learned much from his style of teaching and mathematical exposition.

Some of the texts which have influenced me in one form or another are Halmos [14], Royden [34], Hewitt and Stromberg [18], Aliprantis and Burkinshaw [1], Friedman [13] and Parthasarathy [28].

I am indebted to the students to whom I have taught this subject over the years for their reactions, remarks, comments and suggestions which have helped in deciding on the style of presentation of the text.

It is a pleasure to acknowledge the support and encouragement I received from my friend Prof. S. Kumaresan (University of Bombay) at various stages in the preparation of this text. He also went through the text, weeding out misprints and mistakes. I am also thankful to my friend Dr. S. Purkayastha (Indian Institute of Technology Bombay) for going through the typeset manuscript and suggesting many improvements. For any shortcoming still left in the text, the author is solely responsible.

I thank C.L. Anthony for processing the entire manuscript in LaTeX. The hard job of preparing the figures was done by P. Devaraj, I am thankful for his help. Thanks are also due to the Department of Mathematics, IIT Bombay for the use of Computer Lab and photocopying facilities. I would like to thank the Curriculum Development Program of the Indian Institute of Technology Bombay for the financial support to prepare the first version of the manuscript. The technical advice received from the production department of Narosa Publishers in preparing the camera ready copy of the manuscript is acknowledged with thanks.

Special thanks are due to my family: my wife Lalita for her help in more ways than one; and my parents for allowing me to choose my career and for their love and encouragement in pursuing the same. It is to them that this book is dedicated.

Finally, I would be grateful for critical comments and suggestions for later improvements.

Mumbai, 1997

Preface to the Second Edition

In revising the first edition, I have resisted the temptation of adding more topics to the text. The main aim has been to rectify the defects of the first edition:

- Efforts have been made to remove the typos and correct the mismatched cross references. I hope there are none now.

- In view of the feedback received from students, at many places phrases like 'trivial to verify', 'easy to see', etc have been expanded with explanations.

- Sequencing of topics in some of the chapters has been altered to make the development of the subject matter more consistent.

- Short notes have been added to give a glimpse of the link between measure theory and probability theory.

- More exercises have been added.

- Four new appendices have been added.

While preparing the first edition of this book, I was often questioned about the 'utility' of spending my valuable 'research time' on writing a book. The response of the students to the first edition and the reviewers' comments have confirmed my confidence that writing a book is as valuable as doing research. I thank all the reviewers of the first edition for their encouraging remarks. Their constructive criticism has helped me a lot in preparing this edition.

I would like to thank Mr. N. K. Mehra, Narosa Publishers, for agreeing to copublish this edition with the AMS.

I take pleasure in offering thanks to Edward G. Dunne, Acquisitions Editor, Book Program AMS, for the help and encouragement received from him.

I thank the editorial and the technical support staff of the AMS for their help and cooperation in preparing this edition.

Once again, the help received from P. Devraj in revising the figures is greatly appreciated. Thanks are also due to Mr. C.L. Anthony and Clarity Reprographers & Traders for typesetting the manuscript in LaTeX.

I would greatly appreciate comments/suggestions from students and teachers about the present edition. I intend to post comments/corrections on the present edition on my homepage at

www.math.iitb.ac.in/∼ikr/books.html

Mumbai, 2002   **Inder K. Rana**

Recipe for a one semester course and interdependence of the chapters

*Lebesgue measure and integration
(40 lectures and 10 problem/discussion hours)

Prologue: Everything

Chapter 1:   Sections 1.1 and 1.2 (depending upon the background of the students), 1.3 and 1.4 can be left for self study.

Chapter 2:   Sections 2.1 and 2.2.

Chapter 3:   Sections 3.1 to 3.3; 3.5 to 3.9; 3.10 and 3.11 (omitting the proofs).

Chapter 4:   Sections 4.1 to 4.3; 4.4 and 4.5 (omitting the proofs); 4.6.

Chapter 5:   Sections 5.1 to 5.6; Parts of 5.7 to 5.9 can be included depending upon the background of students and the emphasis of the course.

Chapter 6:   Sections 6.1; 6.2 (omitting proofs); 6.3 (stating the theorem 6.3.6 and giving applications: 6.3.8, 6.3.10 to 6.3.13, 6.3.16 (omitting proof).

Chapter 7:   Sections 7.1 to 7.4.

Interdependence of the chapters

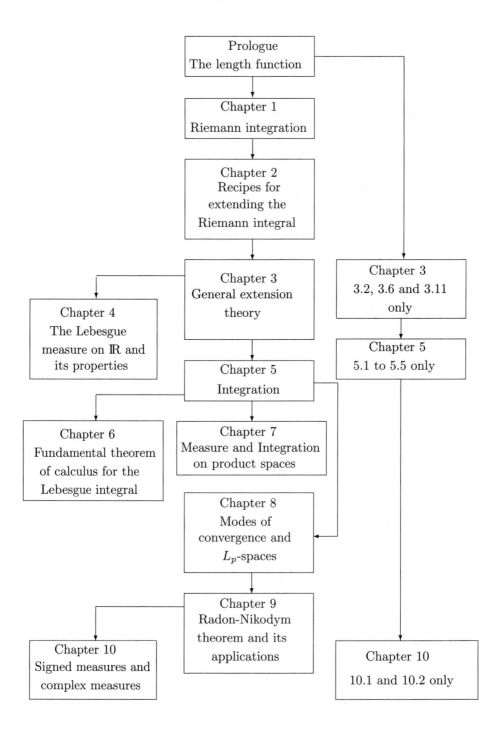

Notations used in the text

The three digit system is used to number the definitions, theorems, propositions, lemmas, exercises, notes and remarks. For example, Theorem 3.2.4 is the 4th numbered statement in section 2 of chapter 3.

The symbol ■ is used to indicate the end of a proof. The symbol $A := B$ or $B =: A$ means that this equality is the definition of A by B. The symbol • before an exercise means that this exercise will be needed in the later discussions. Sections, theorems, propositions, etc., which are marked * can be omitted on first reading.

The phrase "the following are equivalent:" means each of the listed statement implies the other. For example in Theorem 1.1.4, it means that each of the statements (i), (ii) and (iii) implies the other.

The notations and symbols used from logic and elementary analysis are as follows:

$\Longrightarrow$	:	implies; gives
$\not\Longrightarrow$	:	does not imply
$\Longleftrightarrow$	:	implies and is implied by; if and only if
$\exists$	:	there exists
$\forall$	:	for all; for every
$x \in A$	:	x belongs to A
$x \notin A$	:	x does not belong to A
$A \subset B$	:	A is a proper subset of B
$A \subseteq B$	:	A is a subset of B
$\mathcal{P}(X)$	:	set of all subsets of X

$\emptyset$:   empty set
$A \setminus B$:   set of elements of A not in B
$A \times B$:   Cartesian product of A and B
$\prod\limits_{i=1}^{n} X_i$:   Cartesian product of sets $X_1, \ldots, X_n$.
$\inf$:   infimum
$\sup$:   supremum
$\bigcup, \cup$:   union
$\bigcap, \cap$:   intersection
$\triangle$:   symmetric difference
A^c :   complement of a set A
$\overline{E}$:   closure of a set E
∂E :   boundary points of a set E
$\limsup\limits_{n \to \infty}$:   limit superior; upper limit
$\liminf\limits_{n \to \infty}$:   limit inferior; lower limit

$$\left. \begin{array}{l} f : X \longrightarrow Y \\ \quad x \longmapsto y \end{array} \right\} : f \text{ is a function from } X \text{ into } Y \text{ and } f(x) = y.$$

$\mathbb{N}$:   the set of natural numbers
$\mathbb{Z}$:   the set of integers
$\mathbb{Q}$:   the set of rational numbers
$\mathbb{R}$:   the set of real numbers
$\mathbb{R}^*$:   the set of extended real numbers
$\mathbb{C}$:   the set of complex numbers
$\mathbb{R}^n$: n-dimensional Euclidean space
$|x|$:   absolute value of x

$$\left. \begin{array}{l} (a,b), (a,b], [a,b), [a,b], (-\infty, \infty), \\ (-\infty, a), (-\infty, a], (a, \infty), [a, \infty) \end{array} \right\} : \text{intervals in } \mathbb{R}.$$

$\{a_n\}_{n \geq 1}$: sequence with n^{th} term a_n.
(X, d) : a metric space.

For the list of other symbols used in the text, see the symbol index given at the end of the text.

The length function

We denote the set of real numbers by $\mathbb{R}$. Let $\mathbb{R}^*$ denote the set of **extended real numbers.** (See appendix A for details.)

Let $\mathcal{I}$ denote the collection of all intervals of $\mathbb{R}$. If an interval $I \in \mathcal{I}$ has end points a and b we write it as $I(a, b)$. By convention, the open interval $(a, a) = \emptyset \ \forall \ a \in \mathbb{R}$. Let $[0, +\infty] := \{x \in \mathbb{R}^* | x \geq 0\} = [0, +\infty) \cup \{+\infty\}$. Define the function $\lambda : \mathcal{I} \longrightarrow [0, \infty]$ by

$$\lambda(I(a, b)) := \begin{cases} |b - a| & \text{if } a, b \in \mathbb{R}, \\ +\infty & \text{if either } a = -\infty \text{ or } b = +\infty \text{ or both.} \end{cases}$$

The function λ, as defined above, is called the **length function** and has the following properties:

Property (1): $\lambda(\emptyset) = 0$.

Property (2): $\lambda(I) \leq \lambda(J)$ *if* $I \subseteq J$.

This is called the **monotonicity property** of λ (or one says that λ is **monotone**) and is easy to verify.

Property (3): *Let* $I \in \mathcal{I}$ *be such that* $I = \bigcup_{i=1}^{n} J_i$, *where* $J_i \cap J_j = \emptyset$ *for* $i \neq j$. *Then*

$$\lambda(I) = \sum_{i=1}^{n} \lambda(J_i).$$

This property of λ is called the **finite additivity of** λ, or one says that λ is **finitely additive**.

To prove this, let I be an infinite interval. Then at least one of the J_i's is an infinite interval and hence $\lambda(I) = +\infty = \sum_{i=1}^{n} \lambda(J_i)$. Next, let I be a finite interval with end points a and $b, a < b$. Then each J_i is a finite interval with end points, say, a_i and b_i where $a_i < b_i$. We may assume, without loss of generality, that $a = a_1 < b_1 = a_2 < b_2 = \cdots = a_n < b_n = b$. Then

$$\lambda(I) = b - a = b_n - a_1 = \sum_{i=1}^{n} (b_i - a_i) = \sum_{i=1}^{n} \lambda(J_i).$$

Property (4): *Let $I \in \mathcal{I}$ be a finite interval such that $I \subseteq \bigcup_{i=1}^{\infty} I_i$, where $I_i \in \mathcal{I}$. Then*

$$\lambda(I) \leq \sum_{i=1}^{\infty} \lambda(I_i).$$

To prove this, we note that if I_i is an infinite interval for some i, then clearly $\lambda(I) \leq +\infty = \sum_{i=1}^{\infty} \lambda(I_i)$. So, assume that each I_i is a finite interval. We further assume for the time being that $I = [a, b]$ and that each I_i is an open interval. Then by the Heine-Borel theorem, there exists some n such that $I \subseteq \bigcup_{i=1}^{n} I_i$. Let $I_i = (a_i, b_i), i = 1, 2, \ldots, n$. Since $a \in I$, there exists some i such that $a \in I_i$. We rename this interval as I_1. If $b \in I_1$, then $\lambda(I) \leq \lambda(I_1) \leq \sum_{i=1}^{\infty} \lambda(I_i)$ and we are through. If not, then $b_1 < b$ and hence $b_1 \in I_i$ for some $i \geq 2$. Proceeding this way, we will have

$$a_1 < a < b_1 < b_2 < \ldots b_{m-1} < b < b_m,$$

for some $m \leq n$, and $a_i < b_{i-1}$ for $i \geq 2$. Hence

$$
\begin{aligned}
\lambda(I) &= b - a \\
&\leq b_m - a_1 \\
&= \sum_{i=2}^{m} (b_i - b_{i-1}) + b_1 - a_1 \\
&\leq \sum_{i=2}^{m} (b_i - a_i) + (b_1 - a_1) \\
&= \sum_{i=1}^{m} \lambda(I_i) \leq \sum_{i=1}^{\infty} \lambda(I_i).
\end{aligned}
$$

In the general case when I is an arbitrary finite interval, given any real number $\epsilon > 1$, we can find a closed interval $J \subset I$ such that $\epsilon \lambda(J) = \lambda(I)$ and an open interval $J_n \supseteq I_n$ such that $\lambda(J_n) = \epsilon \lambda(I_n)$ for every $n \geq 1$. Then $J \subseteq \bigcup_{n=1}^{\infty} J_n$ and by the earlier case, $\lambda(J) \leq \sum_{n=1}^{\infty} \lambda(J_n)$. Hence

$$\lambda(I) = \epsilon \lambda(J) \leq \epsilon \sum_{n=1}^{\infty} \lambda(J_n) = \epsilon^2 \sum_{n=1}^{\infty} \lambda(I_n).$$

Since this holds for every $\epsilon > 1$, letting $\epsilon \to 1$, we get

$$\lambda(I) \leq \sum_{n=1}^{\infty} \lambda(I_n).$$

Property (5): *Let $I \in \mathcal{I}$ be a finite interval such that $I = \bigcup_{n=1}^{\infty} I_n$, where $I_n \in \mathcal{I}$ and $I_n \cap I_m = \emptyset$ for $n \neq m$. Then*

$$\lambda(I) = \sum_{n=1}^{\infty} \lambda(I_n).$$

To see this, we note that by property (4), $\lambda(I) \leq \sum_{n=1}^{\infty} \lambda(I_n)$. To prove the reverse inequality, let I have left-endpoint a and right-endpoint b. Let I_i have left-endpoint a_i and right-endpoint $b_i, i \geq 1$. Since $I_n \cap I_m = \emptyset$ for $n \neq m$, we can assume without loss of generality that $\forall\, k \geq 1$,

$$a \leq a_1 < b_1 \leq a_2 \leq \ldots \leq b_k \leq b.$$

Then for every $k \geq 1$ we have

$$\sum_{n=1}^{k} \lambda(I_n) = \sum_{n=1}^{k} (b_n - a_n) \leq (b - a) \leq \lambda(I).$$

Hence $\sum_{n=1}^{\infty} \lambda(I_n) \leq \lambda(I)$.

Property (6): *Let $I \in \mathcal{I}$ be any interval. Then*
$$\lambda(I) = \sum_{n=-\infty}^{\infty} \lambda(I \cap [n, n+1)).$$

If I is a finite interval, then $I = \bigcup_{n=k}^{\ell} (I \cap [n, n+1))$ for some integers k and ℓ, and by property (5) we have the required property. If I is an infinite interval, then $\lambda(I) = +\infty$ and for an infinite number of n's we will have $I \cap [n, n+1) = [n, n+1)$. Thus

$$\sum_{n=-\infty}^{+\infty} \lambda(I \cap [n, n+1)) = +\infty = \lambda(I).$$

Property (7): *Let $I \in \mathcal{I}$ be any interval such that $I = \bigcup_{n=1}^{\infty} I_n$, $I_n \in \mathcal{I}$ and $I_n \cap I_m = \emptyset$ for $n \neq m$. Then*

$$\lambda(I) = \sum_{n=1}^{\infty} \lambda(I_n).$$

This property of λ is called the **countable additivity of** λ, or one says that λ is **countably additive**. If I is finite, we have already proved it in property (5). If I is infinite, we use properties (5) and (6) to obtain the required equality.

Property (8): *Let $I \in \mathcal{I}$ and $I \subseteq \bigcup_{n=1}^{\infty} I_n$, $I_n \in \mathcal{I}$. Then*

$$\lambda(I) \leq \sum_{n=1}^{\infty} \lambda(I_n).$$

This property of λ is called the **countable subadditivity** of λ, or one says that λ is **countably subadditive**. When I is a finite interval, we have already proved it in property (4). The only case we have to consider is when I is infinite and all the I_n's are finite. In this case, we write

$$I = \bigcup_{k=-\infty}^{+\infty} (I \cap [k, k+1))$$

and note that for every k, $I \cap [k, k+1) \subseteq \bigcup_{n=1}^{\infty}(I_n \cap [k, k+1))$. Using properties (5) and (6), we have

$$
\begin{aligned}
\lambda(I) &= \sum_{k=-\infty}^{+\infty} \lambda(I \cap [k, k+1)) \\
&\leq \sum_{k=-\infty}^{+\infty} \sum_{n=1}^{\infty} \lambda(I_n \cap [k, k+1)) \\
&= \sum_{n=1}^{\infty} \sum_{k=-\infty}^{+\infty} \lambda(I_n \cap [k, k+1)) \\
&= \sum_{n=1}^{\infty} \lambda(I_n).
\end{aligned}
$$

The above properties show that λ, the length function, is a nonnegative, monotone, countably additive and countably subadditive function. We remark that $\lambda(\{x\}) = 0$ for every $x \in \mathbb{R}$, for $\{x\} = [x, x]$. Finally, we state a property of λ which depends upon the group structure on $\mathbb{R}$.

Property (9): $\lambda(I) = \lambda(I + x)$, *for every $I \in \mathcal{I}$ and $x \in \mathbb{R}$, where $I + x :=$* $\{y + x \mid y \in I\}$.

This property of the length function is called **translation invariance**, or one says that λ is **translation invariant**.

Chapter 1

Riemann integration

1.1. The Riemann integral: A review

The geometric problem that leads to the concept of Riemann integral is the following: given a bounded function $f : [a, b] \longrightarrow \mathbb{R}$, how to define the area of the region bounded by the graph of the function and the lines $x = a$ and $x = b$? For example if $f(x) \geq 0$ and $a \leq x \leq b$, one would like to find the area of the region (Figure 1)

$$S(f) := \{(x, y) \in \mathbb{R}^2 \,|\, a \leq x \leq b, \ 0 \leq y \leq f(x)\}.$$

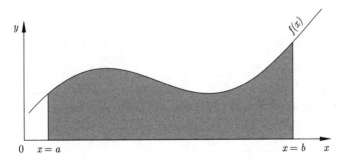

Figure 1: Area $S(f)$

Heuristically, this can be done by approximating the required area by the union of rectangular areas from the inside and outside of $S(f)$ (see Figures 2 and 3). The required area is then captured between these approximating areas. As the number of rectangles is 'increased', one gets 'better' approximations and one hopes to find the required area by a 'limiting' process. These intuitive ideas can be made precise as follows.

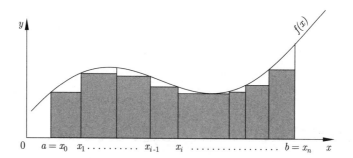

Figure 2: Approximation from inside

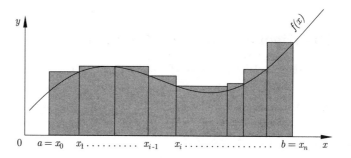

Figure 3: Approximation from outside

Throughout this section, $f : [a, b] \longrightarrow \mathbb{R}$ will be a fixed bounded function. A finite set of points $P = \{x_0, x_1, \ldots, x_n\}$ is called a **partition** of $[a, b]$ if

$$a = x_0 < x_1 < \cdots < x_n = b.$$

For a partition $P = \{x_0, x_1, \ldots, x_n\}$ of $[a, b]$,

$$\|P\| := \max_{1 \leq i \leq n} \{(x_i - x_{i-1})\}$$

is called the **norm of the partition** P. Let $P = \{x_0, x_1, \ldots, x_n\}$ be a partition of $[a, b]$. Let

$$m_i := \inf\{f(x) \mid x_{i-1} \leq x \leq x_i\}$$

and

$$M_i := \sup\{f(x) \mid x_{i-1} \leq x \leq x_i\}.$$

Define

$$L(P, f) := \sum_{i=1}^{n} m_i(x_i - x_{i-1})$$

and

$$U(P, f) := \sum_{i=1}^{n} M_i(x_i - x_{i-1}).$$

Since f is assumed to be bounded, each m_i and $M_i, 1 \le i \le n$, exists and hence each of $L(P, f)$ and $U(P, f)$ is well-defined. The numbers $U(P, f)$ and $L(P, f)$ are called, respectively, the **upper sum** and the **lower sum** of f with respect to the partition P. Geometrically, $L(P, f)$ approximates the required area from 'inside' (see Figure 2), and $U(P, f)$ approximates the required area from 'outside' (see Figure 3).

If P_1 and P_2 are two partitions of $[a, b]$ such that $P_1 \subseteq P_2$, i.e., every point in P_1 is also a point in P_2, then P_2 is called a **refinement** of P_1. Given any two partitions P_1 and P_2, $P_1 \cup P_2$ is also a partition of $[a, b]$. In fact, $P_1 \cup P_2$ is a refinement of both P_1 and P_2 and is called the **common refinement** of P_1 and P_2. We first prove the intuitively obvious result: as we refine a partition, the approximations $U(P, f)$ and $L(P, f)$ improve.

1.1.1. Proposition:

(i) *For every partition P of $[a, b]$,*

$$m(b - a) \le L(P, f) \le U(P, f) \le M(b - a),$$

where $m := \inf\{f(x) \mid a \le x \le b\}$ and $M := \sup\{f(x) \mid a \le x \le b\}$.

(ii) *For any two partitions P_1 and P_2 of $[a, b]$, if P_2 is a refinement of P_1, then*

$$L(P_1, f) \le L(P_2, f) \le U(P_2, f) \le U(P_1, f).$$

(iii) *For any two partitions P_1 and P_2 of $[a, b]$,*

$$L(P_1, f) \le U(P_2, f).$$

(iv) *Let*

$$\alpha := \sup\{L(P, f) \mid P \text{ a partition of } [a, b]\}$$

and

$$\beta := \inf\{U(P, f) \mid P \text{ a partition of } [a, b]\}.$$

Then both α and β exist, and $\alpha \le \beta$.

Proof: (i) Let $P = \{x_0, x_1, \cdots, x_n\}$ be any partition of $[a, b]$. If $m_i := \inf\{f(x) \mid x_{i-1} \le x \le x_i\}$ and $M_i := \sup\{f(x) \mid x_{i-1} \le x \le x_i\}$, then $m \le m_i \le M_i \le M$ for $1 \le i \le n$. Thus (see Figure 4)

$$m(x_i - x_{i-1}) \le m_i(x_i - x_{i-1}) \le M_i(x_i - x_{i-1}) \le M(x_i - x_{i-1}).$$

Hence

$$m(b - a) \le \sum_{i=1}^{n} m_i(x_i - x_{i-1}) \le \sum_{i=1}^{n} M_i(x_i - x_{i-1}) \le M(b - a).$$

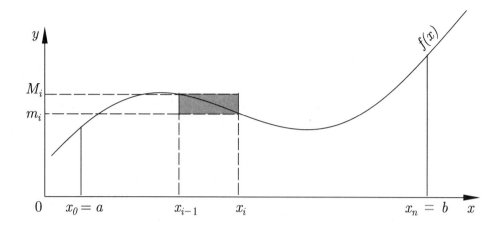

Figure 4

This proves (i).

(ii) Let P_1 and P_2 be any two partitions of $[a, b]$ such that P_2 is a refinement of P_1. First consider the case that the partition P_2 has just one point more than P_1 (see Figure 5).

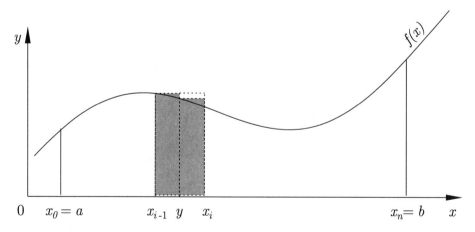

Figure 5

Let $P_1 = \{x_0, x_1, \cdots, x_{i-1}, x_i, \cdots, x_n\}$ and $P_2 = \{x_0, x_1, \cdots, x_{i-1}, y, x_i, \cdots, x_n\}$. It is easy to see that

$$\sup\{f(x) \,|\, x_{i-1} \leq x \leq y\} \leq \sup\{f(x) \,|\, x_{i-1} \leq x \leq x_i\}$$

and

$$\sup\{f(x) \,|\, y \le x \le x_i\} \le \sup\{f(x) \,|\, x_{i-1} \le x \le x_i\}.$$

Hence

$$
\begin{aligned}
U(P_1, f) &= \sum_{j=1}^{n} \sup\{f(x) \,|\, x_{j-1} \le x \le x_j\}(x_j - x_{j-1}) \\
&= \sum_{\substack{j=1 \\ j \ne i}}^{n} \sup\{f(x) \,|\, x_{j-1} \le x \le x_j\}(x_j - x_{j-1}) \\
&\qquad + \sup\{f(x) \,|\, x_{i-1} \le x \le x_i\}(x_i - x_{i-1}) \\
&= \sum_{\substack{j=1 \\ j \ne i}}^{n} \sup\{f(x) \,|\, x_{j-1} \le x \le x_j\}(x_j - x_{j-1}) \\
&\qquad + \sup\{f(x) \,|\, x_{i-1} \le x \le x_i\}(x_i - y) \\
&\qquad + \sup\{f(x) \,|\, x_{i-1} \le x \le x_i\}(y - x_{i-1}) \\
&\ge \sum_{\substack{j=1 \\ j \ne i}}^{n} \sup\{f(x) \,|\, x_{j-1} \le x \le x_j\}(x_j - x_{j-1}) \\
&\qquad + \sup\{f(x) \,|\, x_i \le x \le y\}(x_i - y) \\
&\qquad + \sup\{f(x) \,|\, x_{i-1} \le x \le y\}(y - x_{i-1}) \\
&= U(P_2, f).
\end{aligned}
$$

In case P_2 has k extra points, the above argument repeated k times will show that $U(P_1, f) \ge U(P_2, f)$ whenever P_2 is a refinement of P_1. Similar arguments will prove that $L(P_2, f) \ge L(P_1, f)$. This proves (ii).

(iii) Let P_1 and P_2 be any two partitions. Then by (ii),

$$L(P_1, f) \le L(P_1 \cup P_2, f) \le U(P_1 \cup P_2, f) \le U(P_2, f).$$

This proves (iii).

(iv) Let

$$\mathcal{L} := \{L(P, f) \,|\, P \text{ a partition of } [a, b]\}$$

and

$$\mathcal{U} := \{U(P, f) \,|\, P \text{ a partition of } [a, b]\}.$$

Since $\mathcal{L}$ and $\mathcal{U}$ are nonempty bounded subsets of $\mathbb{R}$, α and β exist. Clearly, $\alpha \le \beta$. ∎

1.1.2. Definition: Let $f : [a, b] \longrightarrow \mathbb{R}$ be a bounded function. The real numbers

$$\underline{\int_a^b} f(x)dx := \sup\{L(P, f) \,|\, P \text{ a partition of } f\}$$

and

$$\overline{\int_a^b} f(x)dx := \inf\{U(P, f) \,|\, P \text{ a partition of } f\}$$

are called the **lower integral** and the **upper integral** of f, respectively. The function f is said to be **Riemann integrable** on $[a, b]$ if

$$\underline{\int_a^b} f(x)dx = \overline{\int_a^b} f(x)dx.$$

The common value in that case is called the **Riemann integral** of f over $[a, b]$ and is denoted by

$$\int_a^b f(x)dx := \underline{\int_a^b} f(x)dx = \overline{\int_a^b} f(x)dx.$$

1.1.3. Examples:

(i) Let $f : [a, b] \longrightarrow \mathbb{R}$ be the constant function, $f(x) \equiv c$. Then for every partition P of $[a, b]$, $U(P, f) = L(P, f) = c(b - a)$. Hence f is Riemann integrable and

$$\int_a^b f(x)dx = c(b - a).$$

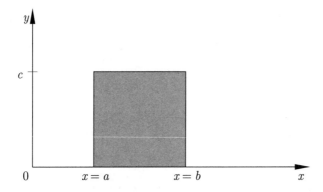

Figure 6

(ii) Let $f : [0, a] \longrightarrow \mathbb{R}$ be defined by $f(x) = x$. Let us consider the partitions $P_n := \{0, a/n, 2a/n, \cdots, (n-1)a/n, a\}, n \geq 1$. Clearly,

$$
\begin{aligned}
U(P_n, f) &= \sum_{j=1}^{n} \left(\frac{ja}{n}\right) \frac{a}{n} \\
&= \frac{a^2}{n^2} \sum_{j=1}^{n} j \\
&= \frac{a^2}{n^2} \left[\frac{n(n+1)}{2}\right] \\
&= \frac{a^2}{2} \left(\frac{n+1}{n}\right).
\end{aligned}
$$

Similarly,

$$
L(P_n, f) = \frac{a^2}{2} \left(\frac{n-1}{n}\right).
$$

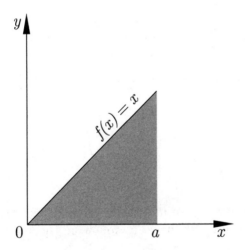

Figure 7

It is easy to see that $\{U(P_n, f)\}_{n\geq 1}$ is a decreasing sequence and $\{L(P_n, f)\}_{n\geq 1}$ is an increasing sequence. Hence

$$
\sup_{n\geq 1}\{L(P_n, f)\} = \lim_{n\to\infty} \frac{a^2}{2} \left(\frac{n-1}{n}\right) = \frac{a^2}{2}
$$

and

$$
\inf_{n\geq 1} \{U(P_n, f)\} = \lim_{n\to\infty} \frac{a^2}{2} \left(\frac{n+1}{n}\right) = \frac{a^2}{2}.
$$

Thus

$$\begin{aligned}
\frac{a^2}{2} &= \sup_{n \geq 1} \{L(P_n, f)\} \\
&\leq \sup_{P} \{L(P, f)\} = \underline{\int_0^a} f(x)dx \\
&\leq \inf_{P} \{U(P, f)\} \\
&\leq \inf_{n \geq 1} \{U(P_n, f)\} = \overline{\int_0^a} f(x)dx \\
&= \frac{a^2}{2}.
\end{aligned}$$

Hence f is Riemann integrable and

$$\int_0^a f(x)dx = \frac{a^2}{2}.$$

(iii) Let $f : [a, b] \longrightarrow \mathbb{R}$ be defined by

$$f(x) := \begin{cases} 0 & \text{if } x \text{ is a rational,} \quad a \leq x \leq b, \\ 1 & \text{if } x \text{ is an irrational,} \quad a \leq x \leq b. \end{cases}$$

It is easy to see that for any partition P of $[a, b]$, $U(P, f) = (b - a)$ and $L(P, f) = 0$. Hence

$$\underline{\int_a^b} f(x)dx = 0 < (b - a) = \overline{\int_a^b} f(x)dx.$$

Thus f is not Riemann integrable.

In general, it is not easy to compute the upper and the lower integrals of a function and verify its integrability. The following theorem is very useful for such verifications.

1.1.4. Theorem: *Let $f : [a, b] \longrightarrow \mathbb{R}$ be a bounded function. The following statements are equivalent:*

(i) *f is Riemann integrable.*

(ii) *For every $\epsilon > 0$ there exists a partition P of $[a, b]$ such that*

$$U(P, f) - L(P, f) < \epsilon.$$

(iii) *There exists a unique real number α such that for every partition P of $[a, b]$*

$$L(P, f) \leq \alpha \leq U(P, f).$$

Proof: We shall prove that (i) $\Leftrightarrow$ (ii) and (iii) $\Leftrightarrow$ (i).

Suppose (i) holds and $\epsilon > 0$ is arbitrary. By definition, there exist partitions P_1 and P_2 of $[a, b]$ such that

$$U(P_2, f) - \epsilon/2 \; < \; \int_a^b f(x)dx \; < \; L(P_1, f) + \epsilon/2.$$

Let $P := P_1 \cup P_2$. Then

$$U(P, f) - L(P, f) \; \leq \; U(P_2, f) - L(P_1, f) \; \leq \; \epsilon.$$

This proves that (ii) holds. Hence (i) $\Rightarrow$ (ii).

The implication (ii) $\Rightarrow$ (i) is easy and is left as an exercise. Next, suppose that (i) holds. Let

$$\underline{\int_a^b} f(x)dx = \overline{\int_a^b} f(x)dx := \alpha.$$

Then $\alpha = \int_a^b f(x)dx$ and it satisfies the required property. To prove the uniqueness, suppose $\exists \; \beta \in \mathbb{R}$ such that for every partition P of $[a, b]$, $L(P, f) \leq \beta \leq U(P, f)$. Then

$$\alpha \; = \; \underline{\int_a^b} f(x)dx \; \leq \; \beta \; \leq \; \overline{\int_a^b} f(x)dx \; = \; \alpha$$

Hence $\alpha = \beta$. This proves (iii). Finally suppose (iii) holds but f is not integrable. Then for every partition P of $[a, b]$,

$$L(P, f) \; \leq \; \underline{\int_a^b} f(x)dx \; < \; \overline{\int_a^b} f(x)dx \; \leq \; U(P, f).$$

But then every number α between $\underline{\int_a^b} f(x)dx$ and $\overline{\int_a^b} f(x)dx$ has the property that $L(P, f) < \alpha < U(P, f)$. This contradicts (iii). Hence (iii) implies that f is Riemann integrable, i.e., (iii) $\Longrightarrow$ (i). ∎

1.1.5. Theorem: *Let $f : [a, b] \longrightarrow \mathbb{R}$ be a bounded function. Then the following statements are true:*

(i) *If there exists a sequence $\{P_n\}_{n \geq 1}$ of partitions of $[a, b]$ such that*

$$\lim_{n \to \infty} \left(U\left(P_n, f\right) - L\left(P_n, f\right) \right) = 0,$$

then f is Riemann integrable and

$$\lim_{n \to \infty} L(P_n, f) = \int_a^b f(x)dx = \lim_{n \to \infty} U(P_n, f).$$

(ii) *If f is Riemann integrable, then there exists a sequence $\{P_n\}_{n \geq 1}$ of partitions of $[a, b]$ such that each P_{n+1} is a refinement of P_n, $\|P_n\| \to 0$ as $n \to \infty$ and*

$$\lim_{n \to \infty} (U(P_n, f) - L(P_n, f)) = 0.$$

Proof: (i) Suppose $\{P_n\}_{n \geq 1}$ is a sequence of partitions such that

$$\lim_{n \to \infty} (U(P_n, f) - L(P_n, f)) = 0.$$

Let $\epsilon > 0$ be given. We can choose n_0 such that $\forall \ n \geq n_0$

$$U(P_n, f) - L(P_n, f) < \epsilon.$$

Hence by theorem 1.1.4, f is Riemann integrable. Further, $\forall \ n \geq n_0$

$$U(P_n, f) - \int_a^b f(x)dx \ \leq \ U(P_n, f) - L(P_n, f) \ < \ \epsilon.$$

Hence

$$\lim_{n \to \infty} U(P_n, f) = \int_a^b f(x)dx.$$

Similarly,

$$\lim_{n \to \infty} L(P_n, f) = \int_a^b f(x)dx.$$

(ii) Suppose f is Riemann integrable. Since

$$\int_a^b f(x)dx \ = \ \sup\{L(P, f) \mid P \text{ a partition of } [a, b]\}$$

$$= \ \inf\{U(P, f) \mid P \text{ a partition of } [a, b]\},$$

we can choose sequences $\{P_n'\}_{n \geq 1}$ and $\{P_n''\}_{n \geq 1}$ of partitions of $[a, b]$ such that

$$\lim_{n \to \infty} L(P_n', f) = \int_a^b f(x)dx = \lim_{n \to \infty} U(P_n'', f).$$

Let $P_n^* = \{x_0, x_1, \ldots, x_n\}$, where $x_0 := a$, $x_k := x_{k-1} + (b - a)/n$ for $1 \leq k \leq n$. (P_n^* is called the **regular partition** of $[a, b]$.) Let $P_0 := \{a, b\}$ and put

$$P_n := P_{n-1} \cup P_n^* \cup \left(\bigcup_{k=1}^{n} (P_n' \cup P_n'') \right), \ \forall \, n \geq 1.$$

Then $\|P_n\| \ \leq \ 1/n \ \forall \ n$ and each P_{n+1} is a refinement of P_n. Further, since

$$U(P_n, f) - L(P_n, f) \ \leq \ U(P_n'', f) - L(P_n', f),$$

clearly

$$\lim_{n \to \infty} (U(P_n, f) - L(P_n, f)) = 0. \ \blacksquare$$

1.1.6. Examples:

(i) Let $f : [a, b] \longrightarrow \mathbb{R}$ be any monotonically increasing function, i.e., $f(x) \geq f(y)$ if $x > y$. Let $P_n = \{x_0, x_1, \dots, x_n\}$ be the regular partition of $[a, b]$, i.e., $x_i - x_{i-1} = (b-a)/n, 1 \leq i \leq n$. Then

$$U(P_n, f) = \sum_{i=1}^{n} f\left(a + \frac{i(b-a)}{n}\right)\left(\frac{b-a}{n}\right)$$

and

$$L(P_n, f) = \sum_{i=1}^{n} f\left(a + \frac{(i-1)(b-a)}{n}\right)\left(\frac{b-a}{n}\right).$$

Hence

$$U(P_n, f) - L(P_n, f)$$
$$= \frac{b-a}{n} \sum_{i=1}^{n} \left[f\left(a + \frac{i(b-a)}{n}\right) - f\left(a + \frac{(i-1)(b-a)}{n}\right) \right]$$
$$= \frac{(b-a)}{n}(f(b) - f(a)).$$

It follows from theorem 1.1.5 that f is Riemann integrable. A similar argument will prove that f is Riemann integrable when f is monotonically decreasing.

(ii) Let $f : [a, b] \longrightarrow \mathbb{R}$ be a continuous function. We show that f is Riemann integrable. Since f is continuous, it is bounded and is uniformly continuous. Let $\epsilon > 0$ be arbitrary. We choose $\delta > 0$ such that

$$|f(x) - f(y)| < \epsilon/(b-a) \text{ whenever } |x - y| < \delta.$$

Let P be any partition of $[a, b]$ such that $\|P\| < \delta$. Let $P = \{x_0, x_1, \dots, x_n\}$. Since f is continuous, it attains its maximum and minimum values M_i and m_i, respectively, on the interval $[x_{i-1}, x_i]$ at some points, say $f(y_i) = M_i$ and $f(z_i) = m_i, 1 \leq i \leq n$. Clearly,

$$(M_i - m_i) < \epsilon/(b-a) \text{ for every } i$$

and

$$U(P, f) - L(P, f) = \sum_{i=1}^{n} (M_i - m_i)(x_i - x_{i-1})$$

$$< \frac{\epsilon}{b-a} \sum_{i=1}^{n} (x_i - x_{i-1}) = \epsilon.$$

Thus f is integrable, by theorem 1.1.4.

1.1.7. Exercise: Analyze whether the following functions are Riemann integrable or not:

(i) $f(x) := \begin{cases} 1 & \text{if} \ \ 0 \le x \le 2, x \ne 1, \\ 2 & \text{if} \qquad\qquad\quad x = 1. \end{cases}$

(ii) $f : [a, b] \to \mathbb{R}$, f has only a finite number of discontinuity points.

(iii) $f : [0, 1] \longrightarrow \mathbb{R}$,

$$f(x) := \begin{cases} 0 & \text{if} \ \ x \text{ is irrational}, 0 \le x \le 1, \\ x & \text{if} \ \ \ x \text{ is rational}, 0 \le x \le 1. \end{cases}$$

1.1.8. Exercise:

(i) Let $f : [a, b] \longrightarrow \mathbb{R}$ be a nonnegative continuous function and let $f(c) > 0$ for some $c \in [a, b]$. Show that $\int_a^b f(x)dx > 0$.

•(ii) Let $f : [a, b] \longrightarrow \mathbb{R}$ be continuous and $f(x) \ge 0 \ \ \forall \ \ x \in [a, b]$. If $\int_a^b f(x)dx = 0$, show that $f(x) \equiv 0$.

1.1.9. Exercise: Let $f, g : [a, b] \longrightarrow \mathbb{R}$ be bounded functions. Prove the following assertions:

(i) $\displaystyle \underline{\int_a^b} (f + g)(x) \ge \underline{\int_a^b} f(x)dx + \underline{\int_a^b} g(x)dx.$

(ii) $\displaystyle \overline{\int_a^b} (f + g)(x)dx \le \overline{\int_a^b} f(x)dx + \overline{\int_a^b} g(x)dx.$

(iii) $\displaystyle \underline{\int_a^b} (\alpha f)(x)dx = \begin{cases} \alpha \ \ \displaystyle\underline{\int_a^b} f(x)dx & \text{if} \ \ \alpha > 0, \\ \\ \alpha \ \ \displaystyle\overline{\int_a^b} f(x)dx & \text{if} \ \ \alpha < 0. \end{cases}$

1.1.10. Exercise: Let $f : [a, b] \longrightarrow \mathbb{R}$ be a bounded function. Define for $x \in [a, b]$,

$$f^+(x) := \begin{cases} f(x) & \text{if} \ \ f(x) \ge 0, \\ 0 & \text{if} \ \ f(x) \le 0 \end{cases}$$

and

$$f^-(x) := \begin{cases} -f(x) & \text{if} \ \ f(x) \le 0, \\ 0 & \text{if} \ \ f(x) \ge 0. \end{cases}$$

The nonnegative functions f^+ and f^- are called, respectively, the **positive** and **negative part** of the function f.

(i) Show that $f = f^+ - f^-$ and $|f| = f^+ + f^-$.

(ii) Let f be Riemann integrable. Show that both f^+ and f^- are also Riemann integrable.

(iii) From (i) deduce that $|f|$ is also Riemann integrable and

$$\left| \int_a^b f(x)dx \right| \leq \int_a^b |f(x)| \, dx.$$

1.1.11. Exercise: Construct a function $f : [a,b] \longrightarrow \mathbb{R}$ such that $|f|$ is Riemann integrable but f is not Riemann integrable.

1.1.12. Exercise: Let $f : [a,b] \longrightarrow \mathbb{R}$ be Riemann integrable. Show that f is also Riemann integrable on $[a,x] \; \forall \; x \in [a,b]$ and the function

$$F(x) := \int_a^x f(t)dt, \quad x \in [a,b],$$

is uniformly continuous.

1.1.13. Exercise: Let $f : [a,b] \longrightarrow \mathbb{R}$ be a bounded function. Show that f is Riemann integrable iff

$$\underline{\int_a^b} f(x)dx = -\underline{\int_a^b} (-f)(x)dx$$

or

$$\overline{\int_a^b} f(x)dx = -\overline{\int_a^b} (-f)(x)dx.$$

We end this section with the definition of integrability as given by Bernhard Riemann in 1854.

1.1.14. Definition: Let $f : [a,b] \longrightarrow \mathbb{R}$ be a bounded function and let $P = \{a = x_0 < x_1 < \cdots < x_n = b\}$ be any partition of $[a,b]$. Let $t_i \in [x_{i-1}, x_i], 1 \leq i \leq n$, be chosen arbitrarily and let

$$S(P,f) := \sum_{i=1}^n f(t_i)(x_i - x_{i-1}).$$

$S(P,f)$ is called a **Riemann sum** of f with respect to the partition P. We say that the function f is R-**integrable** if there exists a real number L having the property that for every $\epsilon > 0$ there exists some $\delta > 0$ such that if P is any partition of $[a,b]$ with $\|P\| < \delta$ and $S(P,f)$ is any Riemann sum of f with respect to the partition P, then $|S(P,f) - L| < \epsilon$. We write this as

$$\lim_{\|P\| \to 0} S(P,f) = L.$$

1.1.15. Theorem (G. Darboux): *Let $f : [a,b] \longrightarrow \mathbb{R}$ be a bounded function. Then f is R-integrable iff f is Riemann integrable, and in that* *case*

$$\int_a^b f(x)dx = \lim_{\|P\| \to 0} S(P, f).$$

Proof: See Apostol [2]. ∎

1.2. Characterization of Riemann integrable functions

Let $\mathcal{R}[a, b]$ denote the set of all functions $f : [a, b] \longrightarrow \mathbb{R}$ which are Riemann integrable. Our next theorem describes some properties of $\mathcal{R}[a, b]$ and the map $f \longmapsto \int_a^b f(x)dx$ for $f \in \mathcal{R}[a, b]$.

1.2.1. Theorem: *Let* $f, g : [a, b] \longrightarrow \mathbb{R}$ *be bounded Riemann integrable functions and* α *be any real number. Then:*

(i) $f + g$ *is also Riemann integrable and*

$$\int_a^b (f + g)(x)dx = \int_a^b f(x)dx + \int_a^b g(x)dx.$$

(ii) αf *is Riemann integrable and*

$$\int_a^b (\alpha f)(x)dx = \alpha \int_a^b f(x)dx.$$

(iii) *If* $f(x) \le g(x) \ \forall \ x \in [a, b]$, *then*

$$\int_a^b f(x)dx \ \le \ \int_a^b g(x)dx.$$

Proof: (i) Since f, g are integrable, given $\epsilon > 0$ we can choose partitions P_1 and P_2 of $[a, b]$ such that

$$U(P_1, f) - L(P_1, f) < \epsilon/2$$

and

$$U(P_2, g) - L(P_2, g) < \epsilon/2.$$

Let $P = P_1 \cup P_2$. Then clearly

$$U(P, f) - L(P, f) < \epsilon/2$$

and

$$U(P, g) - L(P, g) < \epsilon/2.$$

Since for any set $A \subseteq [a, b]$,

$$\sup\{f(x) + g(x) \mid x \in A\} \ \le \ \sup\{f(x) \mid x \in A\} + \sup\{g(x) \mid x \in A\}$$

and

$$\inf\{f(x) + g(x) \mid x \in A\} \ \ge \ \inf\{f(x) \mid x \in A\} + \inf\{g(x) \mid x \in A\},$$

we have

$$U(P, f+g) \leq U(P, f) + U(P, g)$$

and

$$L(P, f+g) \geq L(P, f) + L(P, g).$$

Hence

$$\begin{aligned} U(P, f+g) &\leq U(P, f) + U(P, g) \\ &\leq L(P, f) + L(P, g) + \epsilon \\ &\leq L(P, f+g) + \epsilon. \end{aligned}$$

Thus $f + g$ is Riemann integrable by theorem 1.1.4. Further,

$$\begin{aligned} \overline{\int_a^b} (f+g)(x)dx &\leq U(P, f+g) \\ &\leq L(P, f) + L(P, g) + \epsilon \\ &\leq \int_{\underline{a}}^b f(x)dx + \int_{\underline{a}}^b g(x)dx + \epsilon. \end{aligned}$$

Since the functions f, g and $f + g$ are all integrable and $\epsilon > 0$ is arbitrary, we have

$$\int_a^b (f+g)(x)dx \leq \int_a^b f(x)dx + \int_a^b g(x)dx. \tag{1.1}$$

Similarly,

$$\begin{aligned} \int_{\underline{a}}^b (f+g)(x)dx &\geq L(P, f+g) \\ &\geq U(P, f) + U(P, g) - \epsilon \\ &\geq \overline{\int_a^b} f(x)dx + \overline{\int_a^b} g(x)dx - \epsilon. \end{aligned}$$

Again, since f, g and $f + g$ are integrable and $\epsilon > 0$ is arbitrary, we have

$$\int_a^b (f+g)(x)dx \geq \int_a^b f(x)dx + \int_a^b g(x)dx. \tag{1.2}$$

Equations (1.1) and (1.2) complete the proof of (i). The proofs of (ii) and (iii) are easy and are left as exercises. ∎

The above theorem tells us that $\mathcal{R}[a, b]$ is a vector space over $\mathbb{R}$ and the map $f \longmapsto \int_a^b f dx$ is a linear, order preserving map from $\mathcal{R}[a, b]$ to $\mathbb{R}$. In view of examples 1.1.6, $\mathcal{R}[a, b]$ includes the class of all monotone functions and the class of all continuous functions. Thus the space $\mathcal{R}[a, b]$ is quite large. In view of exercise 1.1.7(ii), it is natural to ask the following question:

Let $f : [a, b] \longrightarrow \mathbb{R}$ be a bounded function which is discontinuous at an infinite set of points in $[a, b]$. Is f Riemann integrable?

Example 1.1.3 (iii) shows that the set D of discontinuities of f cannot be too large, e.g., D cannot be equal to $[a, b]$. What about if D is countably infinite? (See example 1.2.14.) To analyze integrability of f on an interval which includes points of discontinuity of f, we should look at the points of discontinuity in a more quantitative way. To do that we introduce the following concept.

1.2.2. Definition: Let $f : [a, b] \longrightarrow \mathbb{R}$ be a bounded function and J a subinterval of $[a, b]$. Let

$$\omega(f, J) := \sup\{f(x) : x \in J\} - \inf\{f(x) : x \in J\}$$

and for $x \in [a, b]$, let

$$\omega(f, x) := \lim_{\substack{\lambda(J) \to 0 \\ x \in J}} \omega(f, J),$$

where $\lambda(J)$ denotes the length of the interval J. The function $\omega(f, J)$ is called the **oscillation of f in the interval J** and $\omega(f, x)$ is called the **oscillation of f** at x. Clearly $\omega(f, x) \geq 0$ for every $x \in [a, b]$.

1.2.3. Examples:

(i) Let $f(x) := \begin{cases} x + 2 & \text{if } x \geq 0, \\ 0 & \text{if } x < 0. \end{cases}$

Then $\omega(f, x) = 0 \ \ \forall \ x \neq 0$ and $\omega(f, 0) = 2$.

(ii) Let $f(x) := \begin{cases} 0 & \text{if } 0 \leq x \leq 1, \\ x & \text{if } 1 < x \leq 2. \end{cases}$

Then $\omega(f, x) = 0$ if $0 \leq x < 1$, $\omega(f, 1) = 1$ and $\omega(f, x) = 0$ if $1 < x \leq 2$.

(iii) Let $f(x) := \begin{cases} \sin 1/x & \text{if } x \neq 0, \\ 0 & \text{if } x = 0. \end{cases}$

Then $\omega(f, 0) = 2$.

1.2.4. Exercise: Let $f : [a, b] \longrightarrow \mathbb{R}$.

(i) Show that f is continuous at $c \in [a, b]$ iff $\omega(f, c) = 0$.

(ii) Let $\omega(f, x) < \epsilon$ for every $x \in [a, b]$. Show there exists $\delta > 0$ such that $|f(x) - f(y)| < \epsilon$ whenever $|x - y| < \delta$.
    (Hint: Use the fact that $[a, b]$ is compact.)

The main aim of introducing the concept of oscillation of a function at a point is that it helps us to analyze the set of discontinuities of f. In some sense, oscillation gives a quantitative measure of discontinuity. For the rest of the chapter, we fix $f : [a, b] \longrightarrow \mathbb{R}$, a bounded function. Let

$$D := \{x \in [a, b] \mid f \text{ is not continuous at } x\}.$$

In view of exercise 1.2.4, we can write

$$D = \{x \in [a, b] \mid \omega(f, x) > 0\} = \bigcup_{n=1}^{\infty} D_n,$$

where

$$D_n := \{x \in [a, b] \mid \omega(f, x) \geq 1/n\},$$

i.e., D_n is the set of those points x at which the oscillation of f exceeds $1/n$. For any $\epsilon > 0$, let us analyze the set

$$D_\epsilon := \{x \in [a, b] \mid \omega(f, x) \geq \epsilon\},$$

when f is Riemann integrable. Since f is Riemann integrable, given any $\eta > 0$ we can choose a partition $P = \{a = x_0 < x_1 < \cdots < x_n = b\}$ of $[a, b]$ such that

$$U(P, f) - L(P, f) < \eta.$$

Let

$$S := \{i \mid 1 \leq i \leq n \text{ and } (x_{i-1}, x_i) \cap D_\epsilon \neq \emptyset\}.$$

Then

$$D_\epsilon \subseteq \bigcup_{i \in S} [x_{i-1}, x_i]$$

and for every $i \notin S, (x_{i-1}, x_i) \cap D_\epsilon = \emptyset$. Note that for $i \in S$, $\exists$ some $c_i \in [x_{i-1}, x_i] \cap D_\epsilon$. Thus

$$(M_i - m_i) \geq \omega(f, c_i) \geq \epsilon,$$

where

$$M_i := \sup\{f(x) \mid x \in [x_{i-1}, x_i]\} \text{ and } m_i := \inf\{f(x) \mid x \in [x_{i-1}, x_i]\}.$$

Hence

$$\eta > U(P, f) - L(P, f) \geq \sum_{i \in S} (M_i - m_i)(x_i - x_{i-1})$$

$$\geq \epsilon \sum_{i \in S} (x_i - x_{i-1}).$$

Thus for any $\eta > 0$, we have intervals $[x_{i-1}, x_i], i \in S$, such that

$$D_\epsilon \subseteq \bigcup_{i \in S} [x_{i-1}, x_i] \text{ and } \sum_{i \in S} (x_i - x_{i-1}) < \eta/\epsilon.$$

In a sense, what we have shown is that if f is Riemann integrable, then D_ϵ can be covered by closed intervals of total length as small as we want. Let us record this in the next proposition.

1.2.5. Proposition: *Let $f : [a, b] \longrightarrow \mathbb{R}$ be a Riemann integrable function and $D_\epsilon := \{x \in [a, b] \mid \omega(f, x) \geq \epsilon\}$. Then for every $\eta > 0$ there exist closed intervals $I_1, I_2, \ldots, I_k \subset [a, b]$ such that*

$$D_\epsilon \subseteq \bigcup_{j=1}^{k} I_j \quad and \quad \sum_{j=1}^{k} \lambda(I_j) < \eta.$$

•1.2.6. Exercise: Let f, D_ϵ be as in proposition 1.2.5. Show that for any given $\eta > 0$ there exist open intervals $I_1, \ldots, I_k$ such that $D_\epsilon \subseteq \bigcup_{j=1}^{k} I_j$ and $\sum_{j=1}^{k} \lambda(I_j) < \eta$.

1.2.7. Corollary: *Let $f : [a, b] \longrightarrow \mathbb{R}$ be Riemann integrable. Then for every $\eta > 0$ there exists a sequence of closed intervals $J_1, J_2, J_3, \ldots$ in $[a, b]$ such that*

$$D := \{x \mid f \text{ is not continuous at } x\} \subseteq \bigcup_{k=1}^{\infty} J_k \quad and \quad \sum_{k=1}^{\infty} \lambda(J_k) < \eta.$$

Proof: Note that $D = \bigcup_{k=1}^{\infty} D_n$, where

$$D_n := \{x \in [a, b] \mid \omega(f, x) \geq 1/n\}.$$

Now, by proposition 1.2.5 applied to D_n for every n, we can find closed intervals $I_1^n, I_2^n, \ldots, I_{k_n}^n$ such that

$$D_n \subseteq \bigcup_{j=1}^{k_n} I_j^n \quad and \quad \sum_{j=1}^{k_n} \lambda(I_j^n) < \eta/2^n.$$

For $n = 1, 2, \ldots$ and $1 \leq j \leq k_n$, let the intervals I_j^n be renamed as $J_1, J_2, \ldots$. Then

$$D = \bigcup_{n=1}^{\infty} D_n \subseteq \bigcup_{n=1}^{\infty} J_n \quad and \quad \sum_{k=1}^{\infty} \lambda(J_k) \leq \sum_{n=1}^{\infty} \sum_{j=1}^{k_n} \lambda(I_j^n) < \eta. \quad \blacksquare$$

In view of the above corollary, we have the following definition.

1.2.8. Definition: A subset $E \subset \mathbb{R}$ is said to be a **null set** if, given $\epsilon > 0$, there exists a countable family of intervals $\{I_n \mid n \geq 1\}$ such that $E \subseteq \bigcup_{n=1}^{\infty} I_n$ and $\sum_{n=1}^{\infty} \lambda(I_n) \leq \epsilon$.

1.2.9. Remark: It is not important in definition 1.2.8 as to what is the nature (i.e., open, closed, etc.) of the intervals. In fact, if E is a null set we can choose intervals of the type we like to satisfy the required properties.

1.2.10. Examples:

(i) Clearly every singleton set $\{x\}$, $x \in \mathbb{R}$, is a null set, for $\{x\} = [x, x] := I$ and $\lambda(I) = 0$. It is easy to check that every finite set is a null set.

(ii) Any countably infinite set $S = \{x_1, x_2, x_3, \dots\}$ is a null set. To see this, let $\epsilon > 0$ be given. Let $I_j := (x_j - \epsilon/2^{j+1}, x_j + \epsilon/2^{j+1})$, $j = 1, 2, \dots$. Then

$$S \subset \bigcup_{j=1}^{\infty} I_j \text{ and } \sum_{j=1}^{\infty} \lambda(I_j) \leq \epsilon.$$

(iii) $\mathbb{Q}$, the set of rational numbers, is a null subset of $\mathbb{R}$.

1.2.11. Exercise:

(i) Show that every subset of a null set is also a null set.

(ii) Let $A_1, A_2, \dots, A_n, \dots$ be null sets. Show that $\bigcup_{n=1}^{\infty} A_n$ is a null set.

(iii) Let $E \subseteq [a, b]$ be any set which has only a finite number of limit points. Can E be uncountable? Can you say E is a null set?

(iv) Let E be a null subset of $\mathbb{R}$ and $x \in \mathbb{R}$. What can you say about the sets $E + x := \{y + x \mid y \in E\}$ and $xE := \{xy \mid y \in E\}$?

1.2.12. Exercise:

(i) Let I be an interval having at least two distinct points. Show that I is not a null set.

(ii) If E contains an interval of positive length, show that it is not a null set. Is the converse true, i.e., if $E \subseteq \mathbb{R}$ is not a null set, then does E contain an interval of positive length?

1.2.13. Example (Cantor sets): Let $I := [0, 1]$ and let $0 < \alpha \leq 1$ be fixed. We remove from the interval $[0, 1]$ successively a collection of open intervals as follows: (i) Remove from $[0, 1]$ the central open interval I_1^1 of length $\alpha/3$. Then

$$I_1^1 := \left(\frac{1}{2} - \frac{\alpha}{2.3}, \frac{1}{2} + \frac{\alpha}{2.3} \right).$$

This will give two disjoint closed intervals J_1^1 and J_2^1 (Figure 8), each of length $(1 - \alpha/3)/2$.

$$\tfrac{1}{2} - \tfrac{\alpha}{2.3} \qquad\qquad \tfrac{1}{2} + \tfrac{\alpha}{2.3}$$

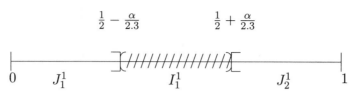

Figure 8: Step one

(ii) Remove the central open intervals I_1^2 and I_2^2 each of length $\alpha/9$ from the intervals J_1^1 and J_2^1, respectively, to get four disjoint closed intervals J_1^2, J_2^2, J_3^2 and J_4^2 (Figure 9) each of length $(1 - \alpha/3 - 2\alpha/9)/4$.

$$I_1^2 \qquad\qquad I_1^1 \qquad\qquad I_2^2$$

Figure 9: Step two

(iii) Proceeding as above, suppose at the nth step we have obtained 2^n disjoint closed intervals $J_1^n, \ldots J_{2^n}^n$ such that each has length $(1 - \alpha/3 - \cdots - 2^{n-1}\alpha/3^n)/2^n$. We remove central open intervals I_k^{n+1}, $1 \le k \le 2^n$, each of length $\alpha/3^{n+1}$ from each of the J_k^n to get 2^{n+1} disjoint closed intervals $J_k^{n+1}, 1 \le k \le 2^{n+1}$. Let

$$A_n := \bigcup_{j=1}^{2^{n-1}} I_j^{n-1}, \; B_n := \bigcup_{k=1}^{2^n} J_k^n \; \text{ and } \; C_\alpha := \bigcap_{n=1}^{\infty} B_n = [0,1] \setminus \left(\bigcup_{n=1}^{\infty} A_n \right).$$

The set A_n consists of those points which are removed at the $(n+1)^{\text{th}}$ stage from the leftover of $[0,1]$ after the nth stage, and B_n is the set of points leftover after the $(n+1)^{\text{th}}$ stage removal has been completed. The set C_α is the set of points left after all the intervals $I_j^n, 1 \le j \le 2^n$ and $n = 1, 2, \ldots$, have been removed from I. The sets C_α are called **Cantor sets**.

Note that $C_\alpha \ne \emptyset$; for example, it includes the endpoints of all the intervals removed. Further, the sum of the lengths of all the intervals removed from I is

$$\sum_{n=0}^{\infty} \alpha 2^n / 3^{n+1} = \alpha.$$

If $0 < \alpha < 1$, then C_α cannot be covered by a countable collection of subintervals of total length less than $1 - \alpha$ (see property (8) of the length function λ in the prologue). Hence C_α is not a null set for $0 < \alpha < 1$.

For $\alpha = 1, C_\alpha$ is a null set. To see this, let $\epsilon > 0$ be arbitrary. We choose a positive integer n sufficiently large so that

$$\sum_{k=n+1}^{\infty} 2^{k-1}/3^k < \epsilon.$$

Then the finite number of intervals $J_k^n, 1 \le k \le 2^n$, will cover C_1. Thus for $\alpha = 1, C_\alpha$ is a null set. The set C_1 is more popularly known as **Cantor's ternary set**. The reason for this is that points of C_1 are precisely those real numbers x in $[0, 1]$ that admit ternary expansions $0 \cdot a_1 a_2 \ldots a_n \ldots$, i.e.,

$$x = \sum_{n=1}^{\infty} a_n/3^n,$$

where each a_n is either 0 or 2. This fact can be used to show that the set C_1 is uncountable. For this, consider the map $f : C_1 \longrightarrow [0, 1]$ defined as follows: for $x \in C_1$, if $x = \sum_{n=1}^{\infty} a_n/3^n$ is its ternary expansion, then $f(x) := y \in [0, 1]$ is the point having the binary expansion

$$y = \sum_{n=1}^{\infty} b_n/2^n,$$

where $b_n = a_n/2$ for every n. It is easy to check that f is a bijective map. Thus C_1 is an uncountable, null subset of $\mathbb{R}$.

The sets C_α, $0 < \alpha \le 1$, are all very useful in constructing examples, as we shall see later. This is mainly because of the following nice topological properties that the sets C_α have.

First of all, each C_α is a closed subset of $\mathbb{R}$, as it is intersection of the closed sets $B_n, n = 1, 2, \ldots$. We show next that C_α is nowhere dense in $[0, 1]$. To see this, note that C_α includes no nonempty open interval. For if $(a, b) \subset C_\alpha$, then $(a, b) \subset B_n \; \forall \; n$. But then $(a, b) \subset J_k^n$ for every n and for some $k, 1 \le k \le 2^n$. Thus $\forall \; n$,

$$(b - a) \; < \; \lambda(J_k^n) \; \le \; 1/2^n,$$

and hence $(a, b) = \emptyset$, a contradiction. That C_α is nowhere dense follows from the fact that if a closed set includes no nonempty interval, then it is nowhere dense.

Finally, we show that C_α is a perfect set. To prove this we shall show that C_α is dense in itself (since C_α is closed). Let $x \in C_\alpha$ be the left endpoint of an interval I_k^n for some $n \ge 1$ and $1 \le k \le 2^{n-1}$. Then $x \in J_k^n \; \forall \; n$, for some $1 \le k \le 2^n$, and x will always be its right endpoint. If x_n denotes the left endpoint of this J_k^n, then clearly $x_n \in C_\alpha$ and x_n converges to x. A similar argument applies if $x \in C_\alpha$ is the right endpoint of some I_k^n. Finally, suppose $x \in C_\alpha$ is such that x is not the endpoint of any I_k^n; then x will be an interior point of J_k^n for each n and some k. Clearly the sequence of endpoints of these J_k^n will converge to x. Hence C_α is dense in itself.

In the terminology of null sets, corollary 1.2.7 states that for a Riemann integrable function f, the set of discontinuities of f is a null set. It is natural to ask the question: Is the converse true, i.e., if f is a bounded function on $[a, b]$ and the set of discontinuities of f is a null set, can we say f is Riemann integrable? The answer to this question is in the affirmative. Before we prove this, let us look at an example of a function on $[0, 1]$ which has an infinite number of discontinuities in every subinterval of $[0, 1]$, yet is Riemann integrable.

1.2.14. Example (Popcorn function): Let $f : [0, 1] \longrightarrow [0, 1]$ be defined as follows:

$$f(x) := \begin{cases} 1 & \text{if } x = 0, \\ 1/q & \text{if } x \in (0, 1] \text{ is a rational } x = p/q \text{ in lowest terms,} \\ 0 & \text{if } x \in [0, 1] \text{ is an irrational.} \end{cases}$$

The function f is continuous at every irrational and discontinuous at every rational point. Let us analyze f for integrability. First note that if I is any open interval that intersects $[0, 1]$, then $f(x) = 0$ for some $x \in [0, 1] \cap I$. Thus $L(P, f) = 0$ for every partition P of $[0, 1]$. Let $\epsilon > 0$ be arbitrary. Let

$$A := \{x \in [0, 1] \mid f(x) \geq \epsilon/2\}.$$

We note that A is a finite set, since it consists of only those rationals $x = p/q$ where $1/q \geq \epsilon/2$ and $0 < p \leq q$. Now we can cover these points of A by open subintervals of $[0, 1]$ such that the total length of these subintervals is less than $\epsilon/2$. Without loss of generality, we may assume that these subintervals are disjoint and are $[x_k, y_k], 1 \leq k \leq n$, where $y_k > x_k, k = 1, 2, \ldots, n - 1$. Consider the partition P of $[0, 1]$ given by

$$P = \{0 = y_0 \leq x_1 < y_1 < \cdots < x_n < y_n \leq x_{n+1} = 1\}.$$

Let

$$M_k := \sup\{f(x) \mid x_k \leq x \leq y_k\}, \text{ for } 1 \leq k \leq n$$

and

$$\tilde{M}_k := \sup\{f(x) \mid y_{k-1} \leq x \leq x_k\}, \text{ for } 1 \leq k \leq n + 1.$$

Then for each k, $M_k \leq 1$ and $\tilde{M}_k \leq \epsilon/2$. Thus

$$
\begin{aligned}
U(P, f) - L(P, f) = U(P, f) &= \sum_{k=1}^{n} M_k(y_k - x_k) + \sum_{k=1}^{n+1} \tilde{M}_k(x_k - y_{k-1}) \\
&\leq \sum_{k=1}^{n} M_k(y_k - x_k) + \epsilon/2 \sum_{k=1}^{n+1} (x_k - y_{k-1}) \\
&< \sum_{k=1}^{n} (y_k - x_k) + \epsilon/2 \\
&< \epsilon/2 + \epsilon/2 = \epsilon.
\end{aligned}
$$

Hence f is integrable on $[0, 1]$ and

$$
\int_0^1 f(x)dx = 0.
$$

A closer look at the above example tells us that f becomes integrable mainly because the set $\{x \in [0,1] \mid \omega(f,x) \geq \epsilon/2\} = \{x \in [0,1] \mid f(x) \geq \epsilon/2\}$ is a null set. Thus in order to analyze the integrability of f we should analyze the sets $D_\epsilon := \{x \in [a,b] \mid \omega(f,x) \geq \epsilon\}$ in detail and expect f to be integrable if D_ϵ is a null set for every $\epsilon > 0$.

1.2.15. Proposition: *Let $f : [a,b] \longrightarrow \mathbb{R}$ be Riemann integrable. Then D_ϵ is a compact set for every $\epsilon > 0$.*

Proof: Since $[a,b]$ is compact and $D_\epsilon \subseteq [a,b]$, it is enough to show that D_ϵ is a closed subset of $[a,b]$. Let $t \in [a,b]$ be any accumulation point of D_ϵ. Suppose $t \notin D_\epsilon$, i.e., $\omega(f,t) < \epsilon$. Then there exists some $\delta_t > 0$ such that

$$
\omega(f, I) < \epsilon, \quad \text{where } I = (t - \delta_t, t + \delta_t) \cap [a,b].
$$

But then for every interval J such that $t \in J \subseteq I$, we have $\omega(f, J) < \epsilon$. Hence

$$
\omega(f, y) < \epsilon \text{ for every } y \in I.
$$

Thus, $I \cap D_\epsilon = \emptyset$, a contradiction to the fact that t is an accumulation point of D_ϵ. Hence $t \in D_\epsilon$ and D_ϵ is a closed subset of $[a,b]$. ∎

1.2.16. Theorem: *Let $f : [a,b] \longrightarrow \mathbb{R}$ be a bounded function such that $D := \{x \in [a,b] \mid \omega(f,x) > 0\}$ is a null set. Then f is Riemann integrable.*

Proof: Let $\epsilon > 0$ be given. In view of theorem 1.1.4, we have to construct a partition P of $[a,b]$ such that $U(P, f) - L(P, f) < \epsilon$. For this we proceed as follows:

Step 1: Since $D = \{x \in [a, b] \mid \omega(f, x) > 0\}$ is a null set, $D_{\epsilon'} := \{x \in [a, b] \mid \omega(f, x) \geq \epsilon'\}$ is also a null set for every $\epsilon' > 0$. Let ϵ' be fixed arbitrarily. We choose open intervals $I_1, I_2, \ldots, I_n, \ldots$ such that

$$D_{\epsilon'} \subseteq \bigcup_{n=1}^{\infty} I_n \text{ and } \sum_{n=1}^{\infty} \lambda(I_n) < \epsilon'.$$

Since $D_{\epsilon'}$ is compact (proposition 1.2.15), we can find a positive integer m such that $D_{\epsilon'} \subseteq \bigcup_{n=1}^{m} I_n$. Let us arrange the endpoints of the intervals $I_n \cap [a, b], n = 1, 2, \ldots, m$, as $a = x_1 < x_2 < \cdots < x_r = b$. Then these points give us a partition P of $[a, b]$. Further, note that if

$$S := \{1 \leq i \leq r \mid [x_{i-1}, x_i] \cap D_{\epsilon'} \neq \emptyset\},$$

then

$$\sum_{i \in S} \lambda(I_i) \leq \sum_{i=1}^{m} \lambda(I_i) < \epsilon'.$$

Step 2: Let $A := \bigcup_{i \notin S} [x_{i-1}, x_i]$. Then $\omega(f, x) < \epsilon'$ for every $x \in A$. Now using exercise 1.2.4(ii), we can find $\delta > 0$ such that $|f(x) - f(y)| < \epsilon'$ whenever $|x - y| < \delta$. Without loss of generality, we assume that the partition P has the property that $\|P\| < \delta$, for if required we can consider a refinement of P. Thus for every $i \notin S$, if $x, y \in [x_{i-1}, x_i]$, then $|f(x) - f(y)| < \epsilon'$.

Step 3: Let $|f(x)| \leq M \; \forall \; x \in [a, b]$. Let

$$M_i := \sup\{f(x) \mid x_{i-1} \leq x \leq x_i\} \text{ and } m_i := \inf\{f(x) \mid x_{i-1} \leq x \leq x_i\}.$$

Then using steps 1 and 2, we get

$$
\begin{aligned}
U(P, f) - L(P, f) &= \sum_{i=1}^{r} (M_i - m_i)(x_i - x_{i-1}) \\
&= \sum_{i \in S} (M_i - m_i)(x_i - x_{i-1}) \\
&\quad + \sum_{i \notin S} (M_i - m_i)(x_i - x_{i-1}) \\
&\leq 2M_i \sum_{i \in S} (x_i - x_{i-1}) + \epsilon' \sum_{i \notin S} (x_i - x_{i-1}) \\
&\leq 2M\epsilon' + \epsilon' \sum_{i=1}^{r} (x_i - x_{i-1}) \\
&= (2M + b - a)\epsilon'.
\end{aligned}
$$

Since ϵ' is arbitrary, we could start with ϵ' such that $(2M + b - a)\epsilon' = \epsilon$, proving that f is Riemann integrable. ∎

1.2.17. Exercise:

(i) Let $D \subset [a, b]$ be a null set. Show that $[a, b] \setminus D$ is dense in $[a, b]$.

(ii) Let $D \subset \mathbb{R}$ be a null set. Can we say $\mathbb{R} \setminus D$ is dense in $\mathbb{R}$?

(iii) Let $f \in \mathcal{R}[a, b]$ be such that the set $\{x \in [a, b] \mid f(x) \neq 0\}$ is a null set. Use (i) to show that

$$\int_a^b f(x)dx = 0.$$

1.2.18. Exercise:

(i) Let f and g be Riemann integrable on $[a, b]$. Show that $f + g$, $f - g$, fg and αf are all Riemann integrable for $\alpha \in \mathbb{R}$. In particular, $\mathcal{R}[a, b]$ is a vector space over $\mathbb{R}$. Further, the map

$$f \longmapsto \int_a^b f(x)\, dx, \ f \in \mathcal{R}[a, b],$$

is a linear map from $\mathcal{R}[a, b]$ to $\mathbb{R}$.

(ii) Let $f \in \mathcal{R}[a, b]$ be such that $f \geq 0$. Show that $\int_a^b f(x)dx \geq 0$. Further,

$$\int_a^b f(x)dx = 0 \ \text{ iff } \ \{x \in [a, b] \mid f(x) > 0\} \ \text{ is a null set.}$$

(Hint: Use exercise 1.2.17(iii) for the 'if' implication and proceed as in the proof of proposition 1.2.5 for the 'only if' implication.)

(iii) Let f, g be bounded functions on $[a, b]$ such that $f \in \mathcal{R}[a, b]$ and $\{x \in [a, b] \mid f(x) \neq g(x)\}$ is a null set. Is g Riemann integrable? If yes, is

$$\int_a^b f(x)dx = \int_a^b g(x)dx?$$

1.2.19. Exercise:

(i) Let $g \in \mathcal{R}[a, b]$ and assume $m \leq g(x) \leq M$ for all $x \in [a, b]$. Let $f : [m, M] \to \mathbb{R}$ be a continuous function and $h = f \circ g$. Show that $h \in \mathcal{R}[a, b]$.

(ii) Let f be as defined in example 1.2.14 and $g(x) = 1$ if $0 < x \leq 1$, $g(0) = 0$. Show that $h = g \circ f$ is not Riemann integrable on $[0, 1]$, although both $f \in \mathcal{R}[0, 1]$ and $g \in \mathcal{R}[0, 1]$.

1.2.20. Exercise: Let f be any monotone function on $[a, b]$. Show that $f \in \mathcal{R}[a, b]$. (Recall a monotone function has only countably many discontinuities. See also example 1.1.6 for a direct proof.)

1.2.21. Exercise: Let X be any nonempty set and A be any subset of X. The function $\chi_A : X \longrightarrow \{0,1\}$ defined by

$$\chi_A(x) := \begin{cases} 1 & \text{if} \quad x \in A, \\ 0 & \text{if} \quad x \notin A, \end{cases}$$

is called the **characteristic function** or the **indicator function** of the set A. Prove the following:

(i) $\chi_{A \cap B} = \chi_A \chi_B$.

(ii) $\chi_{A \cup B} = \chi_A + \chi_B - \chi_{A \cap B}$.

(iii) $\chi_{A \triangle B} = |\chi_A - \chi_B|$, where

$$A \triangle B = (A \cup B) \setminus (A \cap B).$$

1.2.22. Exercise: Let $S \subseteq [a,b]$ be any nonempty set and let ∂S be the boundary of S. Show that $\chi_S \in \mathcal{R}[a,b]$ iff ∂S is a null set.

1.2.23. Exercise: Let $0 < \alpha \le 1$ and let $f = \chi_{C_\alpha}$ be the characteristic function of the Cantor set C_α (see example 1.2.13). Show that $f \in \mathcal{R}[0,1]$ iff $\alpha = 1$, and in that case $\int_0^1 f(x)dx = 0$. Compute $\underline{\int_0^1} f(x)dx$ and $\overline{\int_0^1} f(x)dx$ when $f = \chi_{C_\alpha}$, $0 < \alpha < 1$.

1.3. Historical notes: The integral from antiquity to Riemann

The origin of the integral lies in the works of the Greek mathematicians. Euclid (300 B.C.) in his book 'The Elements' and later Archemedes (287 - 212 B.C.) in his treatise 'The Method' gave techniques of computing areas and volumes which essentially amounted to computing definite integrals like $\int_a^b x dx$ and $\int_a^b x^2 dx$. However, the techniques were purely geometric and no general method of computing the areas and the volumes was given.

Till the seventeenth century, concepts like area and volume were not defined. They were only understood geometrically, and particular methods were given to compute them. The discovery of calculus in the seventeenth century, which culminated in the work of Issac Newton, Gottfried Wilhelm Leibniz and Leonhard Euler, defined the integral only as the inverse of the derivative, i.e., one wrote $\int_a^b f(x)dx = F(b) - F(a)$, if one could find F such that $F' = f$. Again, this gave only a method of computing the area below the curve $y = f(x)$, between $x = a$ and $x = b$, provided one could find F (called an **antiderivative** of f) such that $F' = f$. The concept of what should be called the area below the curve was not defined. It should be mentioned here that at that point of time even the concept of a function (as we understand it today) was not clear. In fact, the need to define a function more precisely had a great hand in the evolution of the integral concept.

An introduction to the notion of function was made by René Descartes (1596-1650), who gave relations between variables in terms of algebraic equations. The need to define a function precisely was felt more strongly during the second half of the eighteenth century, when the works of Jean d'Alembert (1747), Leonhard Euler (1748) and Daniel Bernoulli (1758) on the vibrating string problem started a debate on the concept of a function. By the end of the eighteenth century, the concept of function as given by Euler in 1755 became acceptable: "If some quantities depend upon other in such a way as to undergo variation when the latter are varied, then the former are called functions of the latter." However, it was still believed that the graph of a function could be traced with a "free motion of the hand", i.e., functions were still believed to be piecewise smooth. In the year 1807, Joseph Fourier rekindled interest in the definition of function. He considered 'arbitrary functions': a function which takes any values and which may or may not be governed by a common law, i.e., not given by a single formula everywhere (but still believed to be differentiable except at a finite number of points in any finite interval). For such a function f defined on $[-\pi, \pi]$, Fourier claimed that one can have the following representation:

$$f(x) = \frac{a_0}{2} + \sum_{n=1}^{\infty} [\, a_n \cos nx + b_n \sin nx \,], \qquad (1.3)$$

where the constants $a_0, a_1, \ldots$, and $b_1, b_2, \ldots$ are given by

$$a_n = \frac{1}{\pi} \int_{-\pi}^{\pi} f(x) \cos nx \, dx \ \text{ and } \ b_m = \frac{1}{\pi} \int_{-\pi}^{\pi} f(x) \sin mx \, dx, \qquad (1.4)$$

for every $n = 0, 1, \ldots$ and for every $m = 1, 2, \ldots$.

To prove his claim, Fourier implicitly assumed that the representation (1.3) is possible, and then to compute a_n and b_n, he assumed term by term integration of the series in (1.3) when multiplied with $\cos nx$ or $\sin nx$. He further assumed that the integrals in (1.4) made sense. In fact, integrability of $f(x) \cos nx$ and $f(x) \sin mx$ presented no difficulty, since for him f had at most a finite number of discontinuity points in $[-\pi, \pi]$. So he could claim the existence of integrals by the eighteenth century viewpoint, i.e., area below the curve - the area concept still being undefined. Though Fourier had broadened the concept of function to include piecewise continuous function, it was only in 1823 that Augustein-Louis Cauchy gave a precise definition of a continuous function and defined the integral of such a function as $\lim_{\|p\| \to \infty} S(P, f)$ (see definition 1.1.14). Not only did Cauchy give the definition of the definite integral and show that for a continuous function it exists, he also showed the existence of antiderivative for continuous functions. To be specific, for the first time a rigorous proof of what came to be known as the 'fundamental theorem of calculus' was given by Cauchy.

The series in (1.3) came to be known as the **Fourier series** and the constants a_n, b_n (given in (1.4)) the **Fourier coefficients** of the function f. The problem of finding conditions under which the Fourier series converges to $f(x)$ attracted many mathematicians, and it played an important role in the development of the concept of integral. Even though Cauchy's notion of integral was able to give meaning to the Fourier coefficients a_n, b_n, it was still believed that functions can have only a finite number of discontinuities in any finite interval, and hence Cauchy's notion of integral can be extended to such functions also. However, Peter Gustav Lejeune-Dirichlet in 1829 gave an example of a function ($f(x) := 1$ if x is rational and $f(x) := 0$ if x is irrational, now known as the **Dirichlet function**) which had an infinite number of discontinuities in every finite interval. Here was an example of a function which was not defined by a formula, nor could its graph be drawn. Later, in 1837, Dirichlet gave the definition of the function which is employed most often now. The example given by Dirichlet not only broadened the concept of a function, but also made mathematician feel the need to treat continuous and discontinuous functions with equal vigor. Also, it made mathematicians think about extending the notion of integral from continuous functions to a more general class of functions in order to analyze the problem of convergence of Fourier series. It was Bernhard Riemann (in 1854) who extended the notion of integral to bounded (not necessarily continuous) functions on intervals, as given in definition 1.1.14. To show that the class of functions for which integral $\int_a^b f(x)dx$ existed was indeed bigger than the class of continuous functions, he gave the following example (see also example 1.2.14).

1.3.1. Example (Riemann): Let $f : [-1/2, 1/2] \longrightarrow \mathbb{R}$ be defined by

$$f(x) := \begin{cases} x & \text{if } -1/2 < x < 1/2, \\ 0 & \text{if } x = 1/2 \text{ or } x = -1/2. \end{cases}$$

Let f be extended to $\mathbb{R}$, such that

$$f(x) := f(x + 1), \quad x \in \mathbb{R}.$$

The graph of f is given in Figure 10 below. Let the function $R : \mathbb{R} \longrightarrow \mathbb{R}$ be defined by

$$R(x) := \sum_{n=1}^{\infty} \frac{f(nx)}{n^2}, \quad x \in \mathbb{R}.$$

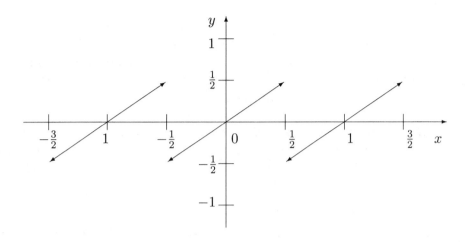

Figure 10: Graph of f

Clearly, for every x,

$$|R(x)| \leq \frac{1}{2}\sum_{n=1}^{\infty}\frac{1}{n^2} < +\infty,$$

showing that R is a bounded function. Also it is easy to see that R is continuous at x if for every k, kx is not an odd multiple of $1/2$, i.e, $x \neq m/2k$, m and $2k$ being relatively prime. Let $x = m/2k$, where m and $2k$ are relatively prime. Then $nx = mn/2k$ will be an odd multiple of $1/2$ if n is an odd multiple of k, i.e., $n = k(2\ell+1)$, $\ell = 1, 2, \ldots$. And at these points, i.e., at $k(2\ell+1)x$, $\ell = 1, 2, \ldots$, the function $f(nx)/n^2$ has a jump of magnitude $1/2n^2$ from the right and $1/2n^2$ from the left. Hence for $x = m/2k$,

$$R(x+) = R(x) - \frac{1}{2k^2}\sum_{\ell=1}^{\infty}\frac{1}{(2l+l)^2} = R(x) - \frac{\pi^2}{16k^2}$$

and

$$R(x-) = R(x) + \frac{1}{2k^2}\sum_{\ell=1}^{\infty}\frac{1}{(2l+1)^2} = R(x) + \frac{\pi^2}{16k^2}.$$

(Here we have used the result due to Euler : $\sum_{\ell=1}^{\infty}\frac{1}{(2l+1)^2} = \frac{\pi^2}{8}$. For a proof see corollary 8.10.8.)

Hence R is discontinuous at x iff $x = m/2k$, m and $2k$ being relatively prime. We note that such points are dense in $\mathbb{R}$. Finally, we show that $R(x)$ is integrable. Let $\epsilon > 0$ be any real number. Then

$$D_\epsilon := \{x \in [a,b] \mid \omega(R,x) > \epsilon\}$$
$$= \{x \in [a,b] \mid x = m/2k, m \text{ and } 2k \text{ relatively prime and } \pi^2/8k^2 > \epsilon\}.$$

Thus D_ϵ is at most a finite set, and hence is a null set. Now by theorem 1.2.16, R is integrable.

Riemann's original definition of integrability of a function f on an interval $[a, b]$ is as given in definition 1.1.14. The equivalent definition of integrability (i.e., definition 1.1.2) is due to Gaston Darboux (1875). He also proved theorem 1.1.15 and the following theorem.

1.3.2. Theorem (Fundamental theorem of calculus for Riemann integrable functions): *Let $f : [a, b] \longrightarrow \mathbb{R}$ be a Riemann integrable function. Let $F(a) := 0$ and $F(x) := \int_a^x f(t)dt, x \in [a, b]$. Then the following hold:*

(i) *F is uniformly continuous.*

(ii) *If f is continuous at $x \in [a, b]$, then F is differentiable at x and $F'(x) = f(x)$.*

(iii) *If G is any differentiable function on $[a, b]$ such that $G'(x) = f(x)$, for every $x \in (a, b)$, then $\forall\, x, y \in [a, b]$*

$$G(y) - G(x) = \int_x^y f(t)dt.$$

Proof: (i) Since f is bounded, let $|f(x)| \leq M$ for every $x \in [a, b]$. Then for $y \geq x$, using exercise 1.1.10(iii), we have

$$|F(y) - F(x)| = \left| \int_x^y f(t)dt \right| \leq \int_x^y |f(t)|\, dt \leq M\, |y - x|.$$

From this the uniform continuity of F follows.

(ii) Let f be continuous at x. Then for $y \neq x$,

$$f(x) - \frac{F(y) - F(x)}{y - x} = \frac{1}{y - x}\left[(y - x)f(x) - \int_x^y f(t)dt \right]$$

$$= \frac{1}{(y - x)}\left[\int_x^y f(x)dt - \int_x^y f(t)dt \right]$$

$$= \frac{1}{y - x}\left[\int_x^y [f(x) - f(t)]dt \right].$$

Thus

$$\left| f(x) - \frac{F(y) - F(x)}{y - x} \right| \leq \frac{1}{|y - x|}\int_x^y |f(x) - f(t)|\, dt.$$

Since f is continuous at x, given $\epsilon > 0$ we can choose $\delta > 0$ such that $|f(x) - f(t)| < \epsilon$ whenever $|x - t| < \delta$. Thus for y such that $|x - y| < \delta$,

$$\left| f(x) - \frac{F(y) - F(x)}{y - x} \right| \leq \frac{\epsilon}{|y - x|}\left| \int_x^y dt \right| = \epsilon.$$

Hence $F'(x)$ exists and

$$F'(x) := \lim_{y \to x} \frac{F(y) - F(x)}{y - x} = f(x).$$

(iii) Since $G'(x) = f(x) \ \forall \ x \in [a, b]$, $G'(x) \in \mathcal{R}[a, b]$. Let $a \le x < y \le b$ be fixed and $\epsilon > 0$ be given. Choose a partition $P = \{x = x_0 < x_1 < \cdots x_n = y\}$ of $[x, y]$ such that

$$U(P, G') - L(P, G') < \epsilon. \tag{1.5}$$

By the mean value theorem for G on each of the intervals $[x_{k-1}, x_k]$, we can choose $c_k \in (x_{k-1}, x_k)$ such that

$$G(x_k) - G(x_{k-1}) = (x_k - x_{k-1})G'(c_k).$$

Thus

$$
\begin{aligned}
G(y) - G(x) &= \sum_{k=1}^{n} [\, G(x_k) - G(x_{k-1}) \,] \\
&= \sum_{k=1}^{n} G'(c_k)(x_k - x_{k-1}).
\end{aligned}
$$

Since

$$L(G', P) \le \sum_{k=1}^{n} G'(c_k)(x_k - x_{k-1}) \le U(G', P),$$

we have

$$L(G', P) \le G(y) - G(x) \le U(G', P). \tag{1.6}$$

Also,

$$L(G', P) \le \int_x^y G'(t)dt = \int_x^y f(t)dt \le U(G', P). \tag{1.7}$$

From (1.5), (1.6) and (1.7), we have

$$\left| \int_x^y f(t)dt - [G(y) - G(x)] \right| < \epsilon.$$

Since $\epsilon > 0$ is arbitrary, we get

$$\int_x^y f(t)dt = G(y) - G(x). \ \blacksquare$$

In the exercises below, we give some of the well known consequences of the fundamental theorem of calculus.

1.3.3. Exercise:

(i) (**Integration by parts**): Let F, G be differentiable on $[a, b]$ such that $F', G' \in \mathcal{R}[a, b]$. Then

$$\int_a^b F(x)G'(x)dx = F(b)G(b) - F(a)G(a) - \int_a^b F'(x)g(x)dx.$$

(ii) (**Leibniz Rule**): Let $f : [a, b] \to \mathbb{R}$ be continuous and $u, v : [c, d] \to [a, b]$ be differentiable. Then $\forall \, \alpha \in [c, d]$,

$$\frac{d}{dx}\left(\int_{u(x)}^{v(x)} f(t)dt\right)\bigg|_{x=\alpha} = f(v(\alpha))v'(\alpha) - f(u(\alpha))u'(\alpha).$$

1.3.4. Exercise:

(i) (**Direct Substitution**): Let $g : [c, d] \to \mathbb{R}$ be a differentiable function with $g' \in \mathcal{R}[c, d]$. Let $f : g([c, d]) \to \mathbb{R}$ be continuous. Then the following integrals exist and are equal.

$$\int_c^d f(g(x))g'(x)dx = \int_{g(c)}^{g(d)} f(t)dt.$$

(ii) (**Inverse Substitution**): Let $g : [c, d] \to \mathbb{R}$ be a continuously differentiable function with $g'(x) \neq 0 \, \forall \, x \in [c, d]$. Let $g[c, d] = [a, b]$ and $f : [a, b] \to \mathbb{R}$ be continuous. Then

$$\int_a^b f(t)dt = \int_{g^{-1}(a)}^{g^{-1}(b)} f(g(x))g'(x)dx.$$

(Hint: $g'(x) \neq 0 \, \forall \, x \in [c, d]$ implies that g is strictly monotone.)

1.4. Drawbacks of the Riemann integral

Using theorem 1.3.2, Hermann Hankel (1871) constructed the function

$$G(x) := \int_0^x R(t)dt,$$

where $R(t)$ is the function considered by Riemann as in example 1.3.1. The function $G(x)$ provided an example of a function which is continuous everywhere but is not differentiable at an infinite set of points, contrary to the popular belief in the 18th century that a continuous function is differentiable everywhere except at a finite number of points. It was Karl Weierstrass (1872) who finally dispelled all doubts by constructing a function on the real line which is continuous everywhere but differentiable nowhere. These developments raised the question about the existence of the derivative for non-continuous functions. The second fallout of theorem 1.3.2 was that one could no longer claim that integration (in the sense of Riemann) is the reverse of differentiation. One could no longer say that a pair of functions F, f on $[a, b]$, $f \in \mathcal{R}[a, b]$, are related by the equation

$$F(y) - F(x) = \int_x^y f(t)dt, \quad a \leq x < y \leq b,$$

iff F is differentiable and $F'(x) = f(x)$. The beauty of the fundamental theorem of calculus, as exhibited by Cauchy, lost its charm. This motivated mathematicians to look at differentiability properties of functions more critically on one hand, and on the other to look for differentiable functions $f : [a, b] \longrightarrow \mathbb{R}$ such that f' is bounded but not integrable. Ulisse Dini (1878) introduced four different concepts of derivative of a function at a point. Using these concepts, he showed that for a bounded integrable function $f : [a, b] \longrightarrow \mathbb{R}$, the function $F(x) := \int_a^x f(t)dt$ has all the four derivatives, they are all bounded, integrable and $F(x) - F(a) = \int_a^x (DF)(t)dt$, where $DF(t)$ is any one of those derivatives. He further pointed out that the condition f' be integrable in theorem 1.3.2(iii) is necessary. He also conjectured that it should be possible to construct functions $f : [a, b] \longrightarrow \mathbb{R}$ which have bounded, non-integrable derivatives. The first example of such a function was given by Vito Volterra (1881). We point out here that it is easy to construct an example of a function $f : [a, b] \longrightarrow \mathbb{R}$ such that f is differentiable but f' is not bounded and hence not integrable, for example $f(x) = x^2 \sin(1/x^2)$ if $x \neq 0$ and $f(0) = 0$ if $x = 0, x \in [0, 1]$, is one such function.

1.4.1. Example (Volterra): **Step 1:** Let $a \in \mathbb{R}$. Define $f_a : \mathbb{R} \longrightarrow \mathbb{R}$ by

$$f_a(x) := \begin{cases} (x - a)^2 \sin \dfrac{1}{x - a} & \text{if } x \neq a, \\ 0 & \text{if } x = a. \end{cases}$$

The graph of the function f_a is as given in Figure 11. It is easy to see that f_a is differentiable everywhere and f_a' vanishes at an infinite number of points near $x = a$.

Step 2: Let $a, b \in \mathbb{R}$ with $a < b$. Let

$$\alpha_a := \sup\{x \mid a < x \leq (a + b)/2 \text{ and } f_a'(x) = 0\}.$$

Define $f_{a,b} : (a, b) \longrightarrow \mathbb{R}$ as follows:

$$f_{a,b}(x) := \begin{cases} f_a(x) & \text{if } a < x \leq \alpha_a, \\ f_a(\alpha_a) & \text{if } \alpha_a \leq x \leq b - (\alpha_a - a), \\ f_a(b + a - x) & \text{if } b - (\alpha_a - a) \leq x < b. \end{cases}$$

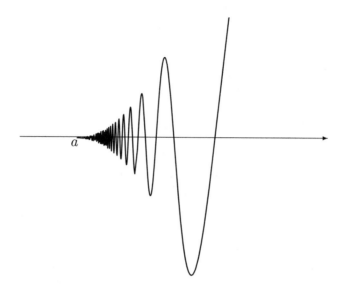

Figure 11: The function f_a

Note that $f_{a,b}(x)$ is defined as $f_a(x)$ in $(a, \alpha_a]$, constant with values $f_a(\alpha_a)$ in $[\alpha_a, (a+b)/2)$, and in $[(a+b)/2, b)$ it is just the reflection of $f_a(x)$ about the line $(a+b)/2$. Since $f_{a,b}(x) = -f_b(x)$ for $x \in [b - (\alpha_a - a), b)$, we have

$$|f_{a,b}(x)| \leq \max\{(b-x)^2, (a-x)^2\}, \ \forall \, x \in (a, b).$$

It is easy to check that $f_{a,b}$ is differentiable everywhere and

$$|f'_{a,b}(x)| \leq 2(b-a) + 1.$$

Further,

$$f_{a,b}(x) = 2(x-a)\sin(1/(x-a)) - \cos(1/x - a), \ \text{for } x \text{ near } a.$$

Thus by choosing n sufficiently large, we can always select x close to a such that $1/(x-a) = n\pi$ and hence $f'_{a,b}(x) = \pm 1$. Similarly near b, $f'_{a,b}(x)$ oscillates infinitely often between $+1$ and -1.

Step 3: Let C_α be the Cantor set, $0 < \alpha < 1$, as constructed in example 1.2.13. Recall that

$$C_\alpha = [0,1] \setminus \left[\bigcup_{n=1}^{\infty} \left(\bigcup_{j=1}^{2^{n-1}} I_j^{n-1} \right) \right],$$

where for each $n = 1, 2, \ldots$ and $1 \leq j \leq 2^{n-1}, I_j^{n-1}$ is one of the open intervals removed from $[0,1]$ at the nth stage. Define $F : [0,1] \longrightarrow \mathbb{R}$ by

$$F(x) := \begin{cases} 0 & \text{if } x \in C_\alpha, \\ f_{a,b}(x) & \text{if } x \in I_j^{n-1} := (a,b) \text{ for some } n \text{ and } j, 1 \leq j \leq 2^{n-1}. \end{cases}$$

If $x \notin C_\alpha$, then clearly, F is differentiable and $F'(x) = f'_{a,b}(x)$ for some $(a, b) \subset [0, 1]$. Let $x \in C_\alpha$ and let $\eta > 0$ be arbitrary. Let $y \in [0, 1]$ be such that $|y - x| < \eta$. If $y \in C_\alpha$, then

$$\left| \frac{F(y) - F(x)}{y - x} \right| = 0.$$

In case $y \notin C_\alpha$, let $y \in I_j^{n-1} := (a, b)$ for some n, j with $1 \leq j \leq 2^{n-1}$. Without loss of generality, let $|a - x| < |b - x|$. Then

$$\left| \frac{F(y) - F(x)}{y - x} \right| = \left| \frac{F(y)}{y - x} \right| = \left| \frac{(y - a)^2 \sin(1/(y - a))}{y - x} \right| \leq |y - x| < \eta.$$

Thus $F'(x) = 0$ for $x \notin C_\alpha$. Hence F is differentiable everywhere and

$$|F'(x)| \leq |f'_{a,b}(x)| \leq 3, \quad \forall \, x \in [0, 1].$$

Finally, F' is not continuous at each $x \in C_\alpha$. To see this, fix $x \in C_\alpha$ and let $\delta > 0$ be arbitrary. Then we can choose $y \notin C_\alpha$ such that $|x - y| < \delta$ and $F'(y) = f'_{a,b}(y) = \pm 1$; here we use the facts that C_α is nowhere dense and that $f'_{a,b}(x)$ fluctuates infinitely often near a and b between ± 1. Thus F' is not continuous on C_α and $\lambda(C_\alpha) = \alpha > 0$. Hence F' is not Riemann integrable, by corollary 1.2.7.

1.4.2. Remark: We recall that Fourier in his works had implicitly assumed that a series of functions can be integrated term by term. Under what conditions this can be justified? The equivalent questions is: Let $\{f_n\}_{n \geq 1}$ be a sequence of Riemann integrable functions on an interval $[a, b]$. Let $f_n(x) \longrightarrow f(x) \; \forall \; x \in [a, b]$. Can we say f is Riemann integrable on $[a, b]$ and

$$\lim_{n \to \infty} \int_a^b f_n(x) dx = \int_a^b f(x) dx?$$

The following exercises show that the answer in general is in the negative.

1.4.3. Exercise:

(i) Let $f_n(x) = ne^{-nx}$ for $x \in [0, 1]$ and $n = 1, 2, \dots$. Show that each f_n is Riemann integrable and $\lim_{n \to \infty} f_n(x) = f(x) = 0 \; \forall \, x \in (0, 1]$, but

$$\int_0^1 f_n dx \quad \text{does not converge to} \quad \int_0^1 f(x) dx.$$

(ii) Let $\{r_1, r_2, \dots\}$ be an enumeration of the rationals in $[0, 1]$. Define $\forall \, n = 1, 2, \dots$,

$$f_n(x) := \begin{cases} 1 & \text{if} \quad x \in \{r_1, r_2, \dots, r_n\}, \\ 0 & \text{if} \quad x \in [0, 1] \setminus \{r_1, r_2, \dots, r_n\}. \end{cases}$$

Show that $\{f_n\}_{n\geq 1}$ is a convergent sequence of Riemann integrable functions and $f(x) =: \lim\limits_{n\to\infty} f_n(x)$ is a bounded function which is not Riemann integrable.

A sufficient condition that allows the interchange of the limit and integration is given by the following theorem.

1.4.4. Theorem: *Let $\{f_n\}_{n\geq 1}$ be a sequence of Riemann integrable functions on $[a,b]$ and let $\{f_n\}_{n\geq 1}$ converge to a function f uniformly on $[a,b]$. Then f is also Riemann integrable on $[a,b]$ and*

$$\int_a^b f(x)dx = \lim_{n\to\infty} \int_a^b f_n(x)dx.$$

Proof: We ask the reader to supply the proof as follows:

(i) Using the uniform convergence of $\{f_n\}_{n\geq 1}$, deduce that f is bounded on $[a,b]$.

(ii) Let $E_n := \{x \in [a,b]| f_n$ is not continuous at $x\}$ and $E := \bigcup_{n=1}^{\infty} E_n$. Show that E is a null set and f is continuous on $[a,b] \setminus E$. Hence $f \in \mathcal{R}[a,b]$

(iii) Show that

$$\lim_{n\to\infty} \left| \int_a^b f_n(x)\, dx - \int_a^b f(x)\, dx \right| = 0.$$

This will prove the theorem. ∎

1.4.5. Exercise: Let $f_n(x) = x^n, 0 \leq x \leq 1, \quad n = 1, 2, \ldots$. Show that f_n is Riemann integrable on $[0,1]$. Show that $\{f_n(x)\}_{n\geq 1}$ converges for every $x \in [0,1]$. Is the limit function f Riemann integrable? Can you conclude that

$$\lim_{n\to\infty} \int_0^1 f_n(x)dx = \int_0^1 f(x)dx?$$

Another sufficient condition for convergence of Riemann integrals is given by the following theorem.

1.4.6. Theorem (Arzela): *Let $\{f_n\}_{n\geq 1}$ be a sequence of Riemann integrable functions on $[a,b]$ such that for some $M > 0, |f_n(x)| < M \ \forall \ x \in [a,b]$ and $\forall \ n = 1, 2, \ldots$. Let $f_n(x) \longrightarrow f(x) \ \forall \ x \in [a,b]$ and let f be Riemann integrable on $[a,b]$. Then*

$$\lim_{n\to\infty} \int_a^b f_n(x)dx = \int_a^b f(x)dx.$$

Proof: We refer to Luxemberg [24] for a proof. We shall deduce this theorem as a consequence of a more general theorem: Lebesgue's dominated convergence theorem (see exercise 5.5.9). ■

As we see from theorems 1.4.4 and 1.4.6, one has to impose quite strong conditions to ensure the validity of interchanging of the limit and the integral sign. For example, in theorem 1.4.6, one has to assume that the limit function is also Riemann integrable. That this condition cannot be dropped follows from exercise 1.4.3(ii) and the next exercise.

1.4.7. Exercise: Let $f_n : [0,1] \longrightarrow \mathbb{R}$ be defined by

$$f_n(x) := \begin{cases} 1 & \text{if} \quad x \neq k/2^n, \\ 0 & \text{if} \quad x = k/2^n \text{ for some } k, 1 \leq k \leq 2^n - 1. \end{cases}$$

Note that for all n we have $0 \leq f_n(x) \leq 1 \ \forall \, x \in [0,1]$. Show that $f_n \in \mathcal{R}[a,b]$ $\forall \, n = 1, 2, \ldots$. Let $f : [0,1] \longrightarrow \mathbb{R}$ be defined by

$$f(x) := \begin{cases} 1 & \text{if} \quad x \neq k/2^n \text{ for any } n, 1 \leq k \leq 2^n, \\ 0 & \text{if} \quad x = k/2^n \text{ for some } n, 1 \leq k \leq 2^n. \end{cases}$$

Show that $f_n(x) \to f(x) \ \forall \, x \in [0,1]$, but $f \notin \mathcal{R}[a,b]$.

We discuss next another drawback of Riemann integration.

Let $C[a,b]$ denote the set of all continuous functions $f : [a,b] \longrightarrow \mathbb{R}$. For $f, g \in C[a,b]$, define

$$d(f,g) := \int_a^b |f(x) - g(x)| \, dx.$$

We leave it to the reader to check that $d(f,g)$ is indeed a metric on $C[a,b]$, i.e., it has the following properties: for f, g and $h \in C[a,b]$,

(i) $d(f,g) \geq 0$, and $d(f,g) = 0$ iff $f = g$.

(ii) $d(f,g) = d(g,f)$.

(iii) $d(f,h) \leq d(f,g) + d(g,h)$.

The metric $d(f,g)$ is called the L_1-**metric on** $C[a,b]$. One would like to know: is $C[a,b]$ complete under this metric? Let $\{f_n\}_{n \geq 1}$ be a Cauchy sequence in $C[a,b]$ in the L_1-metric, i.e., such that $d(f_n, f_m) \longrightarrow 0$ as $n, m \longrightarrow \infty$. The question is, does there exist some function $f \in C[a,b]$ such that $d(f_n, f) \longrightarrow 0$ as $n \longrightarrow \infty$? Let us consider the following particular situation: let $a = 0, b = 1$. For every $n \geq 1$, consider the function $f_n : [0,1] \longrightarrow \mathbb{R}$ defined by

$$f_n(x) := \begin{cases} 0 & \text{if } 0 \leq x \leq 1/2, \\ n(x - 1/2) & \text{if } 1/2 \leq x \leq 1/2 + 1/n, \\ 1 & \text{if } 1/2 + 1/n \leq x \leq 1. \end{cases}$$

The graph of f_n is given in Figure 12. Suppose that there exists a function $f : [0,1] \longrightarrow \mathbb{R}$ which is continuous and $d(f_n, f) \longrightarrow 0$ as $n \to \infty$. Then $\forall \, n \geq 1$,

$$\int_0^{1/2} |f(x)|dx = \int_0^{1/2} |f_n(x) - f(x)|dx$$

$$\leq \int_0^1 |f_n(x) - f(x)|dx.$$

Thus

$$\int_0^{1/2} |f(x)|dx = 0.$$

Hence by exercise 1.1.8,

$$f(x) = 0, \, \forall \, 0 \leq x < 1/2.$$

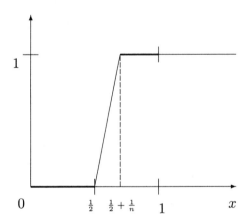

Figure 12 : The function f_n

On the other hand, if $1 \geq x > 1/2$ and the integer n_0 is such that $1/2 + 1/n_0 < x$, then $\forall \, n \geq n_0$,

$$\int_x^1 |1 - f(x)| \, dx = \int_x^1 |f_n(x) - f(x)| \, dx$$

$$\leq \int_0^1 |f_n(x) - f(x)| \, dx.$$

Hence

$$\int_x^1 |1 - f(x)| \, dx = 0 \text{ for every } 1/2 < x \le 1.$$

This implies, by exercise 1.1.8,

$$f(x) = 1 \text{ for every } 1/2 < x \le 1.$$

Thus $f \notin C[0,1]$. This shows that the space $C[a,b]$ is not complete with respect to the L_1-metric.

1.4.8. Exercise (Incompleteness of $\mathcal{R}[a,b]$ in the L_1-metric):

(i) Show that $d(f,g)$ makes sense for $f, g \in \mathcal{R}[a,b]$, but is not a metric on $\mathcal{R}[a,b]$. (Hint: Properties (i), (ii) and (iii) hold, except that $d(f,g) = 0$ need not imply that $f(x) = g(x) \; \forall \, x \in [a,b]$. It is only what is called a **pseudo-metric**.)

(ii) For $f, g \in \mathcal{R}[a,b]$, we say f is equivalent to g and write $f \sim g$ if $\{x \in [a,b] | f(x) \ne g(x)\}$ is a null set. Show that $\sim$ is an equivalence relation on $\mathcal{R}[a,b]$ and

$$\int_a^b f(x) dx = \int_a^b g(x) dx \text{ if } f \sim g.$$

Let $\tilde{\mathcal{R}}[a,b]$ denote the set of all equivalence classes and let $\tilde{f}$ denote the equivalence class which contains $f \in \mathcal{R}[a,b]$. Let

$$\tilde{d}(\tilde{f}, \tilde{g}) := \int_a^b |f(x) - g(x)| \, dx,$$

for $\tilde{f}, \tilde{g} \in \tilde{\mathcal{R}}[a,b]$. Show that $\tilde{d}$ is a well-defined metric on $\tilde{\mathcal{R}}[a,b]$, called the L_1-**metric**.

(iii) Show that $\tilde{\mathcal{R}}[a,b]$ is not complete under the metric $\tilde{d}$ as follows: Consider the Cantor set $C_\alpha, 0 < \alpha < 1$, as constructed in example 1.2.13. Recall that $C_\alpha = \bigcap_{n=1}^\infty B_n = [0,1] \setminus (\bigcup_{n=1}^\infty A_n)$. Let $f_n = \chi_{B_n}$ for every $n \ge 1$.

(a) Show that $f_n \in \mathcal{R}[a,b]$ with

$$\int_0^1 f_n(x) dx > 1 - \alpha \; \forall \, n, \text{ and } \lim_{n \to \infty} \int_0^1 |f_n(x) - f_m(x)| dx = 0.$$

(b) Show that there does not exist any function $f \in \mathcal{R}[0,1]$ such that

$$\lim_{n \to \infty} \int_0^1 |f_n(x) - f(x)| \, dx = 0, \tag{1.8}$$

as follows:
Suppose there exists $f \in \mathcal{R}[a,b]$ such that (1.8) holds. Then

(b_1) $\displaystyle\int_0^1 f(x)dx = \lim_{n\to\infty} \int_0^1 f_n(x)dx \geq 1 - \alpha.$

(b_2) There exists a function $g \in \mathcal{R}[a,b]$ such that $g(x) = 0$, for every $x \in \bigcup_{n=1}^\infty A_n$ and $f \sim g$. Using this, deduce that

$$\int_0^1 f(x)dx = \underline{\int_0^1} g(x)dx = 0,$$

which is in contradiction to (b_1).

The above exercise shows that $\mathcal{R}[a,b]$ is not a complete metric space with respect to the metric $\tilde{d}$. Since every metric space can be completed, one wonders about the completion of the metric space $\tilde{\mathcal{R}}[a,b]$. A concrete realization of the completion of $\tilde{\mathcal{R}}[a,b]$ is one of the outcomes of Lebesgue's theory of integration (see section 5.6).

Some other drawbacks of the Riemann integral are: it is defined only for bounded functions; it is defined for functions on bounded intervals only; functions, even if they are defined on bounded intervals and have finite range (e.g., Dirichlet's function) are not necessarily integrable; and so on.

From the year 1854 onwards, when Riemann extended the definition of integral due to Cauchy, many mathematicians contributed in the effort to extend the notion of integral in order to remove these drawbacks. The efforts of these mathematicians: Camille Jordan, Emile Borel, René Baire, Johann Radon to name a few, culminated in the work of Henri Lebesgue, who in 1902 announced a generalization of the Riemann integral. In 1920, Friedrich Riesz gave an alternative method of constructing this extended integral. The approach of Lebesgue, which was later (1914) made abstract by Constantin Carathéodory, is more set theoretic, while the approach of Riesz is purely function theoretic. We outline these approaches in the next chapter.

Chapter 2

Recipes for extending the Riemann integral

2.1. A function theoretic view of the Riemann integral

Let us recall that $\mathcal{R}[a, b]$, the set of Riemann integrable functions on the interval $[a, b]$, has the following properties:

(i) $\mathcal{R}[a, b]$ is a vector space over $\mathbb{R}$.

(ii) The map $f \longmapsto \int_a^b f(x)\,dx, f \in \mathcal{R}[a, b]$, is a nonnegative linear map from $\mathcal{R}[a, b]$ to $\mathbb{R}$.

(iii) Whenever functions $f_n, g \in \mathcal{R}[a, b]$, $\quad n = 1, 2, \ldots$, are such that $|f_n(x)| \leq |g(x)|$ and $\lim_{n\to\infty} f_n(x) = g(x) \quad \forall\, x \in [a, b]$, then

$$\lim_{n\to\infty} \int_a^b f_n(x)\,dx = \int_a^b g(x)\,dx.$$

(The property (iii) follows from theorem 1.4.6. Let us call it as **dominated convergence property**.)

In view of the discussion in section 1.4, our aim is to extend the notion of Riemann integral to a class of functions bigger than $\mathcal{R}[a, b]$, keeping the properties (i), (ii), (iii) intact. We state it as the following:

Extension Problem: Construct a class $\mathcal{L}$ of functions from $\mathbb{R}$ to $\mathbb{R}$ and define a map $I : \mathcal{L} \longrightarrow \mathbb{R}$ with the following properties:

(i) $\mathcal{L}$ is a vector space over $\mathbb{R}$ and $\mathcal{R}[a, b]$ is a subspace of $\mathcal{L}$.

(ii) $I : \mathcal{L} \longrightarrow \mathbb{R}$ is nonnegative and linear, i.e.,

$$I(f) \geq 0 \ \forall \ f \in \mathcal{L} \text{ with } f \geq 0$$

and

$$I(\alpha f + \beta g) = \alpha I(f) + \beta I(g), \ \forall \ f, g \in \mathcal{L}; \ \alpha, \beta \in \mathbb{R}.$$

(iii) For $f \in \mathcal{R}[a,b]$,

$$I(f) = \int_a^b f(x) \, dx.$$

(iv) $I(f)$ is free from the defects of the Riemann integral.

(In (i) and (ii), even though f is defined only on $[a,b]$, we can regard it as a function on $\mathbb{R}$ by putting $f(x) = 0 \ \forall \ x \in \mathbb{R} \setminus [a,b]$.)

In view of (iii) we can call $I(f)$ the extended integral of f.

To solve the extension problem, let us look at the Riemann integral from a different viewpoint. Let $f : [a,b] \longrightarrow \mathbb{R}$ be a bounded function. Given a partition $P = \{a = x_0 < x_1 < \cdots x_n = b\}$ of $[a,b]$, for $x \in [a,b]$, let

$$\Phi_P(x) := m_1 \, \chi_{[x_0,x_1]}(x) + \sum_{i=2}^n m_i \, \chi_{(x_{i-1},x_i]}(x)$$

and

$$\Psi_P(x) := M_1 \, \chi_{[x_0,x_1]}(x) + \sum_{i=2}^n M_i \, \chi_{(x_{i-1},x_i]}(x).$$

Here

$$m_1 := \inf\{f(x) \mid x_0 \leq x \leq x_1\},$$
$$M_1 := \sup\{f(x) \mid x_0 \leq x \leq x_1\},$$
$$m_i := \inf\{f(x) \mid x_i < x \leq x_{i+1}\},$$
$$M_i := \sup\{f(x) \mid x_i < x \leq x_{i+1}\}, \quad 1 \leq i \leq n.$$

Then for every $x \in [a,b]$, $\Phi_P(x) \leq f(x) \leq \Psi_p(x)$ and $\Phi_P, \Psi_P \in \mathcal{R}[a,b]$. Further,

$$\int_a^b \Phi_P(x)dx = L(P,f) \quad \text{and} \quad \int_a^b \Psi_P(x)dx = U(P,f),$$

where $L(P,f)$ and $U(P,f)$ are the lower and upper sums of f with respect to the partition P.

In case f is Riemann integrable, by theorem 1.1.4 there exists a sequence of partitions $\{P_n\}_{n \geq 1}$ such that each P_{n+1} is a refinement of P_n, $\|P_n\| \to 0$ as $n \to \infty$ and

$$\int_a^b f(x)dx = \lim_{n\to\infty} L(P_n,f) = \lim_{n\to\infty} U(P_n,f).$$

Note that $\forall\, n \geq 1$ and $\forall\, x \in [a,b]$,

$$\Phi_{P_n}(x) \;\leq\; \Phi_{P_{n+1}}(x) \;\leq\; f(x) \;\leq\; \Psi_{P_{n+1}}(x) \leq \Psi_{P_n}(x).$$

Thus $\{\Phi_{P_n}\}_{n\geq 1}$ is an increasing sequence of functions bounded above by f and $\{\Psi_{P_n}\}_{n\geq 1}$ is a decreasing sequence of functions bounded below by f at every point in $[a,b]$. Further,

$$\int_a^b f(x)dx \;=\; \lim_{n\to\infty} \int_a^b \Phi_{P_n}(x)dx \;=\; \lim_{n\to\infty} \int_a^b \Psi_{P_n}(x)dx. \qquad (2.1)$$

The functions Φ_P and Ψ_P are functions of a special type:

2.1.1. Definition: A function $\Phi : [a,b] \to \mathbb{R}$ is called a **step function** if there exists a partition $P = \{a = x_0 < x_1 < \cdots < x_n = b\}$ of $[a,b]$ such that Φ is constant, say C_i, on every open interval $(x_i, x_{i+1}), 0 \leq i \leq n-1$.

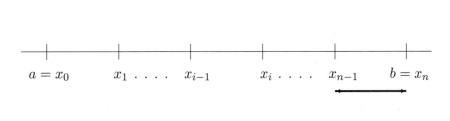

Figure 13 : Graph of a step function

Thus Φ_{P_n} and Ψ_{P_n}, as defined above, are examples of step functions, and in view of (2.1) we can treat the integrals of the step functions as the building blocks for the Riemann integral of f. In order to enlarge the space $\mathcal{R}[a,b]$ and to extend the notion of integral, it is natural to extend the space of building blocks itself. There are two well-known methods for doing this. We give an outline of each method.

2.2. Lebesgue's recipe

Let us note that a step function takes only finitely many values, and these are taken on disjoint open intervals. As far as the integral is concerned, we can disregard the values of the step function at the partition points. In fact, at these points the step function can be given an arbitrary value, without changing its Riemann integral. Thus if $\Phi : [a,b] \longrightarrow \mathbb{R}$ is a step function such that $\Phi(x) = C_k$ for $x \in (x_{k-1}x_k)$, where $a = x_0 < x_1 < \cdots < x_n = b$, then we can represent Φ as follows:

$$\Phi(x) = \sum_{k=1}^{n} C_k \chi_{I_k}(x), \quad x \in [a, b], \tag{2.2}$$

where $I_k = [x_{k-1}, x_k)$ for $1 \le k \le n - 1$ and $I_n = [x_{n-1}, x_n]$. Note that $[a, b] = \bigcup_{k=1}^{n} I_k$, with $I_i \cap I_j = \emptyset$ for $i \ne j$. In order to extend the class of building blocks for our new integral, we can consider functions of the type $s := \sum_{i=1}^{n} C_i \chi_{A_i}$, where n is a positive integer and the A_i's are subsets of $[a, b]$ such that $A_i \cap A_j = \emptyset$ for $i \ne j$ and $\bigcup_{i=1}^{n} A_i = [a, b]$. Let us call such functions **generalized step functions** or **simple functions**. The advantage of such functions is that they take only finitely many values (like step functions) on disjoint sets (which are not necessarily intervals, as those for the step functions are). Also, they make sense for any subset E of $\mathbb{R}$. For example, if $E = \bigcup_{i=1}^{n} A_i$, where $A_i \cap A_j = \emptyset$ for $i \ne j$, then we can call $s = \sum_{i=1}^{m} C_i \chi_{A_i}$ a simple function on E. Let us denote by $\mathbb{L}_0$ the collection of simple functions on $\mathbb{R}$. Note that a step function on $[a, b]$ can be treated as a simple function on $\mathbb{R}$ by defining it to be zero outside $[a, b]$. Thus $\mathbb{L}_0$ includes the class of step functions on $\mathbb{R}$. Further, noting that for a step function Φ on $[a, b]$ as given by (2.2) above, since

$$\int_a^b \Phi(x)dx = \sum_{i=1}^{n} C_i \lambda(I_i), \tag{2.3}$$

we can extend the notion of integral to simple functions as follows: for $s \in \mathbb{L}_0$ with $s = \sum_{i=1}^{n} C_i \chi_{A_i}$, let the extended integral be

$$\int s d\lambda := \sum_{i=1}^{n} C_i \lambda(A_i). \tag{2.4}$$

Of course in (2.4) the quantities $\lambda(A_i), 1 \le i \le n$, are undefined. Comparing equation (2.4) with equation (2.3) and keeping in mind that we have to have $\int \Phi d\lambda = \int_a^b \Phi(x)dx$ in case Φ is a step function, it is natural to expect $\lambda(A_i)$ to be the 'length of the set A_i'. Thus the first step in our extension program should be: try to extend the notion of length from intervals to a bigger class of subsets of $\mathbb{R}$. This we will discuss in chapters 3 and 4. Supposing we are able to define the notion of length for a class $\mathcal{A}$ of subsets of $\mathbb{R}$ such that $\mathcal{A}$ includes intervals, we can consider functions of the type $\sum_{i=1}^{n} C_i \chi_{A_i}$, with each $A_i \in \mathcal{A}$. Such functions are called **simple measurable functions**. For such a function we define the new integral by (2.4). Since $\lambda(A_i)$ could be $+\infty$, to make the sum in (2.4) meaningful, we assume that $C_i \ge 0 \ \forall \ i$. That is, we consider only nonnegative simple measurable functions. Since we expect our integral to behave nicely under limiting operations, we consider functions $f : \mathbb{R} \longrightarrow \mathbb{R}$ for which one can construct sequences $\{s_n\}_{n \ge 1}$ of nonnegative simple functions such that $0 \le s_n \le f$ and $s_n(x) \longrightarrow f(x) \ \forall \ x \in \mathbb{R}$.

Note that this automatically forces f to be nonnegative. For such functions f, we can define

$$\int f d\lambda := \lim_{n \to \infty} \int s_n d\lambda.$$

This raises many questions: Is $\int f d\lambda$ well-defined, i.e., is it independent of the choice of the sequence $\{s_n\}_{n \geq 1}$? For what nonnegative functions $f : \mathbb{R} \longrightarrow \mathbb{R}$, is construction of such sequences possible? A function for which construction of such a sequence is possible is called a **measurable function** and will be discussed in chapter 5. Note that the integral $\int f d\lambda$ could be $+\infty$ for $f \geq 0$ and f measurable. For a general function $f : \mathbb{R} \longrightarrow \mathbb{R}$, one considers the **positive part** f^+ and the **negative part** f^-, defined by $f^+(x) := f(x)$ if $f(x) \geq 0$ and $f^+(x) = 0$ if $f(x) < 0$. Let $f^-(x) := f^+(x) - f(x)$. Then $f = f^+ - f^-$. One notes that f^+ and f^- are both nonnegative functions. If both f^+ and f^- are measurable, we say f is a measurable function. For a measurable function f, the required linearity property of the integral demands that we should define

$$\int f d\lambda := \int f^+ d\lambda - \int f^- d\lambda.$$

A problem arises in the case $\int f^+ d\lambda = \int f^- d\lambda = +\infty$. To overcome this, one says f is**Lebesgue integrable** if $\int f^+ d\lambda < +\infty$ and $\int f^- d\lambda < +\infty$. Then the class of Lebesgue integrable function is the required class of functions for which $\int f d\lambda$ is well-defined. The detailed construction of this integral and the proof that this integral really works, i.e., indeed extends the Riemann integral and removes its drawbacks, will be analyzed in chapters 5 and 6.

2.3. Riesz-Daniel recipe

There is another way of characterizing the Riemann integrability of functions. Since $\sup A = -\inf(-A)$ for any subset A of $\mathbb{R}$, f is Riemann integrable on $[a, b]$ if and only if

$$\overline{\int_a^b} f \, dx = - \left[\underline{\int_a^b} (-f) dx \right] \tag{2.5}$$

(as the expression on the right side is the lower integral of f). Thus among all functions on $[a, b]$ we consider the subset of those which satisfy equation (2.5). This subset turns out to be a vector space, and the integral is linear on it.

One way of extending the definition of Riemann integral would be not to insist on being able to approximate from both 'inside' and 'outside', but be content with approximating the area either from 'inside' or from 'outside' only.

Let us call a function $\Phi : \mathbb{R} \longrightarrow \mathbb{R}$ a **step function** on $\mathbb{R}$ if $\exists\, a, b \in \mathbb{R}$ with $a < b$ such that $\Phi(x) = 0$ for $x \notin [a, b]$ and Φ restricted to $[a, b]$ is a step function as defined in 2.1.1. For a step function Φ on $\mathbb{R}$, let $\int \Phi d\lambda$ be defined as in equation (2.3). With step function on $\mathbb{R}$ as building blocks, let us try to approximate the 'area' from 'inside' only. Thus we are tempted to define (tentatively) the extended integral $\int f d\lambda$ as follows:

$$\int f d\lambda := \sup \int \Phi d\lambda,$$

where the supremum is taken over all step functions Φ such that $\Phi \le f$. We may then call f integrable if $\int f$ is finite. But this naive approach has a problem: when f is integrable $-f$ need not be integrable, and in particular $\int f d\lambda = -\int (-f) d\lambda$ may not hold. To overcome this problem, we proceed as follows:

Let $\mathcal{L}^+$ denote the set of all those functions f for which there exists a sequence $\{\Phi_n\}_{n \ge 1}$ of step functions such that $\{\Phi_n\}_{n \ge 1}$ increases to f and $\lim_{n \to \infty} \int \Phi_n d\lambda$ exists. Note that $\mathcal{L}^+$ includes the class of step functions. We then define $\int f d\lambda$ for $f \in \mathcal{L}^+$ by setting

$$\int f d\lambda := \lim_{n \to \infty} \int \Phi_n d\lambda.$$

One then shows that this is well-defined. It is easy to see that $\mathcal{L}^+$ is closed under addition and scalar multiplication by positive reals. To get a vector space out of this, we simply take $\mathcal{L} := \mathcal{L}^+ - \mathcal{L}^+$. That is, $\mathcal{L}$ consists of functions h which can be written as $h = f - g$, where $f, g \in \mathcal{L}^+$, and extend the integral in an obvious way:

$$\int h\, d\lambda = \int f\, d\lambda - \int g\, d\lambda.$$

Of course, one has to show that this integral is well-defined.

Notice that if we take $f_n \in \mathcal{L}^+$ such that $\{f_n\}_{n \ge 1}$ increases to f with $\int f_n$ bounded by some constant $\forall\, n$, then it is almost clear that $f \in \mathcal{L}^+$ and that we have

$$\int f\, d\lambda = \lim_{n \to \infty} \int f_n\, d\lambda.$$

This is a special case of the so-called *monotone convergence theorem*. With a little more effort, one can prove a similar result with no restrictions on f_n except that $f_n \in \mathcal{L}$. This shows that this method cannot enlarge $\mathcal{L}$ any further.

We refer the reader for more details about this way of developing the Lebesgue integral to Daniel [10], Riesz [31], [32], [33] and Stone [39].

Chapter 3

General extension theory

3.1. First extension

3.1.1. In chapter 2 we saw that the first step towards extending the notion of Riemann integral is to extend the length function λ from intervals to a larger class of subsets of $\mathbb{R}$. Suppose $E \subseteq \mathbb{R}$ is such that it is union of a finite number of pairwise disjoint intervals. Then it is natural to define the length of E to be the sum of the lengths of these intervals. Mathematically, let $E = \bigcup_{k=1}^{n} I_k$, where $I_k \in \mathcal{I}$ and $I_k \cap I_\ell = \emptyset$ for $1 \leq k \neq \ell \leq n$. Since the extended notion of length of E, denoted by $\tilde{\lambda}(E)$, is expected to be finitely additive, we will have

$$\tilde{\lambda}(E) = \sum_{k=1}^{n} \tilde{\lambda}(I_k) = \sum_{k=1}^{n} \lambda(I_k). \tag{3.1}$$

Thus, if $E = \bigcup_{k=1}^{n} I_k$, where the I_k's are pairwise disjoint intervals, the above forces us to define

$$\tilde{\lambda}(E) := \sum_{k=1}^{n} \lambda(I_k). \tag{3.2}$$

Before we proceed further, we should check that $\tilde{\lambda}$ as in equation (3.2) is well-defined. Let $E = \bigcup_{k=1}^{n} I_k = \bigcup_{\ell=1}^{m} J_\ell$, where $I_k, J_\ell \in \mathcal{I}$ with $I_{k_1} \cap I_{k_2} = \emptyset$ for $1 \leq k_1 \neq k_2 \leq n$ and $J_{\ell_1} \cap J_{\ell_2} = \emptyset$ for $1 \leq \ell_1 \neq \ell_2 \leq m$. Then $\sum_{k=1}^{n} \lambda(I_k) = \sum_{\ell=1}^{m} \lambda(J_\ell)$. To check this, we note that $I_k = \bigcup_{\ell=1}^{m}(I_k \cap J_\ell)$ for every k and $J_\ell = \bigcup_{k=1}^{n}(I_k \cap J_\ell)$ for every ℓ, where the intervals $I_k \cap J_\ell$

are pairwise disjoint. Now using finite additivity of λ, we have

$$\sum_{k=1}^{n} \lambda(I_k) = \sum_{k=1}^{n} \sum_{\ell=1}^{m} \lambda(I_k \cap J_\ell) = \sum_{\ell=1}^{m} \lambda(J_\ell).$$

Note that here we have used the fact that for $I_k, J_\ell \in \mathcal{I}$, $I_k \cap J_\ell \in \mathcal{I}$. Thus $\tilde{\lambda}$, given by equation (3.2), is well-defined on the collection

$$\mathcal{F}(\mathcal{I}) := \left\{ E \subseteq \mathbb{R} \,\middle|\, E = \bigcup_{k=1}^{n} I_k, I_k \in \mathcal{I}, I_k \cap I_\ell = \emptyset \text{ for } k \neq \ell, n \in \mathbb{N} \right\}.$$

Clearly, $\mathcal{I} \subset \mathcal{F}(\mathcal{I})$, and $\tilde{\lambda}(E) = \lambda(E)$ if $E \in \mathcal{I}$. Further, $\tilde{\lambda} : \mathcal{F}(\mathcal{I}) \longrightarrow [0, \infty]$ has properties similar to that of λ, i.e., $\tilde{\lambda}$ is monotone, countably additive and countably subadditive. Some of the properties of the classes $\mathcal{I}$ and $\mathcal{F}(\mathcal{I})$ and the function $\tilde{\lambda}$ are given in the following propositions.

3.1.2. Proposition: *The class $\mathcal{I}$ has the following properties:*

(i) $\emptyset, \mathbb{R} \in \mathcal{I}$.

(ii) *If $I, J \in \mathcal{I}$, then $I \cap J \in \mathcal{I}$.*

(iii) *If $I \in \mathcal{I}$, then $I^c = J_1 \cup J_2$, where $J_1, J_2 \in \mathcal{I}$ and $J_1 \cap J_2 = \emptyset$.*

Proof: Exercise. ■

3.1.3. Proposition: *The class $\mathcal{F}(I)$ has the following properties:*

(i) $\mathcal{I} \subseteq \mathcal{F}(\mathcal{I})$.

(ii) $\emptyset \in \mathcal{F}(\mathcal{I})$ *and* $\mathbb{R} \in \mathcal{F}(\mathcal{I})$.

(iii) $E_1, E_2 \in \mathcal{F}(\mathcal{I})$, *then* $E_1 \cap E_2 \in \mathcal{F}(\mathcal{I})$.

(iv) *If $E \in \mathcal{F}(\mathcal{I})$, then $E^c \in \mathcal{F}(\mathcal{I})$.*

(v) $\mathcal{F}(\mathcal{I})$ *is the smallest class of subsets of $\mathbb{R}$ such that* (i), (ii), (iii) *and* (iv) *hold.*

Proof: (i), (ii) and (iii) are straightforward. If $E \in \mathcal{F}(\mathcal{I})$ and $E = \bigcup_{k=1}^{n} I_k$ with $I_k \cap I_\ell = \emptyset$ for $1 \leq k \neq \ell \leq n$, then

$$E^c = \bigcap_{k=1}^{n} I_k^c.$$

Also, $\forall \, k$,

$$I_k^c = J_k^1 \bigcup J_k^2,$$

where $J_k^1, J_k^2 \in \mathcal{I}$ and $J_k^1 \cap J_k^2 = \emptyset$. Thus

$$E^c = \bigcap_{k=1}^{n} (J_k^1 \cup J_k^2) = \bigcup_{i,j=1}^{2} \left(\bigcup_{k,l=1 \; k \neq \ell}^{n} (J_k^i \cap J_\ell^j) \right).$$

Thus E^c is a union of a finite number of pairwise disjoint intervals. Hence, $E^c \in \mathcal{F}(\mathcal{I})$. This proves (iv).

Finally, let $\mathcal{C}$ be any other collection of sets such that $\mathcal{I} \subset \mathcal{C}$ and $\mathcal{C}$ has properties (ii), (iii) and (iv). If $E_1, E_2 \in \mathcal{C}$, then

$$E_1 \cup E_2 = (E_1^c \cap E_2^c)^c$$

and hence $E_1 \cup E_2 \in \mathcal{C}$. Let $E \in \mathcal{F}(\mathcal{I})$ and $E = \bigcup_{k=1}^{n} I_k$ with $I_k \in \mathcal{I}, I_k \cap I_\ell = \emptyset$ for $k \neq \ell$. Then $I_k \in \mathcal{C}$ and hence $E \in \mathcal{C}$, showing that $\mathcal{F}(\mathcal{I}) \subseteq \mathcal{C}$. This proves (v). ∎

3.1.4 Proposition: *The function* $\tilde{\lambda} : \mathcal{F}(I) \to \mathbb{R}$, *as defined in equation (3.2), has the following properties:*

(i) $\tilde{\lambda}(I) = \lambda(I) \; \forall \; I \in \mathcal{I}$.

(ii) $\tilde{\lambda}$ *is countably additive, i.e.,*

$$\tilde{\lambda}(E) = \sum_{i=1}^{\infty} \tilde{\lambda}(E_i),$$

whenever $E \in \mathcal{F}(\mathcal{I})$ *is such that* $E = \bigcup_{i=1}^{\infty} E_i$ *with each* $E_i \in \mathcal{F}(\mathcal{I})$, $E_i \cap F_j = \emptyset$ *for* $i \neq j$.

Proof: (i) is obvious. To prove (ii), let $\forall \; i, E_i = \bigcup_{j=1}^{k_i} I_j^i$, where $I_1^i, \ldots, I_{k_i}^i$ are pairwise disjoint intervals. Then $\{I_j^i \mid 1 \leq i \leq n, 1 \leq j \leq k_i\}$ is a collection of pairwise disjoint intervals. Let

$$E = \bigcup_{r=1}^{\ell} K_r,$$

where $K_1, \ldots, K_\ell$ are pairwise disjoint intervals. Then for every r

$$K_r = \bigcup_{i=1}^{\infty} \bigcup_{j=1}^{k_i} (K_r \cap I_j^i)$$

and for every i

$$E_i = \bigcup_{r=1}^{\ell} \bigcup_{j=1}^{k_i} (K_r \cap I_j^i).$$

Thus, using the countable additivity of λ and the definition of $\tilde{\lambda}$, we have

$$
\begin{aligned}
\tilde{\lambda}(E) &= \sum_{r=1}^{\ell} \lambda(K_r) \\
&= \sum_{r=1}^{\ell} \sum_{i=1}^{\infty} \sum_{j=1}^{k_i} \lambda(K_r \cap I_j^i) \\
&= \sum_{i=1}^{\infty} \left(\sum_{j=1}^{k_i} \sum_{r=1}^{\ell} \lambda(K_r \cap I_j^i) \right) \\
&= \sum_{i=1}^{\infty} \tilde{\lambda}(E_i). \quad \blacksquare
\end{aligned}
$$

3.1.5. Exercise: Show that $\tilde{\lambda}$ as in proposition 3.1.4 has the following properties:

(i) $\tilde{\lambda}$ is finitely additive, i.e.,

$$
\tilde{\lambda}(E) = \sum_{i=1}^{n} \tilde{\lambda}(E_i),
$$

whenever $E_1, \ldots, E_n$ are pairwise disjoint sets in $\mathcal{F}(\mathcal{I})$ and $E = \bigcup_{i=1}^{n} E_i \in \mathcal{F}(\mathcal{I})$.

(ii) $\tilde{\lambda}$ is monotone, i.e., if $E, F \in \mathcal{F}(\mathcal{I})$ and $E \subseteq F$, then $\tilde{\lambda}(E) \le \tilde{\lambda}(F)$.

(iii) $\tilde{\lambda}$ is countably subadditive, i.e.,

$$
\tilde{\lambda}(E) \le \sum_{i=1}^{\infty} \tilde{\lambda}(E_i),
$$

whenever $E_1, E_2 \ldots$ are pairwise disjoint sets in $\mathcal{F}(\mathcal{I})$, $E \in \mathcal{F}(\mathcal{I})$ and $E \subseteq \bigcup_{i=1}^{\infty} E_i$.

3.2. Semi-algebra and algebra of sets

Motivated by the properties of the collections $\mathcal{I}$ and $\mathcal{F}(\mathcal{I})$, we have the following:

3.2.1. Definition: Let X be a nonempty set and let $\mathcal{C}$ be a collection of subsets of X. We say $\mathcal{C}$ is a **semi-algebra** of subsets of X if it has the following properties:

(i) $\emptyset, X \in \mathcal{C}$.

(ii) $A \cap B \in \mathcal{C}$ for every $A, B \in \mathcal{C}$.

(iii) For every $A \in \mathcal{C}$ there exist $n \in \mathbb{N}$ and sets $C_1, C_2, \ldots, C_n \in \mathcal{C}$ such that $C_i \cap C_j = \emptyset$ for $i \ne j$ and $A^c = \bigcup_{i=1}^{n} C_i$.

3.2.2. Definition: Let X be a nonempty set and $\mathcal{F}$ a collection of subsets of X. The collection $\mathcal{F}$ is called an **algebra** of subsets of X if $\mathcal{F}$ has the following properties:

   (i) $\emptyset, X \in \mathcal{F}$.

   (ii) $A \cap B \in \mathcal{F}$, whenever $A, B \in \mathcal{F}$.

   (iii) $A^c \in \mathcal{F}$, whenever $A \in \mathcal{F}$.

3.2.3. Examples:

(i) The collection $\mathcal{I}$ of all intervals forms a semi-algebra of subsets of $\mathbb{R}$. For $a, b \in \mathbb{R}$ with $a < b$, consider the collection $\tilde{\mathcal{I}}$ of all intervals of the form $(a, b], (-\infty, b], (a, \infty), (-\infty, +\infty)$. We call $\tilde{\mathcal{I}}$ the collection of all left-open, right-closed intervals of $\mathbb{R}$. It is easy to check that $\tilde{\mathcal{I}}$ is also a semi-algebra of subsets of $\mathbb{R}$.

(ii) The collection $\mathcal{F}(\mathcal{I})$, as discussed in 3.1.1, is an algebra of subsets of $\mathbb{R}$. So is the class $\mathcal{F}(\tilde{\mathcal{I}}) := \{E \subseteq \mathbb{R} \mid E = \bigcup_{k=1}^{n} I_k$ with $I_k \in \tilde{\mathcal{I}}$ and $I_k \cap I_\ell = \emptyset$ for $1 \leq k \neq \ell \leq n, n \in \mathbb{N}\}$.

(iii) Let X be any nonempty set. The collections $\{\emptyset, X\}$ and $\mathcal{P}(X) := \{E \mid E \subseteq X\}$ are trivial examples of algebras of subsets of X. The collection $\mathcal{P}(X)$ is called the **power set** of X.

(iv) Let X be any nonempty set. Let

$$\mathcal{C} := \{E \subseteq X \mid \text{ either } E \text{ or } E^c \text{ is finite}\}.$$

Then $\mathcal{C}$ is an algebra of subsets of X. In case X is a finite set, then $\mathcal{C} = \mathcal{P}(X)$. Suppose X is not finite. Clearly $\emptyset, X \in \mathcal{C}$, and $E^c \in \mathcal{C}$ if $E \in \mathcal{C}$. Finally, suppose $E_1, E_2 \in \mathcal{C}$. If either E_1 is finite or E_2 is finite, then obviously $E_1 \cap E_2 \in \mathcal{C}$. If both E_1^c and E_2^c are finite, then $(E_1 \cap E_2)^c = E_1^c \cup E_2^c$ is finite and thus $E_1 \cap E_2 \in \mathcal{C}$. Hence $\mathcal{C}$ is an algebra.

(v) Let X and Y be two nonempty sets, and $\mathcal{F}$ and $\mathcal{G}$ semi-algebras of subsets of X and Y, respectively. Let

$$\mathcal{F} \times \mathcal{G} = \{F \times G \mid F \in \mathcal{F}, G \in \mathcal{G}\}.$$

We show that $\mathcal{F} \times \mathcal{G}$ is a semi-algebra of subsets of $X \times Y$. Clearly $X \times Y \in \mathcal{F} \times \mathcal{G}$. Next, let $A, B \in \mathcal{F} \times \mathcal{G}$. Let $A = F_1 \times G_1$ and $B = F_2 \times G_2$, where $F_1, F_2 \in \mathcal{F}$ and $G_1, G_2 \in \mathcal{G}$. Then

$$A \times B = (F_1 \times G_1) \cap (F_2 \times G_2) = (F_1 \cap F_2) \times (G_1 \cap G_2).$$

Since $\mathcal{F}, \mathcal{G}$ are semi-algebras, $F_1 \cap F_2 \in \mathcal{F}$ and $G_1 \cap G_2 \in \mathcal{G}$. Hence it follows that $A \times B \in \mathcal{F} \times \mathcal{G}$. Next, let $A = F \times G \in \mathcal{F} \times \mathcal{G}$, where $F \in \mathcal{F}$ and $G \in \mathcal{G}$.

Since $\mathcal{F}, \mathcal{G}$ are semi-algebras, we have pairwise disjoint sets $F_1, \ldots, F_n \in \mathcal{F}$ and pairwise disjoint sets $G_1, \ldots, G_m \in \mathcal{G}$ such that

$$F^c = \bigcup_{i=1}^{n} F_i \quad \text{and} \quad G^c = \bigcup_{j=1}^{m} G_j.$$

Thus

$$
\begin{aligned}
(F \times G)^c &= (F^c \times Y) \cup (F \times G^c) \\
&= \left(\left(\bigcup_{i=1}^{n} F_i \right) \times Y \right) \cup \left(F \times \left(\bigcup_{j=1}^{m} G_j \right) \right) \\
&= \left(\bigcup_{i=1}^{n} (F_i \times Y) \right) \cup \left(\bigcup_{j=1}^{m} (F \times G_j) \right).
\end{aligned}
$$

Clearly, for every i and j, $F_i \times Y \in \mathcal{F} \times \mathcal{G}$ and $F \times G_j \in \mathcal{F} \times \mathcal{G}$. Further, all these sets are pairwise disjoint. This proves that $\mathcal{F} \times \mathcal{G}$ is a semi-algebra.

•**3.2.4. Exercise:**

(a) Let $\mathcal{F}$ be any collection of subsets of a set X. Show that $\mathcal{F}$ is an algebra iff the following hold:

   (i) $\phi, X \in \mathcal{F}$.
   (ii) $A^c \in \mathcal{F}$ whenever $A \in \mathcal{F}$.
   (iii) $A \cup B \in \mathcal{F}$ whenever $A, B \in \mathcal{F}$.

(b) Let $\mathcal{F}$ be an algebra of subsets of X. Show that

   (i) If $A, B \in \mathcal{F}$ then $A \triangle B := (A \setminus B) \cup (B \setminus A) \in \mathcal{F}$.
   (ii) If $E_1, E_2, \ldots, E_n \in \mathcal{F}$ then $\exists\ F_1, F_2, \ldots, F_n \in \mathcal{F}$ such that $F_i \subseteq E_i$ for each i, $F_i \cap F_j = \emptyset$ for $i \neq j$ and $\bigcup_{i=1}^{n} E_i = \bigcup_{j=1}^{n} F_j$.

   The next exercise describes some methods of constructing algebras and semi-algebras.

•**3.2.5. Exercise:**

(i) Let X be a nonempty set. Let $\emptyset \neq E \subseteq X$ and let $\mathcal{C}$ be a semi-algebra (algebra) of subsets of X. Let

$$\mathcal{C} \cap E := \{A \cap E \mid A \in \mathcal{C}\}.$$

Show that $\mathcal{C} \cap E$ is a semi-algebra (algebra) of subsets of E. Note that $\mathcal{C} \cap E$ is the collection of those subsets of E which are elements of $\mathcal{C}$.

(ii) Let X, Y be two nonempty sets and $f : X \longrightarrow Y$ be any map. For $E \subseteq Y$, we write $f^{-1}(E) := \{x \in X \mid f(x) \in E\}$. Let $\mathcal{C}$ be any semi-algebra (algebra) of subsets of Y. Show that

$$f^{-1}(\mathcal{C}) := \{f^{-1}(E) \mid E \in \mathcal{C}\}$$

is a semi-algebra (algebra) of subsets of X.

(iii) Give examples of two nonempty sets X, Y and algebras $\mathcal{F}, G$ of subsets of X and Y, respectively such that $\mathcal{F} \times G := \{A \times B \mid A \in \mathcal{F}, B \in G\}$ is not an algebra. (It will of course be a semi-algebra, as shown in example 3.2.3(v).)

(iv) Let $\{\mathcal{F}_\alpha\}_{\alpha \in I}$ be a family of algebras of subsets of a set X. Let $\mathcal{F} := \bigcap_{\alpha \in I} \mathcal{F}_\alpha$. Show that $\mathcal{F}$ is also an algebra of subsets of X.

(v) Let $\{\mathcal{F}_n\}_{n \geq 1}$ be a sequence of algebras of subsets of a set X. Under what conditions on $\mathcal{F}_n$ can you conclude that $\mathcal{F} := \bigcup_{n=1}^{\infty} \mathcal{F}_n$ is also an algebra?

3.2.6. Exercise: Let $\mathcal{C}$ be a semi-algebra of subsets of a set X. A set $A \subseteq X$ is called a σ-**set** if there exist sets $C_i \in \mathcal{C}, i = 1, 2, \ldots$, such that $C_i \cap C_j = \emptyset$ for $i \neq j$ and $\bigcup_{i=1}^{\infty} C_i = A$. Prove the following:

(i) For any finite number of sets $C, C_1, C_2, \ldots, C_n$ in $\mathcal{C}$, $C \setminus (\bigcup_{i=1}^{n} C_i)$ is a finite union of pairwise disjoint sets from $\mathcal{C}$ and hence is a σ-set.

(ii) For any sequence $\{C_n\}_{n \geq 1}$ of sets in $\mathcal{C}$, $\bigcup_{n=1}^{\infty} C_n$ is a σ-set.

(iii) A finite intersection and a countable union of σ-sets is a σ-set.

3.2.7. Proposition: *Let $\mathcal{C}$ be any collection of subsets of a set X. Then there exists a unique algebra $\mathcal{F}$ of subsets of X such that $\mathcal{C} \subseteq \mathcal{F}$ and if A is any other algebra such that $\mathcal{C} \subseteq A$, then $\mathcal{F} \subseteq A$.*

Proof: Note that there exists at least one σ-algebra of subsets of X which includes $\mathcal{C}$, namely $\mathcal{P}(X)$. Consider $\mathcal{A}$, the intersection of all those algebras of subsets of X which include $\mathcal{C}$. Then it follows from exercise 3.2.5(iv) that $\mathcal{A}$ is the required algebra. ∎

3.2.8. Definition: Let $\mathcal{C}$ be any collection of subsets of a set X. Then the unique algebra given by proposition 3.2.7 is called the **algebra generated by** $\mathcal{C}$ and is denoted by $\mathcal{F}(\mathcal{C})$.

3.2.9. Example: The algebra generated by $\mathcal{I}$, the class of all intervals, is $\{E \subseteq \mathbb{R} \mid E = \bigcup_{k=1}^{n} I_k, I_k \in I, I_k \cap I_\ell = \emptyset \text{ if } 1 \leq k \neq \ell \leq n\}$, as proved in proposition 3.1.3.

A similar result holds in general. See the next exercise.

3.2.10. Exercise:

(i) Let $\mathcal{C}$ be any semi-algebra of subsets of a set X. Show that $\mathcal{F}(\mathcal{C})$, the algebra generated by $\mathcal{C}$, is given by $\{E \subseteq X \mid E = \bigcup_{i=1}^{n} C_i, C_i \in \mathcal{C}$ and $C_i \cap C_j = \emptyset$ for $i \neq j, n \in \mathbb{N}\}$.

(ii) Let X be any nonempty set and $\mathcal{C} = \{\{x\} \mid x \in X\} \bigcup \{\emptyset, X\}$. Is $\mathcal{C}$ a semi-algebra of subsets of X? What is the algebra generated by $\mathcal{C}$? Does your answer depend upon whether X is finite or not? (See example 3.2.3(iv).)

(iii) Let Y be any nonempty set and let X be the set of all sequences with elements from Y, i.e.,

$$X = \{\underline{x} = \{x_n\}_{n \geq 1} \mid x_n \in Y, n = 1, 2, \dots\}.$$

For any positive integer k let $A \subseteq Y^k$, the k-fold Cartesian product of Y with itself, and let $i_1 < i_2 < \cdots < i_k$ be positive integers. Let

$$C(i_1, i_2, \dots, i_k; A) := \{\underline{x} = (x_n)_{n \geq 1} \in X \mid (x_{i_1}, \dots, x_{i_k}) \in A\}.$$

We call $C(i_1, i_2, \dots, i_k; A)$ a k-**dimensional cylinder set** in X with base A. Prove the following assertions:

(a) Every k-dimensional cylinder can be regarded as an n-dimensional cylinder also for $n \geq k$.

(b) Let $\mathcal{A} = \{E \subset X \mid E$ is an n-dimensional cylinder set for some $n\}$. Then $\mathcal{A} \cup \{\emptyset, X\}$ is an algebra of subsets of X.

•(iv) Let $\mathcal{C}$ be any collection of subsets of a set X and let $E \subseteq X$. Let $\mathcal{C} \cap E := \{C \cap E \mid C \in \mathcal{C}\}$. Then the following hold:

(a) $\mathcal{C} \cap E \subseteq \mathcal{F}(\mathcal{C}) \cap E := \{A \cap E \mid A \in \mathcal{F}(\mathcal{C})\}$. Deduce that $\mathcal{F}(\mathcal{C} \cap E) \subseteq \mathcal{F}(\mathcal{C}) \cap E$.

(b) Let $\mathcal{A} = \{A \subseteq X \mid A \cap E \in \mathcal{F}(\mathcal{C} \cap E)\}$. Then $\mathcal{A}$ is an algebra of subsets of X, $\mathcal{C} \subseteq \mathcal{A}$ and $\mathcal{A} \cap E = \mathcal{F}(\mathcal{C} \cap E)$.

(c) Using (a) and (b), deduce that $\mathcal{F}(\mathcal{C}) \cap E = \mathcal{F}(\mathcal{C} \cap E)$.

3.2.11. Remark: Exercise 3.2.10(i) gives a description of $\mathcal{F}(\mathcal{C})$, the algebra generated by a semi-algebra $\mathcal{C}$. In general, no description is possible for $\mathcal{F}(\mathcal{C})$ when $\mathcal{C}$ is not a semi-algebra. See also theorem 4.5.1.

3.3. Extension from semi-algebra to the generated algebra

In section 3.1, we showed that the length function, which is initially defined on the semi-algebra $\mathcal{I}$ of all intervals, can be extended to a set function on $\mathcal{F}(\mathcal{I})$, the algebra generated. Further, the extended function has the properties similar to that of the length function. We want to do the same for functions defined on arbitrary semi-algebras. We make the following definitions.

3.3.1. Definition: Let $\mathcal{C}$ be a class of subsets of a set X. A function $\mu : \mathcal{C} \longrightarrow [0, +\infty]$ is called a **set function**. Further,

(i) μ is said to be **monotone** if $\mu(A) \leq \mu(B)$ whenever $A, B \in \mathcal{C}$ and $A \subseteq B$.

(ii) μ is said to be **finitely additive** if

$$\mu\left(\bigcup_{i=1}^{n} A_i\right) = \sum_{i=1}^{n} \mu(A_i).$$

whenever $A_1, A_2, \ldots, A_n \in \mathcal{C}$ are such that $A_i \cap A_j = \emptyset$ for $i \neq j$ and $\bigcup_{i=1}^{n} A_i \in \mathcal{C}$.

(iii) μ is said to be **countably additive** if

$$\mu\left(\bigcup_{n=1}^{\infty} A_n\right) = \sum_{n=1}^{\infty} \mu(A_n)$$

whenever $A_1, A_2, \ldots$ in $\mathcal{C}$ with $A_i \cap A_j = \emptyset$ for $i \neq j$ and $\bigcup_{n=1}^{\infty} A_n \in \mathcal{C}$.

(iv) μ is said to be **countably subadditive** if

$$\mu(A) \leq \sum_{n=1}^{\infty} \mu(A_n).$$

whenever $A \in \mathcal{C}$, $A = \bigcup_{n=1}^{\infty} A_n$ with $A_n \in \mathcal{C}$ for every n.

(v) μ is called a **measure** on $\mathcal{C}$ if $\emptyset \in \mathcal{C}$ with $\mu(\emptyset) = 0$ and μ is countably additive on $\mathcal{C}$.

3.3.2. Exercise:

(i) Let $\mathcal{C}$ be a collection of subsets of a set X and $\mu : \mathcal{C} \to [0, \infty]$ be a set function. If μ is a measure on $\mathcal{C}$, show that μ is finitely additive. Is μ monotone? Countably subadditive?

(ii) If $\mathcal{C}$ be a semi-algebra, then μ is countably subadditive iff $\forall \, A \in \mathcal{C}$ with $A \subseteq \bigcup_{i=1}^{\infty} A_i$, $A_i \in \mathcal{C}$ implies

$$\mu(A) \leq \sum_{i=1}^{\infty} \mu(A_i).$$

Our next theorem is an abstract version of the extension of the length function given in proposition 3.1.4.

3.3.3. Theorem: *Given a measure μ on a semi-algebra $\mathcal{C}$, there exists a unique measure $\tilde{\mu}$ on $\mathcal{F}(\mathcal{C})$ such that $\tilde{\mu}(E) = \mu(E)$ for every $E \in \mathcal{C}$.*

The measure $\tilde{\mu}$ is called the **extension** of μ.

Proof: We note that every $E \in \mathcal{F}(\mathcal{C})$ can be represented as $E = \bigcup_{i=1}^{n} E_i$ for pairwise disjoint sets $E_1, \ldots, E_n \in \mathcal{C}$. Thus we can define

$$\tilde{\mu}(E) := \sum_{i=1}^{\infty} \mu(E_i).$$

Now proceeding as in 3.1.1 and proposition 3.1.4 for $\tilde{\lambda}$, we can show that $\tilde{\mu}$ is well-defined and has the required properties. ∎

3.3.4. Exercise: Let $X = (0, 1]$ and let $\mathcal{A} = \mathcal{F}(\tilde{\mathcal{I}} \cap (0, 1])$ be the algebra generated by all left-open, right-closed intervals in $(0, 1]$. For every $x \in (0, 1]$, let $x = \sum_{n=1}^{\infty} x_n/2^n$, $x_n \in \{0, 1\}$, be its binary expansion with the convention that we always choose the expansion which does not terminate in zeros. For example, the number $1/2$ has two expansions:

$$1/2 = \sum_{n=1}^{\infty} x_n/2^n = \sum_{n=1}^{\infty} y_n/2^n,$$

where $x_1 = 0, x_n = 1 \ \forall \ n \geq 2$ and $y_1 = 1, y_n = 0 \ \forall \ n \geq 2$. We choose the first one. Then we can identify x with the sequence $\{x_n\}_{n \geq 1}$. Let $n \geq 1$ be fixed and let $u_1, u_2, \ldots, u_n \in \{0, 1\}$. Let $A = \{x = \{x_n\}_{n \geq 1} \in X \mid x_i = u_i, 1 \leq i \leq n\}$. Show that $A \in \tilde{\mathcal{I}} \cap (0, 1]$. Let

$$B(n, k) := \left\{ x = \{x_m\}_{m \geq 1} \in X \ \middle| \ \sum_{i=1}^{n} x_i = k \right\}.$$

Show that $B(n, k) \in \mathcal{A}$ for every n and k, $k \leq n$. Show that $\tilde{\lambda}(A) = 1/2^n$ and $\tilde{\lambda}(B(n, k)) = \binom{n}{k}/2^n$, where $\tilde{\lambda}$ is the extension of the length function λ as given in proposition 3.1.4. Let

$$C = \left\{ x = \{x_n\}_{n \geq 1} \in X \ \middle| \ \lim_{n \to \infty} \frac{1}{n} \sum_{i=1}^{n} x_i = 1/2 \right\}.$$

Show that

$$C = \bigcap_{k=1}^{\infty} \bigcup_{m=1}^{\infty} \bigcap_{n=m}^{\infty} \left\{ x = \{x_n\}_{n \geq 1} \in X \ \middle| \ \left| \frac{1}{n} \sum_{i=1}^{n} f_i(x) \right| < \frac{1}{k} \right\},$$

where

$$f_i(x) = \begin{cases} +1 & \text{if } x_i = 1, \\ -1 & \text{if } x_i = 0. \end{cases}$$

Note that $f_i(x) = 2x_i - 1$ if $x = \{x_n\}_{n \geq 1}$. Does $C \in \mathcal{A}$?

3.4. Impossibility of extending the length function to all subsets of the real line

In section 3.1 the notion of length was extended from the semi-algebra $\mathcal{I}$ of intervals to the collection $\mathcal{F}(I)$, the algebra generated by $\mathcal{I}$. We point out that the length function is countably additive and $\lambda(\{x\}) = 0$ for every $x \in \mathbb{R}$. In this section we present a result due to S.M. Ulam (1930) [41] which, under the assumption of the "continuum hypothesis", implies that it is not possible to extend the length function to all subsets of $\mathbb{R}$. Recall that the continuum hypothesis implies that it is possible to define a well-order $<$ on $\mathbb{R}$ such that $\forall\, y \in \mathbb{R}$, the set $\{x \in \mathbb{R} \mid x < y\}$ is countable (see appendix C) .

3.4.1. Theorem (Ulam): *Let μ be a measure defined on all subsets of $\mathbb{R}$ such that $\mu((n, n+1]) < \infty$ $\forall\, n \in \mathbb{Z}$ and $\mu(\{x\}) = 0$ for every $x \in \mathbb{R}$. Then $\mu(E) = 0$ for every $E \subseteq \mathbb{R}$.*

Proof: It is enough to show that $\mu((n, n+1]) = 0$ for every $n \in \mathbb{Z}$. Let $n_0 \in \mathbb{Z}$ be fixed and let $X := (n_0, n_0 + 1]$. The main idea of the proof is to express X as a countable union of sets each having μ-measure zero.

Since X also has cardinality that of $\mathbb{R}$, by definition, there exists a well-order $<$ on X such that for every $x \in X$, the set $\{y \in X \mid y < x\}$ is countable. Let $\phi_x : \{y \in X \mid y < x\} \longrightarrow \mathbb{N}$ be any one-one map. Then for $x, y \in X$ with $y < x, \phi_x(y)$ is a natural number. Further, for $x, y, z \in X$, if $x < y < z$ then $\phi_z(y) \neq \phi_z(x)$. For $x \in X$ and $n \in \mathbb{N}$, define

$$F_x^n := \{y \in X \mid y > x \text{ and } \phi_y(x) = n\}.$$

Then for every fixed $x \in X$,

$$X = \left(\bigcup_{n=1}^{\infty} F_x^n \right) \bigcup \{y \in X \mid y \leq x\}.$$

Since the set $\{y \in X \mid y \leq x\}$ is countable and $\mu(\{y\}) = 0$ for every $y \in Y$, $\mu\{y \in X \mid y \leq x\} = 0$. To complete the proof we have only to show that there exists some $x \in X$ such that $\forall\, n \in \mathbb{N}, \mu(F_x^n) = 0$. To show this, note that for $x \neq y$ and $n \in \mathbb{N}$, if $z \in F_y^n \cap F_x^n$, then $\phi_z(x) = \phi_z(y) = n$. Since $x \neq y$, either $x < y$ or $y < x$ and hence either $x < y < z$ or $y < x < z$. In either case, $\phi_z(x) = \phi_z(y) = n$ will be contradicted. Thus for every $n \in \mathbb{N}$, the family $\{F_x^n\}_{x \in X}$ is a pairwise disjoint family of subsets of X. Since $\mu(X) < +\infty$ and X is uncountable, $\mu(F_x^n) > 0$ is possible only for a countable number of x's. Thus $\{x \in X \mid \mu(F_x^n) > 0 \text{ for some } n\}$ is at most countable. Hence there exists $x \in X$ such that $\mu(F_x^n) = 0$ for every $n \in \mathbb{N}$. Thus $\mu(X) = 0$. ∎

3.4.2. Remark: Ulam's theorem shows the impossibility of extending the length function from intervals to all subsets of $\mathbb{R}$, assuming the continuum hypothesis. We shall see later in section 4.6 that similar results can be proved if one assumes the 'axiom of choice' (see appendix B). Ulam's result uses the property of λ that $\lambda(\{x\}) = 0 \ \forall \ x \in \mathbb{R}$, and the fact that $\lambda([n, n+1]) < +\infty$ for every $n \in \mathbb{Z}$. In the later results we shall use the translation invariance property of the length function λ.

3.5. Countably additive set functions on intervals

We have shown in the prologue that the length function is a countably additive set function on the class of all intervals. One can ask the question: do there exist countably additive set functions on intervals, other than the length function? The answer is given by the following:

3.5.1. Proposition: *Let* $F : \mathbb{R} \longrightarrow \mathbb{R}$ *be a monotonically increasing function. Let* $\mu_F : \tilde{\mathcal{I}} \longrightarrow [0, \infty]$ *be defined by*

$$
\begin{aligned}
\mu_F\,(a,b\,] &:= F(b) - F(a), \\
\mu_F\,(-\infty, b\,] &:= \lim_{x \to \infty} [F(b) - F(-x)], \\
\mu_F\,(a, \infty) &:= \lim_{x \to \infty} [F(x) - F(a)], \\
\mu_F(-\infty, \infty) &:= \lim_{x \to \infty} [F(x) - F(-x)].
\end{aligned}
$$

Then μ_F *is a well-defined finitely additive set function on* $\tilde{\mathcal{I}}$. *Further,* μ_F *is countably additive if* F *is right continuous.*

One calls μ_F **the set function induced by** F.

Proof: Clearly, $\mu_F : \tilde{\mathcal{I}} \longmapsto [0, \infty]$ is a well-defined function. The other facts about μ_F can be proved on the lines that the length function λ has these properties, as proved in the prologue. (Note that the length function corresponds to the case $F(x) = x$, $\forall \ x$, the intervals involved are left-open and right-closed, and F is right continuous.) We leave the details as an exercise. ■

3.5.2. Exercise: Let $F(x) = [x]$, the integral part of $x, x \in \mathbb{R}$. Describe the set function μ_F.

The converse of proposition 3.5.1 is also true.

3.5.3. Proposition: *Let* $\mu : \tilde{\mathcal{I}} \longrightarrow [0, \infty]$ *be a finitely additive set function such that* $\mu(a, b] < +\infty$ *for every* $a, b \in \mathbb{R}$. *Then there exists a monotonically*

increasing function $F : \mathbb{R} \longrightarrow \mathbb{R}$ such that $\mu(a, b] = F(b) - F(a) \ \forall \ a, b \in \mathbb{R}$.
If μ is also countably additive, then F is right-continuous.

Proof: Since the function $F : \mathbb{R} \longrightarrow \mathbb{R}$ that we are looking for has to have
the property that $\mu(a, b] = F(b) - F(a) \ \forall \ a, b \in \mathbb{R}$, we fix $a \in \mathbb{R}$, say $a = 0$,
and let $b \in \mathbb{R}$ vary. This motivates the definition of a function F as follows:

$$F(x) := \begin{cases} \mu(0, x] & \text{if } x > 0, \\ 0 & \text{if } x = 0, \\ -\mu(x, 0] & \text{if } x < 0. \end{cases}$$

It is easy to check that F is a monotonically increasing function and $\mu(a, b] = F(b) - F(a)$ for every $a, b \in \mathbb{R}$. We need only to check that F is right
continuous if μ is countably additive. For this let $x \in \mathbb{R}$ and let $\{x_n\}_{n \geq 1}$
be a decreasing sequence in $\mathbb{R}$ with $\lim_{n \to \infty} x_n = x$. Then $\{F(x_n)\}_{n \geq 1}$ is a
decreasing sequence and is bounded below by $F(x)$. Thus $\lim_{n \to \infty} F(x_n)$ exists.
To compute this limit we consider two cases.

If $x \geq 0$, then

$$0 \leq x < \cdots \leq x_n \leq \cdots \leq x_2 \leq x_1.$$

Using the countable additivity property of μ, we have

$$\begin{aligned} F(x_1) = \mu\,(0,\ x_1] &= \mu\,(0,\ x] + \mu\,(x,\ x_i] \\ &= F(x) + \mu\left(\bigcup_{n=1}^{\infty} (x_{n+1},\ x_n]\right) \\ &= F(x) + \sum_{n=1}^{\infty} \mu\,(x_{n+1},\ x_n] \\ &= F(x) + \lim_{k \to \infty} \sum_{n=1}^{k} \mu\,(x_{n+1},\ x_n] \\ &= F(x) + \lim_{k \to \infty} \sum_{n=1}^{k} [F(x_n) - F(x_{n+1})] \\ &= F(x) + F(x_1) - \lim_{k \to \infty} F(x_{k+1}). \end{aligned}$$

Hence

$$\lim_{k \to \infty} F(x_k) = F(x).$$

In case $x < 0$, since $\{x_n\}_{n \geq 1}$ decreases to x, we may assume without loss
of generality that $x_1 < 0$. Then

$$x \leq \cdots \leq x_{n+1} \leq x_n \leq \cdots \leq x_1 < 0$$

and by the countable additivity of μ we have

$$
\begin{aligned}
-F(x) &= \mu\,(x,\ 0] = \mu\,(x,\ x_1] + \mu\,(x_1,0] \\
&= \mu\left(\bigcup_{n=2}^{\infty} (x_n, x_{n-1}]\right) - F(x_1) \\
&= \sum_{n=2}^{\infty} \mu\,(x_n,\ x_{n-1}] - F(x_1) \\
&= \lim_{k\to\infty} \sum_{n=2}^{k} \mu\,(x_n,\ x_{n-1}] - F(x_1) \\
&= \lim_{k\to\infty} \sum_{n=2}^{k} [F(x_{n-1}) - F(x_n)] - F(x_1) \\
&= \lim_{k\to\infty} [F(x_1) - F(x_k)] - F(x_1) \\
&= - \lim_{k\to\infty} F(x_k).
\end{aligned}
$$

This proves that F is right continuous. ∎

3.5.4. Remarks:

(i) In case $\mu(\mathbb{R}) < +\infty$, a more canonical choice for the required function F in proposition 3.5.3 is given by $F(x) := \mu(-\infty, x]$, $x \in \mathbb{R}$.

(ii) Propositions 3.5.1 and 3.5.3 completely characterize the non-trivial countably additive set functions on intervals in terms of functions $F : \mathbb{R} \longrightarrow \mathbb{R}$ which are monotonically increasing and right continuous. Such functions are called **distribution functions** on $\mathbb{R}$. The set function μ_F induced by the distribution function F is non-trivial in the sense that it assigns finite non-zero values to bounded intervals.

3.5.5. Exercise: Let F be a distribution function and $\alpha \in \mathbb{R}$. Show that $F_1 := F + \alpha$ is also a distribution function and $\mu_F = \mu_{F_1}$. Is the converse true?

3.6. Countably additive set functions on algebras

In this section we give some general properties of a set function μ defined on an algebra $\mathcal{A}$ of subsets of an arbitrary set X. These properties do not depend upon the particular choice of $X, \mathcal{A}$ or μ.

3.6.1. Theorem: *Let $\mathcal{A}$ be an algebra of subsets of a set X and let $\mu : \mathcal{A} \longrightarrow [0, \infty]$ be a set function. Then the following hold:*

(i) *If μ is finitely additive and $\mu(B) < +\infty$, then $\mu(B-A) = \mu(B) - \mu(A)$ for every $A, B \in \mathcal{A}$ with $A \subseteq B$. In particular, $\mu(\emptyset) = 0$ if μ is finitely additive and $\mu(B) < +\infty$ for some $B \in \mathcal{A}$.*

(ii) *If μ is finitely additive, then μ is also monotone.*

(iii) *Let $\mu(\emptyset) = 0$. Then μ is countably additive iff μ is both finitely additive and countably subadditive.*

Proof: Proofs of (i) and (ii) are straightforward and are left as exercises. To prove (iii), let μ be countably additive and let $A = \bigcup_{i=1}^{n} A_i$, $A_i \in \mathcal{A}$, with $A_i \cap A_j = \emptyset$ for $i \neq j$. Then $A = \bigcup_{i=1}^{\infty} A_i$, with each $A_i = \emptyset$ for $i > n$, and

$$\mu(A) = \sum_{i=1}^{\infty} \mu(A_i) = \sum_{i=1}^{n} \mu(A_i).$$

To prove the countable subadditivity, let $A \in \mathcal{A}$ be such that $A = \bigcup_{i=1}^{\infty} A_i$ with $A_i \in \mathcal{A}$, $\forall\, i$. We write

$$B_1 := A_1 \text{ and } B_n := \left(A_n - \left(\bigcup_{i=1}^{n-1} A_i \right) \right) \cap A \text{ for } n \geq 2.$$

Then $B_n \in \mathcal{A}$ for every n and $B_n \cap B_m = \emptyset$ for $n \neq m$ with

$$\bigcup_{n=1}^{\infty} B_n = \bigcup_{n=1}^{\infty} A_n.$$

Now using (ii) and the countable additivity of μ,

$$\mu(A) = \mu\left(\bigcup_{n=1}^{\infty} B_n \right) = \sum_{n=1}^{\infty} \mu(B_n) \leq \sum_{n=1}^{\infty} \mu(A_n).$$

This proves that μ is countably subadditive.

Conversely, let μ be finitely additive and countably subadditive. Let $A = \bigcup_{n=1}^{\infty} A_n$, where $A, A_n \in \mathcal{A}$ for every n and $A_n \cap A_m = \emptyset$ for $n \neq m$. By countable subadditivity,

$$\mu(A) \leq \sum_{n=1}^{\infty} \mu(A_n).$$

Also, $\bigcup_{i=1}^{n} A_i \subseteq A$ for every n. Since $\bigcup_{i=1}^{n} A_i \in \mathcal{A}$, by (ii) and finite additivity, we have for every n,

$$\mu(A) \geq \mu\left(\bigcup_{i=1}^{n} A_i \right) = \sum_{i=1}^{n} \mu(A_i).$$

Letting $n \to \infty$, we get $\mu(A) \geq \sum_{i=1}^{\infty} \mu(A_i)$. This proves that μ is countably additive. ∎

3.6.2. Remark: The proof of theorem 3.6.1 includes a proof of the following fact which is used in many other arguments: for any sequence $\{A_n\}_{n\geq 1}$ of elements of an algebra $\mathcal{A}$, there exists a sequence $\{B_n\}_{n\geq 1}$ of pairwise disjoint sets in $\mathcal{A}$ such that $B_n \subseteq A_n \ \forall \ n$ and $\bigcup_{n=1}^{\infty} A_n = \bigcup_{n=1}^{\infty} B_n$. (See exercise 3.2.4.(b).)

In theorem 3.6.1 we saw a necessary and sufficient condition for a finitely additive set function defined on an algebra to be countably additive. Another characterization of countable additivity of set functions defined on algebras is given in the next theorem.

3.6.3. Theorem: *Let $\mathcal{A}$ be an algebra of subsets of a set X and let $\mu : \mathcal{A} \longrightarrow [0, \infty]$ be such that $\mu(\emptyset) = 0$.*

(a) *If μ is countably additive then the following hold:*
    (i) *For any $A \in \mathcal{A}$, if $A = \bigcup_{n=1}^{\infty} A_n$, where $A_n \in \mathcal{A}$ and $A_n \subseteq A_{n+1} \ \forall \ n$, then*

$$\mu(A) = \lim_{n\to\infty} \mu(A_n).$$

This is called the **continuity from below** of μ at A.
    (ii) *For any $A \in \mathcal{A}$, if $A = \bigcap_{n=1}^{\infty} A_n$, where $A_n \in \mathcal{A}$ with $A_n \supseteq A_{n+1} \ \forall \ n$ and $\mu(A_n) < +\infty$ for some n, then*

$$\lim_{n\to\infty} \mu(A_n) = \mu(A).$$

This is called the **continuity from above** of μ at A.

Conversely,

(b) *If μ is finitely additive and (i) holds, then μ is countably additive.*

(c) *If $\mu(X) < +\infty, \mu$ is finitely additive and (ii) holds, then μ is countably additive.*

Proof: (a) Suppose μ is countably additive and let $A \in \mathcal{A}, A = \bigcup_{n=1}^{\infty} A_n$, where $A_n \in \mathcal{A}$ with $A_n \subseteq A_{n+1} \ \forall \ n$. Let $B_1 := A_1$ and $B_n := A_n - A_{n-1}$ for $n \geq 2$. Then $\{B_n\}_{n\geq 1}$ is a sequence of pairwise disjoint sets in $\mathcal{A}$ such that $A_n = \bigcup_{k=1}^{n} B_k \ \forall \ n$ and $A = \bigcup_{n=1}^{\infty} B_n$. Thus using countable and finite additivity of μ, we have

$$\mu(A) = \sum_{k=1}^{\infty} \mu(B_k) = \lim_{n\to\infty} \sum_{k=1}^{n} \mu(B_k) = \lim_{n\to\infty} \mu\left(\bigcup_{k=1}^{n} B_k\right) = \lim_{n\to\infty} \mu(A_n).$$

This proves (i).

(ii) Let $A = \bigcap_{n=1}^{\infty} A_n$, where $A_n \in \mathcal{A}$ with $A_n \supseteq A_{n+1}$ for every n, and let $\mu(A_{n_0}) < +\infty$. We write $B_n := A_{n_0} - A_n$ for every $n \geq n_0$. Then

$B_n \in \mathcal{A}, B_n \subseteq B_{n+1}$ for every $n \geq n_0$, and $\bigcup_{n=n_0}^{\infty} B_n = A_{n_0} - A$. Thus using (i) and theorem 3.6.1 (i), we have

$$
\begin{aligned}
\mu(A_{n_0}) - \mu(A) &= \mu(A_{n_0} - A) \\
&= \lim_{n \to \infty} \mu(B_n) \\
&= \lim_{n \to \infty} \mu(A_{n_0} - A_n) \\
&= \lim_{n \to \infty} [\mu(A_{n_0}) - \mu(A_n)] \\
&= \mu(A_{n_0}) - \lim_{n \to \infty} \mu(A_n).
\end{aligned}
$$

Hence $\mu(A) = \lim_{n \to \infty} \mu(A_n)$. This proves (a) completely.

(b) Let μ be finitely additive and let (i) hold. We have to show that μ is countably additive. Let $A \in \mathcal{A}$, $A = \bigcup_{n=1}^{\infty} A_n$, where $A_n \in \mathcal{A}$ for every n and $A_n \cap A_m = \emptyset$ for $n \neq m$. Then $A = \bigcup_{n=1}^{\infty} (\bigcup_{k=1}^{n} A_k)$, and by the given hypothesis, since $\bigcup_{k=1}^{n} A_k$ is increasing, we have

$$
\mu(A) = \lim_{n \to \infty} \mu \left(\bigcup_{k=1}^{n} A_k \right) = \lim_{n \to \infty} \left(\sum_{k=1}^{n} \mu(A_k) \right) = \sum_{k=1}^{\infty} \mu(A_k).
$$

This proves (b).

(c) Again, let $A \in \mathcal{A}$, $A = \bigcup_{n=1}^{\infty} A_n$, where $A_n \in \mathcal{A}$ for every n and $A_n \cap A_m = \emptyset$ for $n \neq m$. Put $B_n := A - (\bigcup_{k=1}^{n} A_k)$. Then $B_n \in \mathcal{A}, B_n \supseteq B_{n+1}$ $\forall n$ and $\bigcap_{n=1}^{\infty} B_n = \emptyset$. Thus by the given hypothesis and theorem 3.6.1(i), we have

$$
\begin{aligned}
0 = \mu(\emptyset) &= \lim_{n \to \infty} \mu(B_n) \\
&= \lim_{n \to \infty} \mu \left(A - \bigcup_{k=1}^{n} A_k \right) \\
&= \mu(A) - \lim_{n \to \infty} \mu \left(\bigcup_{k=1}^{n} A_k \right) \\
&= \mu(A) - \lim_{n \to \infty} \sum_{k=1}^{n} \mu(A_k) \\
&= \mu(A) - \sum_{k=1}^{\infty} \mu(A_k).
\end{aligned}
$$

Hence $\mu(A) = \sum_{k=1}^{\infty} \mu(A_k)$. This proves the theorem completely. ∎

3.6.4. Exercise:

(i) In the proofs of part (ii) and part (c) of theorem 3.6.3, where do you think we used the hypothesis that $\mu(X) < +\infty$? Do you think this condition is necessary?

(ii) Let $\mathcal{A}$ be an algebra of subsets of a set X and $\mu : \mathcal{A} \to [0, \infty]$ be a finitely additive set function such that $\mu(X) < +\infty$. Show that the following statements are equivalent:

    (a) $\lim_{k \to \infty} \mu(A_k) = 0$, whenever $\{A_k\}_{k \geq 1}$ is a sequence in $\mathcal{A}$ with $A_k \supseteq A_{k+1} \; \forall \; k$, and $\bigcap_{k=1}^{\infty} A_k = \emptyset$.

    (b) μ is countably additive.

3.6.5.   Exercise: Extend the claim of theorem 3.6.3 when $\mathcal{A}$ is only a semi-algebra of subsets of X.

(Hint: Use exercise 3.2.6 or theorems 3.3.3 and 3.6.3.)

3.6.6.   Exercise: Let $\mathcal{A}$ be an algebra of subsets of a set X which is also closed under countable unions (such an algebra is called a σ**-algebra**, see definition 3.9.1), and $\mu : \mathcal{A} \to [0, \infty]$ be a measure. For any sequence $\{E_n\}_{n \geq 1}$ in $\mathcal{A}$, show that

    (i) $\mu \left(\liminf_{n \to \infty} E_n \right) \leq \liminf_{n \to \infty} \mu(E_n)$.
    (ii) $\mu \left(\limsup_{n \to \infty} E_n \right) \geq \limsup_{n \to \infty} \mu(E_n)$.

(Hint: For a sequence $\{E_n\}_{n \geq 1}$ of subsets of a set X,

$$\liminf_{n \to \infty} E_n := \bigcup_{n=1}^{\infty} \bigcap_{k=n}^{\infty} E_k \subseteq \limsup_{n \to \infty} E_n := \bigcap_{n=1}^{\infty} \bigcup_{k=n}^{\infty} E_k.)$$

    Here are some more examples of finitely/countably additive set functions:

3.6.7. Example: Let X be any infinite set and let $x_n \in X, n = 1, 2, \ldots$. Let $\{p_n\}_{n \geq 1}$ be a sequence of nonnegative real numbers. For any $A \subseteq X$, define

$$\mu(A) := \sum_{\{i \mid x_i \in A\}} p_i.$$

It is easy to show that μ is a countably additive set function on the algebra $\mathcal{P}(X)$. We say μ is a **discrete measure** with 'mass' p_i at x_i. The measure μ is finite (i.e., $\mu(X) < +\infty$) iff $\sum_{i=1}^{\infty} p_i < +\infty$. If $\sum_{i=1}^{\infty} p_i = 1$, the measure μ is called a **discrete probability measure/distribution**. Note that $\mu(\{x_i\}) = p_i \; \forall \; i$ and $\mu(\{x\}) = 0$ if $x \neq x_i$. So, one can regard μ as a set function defined on the subsets of the set $Y := \{x_n : n \geq 1\}$. Some of the special cases when $X = \{0, 1, 2, \dots\}$ are:

(a) **Binomial distribution:** $Y := \{0, 1, 2, \dots, n\}$ and, for $0 < p < 1$,

$$p_k = \binom{n}{k} p^k (1-p)^{n-k}, 0 \leq k \leq n.$$

(b) **Poisson distribution:** $Y := \{0, 1, 2, \dots\}$ and

$$p_k := \lambda^k e^{-\lambda}/k!$$

for $k = 0, 1, 2, \dots$, where $\lambda > 0$.

(c) **Uniform distribution:** $Y := \{1, 2, \dots, n\}$,

$$p_k := 1/k \ \forall \ k.$$

3.6.8. Exercise: Let X be any countably infinite set and let

$$\mathcal{C} = \{\{x\} \mid x \in X\}.$$

Show that the algebra generated by $\mathcal{C}$ is

$$\mathcal{F}(\mathcal{C}) := \{A \subseteq X \mid A \text{ or } A^c \text{ is finite}\}.$$

Let $\mu : \mathcal{F}(\mathcal{C}) \longrightarrow [0, \infty)$ be defined by

$$\mu(A) := \begin{cases} 0 & \text{if } A \text{ is finite,} \\ 1 & \text{if } A^c \text{is finite.} \end{cases}$$

Show that μ is finitely additive but not countably additive. If X is an uncountable set, show that μ is also countably additive.

3.6.9. Exercise: Let $X = \mathbb{N}$, the set of natural numbers. For every finite set $A \subseteq X$, let $\#A$ denote the number of elements in A. Define for $A \subseteq X$,

$$\mu_n(A) := \frac{\#\{m : 1 \leq m \leq n, m \in A\}}{n}.$$

Show that μ_n is countably additive for every n on $\mathcal{P}(X)$. In a sense, μ_n is the proportion of integers between 1 to n which are in A. Let

$$\mathcal{C} = \{A \subseteq X \mid \lim_{n \to \infty} \mu_n(A) \text{ exists}\}.$$

Show that $\mathcal{C}$ is closed under taking complements, finite disjoint unions and proper differences. Is it an algebra?

3.6.10. Exercise: Let $\mu : \tilde{\mathcal{I}} \cap (0, 1] \longrightarrow [0, \infty]$ be defined by

$$\mu(a, b] := \begin{cases} b - a & \text{if } a \neq 0, 0 < a < b \leq 1, \\ +\infty & \text{otherwise.} \end{cases}$$

(Recall that $\tilde{\mathcal{I}} \cap (0, 1]$ is the class of all left-open right-closed intervals in $(0, 1]$.) Show that μ is finitely additive. Is μ countably additive also?

3.6.11. Exercise: Let X be a nonempty set.

(a) Let $\mu : \mathcal{P}(X) \longrightarrow [0, \infty)$ be a finitely additive set function such that $\mu(A) = 0$ or 1 for every $A \in \mathcal{P}(X)$. Let

$$\mathcal{U} = \{A \in \mathcal{P}(X) \mid \mu(A) = 1\}.$$

Show that $\mathcal{U}$ has the following properties:
 (i) $\emptyset \notin \mathcal{U}$.
 (ii) If $A \in X$ and $B \supseteq A$, then $B \in \mathcal{U}$.
 (iii) If $A, B \in \mathcal{U}$, then $A \cap B \in \mathcal{U}$.
 (iv) For every $A \in \mathcal{P}(X)$, either $A \in \mathcal{U}$ or $A^c \in \mathcal{U}$.
 (Any $\mathcal{U} \subseteq \mathcal{P}(X)$ satisfying (i) to (iv) is called an **ultrafilter** in X.)

(b) Let $\mathcal{U}$ be any ultrafilter in X. Define $\mu : \mathcal{P}(X) \longrightarrow [0, \infty)$ by

$$\mu(A) := \begin{cases} 1 & \text{if } A \in \mathcal{U}, \\ 0 & \text{if } A \notin \mathcal{U}. \end{cases}$$

Show that μ is finitely additive.

3.6.12. Exercise: Let $\mathcal{A}$ be an algebra of subsets of a set X.

(i) Let μ_1, μ_2 be measures on $\mathcal{A}$, and let α and β be non-negative real numbers. Show that $\alpha\mu_1 + \beta\mu_2$ is also a measure on $\mathcal{A}$.

(ii) For any two measures μ_1, μ_2 on $\mathcal{A}$, we say $\mu_1 \leq \mu_2$ if $\mu_1(E) \leq \mu_2(E)$, $\forall\ E \in \mathcal{A}$. Let $\{\mu_n\}_{n \geq 1}$ be a sequence of measures on $\mathcal{A}$ such that $\mu_n \leq \mu_{n+1}$, $\forall\ n \geq 1$. Define $\forall\ E \in \mathcal{A}$,

$$\mu(E) := \lim_{n \to \infty} \mu_n(E).$$

Show that μ is also a measure on $\mathcal{A}$ and $\forall\ E \in \mathcal{B}$,

$$\mu(E) = \sup \{\mu_n(E) \mid n \geq 1\}.$$

*3.6.13. Exercise: Let X be a compact topological space and $\mathcal{A}$ be the collection of all those subsets of X which are both open and closed. Show that $\mathcal{A}$ is an algebra of subsets of X. Further, every finitely additive set function on $\mathcal{A}$ is also countably additive.

3.7. The induced outer measure

In section 3.1 we have seen how to extend the notion of length from the class of intervals to the algebra generated by intervals. This idea was made abstract in section 3.3, where we showed how to extend a countably additive set function μ from a semi-algebra $\mathcal{C}$ of subsets of a set X to $\mathcal{F}(\mathcal{C})$, the algebra generated by $\mathcal{C}$. In order to extend the notion of length further, we first try to approximate the size of any arbitrary subset A of $\mathbb{R}$ using sets whose size (i.e., the length) is already known, i.e., the intervals. To do this, given a set E we cover it by intervals and calculate the total of the lengths of these covering intervals. This will give us an approximation of the size of E. We take the infimum of such approximate sizes and call it the outer measure of E. Since dealing with the length function on $\tilde{\mathcal{I}}$ or an arbitrary measure μ on an algebra $\mathcal{A}$ of subsets of a set X does not make any difference in the process, for the rest of the section μ will be assumed to be a given measure on an algebra $\mathcal{A}$ of subsets of a set X. Our aim is to try to extend μ to a class of subsets of X which is larger than $\mathcal{A}$. Intuitively, sets A in $\mathcal{A}$ are those whose size $\mu(A)$ can be measured accurately. The approximate size of any set $E \subseteq X$ is given by the outer measure as defined next. Recall (see appendix A) that for any nonempty set $A \subseteq [0, +\infty]$, we write $\inf(A) := \inf A \cap [0, +\infty)$ if $A \cap [0, +\infty) \neq \emptyset$, and $\inf(A) := +\infty$ otherwise.

3.7.1. Definition: Let $\mathcal{A}$ be an algebra of subsets of a set X and $\mu : \mathcal{A} \longrightarrow [0, \infty]$ be a measure on $\mathcal{A}$. For $E \subseteq X$, define

$$\mu^*(E) := \inf \left\{ \sum_{i=1}^{\infty} \mu(A_i) \,\middle|\, A_i \in \mathcal{A}, \, \bigcup_{i=1}^{\infty} A_i \supseteq E \right\}.$$

The set function μ^* is called the **outer measure induced by** μ.

3.7.2. Remarks:

(i) Given any $E \subseteq X$, there exists at least one covering $\{A_i\}_{i \geq 1}$ of E by elements of A, namely $\{X\}$. Thus $\mu^*(E)$ is well-defined.

(ii) The set function $\mu^*(E)$ can take the value $+\infty$ for some sets E.

3.7.3. Exercise: Show that

$$\mu^*(E) = \inf \left\{ \sum_{i=1}^{\infty} \mu(A_i) \,\middle|\, A_i \in \mathcal{A}, \, A_i \cap A_j = \emptyset \text{ for } i \neq j \text{ and } \bigcup_{i=1}^{\infty} A_i \supseteq E \right\}.$$

3.7.4. Proposition (Properties of outer measure): *The set function* $\mu^* : \mathcal{P}(X) \longrightarrow [0, \infty]$ *has the following properties:*

(i) $\mu^*(\emptyset) = 0$ *and* $\mu^*(A) \geq 0 \;\forall\, A \subseteq X$.

(ii) μ^* *is monotone, i.e.,*

$$\mu^*(A) \leq \mu^*(B) \quad \text{whenever} \quad A \subseteq B \subseteq X.$$

(iii) μ^* *is countably subadditive, i.e.,*

$$\mu^*(A) \leq \sum_{i=1}^{\infty} \mu^*(A_i) \quad \text{whenever} \quad A = \bigcup_{i=1}^{\infty} A_i.$$

(iv) μ^* *is an extension of* μ , *i.e.*,

$$\mu^*(A) = \mu(A) \quad if \ \ A \in \mathcal{A}.$$

Proof: Properties (i) and (ii) are obvious. To prove (iii), let $A = \bigcup_{i=1}^{\infty} A_i$. If $\mu^*(A_i) = +\infty$ for some i, then clearly

$$\sum_{i=1}^{\infty} \mu^*(A_i) \ = \ +\infty \ \geq \ \mu^*(A).$$

So, suppose $\mu^*(A_i) < +\infty$ for every i. Then given $\epsilon > 0$, we can find sets $\{A_j^i\}_{j\geq 1}$ such that $A_i \subseteq \bigcup_{j=1}^{\infty} A_j^i$ with each $A_j^i \in \mathcal{A}$ and

$$\mu^*(A_i) \ + \ \epsilon/2^i \ > \ \sum_{j=1}^{\infty} \mu(A_j^i).$$

But, then $A = \bigcup_{i=1}^{\infty} A_i \subseteq \bigcup_{i=1}^{\infty} \bigcup_{j=1}^{\infty} A_j^i$ and

$$\sum_{i=1}^{\infty} \mu^*(A_i) + \sum_{i=1}^{\infty} \epsilon/2^i \ > \ \sum_{i=1}^{\infty} \sum_{j=1}^{\infty} \mu(A_j^i) \ \geq \ \mu^*(A),$$

i.e.,

$$\mu^*(A) \ < \ \sum_{i=1}^{\infty} \mu^*(A_i) + \epsilon.$$

Since this holds for every $\epsilon > 0$, we get

$$\mu^*(A) \ \leq \ \sum_{i=1}^{\infty} \mu^*(A_i).$$

This proves (iii).

To prove (iv), let $A \in \mathcal{A}$. Clearly $\mu^*(A) \leq \mu(A)$. To complete the proof we show that $\mu^*(A) \geq \mu(A)$. Clearly, $\mu^*(A) \geq \mu(A)$ in case $\mu^*(A) = +\infty$. If $\mu^*(A) < +\infty$ and $\epsilon > 0$ is given, we can choose pairwise disjoint sets $A_n \in \mathcal{A}, n = 1, 2, \ldots$, such that $A \subseteq \bigcup_{n=1}^{\infty} A_n$ and

$$\mu^*(A) + \epsilon \ > \ \sum_{n=1}^{\infty} \mu(A_n). \tag{3.3}$$

Since $\left\{\bigcup_{n=1}^{k}(A_n \cap A)\right\}_{k \geq 1}$ increases to A, using theorem 3.6.3(i) we have

$$
\begin{aligned}
\sum_{n=1}^{\infty} \mu(A_n) &= \lim_{k \to \infty} \sum_{n=1}^{k} \mu(A_n) \\
&= \lim_{n \to \infty} \mu\left(\bigcup_{n=1}^{k} A_n\right) \\
&\geq \lim_{n \to \infty} \mu\left(\bigcup_{n=1}^{k} (A_n \cap A)\right) \\
&= \mu\left(\bigcup_{n=1}^{\infty} (A_n \cap A)\right) \\
&= \mu(A). \quad\quad\quad (3.4)
\end{aligned}
$$

From (3.3) and (3.4) we have $\forall\, \epsilon > 0$,

$$
\mu^*(A) + \epsilon > \mu(A).
$$

Since $\epsilon > 0$ is arbitrary, letting $\epsilon \to 0$, we get

$$
\mu^*(A) \geq \mu(A). \quad \blacksquare
$$

3.7.5. Remarks:

(i) A set function ν defined on all subsets of a set X is called an **outer measure** if ν has properties (i), (ii) and (iii) in proposition 3.7.4. The outer measure μ^* induced by μ is characterized by the property that if ν is any outer measure on X such that $\nu(A) = \mu(A)\ \forall\ A \in \mathcal{A}$, then $\mu^*(A) \geq \nu(A)$. In other words, μ^* is the largest of all the outer measures which agree with μ on $\mathcal{A}$.

(ii) In the definition of $\mu^*(E)$ the infimum is taken over the all possible countable coverings of E. To see that finite coverings will not suffice, consider $E := \mathbb{Q} \cap (0, 1)$, the set of all rationals in $(0, 1)$, and let $I_1, I_2, \ldots, I_n$ be any finite collection of open intervals such that $E \subseteq \bigcup_{i=1}^{n} I_i$. Then it is easy to see that $\sum_{i=1}^{n} \lambda(I_i) \geq 1$. This will imply $\lambda^*(E) \geq 1$ if only finite coverings are considered in the definition of λ^*, which contradicts the fact that $\lambda^*(E) = 0$, E being a countable set.

3.7.6. Example: Let

$$
\mathcal{A} := \{A \subseteq \mathbb{R} \mid \text{Either } A \text{ or } A^c \text{ is countable}\}.
$$

It is easy to see that $\mathcal{A}$ is an algebra of subsets of $\mathbb{R}$. (In fact $\mathcal{A}$ is what is called a σ-algebra, see example 3.9.2.) For $A \in \mathcal{A}$, let $\mu(A) = 0$ if A is countable and $\mu(A) = 1$ if A^c is countable. We claim that μ is a measure on $\mathcal{A}$. For that, let $A \in \mathcal{A}$ be such that $A = \bigcup_{i=1}^{\infty} A_i$, where each $A_i \in \mathcal{A}$ and $A_i \cap A_j = \emptyset$ for $i \neq j$. We want to show that $\mu(A) = \sum_{i=1}^{\infty} \mu(A_i)$. If each A_i is countable, then A is countable and hence

$$\mu(A) = 0 = \sum_{i=1}^{\infty} \mu(A_i).$$

Next, suppose that A_i^c is countable for some i_0. Since $A_{i_0} \cap A_j = \emptyset$ for $j \neq i_0$, we have $A_j \subset A_{i_0}^c$ and hence $\mu(A_j) = 0 \; \forall \; j \neq i_0$. Also $A^c \subset A_{i_0}^c$. Thus A^c is countable and $\mu(A) = 1$. This proves that μ is a measure on $\mathcal{A}$. Let μ^* be the outer measure induced by μ on $\mathcal{P}(\mathbb{R})$. It follows from proposition 3.7.4 that μ^* is countably subadditive on $\mathcal{P}(\mathbb{R})$. Is μ^* countably additive? To find an answer to this, let us first understand μ^* better in this case. If $A \subset \mathbb{R}$ is countable, then clearly $A \in \mathcal{A}$, and hence $\mu^*(A) = \mu(A) = 0$. If $A \subseteq \mathbb{R}$ is an uncountable set, then clearly

$$\mu^*(A) \; \leq \; \mu^*(\mathbb{R}) = 1.$$

Further, if $A_i \in \mathcal{A}, i \geq 1$, are such that $A \subseteq \bigcup_{i=1}^{\infty} A_i$, then A being uncountable implies that for some i_0, A_{i_0} is not countable. Since $A_{i_0} \in \mathcal{A}$, we have that $A_{i_0}^c$ is countable. Thus

$$\sum_{i=1}^{\infty} \mu(A_i) \; \geq \; \mu(A_{i_0}) \; \geq \; 1.$$

Hence $\mu^*(A) \geq 1$. Thus $\mu^*(A) = 1$ iff A is uncountable. Now $\mathbb{R} = (-\infty, 0] \cup (0, \infty)$ and

$$\mu^*(\mathbb{R}) = 1 < 2 = \mu(-\infty, 0] + \mu(0, \infty).$$

This shows that μ^* need not be even finitely additive on all subsets.

3.7.7. Exercise: Let X be any nonempty set and let $\mathcal{A}$ be any algebra of subsets of X. Let $x_0 \in X$ be fixed. For $A \in \mathcal{A}$, define

$$\mu(A) := \begin{cases} 0 & \text{if } x_0 \notin A, \\ 1 & \text{if } x_0 \in A. \end{cases}$$

Show that μ is countably additive. Let μ^* be the outer measure induced by μ. Show that $\mu^*(A)$ is either 0 or 1 for every $A \subseteq X$, and $\mu^*(A) = 1$ if $x_0 \in A$. Can you conclude that $\mu^*(A) = 1$ implies $x_0 \in A$? Show that this is possible if $\{x_0\} \in \mathcal{A}$.

3.8. Choosing nice sets: Measurable sets

We come back to our construction: given a measure on an algebra $\mathcal{A}$ of subsets of a set X, try to define a measure $\overline{\mu}$ on some class $\mathcal{S}$ of subsets of X such that $\mathcal{A} \subseteq \mathcal{S}$ and $\overline{\mu}(A) = \mu(A), \; \forall \; A \in \mathcal{A}$. As a first step in this direction, we defined the notion of μ^*, the outer measure induced by μ on all subsets of X. We saw that $\mu^*(A) = \mu(A)$, $\forall\ A \in \mathcal{A}$, but in general μ^* need not be even finitely additive on $\mathcal{P}(X)$. So, as a consolation, let us try to identify some subclass $\mathcal{S}$ of $\mathcal{P}(X)$ such that μ^* restricted to $\mathcal{S}$ will be countable additive. This is the class $\mathcal{S}$ which we call the class of 'nice' subsets of X. But the problem is how to pick these 'nice' sets?

Since μ^* is already countably subadditive, to ensure its countable additivity on a collection $\mathcal{S}$, which can be assumed to be an algebra, it is enough to ensure its finite additivity on it (see theorem 3.6.1). Let us suppose that there is a class $\mathcal{S}$ of subsets of X such that $\mathcal{S} \supseteq \mathcal{A}$ and μ^* is finitely additive on $\mathcal{S}$ with $\mu^*(A) = \mu(A)$, $\forall\ A \in \mathcal{A}$. Then for any set $Y \subseteq X$ and $E \in \mathcal{S}$, by the subadditive property of μ^*,

$$\mu^*(Y) \leq \mu^*(Y \cap E) + \mu^*(Y \cap E^c). \tag{3.5}$$

Also if $\mu^*(Y) = +\infty$, then

$$\mu^*(Y) = +\infty \geq \mu^*(Y \cap E) + \mu^*(Y \cap E^c). \tag{3.6}$$

In case $\mu^*(Y) < +\infty$, given $\epsilon > 0$, we can choose pairwise disjoint sets $A_1, A_2, \ldots$ in $\mathcal{A}$ such that $Y \subseteq \bigcup_{i=1}^{\infty} A_i$ and

$$\mu^*(Y) + \epsilon \geq \sum_{i=1}^{\infty} \mu(A_i). \tag{3.7}$$

Now using the facts that $\mu^*(A) = \mu(A)$ $\forall\ A \in \mathcal{A}$ and that μ^* is finitely additive on $\mathcal{S}$, we have $\forall\ i$

$$\mu^*(A_i) = \mu^*(A_i \cap E) + \mu^*(A_i \cap E^c). \tag{3.8}$$

Thus, using (3.7) and (3.8) we have $\forall\ Y \subseteq X$

$$
\begin{aligned}
\mu^*(Y) + \epsilon &\geq \sum_{i=1}^{\infty} \mu^*(A_i) \\
&= \sum_{i=1}^{\infty} [\mu^*(A_i \cap E) + \mu^*(A_i \cap E^c)] \\
&= \sum_{i=1}^{\infty} \mu^*(A_i \cap E) + \sum_{i=1}^{\infty} \mu^*(A_i \cap E^c) \\
&\geq \mu^*\left(\left(\bigcup_{i=1}^{\infty} A_i\right) \cap E\right) + \mu^*\left(\left(\bigcup_{i=1}^{\infty} A_i\right) \cap E^c\right) \\
&\geq \mu^*(Y \cap E) + \mu^*(Y \cap E^c).
\end{aligned}
\tag{3.9}
$$

Hence, $\forall\ Y \subseteq X$ and $E \in \mathcal{S}$, from (3.5), (3.6) and (3.9) we have

$$\mu^*(Y) = \mu^*(Y \cap E) + \mu^*(Y \cap E^c). \tag{3.10}$$

Thus the 'nice' sets satisfy the above property. We can put this property as the definition of 'nice sets'. Thus a set $E \subseteq X$ is a 'nice' set if we use it as a knife to cut any subset Y of X into two parts, $Y \cap E$ and $Y \cap E^c$, so that their sizes $\mu^*(Y \cap E)$ and $\mu^*(Y \cap E^c)$ add up to give the size $\mu^*(Y)$ of Y. Thus a 'nice' set is in a sense a 'sharp' knife. This motivates our next definition.

3.8.1. Definition: A subset $E \subseteq X$ is said to be μ^*-**measurable** if for every $Y \subseteq X$,

$$\mu^*(Y) = \mu^*(Y \cap E) + \mu^*(Y \cap E^c). \tag{3.11}$$

We denote by $\mathcal{S}^*$ the class of all μ^*-measurable subsets of X. Note that $E \in \mathcal{S}^*$ iff $E^c \in \mathcal{S}^*$, due to the symmetry in equation (3.11).

3.8.2. Theorem: *Let $E \subseteq X$. Show that the following statements are equivalent:*

(i) $E \in \mathcal{S}^*$.

(ii) *For every $Y \subseteq X$,*

$$\mu^*(Y) \geq \mu^*(Y \cap E) + \mu^*(Y \cap E^c).$$

(iii) *For every $Y \subseteq X$, with $\mu^*(Y) < +\infty$,*

$$\mu^*(Y) \geq \mu^*(Y \cap E) + \mu^*(Y \cap E^c).$$

(iv) *For every $A \in \mathcal{A}$,*

$$\mu(A) \geq \mu^*(A \cap E) + \mu^*(A \cap E^c).$$

Proof: Clearly (i) is equivalent to (ii), since μ^* is subadditive. The implications (ii) implies (iii) implies (iv) are also obvious. To complete the proof, we prove (iv) $\Rightarrow$ (ii). Let $Y \subseteq X$. If $\mu^*(Y) = +\infty$, then clearly

$$\mu^*(Y) = \infty \geq \mu^*(Y \cap E) + \mu^*(Y \cap E^c).$$

Next suppose $\mu^*(Y) < +\infty$. Let $\epsilon > 0$. Choose sets $A_i \in \mathcal{A}, i = 1, 2, \dots$, such that $Y \subseteq \bigcup_{i=1}^{\infty} A_i$ and

$$\mu^*(Y) + \epsilon > \sum_{i=1}^{\infty} \mu(A_i).$$

Since, by the given hypothesis, $\forall\, i \geq 1$

$$\mu(A_i) \geq \mu^*(A_i \cap E) + \mu^*(A_i \cap E^c),$$

we have

$$\mu^*(Y) + \epsilon \; > \; \sum_{i=1}^{\infty} \mu(A_i)$$

$$\geq \; \sum_{i=1}^{\infty} \mu^*(A_i \cap E) + \sum_{i=1}^{\infty} \mu^*(A_i \cap E)$$

$$\geq \; \mu^*(Y \cap E) + \mu^*(Y \cap E^c).$$

Since $\epsilon > 0$ is arbitrary, we have

$$\mu^*(Y) \; \geq \; \mu^*(Y \cap E) + \mu^*(Y \cap E^c).$$

Hence (ii) holds. ∎

We finally check that $\mathcal{S}^*$ is indeed the required collection of 'nice' sets.

3.8.3. Proposition: *The collection $\mathcal{S}^*$ has the following properties:*

(i) $\mathcal{A} \subseteq \mathcal{S}^*.$

(ii) $\mathcal{S}^*$ *is an algebra of subsets of X, and μ^* restricted to $\mathcal{S}^*$ is finitely additive.*

(iii) *If $A_n \in \mathcal{S}^*, n = 1, 2, \ldots$, then $\bigcup_{n=1}^{\infty} A_n \in \mathcal{S}^*$ and μ^* restricted to $\mathcal{S}^*$ is countably additive.*

(iv) *Let $\mathcal{N} := \{E \subseteq X \mid \mu^*(E) = 0\}$. Then $\mathcal{N} \subseteq \mathcal{S}^*.$*

Proof: (i) Let $E \subseteq X$ be arbitrary and let $A \in \mathcal{A}$. Let $A_i \in \mathcal{A}, i \geq 1$, be such that $\bigcup_{i=1}^{\infty} A_i \supseteq E$ and $A_i \cap A_j = \emptyset$ for $i \neq j$. Then, using additivity of μ, we have

$$\sum_{i=1}^{\infty} \mu(A_i) \; = \; \sum_{i=1}^{\infty} \mu(A_i \cap A) + \sum_{i=1}^{\infty} \mu(A_i \cap A^c)$$

$$\geq \; \mu^*(E \cap A) + \mu^*(E \cap A^c).$$

Since this holds for any pairwise disjoint covering $\{A_i\}_{i \geq 1}$ of E by elements of $\mathcal{A}$, we have

$$\mu^*(E) \; \geq \; \mu^*(E \cap A) + \mu^*(E \cap A^c).$$

Also, since μ^* is countably subadditive, for any $A \in \mathcal{A}$ we have

$$\mu^*(E) \; = \; \mu^*(E \cap A) + \mu^*(E \cap A^c).$$

Hence $A \in \mathcal{S}^*$. This proves (i).

(ii) Clearly $\emptyset \in \mathcal{S}^*$, and if $A \in \mathcal{S}^*$ then $A^c \in \mathcal{S}^*$. Finally, let $A_1, A_2 \in \mathcal{S}^*$. To show that $A_1 \cup A_2 \in \mathcal{S}^*$, we have to show that for every $E \subseteq X$ with $\mu^*(E) < +\infty$,

$$\mu^*(E) = \mu^*(E \cap (A_1 \cup A_2)) + \mu^*(E \cap (A_1 \cup A_2)^c). \qquad (3.12)$$

Since $A_1 \in \mathcal{S}^*$, we have, $\forall E \subseteq X$ with $\mu(E) < +\infty$,

$$\mu^*(E) = \mu^*(E \cap A_1) + \mu^*(E \cap A_1^c).$$

Changing E to $E \cap (A_1 \cup A_2)$, we get

$$\begin{aligned}
\mu^*(E \cap (A_1 \cup A_2)) \\
&= \mu^*((E \cap (A_1 \cup A_2)) \cap A_1) + \mu^*((E \cap (A_1 \cup A_2)) \cap A_1^c) \\
&= \mu^*(E \cap A_1) + \mu^*(E \cap A_2 \cap A_1^c). \qquad (3.13)
\end{aligned}$$

Also, since $A_2 \in \mathcal{S}^*$, we have

$$\mu^*(E \cap A_1^c) = \mu^*(E \cap A_1^c \cap A_2) + \mu^*(E \cap A_1^c \cap A_2^c). \qquad (3.14)$$

From (3.13) and (3.14), we get

$$\begin{aligned}
\mu^*(E \cap (A_1 \cup A_2)) + \mu^*(E \cap A_1^c \cap A_2^c) &= \mu^*(E \cap A_1) + \mu^*(E \cap A_1^c) \\
&= \mu^*(E).
\end{aligned}$$

Thus (3.12) holds, i.e., $A_1 \cup A_2 \in \mathcal{S}^*$. In particular, if $A_1, A_2 \in \mathcal{S}^*$ and $A_1 \cap A_2 = \emptyset$, then by equation (3.13) with $E = A_1 \cup A_2$, we have

$$\mu^*(A_1 \cup A_2) = \mu^*(A_1) + \mu^*(A_2).$$

This proves (ii) completely.

To prove (iii), let $A_i \in \mathcal{S}^*, i = 1, 2, \dots$, and let $A := \bigcup_{i=1}^{\infty} A_i$. We note that, since $\mathcal{S}^*$ is an algebra, A can be expressed as a countable union of pairwise disjoint elements of $\mathcal{S}^*$ (remark 3.6.2). Thus to show that $A \in \mathcal{S}^*$, we may assume without loss of generality that $A_i \cap A_j = \emptyset$ for $i \neq j$. Now, using the fact that each $A_i \in \mathcal{S}^*$ and $A_i \cap A_j = \emptyset$ for $i \neq j$, we have for every $E \subseteq X$,

$$\begin{aligned}
\mu^*(E) &= \mu^*(E \cap A_1) + \mu^*(E \cap A_1^c) \\
&= \mu^*(E \cap A_1) + \mu^*(E \cap A_1^c \cap A_2) + \mu^*(E \cap A_1^c \cap A_2^c) \\
&= \mu^*(E \cap A_1) + \mu^*(E \cap A_2) + \mu^*(E \cap A_1^c \cap A_2^c) \\
&\quad \cdots\cdots \\
&\quad \cdots\cdots \\
&= \sum_{i=1}^{n} \mu^*(E \cap A_i) + \mu^*\left(E \cap \left(\bigcap_{i=1}^{n} A_i^c\right)\right) \\
&= \sum_{i=1}^{n} \mu^*(E \cap A_i) + \mu^*\left(E \cap \left(\bigcup_{i=1}^{n} A_i\right)^c\right) \\
&\geq \sum_{i=1}^{n} \mu^*(E \cap A_i) + \mu^*\left(E \cap \left(\bigcup_{i=1}^{\infty} A_i\right)^c\right).
\end{aligned}$$

Since this holds $\forall\, n$, letting $n \longrightarrow \infty$ and noting that μ^* is countably subadditive, we have $\forall\, E \subseteq X$,

$$\mu^*(E) \geq \sum_{i=1}^{\infty} \mu^*(E \cap A_i) + \mu^*\left(E \cap \left(\bigcup_{i=1}^{\infty} A_i\right)^c\right) \qquad (3.15)$$

$$\geq \mu^*\left(E \cap \left(\bigcup_{i=1}^{\infty} A_i\right)\right) + \mu^*\left(E \cap \left(\bigcup_{i=1}^{\infty} A_i\right)^c\right).$$

This proves (in view of theorem 3.8.2) that $\bigcup_{i=1}^{\infty} A_i \in \mathcal{S}^*$. In particular, if we take $E = \bigcup_{i=1}^{\infty} A_i$ in (3.15), then

$$\mu^*\left(\bigcup_{i=1}^{\infty} A_i\right) \geq \sum_{i=1}^{\infty} \mu^*(A_i).$$

Since $\mu^*\left(\bigcup_{i=1}^{\infty} A_i\right) \leq \sum_{i=1}^{\infty} \mu^*(A_i)$ holds because of the countable subadditivity property of μ^*, we get that μ^* is countably additive on $\mathcal{S}^*$. This proves (iii).

The proof of (iv) is easy and left as an exercise. ∎

We have proved in the above proposition that $\mathcal{S}^* \supseteq \mathcal{A}$ and $\mathcal{S}^*$ is not only an algebra, it is also closed under countable unions. Algebras with this additional property are called σ-algebras, and are going to play an important role in the rest of the discussion. We analyze them in detail in the next section. We close this section by giving an equivalent definition of measurable sets when $\mu(X) < +\infty$.

3.8.4. Theorem: *Let* $\mu(X) < +\infty$. *Then* $E \subseteq X$ *is* μ^*-*measurable iff*

$$\mu(X) = \mu(E) + \mu(E^c)$$

Proof: Suppose E is μ^*-measurable. Then $\forall\, Y \subseteq X$

$$\mu^*(Y) = \mu^*(Y \cap E) + \mu^*(Y \cap E^c).$$

In particular, for $Y = X$, we have

$$\mu^*(X) = \mu^*(E) + \mu^*(E^c).$$

Conversely, let $E \subseteq X$ be such that above equation holds. Since every set $A \in \mathcal{A}$ is measurable, we have

$$\mu^*(E) = \mu^*(E \cap A) + \mu^*(E \cap A^c)$$

and

$$\mu^*(E^c) = \mu^*(E^c \cap A) + \mu^*(E^c \cap A^c).$$

Adding these two equalities and using the given hypothesis, we have

$$
\begin{aligned}
\mu^*(X) &= \mu^*(E) + \mu^*(E^c) \\
&= [\mu^*(E \cap A) + \mu^*(E^c \cap A)] + [\mu^*(E \cap A^c) + \mu^*(E^c \cap A^c)] \\
&\geq \mu^*(A) + \mu^*(A^c) \geq \mu^*(X).
\end{aligned}
$$

The last inequality follows because μ^* is subadditive. Hence

$$
\mu^*(A) + \mu^*(A^c) = \mu^*(E \cap A) + \mu^*(E^c \cap A) + \mu^*(E \cap A^c) + \mu^*(E^c \cap A^c).
$$

But

$$
\mu^*(A^c) \leq \mu^*(E \cap A^c) + \mu^*(E^c \cap A^c).
$$

Thus

$$
\mu^*(A) \geq \mu^*(E \cap A) + \mu^*(E^c \cap A).
$$

Now it follows from theorem 3.8.2 (iv) that E is measurable. ∎

3.8.5. Exercise: Identify the collection of μ^*-measurable sets for μ as in example 3.7.6.

Theorems 3.7.4.(iv) and 3.8.3 give us a method of constructing an extension of a measure μ defined on an algebra $\mathcal{A}$ to a class $\mathcal{S}^* \supseteq \mathcal{A}$. We analyze the properties of the class $\mathcal{S}^*$ in the next section.

3.9. The σ-algebras and extension from the algebra to the generated σ-algebra

Properties of $\mathcal{S}^*$, the class of μ^*-measurable subsets (as discussed in theorem 3.8.3, motivate the following:

3.9.1. Definition: Let X be any nonempty set and let $\mathcal{S}$ be a class of subsets of X with the following properties:

(i) $\emptyset$ and $X \in \mathcal{S}$.

(ii) $A^c \in \mathcal{S}$ whenever $A \in \mathcal{S}$.

(iii) $\bigcup_{i=1}^{\infty} A_i \in \mathcal{S}$ whenever $A_i \in \mathcal{S}$, $i = 1, 2, \ldots$.

Such a class $\mathcal{S}$ is called a **sigma algebra** (written as σ-algebra) of subsets of X.

3.9.2. Examples:

(i) As proved in proposition 3.8.3, the class $\mathcal{S}^*$ of all μ^*-measurable subsets of X forms a σ-algebra.

(ii) Let X be any set. Then $\{\emptyset, X\}$ and $\mathcal{P}(X)$ are obvious examples of σ-algebras of subsets of X.

(iii) Let X be any uncountable set and let $\mathcal{S} = \{A \subseteq X \mid A$ or A^c is countable$\}$. Then $\mathcal{S}$ is a σ-algebra of subsets of X. To see this we note that clearly $\emptyset, X \in \mathcal{S}$, and $A \in \mathcal{S}$ iff $A^c \in \mathcal{S}$. Let $A_n \in \mathcal{S}, n = 1, 2, \ldots$. If each A_n is countable, then $A := \bigcup_{n=}^{\infty} A_n$ is countable and hence $A \in \mathcal{S}$. In case some A_k is such that A_k^c is countable, then $(\bigcup_{n=1}^{\infty} A_n)^c \subseteq A_k^c$ implies that $\bigcup_{n=1}^{\infty} A_k \in \mathcal{S}$.

(iv) Let X be any set and let $\mathcal{C}$ be any class of subsets of X. Let $\mathcal{S}(\mathcal{C}) := \bigcap \mathcal{S}$, where the intersection is taken over all σ-algebras $\mathcal{S}$ of subsets of X such that $\mathcal{S} \supseteq \mathcal{C}$ (note that $\mathcal{P}(X)$ is one such σ-algebra). It is easy to see that $\mathcal{S}(\mathcal{C})$ is also a σ-algebra of subsets of X and $\mathcal{S}(\mathcal{C}) \supseteq \mathcal{C}$. In fact, if $\mathcal{S}$ is any σ-algebra of subsets of X such that $\mathcal{S} \supseteq \mathcal{C}$, then clearly $\mathcal{S} \supseteq \mathcal{S}(\mathcal{C})$. Thus $\mathcal{S}(\mathcal{C})$ is the smallest σ-algebra of subsets of X containing $\mathcal{C}$, and is called the **σ-algebra generated by** $\mathcal{C}$. In general it is not possible to represent an element of $\mathcal{S}(\mathcal{C})$ explicitly in terms of elements of $\mathcal{C}$. See also theorem 4.5.2.

3.9.3. Exercise:

(i) Let $\mathcal{S}$ be a σ-algebra of subsets of X and let $Y \subseteq X$. Show that $\mathcal{S} \cap Y := \{E \cap Y \mid E \in \mathcal{S}\}$ is a σ-algebra of subsets of Y.

(ii) Let $f : X \to Y$ be a function and $\mathcal{C}$ a nonempty family of subsets of Y. Let $f^{-1}(\mathcal{C}) := \{f^{-1}(C) \mid C \in \mathcal{C}\}$. Show that $\mathcal{S}(f^{-1}(\mathcal{C})) = f^{-1}(\mathcal{S}(\mathcal{C}))$.

(iii) Let X be an uncountable set and $\mathcal{C} = \{\{x\} \mid x \in X\}$. Identify the σ-algebra generated by $\mathcal{C}$.

3.9.4. Exercise: Let $\mathcal{C}$ be any class of subsets of a set X and let $Y \subseteq X$. Let $\mathcal{A}(\mathcal{C})$ be the algebra generated by $\mathcal{C}$.

  (i) Show that $\mathcal{S}(\mathcal{C}) = \mathcal{S}(\mathcal{A}(\mathcal{C}))$.

  (ii) Let $\mathcal{C} \cap Y := \{E \cap Y \mid E \in \mathcal{C}\}$. Show that $\mathcal{S}(\mathcal{C} \cap Y) \subseteq \mathcal{S}(\mathcal{C}) \cap Y$.

  (iii) Let

$$\mathcal{S} := \{E \cup (B \cap Y^c) \mid E \in \mathcal{S}(\mathcal{C} \cap Y), B \in \mathcal{C}\}.$$

    Show that $\mathcal{S}$ is a σ-algebra of subsets of X such that $\mathcal{C} \subseteq \mathcal{S}$ and $\mathcal{S} \cap Y = \mathcal{S}(\mathcal{C} \cap Y)$.

  (iv) Using (i), (ii) and (iii), conclude that $\mathcal{S}(\mathcal{C} \cap Y) = \mathcal{S}(\mathcal{C}) \cap Y$.

3.9.5. Proposition: *Let $\mathcal{C}$ be a class of subsets of a set X such that $\emptyset \in \mathcal{C}$. Then $E \in \mathcal{S}(\mathcal{C})$ iff $\exists$ sets $C_1, C_2, \ldots$ in $\mathcal{C}$ such that $E \in \mathcal{S}(\{C_1, C_2, \ldots\})$.*

Proof: Let

$$\mathcal{B} := \{E \in \mathcal{S}(\mathcal{C}) \mid E \in \mathcal{S}(\{C_1, C_2, \ldots\}) \text{ for some } C_1, C_2, \ldots \in \mathcal{C}\}.$$

Clearly $\mathcal{C} \subseteq \mathcal{B}$. Also, if $E \in \mathcal{B}$ and $E \in \mathcal{S}(\{C_1, C_2, \dots\})$, then by definition, $E^c \in \mathcal{S}(\{C_1, C_2, \dots\})$. Hence $E^c \in \mathcal{B}$. Finally, let $E_j \in \mathcal{B}, j = 1, 2, \dots$. If $E_j \in \mathcal{S}(\{C_1^j, C_2^j, \dots\})$, $C_i^j \in \mathcal{C} \;\forall\; i, j$, then $E_j \in \mathcal{S}\{C_i^j \mid j = 1, 2, \dots, i = 1, 2, \dots\}$. Hence

$$\bigcup_{j=1}^{\infty} E_j \in \mathcal{S}\{C_i^j \mid j = 1, 2, \dots; i = 1, 2, \dots\}.$$

Thus $\bigcup_{j=1}^{\infty} E_j \in \mathcal{B}$. This proves that $\mathcal{B}$ is a σ-algebra. Since $\mathcal{C} \subseteq \mathcal{B}$, by definition we have $\mathcal{S}(\mathcal{C}) \subseteq \mathcal{B}$. Hence $\mathcal{S}(\mathcal{C}) = \mathcal{B}$. ■

3.9.6. Note: The technique used in the proof of proposition 3.9.5 is very useful and is often used to prove various properties of σ-algebras under consideration. The sets satisfying the required property are collected together. One shows that this collection itself is a σ-algebra and includes a subfamily of the original σ-algebra which generates it. The claim then follows by the definition of the generated σ-algebra. We call this the **σ-algebra technique**. Another example of this technique is found in the next exercise.

3.9.7. Exercise: Let X be any topological space. Let $\mathcal{U}$ denote the class of all open subsets of X and $\mathcal{C}$ denote the class of the all closed subsets of X.

(i) Show that
$$\mathcal{S}(\mathcal{U}) = \mathcal{S}(\mathcal{C}).$$

This is called the σ-algebra of **Borel subsets** of X and is denoted by $\mathcal{B}_X$.

(ii) Let $X = \mathbb{R}$. Let $\mathcal{I}$ be the class of all intervals and $\tilde{\mathcal{I}}$ the class of all left-open right-closed intervals. Show that $\mathcal{I} \subset \mathcal{S}(\mathcal{U})$, $\mathcal{I} \subset \mathcal{S}(\tilde{\mathcal{I}})$, $\tilde{\mathcal{I}} \subset \mathcal{S}(\mathcal{I})$ and hence deduce that
$$\mathcal{S}(\mathcal{I}) = \mathcal{S}(\tilde{\mathcal{I}}) = \mathcal{B}_{\mathbb{R}}.$$

3.9.8. Exercise:

(i) Let $\mathcal{I}_r$ denote the class of all open intervals of $\mathbb{R}$ with rational endpoints. Show that $\mathcal{S}(\mathcal{I}_r) = \mathcal{B}_{\mathbb{R}}$.

(ii) Let $\mathcal{I}_d$ denote the class of all subintervals of $[0, 1]$ with dyadic endpoints (i.e., points of the form $m/2^n$ for some integers m and n). Show that $\mathcal{S}(\mathcal{I}_d) = \mathcal{B}_{\mathbb{R}} \cap [0, 1]$.

Combining proposition 3.7.4(iv), proposition 3.8.3 and example 3.9.2(i), we have the following proposition.

3.9.9. Proposition: *Let $\mathcal{A}$ be an algebra of subsets of a set X and μ a measure on $\mathcal{A}$. Then there exist a σ-algebra $\mathcal{S}^*$ (the σ-algebra of μ^*-measurable subsets of X) and a measure μ^* on $\mathcal{S}^*$ such that $\mathcal{A} \subseteq \mathcal{S}^*$ and $\mu^*(A) = \mu(A)$ for every $A \in \mathcal{A}$.*

The above proposition tells us that μ^* is a measure and is an extension of the measure μ from an algebra $\mathcal{A}$ to a σ-algebra $\mathcal{S}^*$. In particular $\mathcal{S}^* \supseteq \mathcal{S}(\mathcal{A})$, the σ-algebra generated by $\mathcal{A}$. At this stage, the following natural questions arise:

Question 1: Is the extension of μ from $\mathcal{A}$ to $\mathcal{S}(\mathcal{A})$ given by proposition 3.9.9 unique?

Question 2: We know that $\mathcal{S}(\mathcal{A}) \subseteq \mathcal{S}^*$. Is there some other relation between the two σ-algebras $\mathcal{S}(\mathcal{A})$ and $\mathcal{S}^*$? Is $\mathcal{S}^*$ much larger than $\mathcal{S}(\mathcal{A})$?

In the remaining sections of this chapter we shall answer these questions. The next example shows that in general the answer to our first question is in the negative.

3.9.10. Example: Let $\mathcal{A} = \mathcal{A}(\tilde{\mathcal{I}})$, the algebra generated by left-open right-closed intervals in $\mathbb{R}$. For $A \in \mathcal{A}$, let $\mu(A) = +\infty$ if $A \neq \emptyset$ and $\mu(\emptyset) = 0$. Then μ is a measure on $\mathcal{A}$. Let $\xi \in \mathbb{R}$ be chosen arbitrarily and fixed. Let $\mathcal{A}_\xi$ denote the algebra of subsets of $\mathbb{R}$ generated by $\mathcal{A}$ and $\{\xi\}$. Define for $A \in \mathcal{A}_\xi$,

$$\mu_\xi(A) := \begin{cases} +\infty & \text{if } A \setminus \{\xi\} \neq \emptyset, \\ 0 & \text{if either } A = \emptyset \text{ or } A = \{\xi\}. \end{cases}$$

It is easy to check that μ_ξ is a measure on $\mathcal{A}_\xi$. If $A \neq \emptyset$ and $A \in \mathcal{A}(\mathcal{I})$, then clearly $A \setminus \{\xi\} \neq \emptyset$ and hence $\mu_\xi(A) = +\infty = \mu(A)$. By proposition 3.9.7, μ_ξ (and hence μ) can be extended to a measure, which we denote by μ_ξ again, on $\mathcal{S}(\mathcal{A})$. Note that $\forall\, x \in X$, $\{x\} \in \mathcal{S}(\mathcal{A})$ with $\mu_\xi(\{x\}) = +\infty$ if $x \neq \xi$ and $\mu_\xi(\{\xi\}) = 0$. Thus for $\xi_1, \xi_2 \in \mathbb{R}$ if $\xi_1 < \xi_2$, then $\mu_{\xi_1}(\{\xi_1\}) = 0$, whereas $\mu_{\xi_2}(\{\xi_1\}) \neq 0$. Hence for every $\xi \in \mathbb{R}$, μ_ξ is an extension of μ and $\mu_{\xi_1} \neq \mu_{\xi_2}$ for $\xi_1 \neq \xi_2$.

3.9.11. Exercise: Let μ and $\mathcal{A}$ be as in example 3.9.10. Show that $\forall\, A \in \mathcal{B}_\mathbb{R}$ there exists a measure μ_A which extends μ to $\mathcal{B}_\mathbb{R}$ and $\mu_A \neq \mu_B$ for $A \neq B$.

3.9.12. Exercise: Let X denote the set of rationals in $(0,1]$ and let $\mathcal{A}$ be as in example 3.9.10. Show that the σ-algebra $X \cap \mathcal{S}(\mathcal{A}) = \mathcal{P}(X)$ and that every nonempty set in the algebra $X \cap \mathcal{A}$ has an infinite number of points. For any $E \in X \cap \mathcal{S}(\mathcal{A})$ and $c > 0$, define $\mu_c(E) = c$ times the number of points in E. Show that μ_c is a measure on $X \cap \mathcal{S}(\mathcal{A}) = \mathcal{S}(X \cap \mathcal{A})$ and it extends the measure μ on $X \cap \mathcal{A}$ given by $\mu(A) = +\infty$ if $A \neq \emptyset$ and $\mu(\emptyset) = 0$. Further, $\mu_{c_1} \neq \mu_{c_2}$ if $c_1 \neq c_2$.

Example 3.9.10, exercises 3.9.11 and 3.9.12 show that in general a measure μ on an algebra $\mathcal{A}$ can have more than one extension to $\mathcal{S}(\mathcal{A})$, the σ-algebra generated by $\mathcal{A}$. In all these examples, the common feature is that the measure μ assigns a large value, namely $(+\infty)$, to nonempty sets. So one asks the modified question: under what conditions on μ is the extension unique? We analyze this problem in the next section.

3.10. Uniqueness of the extension

To look for the condition on μ which may ensure the uniqueness of the extension, we analyze for the particular case of μ, namely the length function λ on $\mathcal{A}(\mathcal{I})$, the algebra generated by all the intervals in $\mathbb{R}$. The length function, though it assigns the value $+\infty$ to unbounded intervals, has the property that we can write $\mathbb{R} = \bigcup_{n=-\infty}^{+\infty}(n, n+1]$ and $\forall~n,~\lambda(n, n+1] = 1 < +\infty$. In other words, the set $\mathbb{R}$ can be decomposed into a countable union of pairwise disjoint sets each having finite length. This motivates the following definition.

3.10.1. Definition: Let $\mathcal{C}$ be a collection of subsets of X and let $\mu :$ $\mathcal{C} \longrightarrow [0, \infty]$ be a set function. We say μ is **totally finite** (or just **finite**) if $\mu(A) < +\infty~\forall~A \in \mathcal{C}$. The set function μ is said to be **sigma finite** (written as σ-**finite**) if there exist pairwise disjoint sets $X_n \in \mathcal{C}, n = 1, 2, \dots$, such that $\mu(X_n) < +\infty$ for every n and $X = \bigcup_{n=1}^{\infty} X_n$.

3.10.2. Example: The length function λ on the class of intervals is σ-finite, whereas none of the set functions considered in example 3.9.10 or exercises 3.9.11 or 3.9.12 are σ-finite. In general, a measure μ defined on an algebra $\mathcal{A}$ of subsets of a set X is finite iff $\mu(X) < +\infty$.

The problem that we want to analyze is the following: Let μ be a σ-finite measure on an algebra $\mathcal{A}$ of subsets of X. Let μ_1 and μ_2 be two measures on $\mathcal{S}(\mathcal{A})$, the σ-algebra generated by the algebra $\mathcal{A}$, such that $\mu_1(A) = \mu_2(A)~\forall~A \in \mathcal{A}$. Is $\mu_1 = \mu_2$? Since μ is σ-finite, we can write $X = \bigcup_{i=1}^{\infty} X_i$, where each $X_i \in \mathcal{A}, X_i \cap X_j = \emptyset$ and $\mu_i(X_j) < +\infty~\forall~i = 1, 2$ and $j = 1, 2, \dots$. Thus for $E \in \mathcal{S}(\mathcal{A})$,

$$\mu_i(E) = \mu_i\left(E \cap \left(\bigcup_{j=1}^{\infty} X_j\right)\right) = \sum_{j=1}^{\infty} \mu_i(E \cap X_j).$$

Thus $\mu_1(E) = \mu_2(E)$ will hold provided we can say that $\mu_1(E \cap X_j) = \mu_2(E \cap X_j) \ \forall \, j$. Equivalently, to have $\mu_1 = \mu_2$ on $\mathcal{S}(\mathcal{A})$, we have only to show that μ_1 and μ_2 are equal on each of the σ-algebras $\mathcal{S}(\mathcal{A}) \cap X_j = \mathcal{S}(\mathcal{A} \cap X_j)$, given that μ_1 and μ_2 are equal on the algebra $\mathcal{A} \cap X_j$. We note that the restriction of μ_1 and μ_2 to each X_j is totally finite. Thus we will have a positive answer to our question provided we can give a positive answer to the question under the additional condition that μ_1 and μ_2 are totally finite. In other words, we may assume without loss of generality that μ_1 and μ_2 are totally finite.

So, let us analyze the situation: μ_1 and μ_2 are totally finite measures on $\mathcal{S}(\mathcal{A})$ such that $\mu_1(A) = \mu_2(A)$ for every $A \in \mathcal{A}$. We want to claim that $\mu_1(E) = \mu_2(E)$ for every $E \in \mathcal{S}(\mathcal{A})$. Let us try to use the σ-algebra technique as mentioned in note 3.9.6. Let

$$\mathcal{M} := \{E \in \mathcal{S}(\mathcal{A}) \mid \mu_1(E) = \mu_2(E)\}.$$

We are given that $\mathcal{A} \subseteq \mathcal{M}$, and we have to show that $\mathcal{S}(\mathcal{A}) \subseteq \mathcal{M}$. It is natural to try to prove that $\mathcal{M}$ is a σ-algebra, so that $\mathcal{A} \subseteq \mathcal{M}$ would then automatically imply, by the definition of $\mathcal{S}(\mathcal{A})$, that $\mathcal{S}(\mathcal{A}) \subseteq \mathcal{M}$, and we will be through. Let us analyze the properties of the class $\mathcal{M}$. If $E \in \mathcal{M}$, can we conclude that $E^c \in \mathcal{M}$? Since $\mathcal{A} \subseteq \mathcal{M}$, we have $X \in \mathcal{M}$ and thus $\mu_1(X) = \mu_2(X)$. Also $E \in \mathcal{M}$ implies $\mu_1(E) = \mu_2(E)$. Since μ_1, μ_2 are finite, we have

$$\mu_1(E^c) = \mu_1(X) - \mu_1(E) = \mu_2(X) - \mu_2(E) = \mu_2(E^c).$$

Hence $E^c \in \mathcal{M}$. Next, let $E_1, E_2 \in \mathcal{M}$. Can we conclude that $E_1 \cup E_2 \in \mathcal{M}$? Apparently, we cannot conclude this in general (we ask the reader to construct examples), i.e., $\mathcal{M}$ need not be a σ-algebra. Thus the σ-algebra technique does not work here. Let us look for some other properties of $\mathcal{M}$. For example, let $E_n \in \mathcal{M}, n \geq 1$, be such that $E_n \subseteq E_{n+1} \ \forall \, n$. Can we say that $\bigcup_{n=1}^{\infty} E_n \in \mathcal{M}$? Well, since μ_1 and μ_2 are measures, using theorem 3.6.3(a), we get

$$\mu_1 \left(\bigcup_{n=1}^{\infty} E_n \right) = \lim_{n \to \infty} \mu_1(E_n)$$

$$= \lim_{n \to \infty} \mu_2(E_n)$$

$$= \mu_2 \left(\bigcup_{n=1}^{\infty} E_n \right).$$

Thus $\bigcup_{n=1}^{\infty} E_n \in \mathcal{M}$. Also, if $E_n \in \mathcal{M}$ and $E_n \supseteq E_{n+1} \ \forall \, n$, then, again noting that μ_1, μ_2 are totally finite, by theorem 3.6.3(b) we have $\bigcap_{n=1}^{\infty} E_n \in \mathcal{M}$. Thus we have proved the following:

3.10.3. Proposition: *Let μ_1 and μ_2 be measures on a σ-algebra $\mathcal{S}$. Then the class $\mathcal{M} = \{E \in \mathcal{S} \mid \mu_1(E) = \mu_2(E)\}$ has the following properties:*

(i) $\emptyset \in \mathcal{M}$.

(ii) *If $A_n \in \mathcal{M}, n = 1, 2, \ldots$, and $A_n \subseteq A_{n+1} \ \forall \ n$, then $\bigcup_{n=1}^{\infty} A_n \in \mathcal{M}$.*

(iii) *Assume further that μ_1 and μ_2 are totally finite. Then for $A_n \in \mathcal{M}$ with $A_n \supseteq A_{n+1}$ for $n = 1, 2, \ldots$, we have $\bigcap_{n=1}^{\infty} A_n \in \mathcal{M}$.*

This motivates the following definition.

3.10.4. Definition: Let X be a nonempty set and $\mathcal{M}$ be a class of subsets of X. We say $\mathcal{M}$ is a **monotone class** if

(i) $\bigcup_{n=1}^{\infty} A_n \in \mathcal{M}$, whenever $A_n \in \mathcal{M}$ and $A_n \subseteq A_{n+1}$ for $n = 1, 2, \ldots$,

(ii) $\bigcap_{n=1}^{\infty} A_n \in \mathcal{M}$, whenever $A_n \in \mathcal{M}$ and $A_n \supseteq A_{n+1}$ for $n = 1, 2, \ldots$.

3.10.5. Examples:

(i) If μ_1 and μ_2 are totally finite measures on a σ-algebra $\mathcal{S}$ and $\mathcal{M} := \{E \in \mathcal{S} \mid \mu_1(E) = \mu_2(E)\}$, then proposition 3.10.3 says that $\mathcal{M}$ is a monotone class.

(ii) Clearly, every σ-algebra is also a monotone class.

(iii) Let X be any uncountable set. Let $\mathcal{M} := \{A \subseteq X \mid A \text{ is countable}\}$. Then $\mathcal{M}$ is a monotone class but not a σ-algebra.

(iv) Let X be any nonempty set and let $\mathcal{C}$ be any collection of subsets of X. Clearly $\mathcal{P}(X)$ is a monotone class of subsets of X such that $\mathcal{C} \subseteq \mathcal{P}(X)$. Let $\mathcal{M}(\mathcal{C}) := \bigcap \mathcal{M}$, where the intersection is over all those monotone classes $\mathcal{M}$ of subsets of X such that $\mathcal{C} \subseteq \mathcal{M}$. Clearly, $\mathcal{M}(\mathcal{C})$ is itself a monotone class, and if $\mathcal{M}$ is any monotone class such that $\mathcal{C} \subseteq \mathcal{M}$, then $\mathcal{M}(\mathcal{C}) \subseteq \mathcal{M}$. Thus $\mathcal{M}(\mathcal{C})$ is the smallest monotone class of subsets of X such that $\mathcal{C} \subseteq \mathcal{M}(\mathcal{C})$. The class $\mathcal{M}(\mathcal{C})$ is called the **monotone class generated by** $\mathcal{C}$.

•**3.10.6. Exercise:** Let $\mathcal{C}$ be any class of subsets of X.

(i) If $\mathcal{C}$ is an algebra which is also a monotone class, show that $\mathcal{C}$ is a σ-algebra.

(ii) $\mathcal{C} \subseteq \mathcal{M}(\mathcal{C}) \subseteq \mathcal{S}(\mathcal{C})$.

(This exercise will be often used in the sequel.)

Let us go back to our original problem which motivated us to define the concept of a monotone class. We had two totally finite measures μ_1 and μ_2

on $\mathcal{S}(\mathcal{A})$, the σ-algebra generated by an algebra $\mathcal{A}$ of subsets of a set X. We were given that $\mu_1(A) = \mu_2(A)$ for every $A \in \mathcal{A}$. To prove that $\mu_1 = \mu_2$, we had to show that $\mathcal{S}(\mathcal{A}) \subseteq \mathcal{M} := \{E \in \mathcal{S}(\mathcal{A}) \mid \mu_1(E) = \mu_2(E)\}$. We saw that $\mathcal{A} \subseteq \mathcal{M}$ and $\mathcal{M}$ is a monotone class. Thus $\mathcal{M}(\mathcal{A}) \subseteq \mathcal{M}$, where $\mathcal{M}(\mathcal{A})$ is the monotone class generated by $\mathcal{A}$. This leads us to a natural question (again motivated by our requirement): is $\mathcal{M}(\mathcal{A}) = \mathcal{S}(\mathcal{A})$? Since every σ-algebra is a monotone class and $\mathcal{A} \subseteq \mathcal{S}(\mathcal{A})$, clearly $\mathcal{M}(\mathcal{A}) \subseteq \mathcal{S}(A)$. Thus the question is, is $\mathcal{S}(\mathcal{A}) \subseteq \mathcal{M}(\mathcal{A})$? The next theorem answers this question in the affirmative.

3.10.7. Theorem (σ-algebra monotone class): *Let $\mathcal{A}$ be an algebra of subsets of a set X. Then $\mathcal{S}(\mathcal{A}) = \mathcal{M}(\mathcal{A})$.*

Proof: As stated above, $\mathcal{M}(\mathcal{A}) \subseteq \mathcal{S}(\mathcal{A})$. We only have to show that $\mathcal{S}(\mathcal{A}) \subseteq \mathcal{M}(\mathcal{A})$. Since $\mathcal{A} \subseteq \mathcal{M}(\mathcal{A})$, to show that $\mathcal{S}(\mathcal{A}) \subseteq \mathcal{M}(\mathcal{A})$ it is enough to show that $\mathcal{M}(\mathcal{A})$ is a σ-algebra. We know $\mathcal{M}(\mathcal{A})$ is a monotone class, and hence to show it is a σ-algebra, it is enough to show that $\mathcal{M}(\mathcal{A})$ is an algebra (see exercise 3.10.6).We use the σ-algebra technique.

We first show that $\mathcal{M}(\mathcal{A})$ is closed under complements. Let

$$\mathcal{B} := \{E \subseteq X \mid E^c \in \mathcal{M}(\mathcal{A})\}.$$

We have to show that $\mathcal{M}(\mathcal{A}) \subseteq \mathcal{B}$. We note that if $E \in \mathcal{A}$, then $E^c \in \mathcal{A} \subseteq \mathcal{M}(\mathcal{A})$. Hence $\mathcal{A} \subseteq \mathcal{B}$. Further, it is easy to check that $\mathcal{B}$ is a monotone class. Hence $\mathcal{M}(\mathcal{A}) \subseteq \mathcal{B}$. Next we check that $\mathcal{M}(\mathcal{A})$ is closed under unions, i.e., if $E, F \in \mathcal{M}(\mathcal{A})$, then $E \cup F \in \mathcal{M}(\mathcal{A})$. For $F \in \mathcal{M}(\mathcal{A})$, let

$$\mathcal{L}(F) := \{A \subseteq X \mid A \cup F \in \mathcal{M}(\mathcal{A})\}.$$

Now, we have to show that $\mathcal{L}(F) \supseteq \mathcal{M}(\mathcal{A})$ for every $F \in \mathcal{M}(\mathcal{A})$. Let us first check it for $F \in \mathcal{A}$. In that case, for every $A \in \mathcal{A}$, the sets $A \cup F, A \cap F^c \in \mathcal{A} \subseteq \mathcal{M}(\mathcal{A})$, proving that $\mathcal{A} \subseteq \mathcal{L}(F)$ if $F \in \mathcal{A}$. It is easy to check that $\mathcal{L}(F)$ is a monotone class for every $F \subseteq X$. Thus for $F \in \mathcal{A}$ we have $\mathcal{A} \subseteq \mathcal{L}(F)$, a monotone class, and hence $\mathcal{M}(\mathcal{A}) \subseteq \mathcal{L}(F)$. Now we note that the class $\mathcal{L}(F)$ is 'symmetric' in the sense that $E \in \mathcal{L}(F)$ iff $F \in \mathcal{L}(E)$. Thus for every $F \in \mathcal{A}$ and $E \in \mathcal{M}(\mathcal{A})$, since $E \in \mathcal{M}(\mathcal{A}) \subseteq \mathcal{L}(F)$, we have $F \in \mathcal{L}(E)$. Thus $\mathcal{A} \subseteq \mathcal{L}(E)$ for every $E \in \mathcal{M}(\mathcal{A})$. Once again exploiting the fact that $\mathcal{L}(E)$ is a monotone class, we have $\mathcal{M}(\mathcal{A}) \subseteq \mathcal{L}(E)$ for every $E \in \mathcal{M}(\mathcal{A})$. This proves that $\mathcal{M}$ is also closed under finite unions. This completes the proof. ∎

As an application of this theorem (as pointed before the statement of the theorem) we have the following:

3.10.8. Theorem: *Let μ be a measure on an algebra $\mathcal{A}$ of subsets of a set A. If μ is σ-finite, then there exists a unique extension of μ to a measure $\bar{\mu}$ on $\mathcal{S}(\mathcal{A})$, the σ-algebra generated by $\mathcal{A}$.*

Proof: Recall that starting with μ, we constructed μ^* on $\mathcal{P}(X)$ and found $\mathcal{S}^*$, the σ-algebra of μ^*-measurable sets such that $\mathcal{S}^* \supseteq \mathcal{A}$, with μ^* being countably additive on $\mathcal{S}^*$ and $\mu^*(A) = \mu(A) \; \forall \; A \in \mathcal{A}$. Thus $\bar{\mu}(E) := \mu^*(E), E \in \mathcal{S}(\mathcal{A})$, gives a measure with the required properties. We only have to show that this is the only one. Let μ_1 and μ_2 be two σ-finite extensions of μ from $\mathcal{A}$ to $\mathcal{S}(\mathcal{A})$, i.e., $\mu_1(A) = \mu_2(A) \; \forall \; A \in \mathcal{A}$. We have to show that $\mu_1(E) = \mu_2(E) \; \forall \; E \in \mathcal{S}(\mathcal{A})$. As noted in the discussion after example 3.10.2, we may assume that μ_1 and μ_2 are in fact totally finite. Let

$$\mathcal{M} := \{E \subseteq X \mid \mu_1(E) = \mu_2(E)\}.$$

Then $\mathcal{A} \subseteq \mathcal{M}$ and $\mathcal{M}$ is a monotone class (proposition 3.10.3). Thus $\mathcal{M}(\mathcal{A}) \subseteq \mathcal{M}$. Now by theorem 3.10.7, $\mathcal{S}(\mathcal{A}) = \mathcal{M}(\mathcal{A}) \subseteq \mathcal{M}$, proving the theorem. ∎

3.10.9. Remark: A σ-finite measure μ on an algebra $\mathcal{A}$ has a unique extension to $\mathcal{S}(\mathcal{A})$, as shown above. In fact, μ has extension to $\mathcal{S}^*$, the σ-algebra of μ^* measurable sets, and we know that $\mathcal{S}^* \supseteq \mathcal{S}(\mathcal{A})$. The natural question arises: what is the difference between the sets in $\mathcal{S}(\mathcal{A})$ and $\mathcal{S}^*$? We had raised this question in the last section also (question 2 after proposition 3.9.9). We shall examine this question in the next section.

3.10.10. Note: In the proof of theorem 3.10.8, though the σ-algebra technique didn't work, we used the monotone class theorem (3.10.7) to prove that $\mu_1(E) = \mu_2(E) \; \forall \; E \in \mathcal{S}(\mathcal{A})$, whenever the sets in $\mathcal{A}$ has this property. This technique is also very useful, and we call it the σ-**algebra monotone class technique**.

3.10.11. Exercise: Let $X = [a, b]$ and let $\mathcal{S}$ be the σ-algebra of subsets of X generated by all subintervals of $[a, b]$. Let μ, ν be finite measures on $\mathcal{S}$ such that $\mu([a, c]) = \nu([a, c]), \; \forall \; c \in [a, b]$. Show that $\mu(E) = \nu(E) \; \forall \; E \in \mathcal{S}$.

3.10.12. Exercise: Let μ_F be the measure on the algebra $\mathcal{A}(\tilde{\mathcal{I}})$ as given in proposition 3.5.1. Let μ_F itself denote the unique extension of μ_F to $\mathcal{L}_F$, the σ-algebra of μ_F^*-measurable sets, as given by theorem 3.10.8. Show that

(i) $\mathcal{B}_{\mathbb{R}} \subseteq \mathcal{L}_F$.

(ii) $\mu_F(\{x\}) = F(x) - \lim_{y \uparrow x} F(y)$. Deduce that the function F is continuous at x iff $\mu_F(\{x\}) = 0$.

(iii) Let F be differentiable with bounded derivative. If $A \subseteq \mathbb{R}$ is a null set, then $\mu_F^*(A) = 0$.

The measure μ_F is called the **Lebesgue-Stieltjes measure** induced by the distribution function F.

3.11. Completion of a measure space

In theorem 3.10.8 we showed that, given a σ-finite measure μ on an algebra $\mathcal{A}$ of subsets of a set X, μ can be extended to a unique measure μ^* on the σ-algebra $\mathcal{S}^*$ of μ^*-measurable subsets of X, and $\mathcal{S}^* \supseteq \mathcal{S}(\mathcal{A})$. In remark 3.10.9 we raised the following question: what is the difference between the sets in $\mathcal{S}^*$ and the sets in $\mathcal{S}(\mathcal{A})$? We answer this question in this section. Let us fix a σ-finite measure μ on an algebra $\mathcal{A}$ for the rest of the section. Let $\mathcal{A}_\sigma$ denote the collection of sets of the form $\bigcup_{i=1}^\infty A_i, A_i \in \mathcal{A}$. Our next proposition gives equivalent ways of describing $\mu^*(E)$ for any set $E \subseteq X, \mu^*$ being the outer measure induced by μ.

3.11.1. Proposition: *For every set $E \subseteq X$,*

$$
\begin{aligned}
\mu^*(E) &= \inf \{\mu^*(A) \mid A \in \mathcal{A}_\sigma, E \subseteq A\} \\
&= \inf \{\mu^*(A) \mid A \in \mathcal{S}(\mathcal{A}), E \subseteq A\} \\
&= \inf \{\mu^*(A) \mid A \in \mathcal{S}^*, E \subseteq A\}.
\end{aligned}
$$

Proof: By the definition of μ^*,

$$
\mu^*(E) = \inf \left\{ \sum_{i=1}^\infty \mu(A_i) \,\middle|\, A_i \in \mathcal{A}, E \subseteq \bigcup_{i=1}^\infty A_i \right\}.
$$

Let $A_i \in \mathcal{A}, i \geq 1$, be such that

$$
A := \bigcup_{i=1}^\infty A_i \supseteq E.
$$

Using remark 3.6.2, we can write $A = \bigcup_{i=1}^\infty B_i$, where $B_i \in \mathcal{A}, B_i \subseteq A_i \; \forall \, i$ and $B_i \cap B_j = \emptyset$ for $i \neq j$. Thus

$$
\sum_{i=1}^\infty \mu(A_i) \geq \sum_{i=1}^\infty \mu(B_i) = \sum_{i=1}^\infty \mu^*(B_i) \geq \mu^*(A).
$$

Note that $A \in \mathcal{A}_\sigma$. Thus

$$
\begin{aligned}
\mu^*(E) &\geq \inf\{\mu^*(A) \mid A \in \mathcal{A}_\sigma, E \subseteq A\} \\
&\geq \inf\{\mu^*(A) \mid A \in \mathcal{S}(\mathcal{A}), E \subseteq A\} \\
&\geq \inf\{\mu^*(A) \mid A \in \mathcal{S}^*, E \subseteq A\} \\
&\geq \mu^*(E). \quad \blacksquare
\end{aligned}
$$

3.11.2. Proposition: *For every $E \subseteq X$, there exists a set $F \in \mathcal{S}(\mathcal{A})$ such that $E \subseteq F, \mu^*(E) = \mu^*(F)$ and $\mu^*(F \setminus E) = 0$.*

The set F is called a **measurable cover** of E.

Proof: Since μ is σ-finite, we can assume that $E = \bigcup_{i=1}^{\infty} E_i$, where $E_i \cap E_j = \emptyset$ for $i \neq j$ and $\mu^*(E_j) < +\infty$ for every j. For every fixed j, by proposition 3.11.1, $\forall \epsilon > 0$ there exists a set $F_\epsilon \in \mathcal{S}(\mathcal{A})$ such that $E_j \subseteq F_\epsilon$ and $\mu^*(E_j) + \epsilon > \mu^*(F_\epsilon)$. In particular for every $\epsilon = 1/n$ we can choose $F_n \in \mathcal{S}(\mathcal{A})$ such that

$$E_j \subseteq F_n \text{ and } \mu^*(E_j) + 1/n > \mu^*(F_n), \ n = 1, 2, \dots .$$

Let $F_j := \bigcap_{n=1}^{\infty} F_n$. Then $E_j \subseteq F_j \in \mathcal{S}(\mathcal{A})$ and, by theorem 3.6.3,

$$\mu^*(E_j) \geq \limsup_{n \to \infty} \mu^*(F_n) = \mu^*(F_j) \geq \mu^*(E_j).$$

Hence $\mu^*(E_j) = \mu^*(F_j)$. Further, let $G \in \mathcal{S}(\mathcal{A})$ be such that $G \subseteq F_j - E_j$. Then $E_j \subseteq F_j - G$ and we have

$$\mu^*(E_j) \leq \mu^*(F_j - G) = \mu^*(F_j) - \mu^*(G) \leq \mu^*(F_j) = \mu^*(E_j).$$

Hence $\mu^*(G) = 0 \ \forall \ G \in \mathcal{S}(\mathcal{A})$ with $G \subseteq F_j - E_j$. Now it follows from proposition 3.11.1 that $\mu^*(F_j - E_j) = 0$. We construct F_j for every j and put $F := \bigcup_{j=1}^{\infty} F_j$. Then $E \subseteq F \in \mathcal{S}(\mathcal{A})$. Since

$$F - E = \left(\bigcup_{j=1}^{\infty} F_j - \bigcup_{j=1}^{\infty} E_j \right) \subseteq \bigcup_{j=1}^{\infty} (F_j - E_j),$$

we have

$$\mu^*(F - E) \leq \sum_{j=1}^{\infty} \mu^*(F_j - E_j) = 0.$$

Finally, since

$$\mu^*(E) \leq \mu^*(F) \leq \mu^*(E) + \mu^*(F - E) = \mu^*(E),$$

it follows that $\mu^*(E) = \mu^*(F)$. ∎

3.11.3. Corollary: *Let $E \subseteq X$. Then there exists a set $K \subseteq E, K \in \mathcal{S}(\mathcal{A})$, such that $\mu^*(A) = 0$ for every set $A \subseteq E \setminus K$.*

The set K is called a **measurable kernel** of E.

Proof: Let G be a measurable cover of E and N be a measurable cover of $G \setminus E$. Let $K := G \setminus N$. Then

$$K = (G \setminus N) \subseteq (G \setminus (G \setminus E)) = E.$$

Further, if $A \subseteq (E \setminus K)$, then

$$A \subseteq (E \setminus (G \setminus N)) = E \cap N \subseteq (N \setminus (G \setminus E)).$$

Since N is a measurable cover of $G \setminus E$, the above implies that $\mu^*(A) = 0$. Hence K is a measurable kernel of E. ∎

As an application of proposition 3.11.2, we have the following extension of theorem 3.6.3(i).

3.11.4. Proposition: *Let $E_1 \subseteq E_2 \subseteq E_3 \subseteq \ldots$ be subsets of X. Then*

$$\mu^* \left(\bigcup_{n=1}^{\infty} E_n \right) = \lim_{n \to \infty} \mu^*(E_n).$$

Proof: Let $E = \bigcup_{n=1}^{\infty} E_n$. By proposition 3.11.2, we can choose sets $A, A_n \in \mathcal{S}(A)$ such that $E \subseteq A, E_n \subseteq A_n \subseteq A$ with $\mu^*(E) = \mu^*(A)$ and $\mu^*(A_n) = \mu^*(E_n) \ \forall \, n \geq 1$. In order to be able to exploit the fact that μ^* is countably additive on $\mathcal{S}(A)$, we put

$$B_n := \bigcap_{m=n}^{\infty} A_m, \ n \geq 1.$$

Since

$$E_n \subseteq E_m \subseteq A_m \ \forall \, m \geq n,$$

we have $E_n \subseteq B_n \subseteq A_n$. Thus

$$\mu^*(B_n) = \mu^*(E_n) = \mu^*(A_n) \ \forall \, n \geq 1$$

and $\{B_n\}_{n \geq 1}$ is an increasing sequence of sets in $\mathcal{S}(A)$. Now by the countable additivity of μ^* on $\mathcal{S}(A)$ and theorem 3.6.3, we have

$$\lim_{n \to \infty} \mu^*(E_n) = \lim_{n \to \infty} \mu^*(B_n) = \mu^* \left(\bigcup_{n=1}^{\infty} B_n \right). \tag{3.16}$$

Since

$$E = \bigcup_{n=1}^{\infty} E_n \subseteq \bigcup_{n=1}^{\infty} B_n \subseteq \bigcup_{n=1}^{\infty} A_n \subseteq A$$

and $\mu^*(E) = \mu^*(A)$, we have

$$\mu^*(E) = \mu^* \left(\bigcup_{n=1}^{\infty} B_n \right). \tag{3.17}$$

The required claim follows from (3.16) and (3.17). ∎

3.11.5. Exercise:

(i) Let $E \subseteq X$, and let G_1, G_2 be two measurable covers of E. Show that $\mu^*(G_1 \Delta G_2) = 0$.

(ii) Let $E \subseteq X$, and let K_1, K_2 be two measurable kernels of E. Show that $\mu^*(K_1 \Delta K_2) = 0$.

(iii) Let $\mathcal{N} := \{E \subseteq X \mid \mu^*(E) = 0\}$. Show that $\mathcal{N}$ is closed under countable unions and

$$\mathcal{S}^* = \mathcal{S}(\mathcal{A}) \cup \mathcal{N} := \{E \cup N \mid E \in \mathcal{S}(\mathcal{A}), N \in \mathcal{N}\},$$

where $\mathcal{S}^*$ is the σ-algebra of μ^*-measurable sets. Further, $\forall\, A \in \mathcal{S}^*$

$$\mu^*(A) = \mu^*(E), \text{ if } A = E \cup N, \text{ with } E \in \mathcal{S}(\mathcal{A}) \text{ and } N \in \mathcal{N}.$$

3.11.6. Definition: Let X be a nonempty set, $\mathcal{S}$ a σ-algebra of subsets of X and μ a measure on $\mathcal{S}$. The pair $(X, \mathcal{S})$ is called a **measurable space** and the triple $(X, \mathcal{S}, \mu)$ is called a **measure space**. Elements of $\mathcal{S}$ are normally called **measurable sets**.

Till now what we have done is that, given a measure on an algebra $\mathcal{A}$ of subsets of a set X, we have constructed the measure spaces $(X, \mathcal{S}(\mathcal{A}), \mu^*)$, $(X, \mathcal{S}^*, \mu^*)$ and exhibited the relations between them. The measure space $(X, \mathcal{S}^*, \mu^*)$ has the property that if $E \subseteq X$ and $\mu^*(E) = 0$, then $E \in \mathcal{S}^*$. This property is called the **completeness of the measure space** $(X, \mathcal{S}^*, \mu^*)$. The measure space $(X, \mathcal{S}(\mathcal{A}), \mu^*)$ need not be complete in general. However, $\mathcal{S}^*$ is obtainable from $\mathcal{S}(\mathcal{A})$ and $\mathcal{N} := \{E \subseteq X \mid \mu^*(E) = 0\}$ by

$$\mathcal{S}^* = \mathcal{S}(\mathcal{A}) \cup \mathcal{N} := \{E \cup N \mid E \in \mathcal{S}(\mathcal{A}), N \in \mathcal{N}\}.$$

One calls $(X, \mathcal{S}^*, \mu^*)$ the **completion** of $(X, \mathcal{S}(\mathcal{A}), \mu)$. This construction can be put in a general context as follows.

3.11.7. Definition: Let $(X, \mathcal{S}, \mu)$ be a measure space and let $\mathcal{N} := \{E \subseteq X \mid E \subseteq N \text{ for some } N \in \mathcal{S} \text{ with } \mu(N) = 0\}$. One says $(X, \mathcal{S}, \mu)$ is **complete** if $\mathcal{N} \subseteq \mathcal{S}$. Elements of $\mathcal{N}$ are called the μ-**null subsets** of X.

The abstraction of the relation between the measure spaces $(X, \mathcal{S}(\mathcal{A}), \mu^*)$ and $(X, \mathcal{S}^*, \mu^*)$ is described in the next theorem.

3.11.8. Theorem: *Let $(X, \mathcal{S}, \mu)$ be a measure space and let $\mathcal{N}$ be the class of μ-null sets (as in definition 3.11.7). Let $\mathcal{S} \triangle \mathcal{N} := \{E \triangle N \mid E \in \mathcal{S}, N \in \mathcal{N}\}$ and $\mathcal{S} \cup \mathcal{N} := \{E \cup N \mid E \in \mathcal{S}, N \in \mathcal{N}\}$. Then $\mathcal{S} \triangle \mathcal{N} = \mathcal{S} \cup \mathcal{N}$ is a σ-algebra of subsets of X. Let $\overline{\mu}(E \triangle N) = \mu(E), \;\; \forall\, E \in \mathcal{S}, N \in \mathcal{N}$. Then $\overline{\mu}$ is a measure on $\mathcal{S} \cup \mathcal{N}$ and $(X, \mathcal{S} \cup \mathcal{N}, \overline{\mu})$ is a complete measure space, called the **completion** of the measure space $(X, \mathcal{S}, \mu)$. (The measure space $(X, \mathcal{S} \cup \mathcal{N}, \overline{\mu})$ is also denoted by $(X, \overline{\mathcal{S}}, \overline{\mu})$.*

Proof: If $E \in \mathcal{S}$ and $N \subseteq A \in \mathcal{S}$ with $\mu(A) = 0$, then the identities

$$E \cup N = (E - A) \triangle (A \cap (E \cup N))$$

and

$$E \triangle N = (E - A) \cup (A \cap (E \triangle N))$$

show that $\mathcal{S} \cup \mathcal{N} = \mathcal{S} \triangle \mathcal{N}$. Now, using this fact, it is easy to show that $\mathcal{S} \cup \mathcal{N} = \mathcal{S} \triangle \mathcal{N}$ is a σ-algebra of subsets of X.

Let $\overline{\mu}(E \triangle N) := \mu(E)$ for every $E \in \mathcal{S}, N \in \mathcal{N}$. To prove that $\overline{\mu}$ is well-defined, let $E_1 \triangle N_1 = E_2 \triangle N_2$, where $E_i \in \mathcal{S}$ and $N_i \in \mathcal{N}, i = 1, 2$. Then, using the fact that $\triangle$ is an associative operation, it follows that

$$\emptyset = (E_1 \triangle N_1) \triangle (E_2 \triangle N_2) = (E_1 \triangle E_2) \triangle (N_1 \triangle N_2).$$

Thus

$$E_1 \triangle E_2 = N_1 \triangle N_2 \subseteq N_1 \cup N_2.$$

Clearly $N_1 \cup N_2 \in \mathcal{N}$, and hence $\mu(E_1 \triangle E_2) = 0$. Thus $\mu(E_1) = \mu(E_1 \cap E_2) = \mu(E_2)$. Equivalently, $\overline{\mu}(E_1 \triangle N_1) = \overline{\mu}(E_2 \triangle N_2)$. Hence $\overline{\mu}$ is well-defined. Further, suppose $\bar{E} \in \mathcal{S} \cup \mathcal{N}$. Let $\bar{E} = E \cup N$, where $E \in \mathcal{S}, N \in \mathcal{N}$ and $N \subseteq A \in \mathcal{S}$ with $\mu(A) = 0$. Then

$$E \cup N = (E - A) \triangle (A \cap (E \cup N)).$$

Thus

$$\overline{\mu}(E \cup N) = \mu(E - A) = \mu(E).$$

Finally, let $E \cup N = \bigcup_{i=1}^{\infty}(E_i \cup N_i)$, where $E, E_i \in \mathcal{S}$ and $N, N_i \in \mathcal{N}$ for every i, with $(E_i \cup N_i) \cap (E_j \cup N_j) = \emptyset$ for $i \neq j$. Then $\overline{\mu}(E \cup N) = \mu(E)$. Also,

$$E \cup N = \left(\bigcup_{i=1}^{\infty} E_i \right) \cup \left(\bigcup_{i=1}^{\infty} N_i \right).$$

Since $\bigcup_{i=1}^{\infty} N_i \in \mathcal{N}$, we have

$$\overline{\mu}(E \cup N) = \mu \left(\bigcup_{i=1}^{\infty} E_i \right)$$

also. Hence

$$\overline{\mu}(E \cup N) = \sum_{i=1}^{\infty} \mu(E_i) = \sum_{i=1}^{\infty} \overline{\mu}(E_i),$$

proving that $\overline{\mu}$ is a measure. That $(X, \mathcal{S} \cup \mathcal{N}, \overline{\mu})$ is a complete measure space, is easy to check. ∎

Finally we describe the relation between μ^* on $\mathcal{P}(X)$ and μ on $\mathcal{A}$.

3.11.9. Proposition: *Let μ be a measure on an algebra $\mathcal{A}$ of subsets of a set X and let μ^* be the induced outer measure. Let $E \in \mathcal{S}^*$ be such that $\mu^*(E) < +\infty$ and let $\epsilon > 0$ be arbitrary. Then there exists a set $F_\epsilon \in \mathcal{A}$ such that $\mu^*(E \triangle F_\epsilon) < \epsilon$.*

Proof: Since $\mu^*(E) < +\infty$, by definition of μ^*, we can find pairwise disjoint sets $F_n \in \mathcal{A}, n = 1, 2, \ldots$, such that $E \subseteq \bigcup_{n=1}^\infty F_n$ and

$$\mu^*(E) + \epsilon \geq \sum_{n=1}^\infty \mu^*(F_n) \geq \mu^*(E).$$

But then $\sum_{n=1}^\infty \mu^*(F_n) < +\infty$, and hence we can find some n_0 such that

$$\sum_{n=n_0+1}^\infty \mu^*(F_n) < \epsilon.$$

If we put $F_\epsilon = \bigcup_{n=1}^{n_0} F_n$, then

$$E \setminus F_\epsilon = E \setminus \left(\bigcup_{n=1}^{n_0} F_n \right) \subseteq \left(\bigcup_{n=1}^\infty F_n \right) - \left(\bigcup_{n=1}^{n_0} F_n \right) = \bigcup_{n=n_0+1}^\infty F_n.$$

Thus

$$\mu^*(E - F_\epsilon) \leq \sum_{n=n_0+1}^\infty \mu^*(F_n) < \epsilon.$$

Also,

$$F_\epsilon \setminus E \subseteq \left(\bigcup_{n=1}^\infty F_n \right) - E.$$

Hence

$$\mu^*(F_\epsilon - E) \leq \sum_{n=1}^\infty \mu^*(F_n) - \mu^*(E),$$

since μ^* is countably additive on $\mathcal{S}^*$. Thus

$$\mu^*(E \triangle F_\epsilon) = \mu^*(E \setminus F_\epsilon) + \mu^*(F_\epsilon \setminus E) \leq 2\epsilon.$$

(Though we wanted to find F such that $\mu^*(E \triangle F_\epsilon) < \epsilon$, we obtained only $\mu^*(E \triangle F_\epsilon) < 2\epsilon$. With appropriate corrections at suitable places we will get the required inequality.) ∎

3.11.10 Note: Whenever $(X, \mathcal{S}, \mu)$ is a finite measure space with $\mu(X) = 1$, it is called a **probability space** and the measure μ is called a **probability**. The reason for this terminology is that the triple $(X, \mathcal{S}, \mu)$ plays a fundamental role in the axiomatic theory of probability. It gives a mathematical model for analyzing statistical experiments. The set X represents the set of all possible outcomes of the experiment, the σ-algebra $\mathcal{S}$ represents the collection of events of interest in that experiment, and for every $E \in \mathcal{S}$, the nonnegative number $\mu(E)$ is the probability that the event E occurs. For more details see Kolmogorov [21] and Parthasarathy [28].

Chapter 4

The Lebesgue measure on $\mathbb{R}$ and its properties

4.1. The Lebesgue measure

We now apply the extension theory of measures, developed in chapter 3, to the particular case when $X = \mathbb{R}, \mathcal{A} = \mathcal{A}(\mathcal{I})$, the algebra generated by all intervals, and μ on $\mathcal{A}$ is the length function λ as described in section 3.1. The outer measure $\overset{*}{\lambda}$, induced by the length function λ, on all subsets of $\mathbb{R}$ is called the **Lebesgue outer measure** and can be described as follows: for $E \subseteq \mathbb{R}$,

$$\overset{*}{\lambda}(E) := \inf\left\{ \sum_{i=1}^{\infty} \lambda(I_i) \,\middle|\, I_i \in \mathcal{I} \,\forall\, i, I_i \cap I_j = \emptyset \text{ for } i \neq j \text{ and } E \subseteq \bigcup_{i=1}^{\infty} I_i \right\}.$$

The σ-algebra of $\overset{*}{\lambda}$-measurable sets, as obtained in section 3.8, is called the σ-algebra of **Lebesgue measurable sets** and is denoted by $\mathcal{L}_{\mathbb{R}}$, or simply by $\mathcal{L}$. The σ-algebra $\mathcal{S}(\mathcal{I}) = \mathcal{S}(\mathcal{A}) := \mathcal{B}_{\mathbb{R}}$, generated by all intervals, is called the σ-algebra of **Borel subsets** of $\mathbb{R}$. We denote the restriction of $\overset{*}{\lambda}$ to $\mathcal{L}$ or $\mathcal{B}_{\mathbb{R}}$ by λ itself. The measure space $(\mathbb{R}, \mathcal{L}, \lambda)$ is called the **Lebesgue measure space** and λ is called the **Lebesgue measure**. We note that since λ on $\mathcal{I}$ is σ-finite (e.g., $\mathbb{R} = \bigcup_{n=-\infty}^{+\infty}(n, n+1])$, the extension of λ to $\mathcal{B}_{\mathbb{R}}$ is unique by theorem 3.10.8. We recall that the σ-algebra $\mathcal{B}_{\mathbb{R}}$ includes all topologically 'nice' subsets of $\mathbb{R}$, such as open sets, closed sets and compact sets. Also, for $E \in \mathcal{B}_{\mathbb{R}}$, if we transform E with respect to the group operation on $\mathbb{R}$, e.g., for $x \in \mathbb{R}$, consider $E + x := \{y + x \mid y \in E\}$, then $E + x \in \mathcal{B}_{\mathbb{R}}$. For this, note that the map $y \longmapsto x + y$ is a homeomorphism of $\mathbb{R}$ onto $\mathbb{R}$, and hence $E + x \in \mathcal{B}$ for every open set E. We leave it for the reader to verify (using

σ-algebra techniques) that this is true for all sets $E \in \mathcal{B}_{\mathbb{R}}$. The relation of λ on $\mathcal{L}$ with λ on topologically nice subsets of $\mathbb{R}$ will be explored in section 4.2, and the question as to whether $E + x \in \mathcal{L}$ for $E \in \mathcal{L}, x \in \mathbb{R}$, i.e., do the group operations on $\mathbb{R}$ preserve the class of Lebesgue measurable sets, will be analyzed in section 4.3. The relation between the σ-algebras $\mathcal{L}$ and $\mathcal{B}_{\mathbb{R}}$ will be discussed in section 4.5. We give below some properties of $\overset{*}{\lambda}$ which are also of interest.

4.1.1. Exercise:

(i) Let $\mathcal{I}_0$ denote the collection of all **open intervals** of $\mathbb{R}$. For $E \subseteq X$, show that

$$\overset{*}{\lambda}(E) = \inf \left\{ \sum_{i=1}^{\infty} \lambda(I_i) \;\middle|\; I_i \in \mathcal{I}_0 \; \forall \, i, \text{ for } i \neq j \text{ and } E \subseteq \bigcup_{i=1}^{\infty} I_i \right\}.$$

(ii) Let $E \subseteq \mathbb{R}$ and let $\epsilon > 0$ be arbitrary. Show that there exists an open set $U_\epsilon \supseteq E$ such that $\lambda(U_\epsilon) \leq \overset{*}{\lambda}(E) + \epsilon$. Can you also conclude that $\lambda(U_\epsilon \setminus E) \leq \epsilon$?

(iii) For $E \subseteq \mathbb{R}$, let

$$\text{diameter}(E) := \sup\{|x - y| \mid x, y \in E\}.$$

Show that $\overset{*}{\lambda}(E) \leq \text{diameter}(E)$.

(iv) Show that for $E \subseteq \mathbb{R}, \overset{*}{\lambda}(E) = 0$ iff E is a null set as in definition 1.2.8.

(v) Let $E \subseteq [0,1]$ be such that $\overset{*}{\lambda}([0,1] \setminus E) = 0$. Show that E is dense in $[0,1]$

(vi) Let $E \subseteq \mathbb{R}$ be such that $\overset{*}{\lambda}(E) = 0$. Show that E has empty interior.

As a particular case of proposition 3.11.4, we have the following.

4.1.2. Proposition: *Let* $\{E_n\}_{n \geq 1}$ *be any increasing sequence of subsets (not necessarily measurable) of* $\mathbb{R}$. *Then*

$$\overset{*}{\lambda}\left(\bigcup_{n=1}^{\infty} E_n \right) = \lim_{n \to \infty} \overset{*}{\lambda}(E_n).$$

We give below an application of the above proposition. For a function $f : [a,b] \longrightarrow \mathbb{R}$, we denote by $f'(x)$ the derivative of f at x, whenever it exists.

*4.1.3. Proposition: *Let $f : [a, b] \longrightarrow \mathbb{R}$ and for any real number $\alpha \geq 0$, let $E_\alpha := \{x \in [a, b] \mid f'(x) \text{ exists and } |f'(x)| \leq \alpha\}$. Then*

$$\overset{*}{\lambda}(f(E_\alpha)) \leq \alpha \overset{*}{\lambda}(E_\alpha).$$

Proof: Let $\epsilon > 0$ be chosen arbitrarily and fixed. For every $n = 1, 2, \dots$, let E_n denote the set of points $x \in E_\alpha$ such that $\forall y \in (a, b)$,

$$0 < |x - y| < 1/n \text{ implies } |f(x) - f(y)| < (\alpha + \epsilon)|x - y|.$$

Clearly, $E_n \subseteq E_{n+1} \ \forall n$ and $\bigcup_{n=1}^{\infty} E_n = E_\alpha$. Thus $\{f(E_n)\}_{n \geq 1}$ is an increasing sequence and $f(E_\alpha) = \bigcup_{n=1}^{\infty} f(E_n)$. By proposition 4.1.2, we get

$$\overset{*}{\lambda}(f(E_\alpha)) = \lim_{n \to \infty} \overset{*}{\lambda}(f(E_n)). \tag{4.1}$$

To compute $\overset{*}{\lambda}(f(E_n))$, let $n \geq 1$ be fixed. We choose a sequence $\{I_k\}_{k \geq 1}$ of intervals such that for each k, $\lambda(I_k) < 1/n$ with $E_n \subset \bigcup_{k=1}^{\infty} I_k$ and

$$\sum_{k=1}^{\infty} \lambda(I_k) < \overset{*}{\lambda}(E_n) + \epsilon.$$

Then by the definition of E_n, $\forall x, y \in E_n \cap I_k$,

$$|f(x) - f(y)| \leq (\alpha + \epsilon)|x - y|.$$

Thus

$$\text{diameter } (f(E_n \cap I_k)) \leq (\alpha + \epsilon)(\text{diameter } (I_k)).$$

Hence

$$\overset{*}{\lambda}(f(E_n \cap I_k)) \leq (\alpha + \epsilon)\lambda(I_k).$$

Therefore,

$$\overset{*}{\lambda}(f(E_n)) \leq \sum_{k=1}^{\infty} \overset{*}{\lambda}(f(E_n \cap I_k))$$

$$\leq (\alpha + \epsilon) \sum_{k=1}^{\infty} \lambda(I_k)$$

$$\leq (\alpha + \epsilon)(\overset{*}{\lambda}(E_n) + \epsilon). \tag{4.2}$$

From (4.1) and (4.2), using proposition 4.1.2, we have

$$\overset{*}{\lambda}(f(E_\alpha)) \leq (\alpha + \epsilon)(\overset{*}{\lambda}(E_\alpha) + \epsilon).$$

Since $\epsilon > 0$ was chosen arbitrarily, we get $\overset{*}{\lambda}(f(E_\alpha)) \leq \alpha \overset{*}{\lambda}(E_\alpha)$. ∎

*4.1.4. Theorem (Saks): *Let $f : \mathbb{R} \longrightarrow \mathbb{R}$ and let $E = \{x \in \mathbb{R} \mid f'(x) \text{ exists and } f'(x) = 0\}$. Then $\overset{*}{\lambda}(f(E)) = 0$.*

Proof: It is enough to prove that $\overset{*}{\lambda}(f(E \cap [a,b])) = 0$ for every $a < b$. Let $a < b$ be fixed. Then $\forall\, n \geq 1$,

$$E \cap [a,b] \subseteq E_n := \left\{ x \in [a,b] \cap E \mid |f'(x)| \leq 1/n \right\}.$$

Hence by proposition 4.1.3,

$$\overset{*}{\lambda}(f(E \cap [a,b])) \;\leq\; \overset{*}{\lambda}(f(E_n)) \;\leq\; \overset{*}{\lambda}(E_n)/n \;\leq\; (b-a)/n.$$

Since this holds $\forall\, n$, $\overset{*}{\lambda}(f(E \cap [a,b]) = 0$. ∎

4.1.5. Note: Saks' theorem tells that the **critical values** (the values $f(x)$, $x \in \mathbb{R}$ such that $f'(x) = 0$) of a function f on $\mathbb{R}$ constitute a null set. This has a converse, which we prove next.

*4.1.6. Theorem: *Let* $f : \mathbb{R} \longrightarrow \mathbb{R}$ *have a derivative on a set* E *and* $\overset{*}{\lambda}(f(E)) = 0$. *Then*

$$\overset{*}{\lambda}(\{x \in E \mid f'(x) \neq 0\}) = 0.$$

Proof: Let $B := \{x \in E \mid |f'(x)| > 0\}$ and for $n = 1, 2, \ldots$, let

$$B_n := \{x \in B \mid |f(x) - f(y)| \geq |x-y|/n \;\forall\, y \text{ with } 0 < |x-y| < 1/n\}.$$

Then $B = \bigcup_{n=1}^{\infty} B_n$. Thus to show that $\overset{*}{\lambda}(B) = 0$, it is enough to show that $\overset{*}{\lambda}(B_n) = 0 \;\forall\, n$. We fix an integer n and note that to show $\overset{*}{\lambda}(B_n) = 0$, it is enough to show that $\overset{*}{\lambda}(I \cap B_n) = 0$ for any interval I of length less than $1/n$. Let $A = I \cap B_n$. We have to show that $\overset{*}{\lambda}(A) = 0$. For this, first note that $f(A) \subseteq f(E)$ implies that $\overset{*}{\lambda}(f(A)) = 0$. Thus given $\epsilon > 0$, we can find intervals $\{I_k\}_{k \geq 1}$ such that $\lambda(I_k) < 1/n \;\forall\, k$ with

$$f(A) \subseteq \bigcup_{k=1}^{\infty} I_k \;\text{ and }\; \sum_{k=1}^{\infty} \lambda(I_k) < \epsilon.$$

Let $A_k := A \cap f^{-1}(I_k)$. Then $A \subseteq \bigcup_{k=1}^{\infty} A_k$ and for $x, y \in A_k$, since $|x - y| < 1/n$, we have $|f(x) - f(y)| \geq |x-y|/n$. Hence

$$
\begin{aligned}
\sup\{|x-y| \mid x, y \in A_k\} \;&\leq\; n|f(x) - f(y)| \\
&\leq\; n\left(\sup\{|s-t| \mid t, s \in f(A_k)\}\right).
\end{aligned}
$$

Thus

$$\overset{*}{\lambda}(A_k) \;\leq\; n\overset{*}{\lambda}(f(A_k)) \;\leq\; n\overset{*}{\lambda}(I_k).$$

Finally,

$$\overset{*}{\lambda}(A) \;\leq\; \sum_{k=1}^{\infty} \overset{*}{\lambda}(A_k) \;\leq\; \sum_{k=1}^{\infty} \overset{*}{\lambda}(I_k) \;\leq\; n\epsilon.$$

Since $\epsilon > 0$ is arbitrary, $\overset{*}{\lambda}(A) = 0$. ∎

An immediate corollary of the above theorem is the following:

*4.1.7. Corollary: If $f : \mathbb{R} \longrightarrow \mathbb{R}$ has a derivative on a set E and f is constant on any subset F of E, then

$$\overset{*}{\lambda}(\{x \in F \mid f'(x) \neq 0\}) = 0.$$

4.2. Relation of Lebesgue measurable sets with topologically nice subsets of $\mathbb{R}$

As a particular case of proposition 3.11.9, we have the following.

4.2.1. Theorem: *Let $E \subseteq \mathbb{R}$ and $\overset{*}{\lambda}(E) < +\infty$. Then, given $\epsilon > 0$, there exists a set F_ϵ which is a finite disjoint union of open intervals and is such that*

$$\overset{*}{\lambda}(E \triangle F_\epsilon) < \epsilon.$$

Proof: By proposition 3.11.9, given $\epsilon > 0$ there exists a set $F \in \mathcal{A}(\mathcal{I})$ such that $\overset{*}{\lambda}(E \triangle F) < \epsilon$. Let $F := \bigcup_{i=1}^{n} I_i$, where $I_i \in \mathcal{I}$ and $I_1, \ldots, I_n$ are disjoint. Let J_i denote the open interval with the same endpoints as I_i and let $F_\epsilon := \bigcup_{i=1}^{n} J_i$. Then

$$\overset{*}{\lambda}(E \triangle F_\epsilon) = \overset{*}{\lambda}(E \triangle F) < \epsilon. ∎$$

We give next some more characterizations of Lebesgue measurable sets.

4.2.2. Theorem: *For any set $E \subseteq \mathbb{R}$ the following statements are equivalent:*

(i) *$E \in \mathcal{L}$, i.e., E is Lebesgue measurable.*

(ii) *For every $\epsilon > 0$, there exists an open set G_ϵ such that*

$$E \subseteq G_\epsilon \quad and \quad \overset{*}{\lambda}(G_\epsilon \setminus E) < \epsilon.$$

(iii) *For every $\epsilon > 0$, there exists a closed set F_ϵ such that*

$$F_\epsilon \subseteq E \quad and \quad \overset{*}{\lambda}(E \setminus F_\epsilon) < \epsilon.$$

(iv) *There exists a G_δ-set G such that*

$$E \subseteq G \quad and \quad \overset{*}{\lambda}(G \setminus E) = 0.$$

(v) *There exists an F_σ-set F such that*

$$F \subseteq E \quad and \quad \overset{*}{\lambda}(E \setminus F) = 0.$$

Proof: We shall prove the following implications:

$$(i) \implies (ii) \implies (iv) \implies (i)$$

and

$$(i) \implies (iii) \implies (v) \implies (i)$$

(i) $\implies$ **(ii)** Let $E \in \mathcal{L}$ and let $\epsilon > 0$ be given. If $\lambda(E) = \overset{*}{\lambda}(E) < +\infty$, then by definition, we can find intervals $I_1, I_2, \ldots, I_n, \ldots$ such that

$$E \subseteq \bigcup_{n=1}^{\infty} I_n \ \text{ and } \ \lambda(E) + \epsilon/2 \ > \ \sum_{n=1}^{\infty} \lambda(I_n).$$

For every n, choose an open interval $J_n \supseteq I_n$ such that

$$\lambda(J_n) \ \leq \ \epsilon/2^{n+1} + \lambda(I_n).$$

Let $G_\epsilon := \bigcup_{n=1}^{\infty} J_n$. Then G_ϵ is an open set with $G_\epsilon \supseteq E$ and $\lambda(G_\epsilon) < +\infty$. Further,

$$
\begin{aligned}
\lambda^*(G_\epsilon \setminus E) \ = \ \lambda(G_\epsilon \setminus E) \ &= \ \lambda(G_\epsilon) - \lambda(E) \\
&\leq \ \sum_{n=1}^{\infty} \lambda(J_n) - \lambda(E) \\
&\leq \ \sum_{n=1}^{\infty} \epsilon/2^{n+1} + \sum_{n=1}^{\infty} \lambda(I_n) - \lambda(E) \\
&< \ \epsilon/2 + \epsilon/2 \ = \ \epsilon.
\end{aligned}
$$

In case $\lambda(E) = \overset{*}{\lambda}(E) = +\infty$, we can write $E = \bigcup_{n=1}^{\infty} E_n$, where $E_n \cap E_m = \emptyset$ for $n \neq m$ and $\overset{*}{\lambda}(E_n) < +\infty$ for every n. Choose, by the earlier case, open set $G_n \supseteq E_n$ such that for every $n = 1, 2, \ldots$

$$\overset{*}{\lambda}(G_n \setminus E_n) \ < \ \epsilon/2^n.$$

Put $G_\epsilon := \bigcup_{n=1}^{\infty} G_n$. Then $G_\epsilon \supseteq E$, G_ϵ is open and $(G_\epsilon \setminus E) \subseteq \bigcup_{n=1}^{\infty}(G_n \setminus E_n)$. Thus

$$\overset{*}{\lambda}(G_\epsilon \setminus E) \ \leq \ \sum_{n=1}^{\infty} \overset{*}{\lambda}(G_n \setminus E_n) \ < \ \epsilon.$$

(i) $\implies$ **(iii)** Let $E \in \mathcal{L}$. Then $E^c \in \mathcal{L}$ and, by (ii) above, there exists an open set $G_\epsilon \supseteq E^c$ such that $\overset{*}{\lambda}(G_\epsilon \setminus E^c) < \epsilon$. Put $K_\epsilon := G_\epsilon^c$. Then $K_\epsilon \subseteq E$ is a closed set, and since $G_\epsilon \setminus E^c = E \setminus K_\epsilon$, we have $\overset{*}{\lambda}(E \setminus K_\epsilon) < \epsilon$. Hence (iii) holds.

(ii) $\implies$ **(iv)** By (ii), for every n, we choose an open set $G_n \supseteq E$ such that $\overset{*}{\lambda}(G_n \setminus E) < 1/n$. Put $G := \bigcap_{n=1}^{\infty} G_n$. Then G is a G_δ-set, $G \supseteq E$, and for every n,

$$\overset{*}{\lambda}(G \setminus E) \ \leq \ \overset{*}{\lambda}(G_n \setminus E) \ < \ 1/n.$$

Hence $\overset{*}{\lambda}(G \setminus E) = 0$. Thus (iv) holds.

(iii) $\implies$ **(v)** By (iii), for every n choose a closed set $K_n \subseteq E$ such that $\overset{*}{\lambda}(E \setminus K_n) < 1/n$. Put $K = \bigcup_{n=1}^{\infty} K_n$. Then K is an F_σ-set with $K \subseteq E$.. Also, for every n,

$$\lambda^*(E \setminus K) \leq \lambda^*(E \setminus K_n) < \frac{1}{n}.$$

Thus $\lambda^*(E \setminus K) = 0$. Hence (v) holds.

(iv) $\implies$ **(i)** By (iv), there exists a G_δ-set $G \supseteq E$ such that $\overset{*}{\lambda}(G \setminus E) = 0$. Thus both $G, G \setminus E \in \mathcal{B}_\mathbb{R} \subseteq \mathcal{L}_\mathbb{R}$. Since $E = G \setminus (G \setminus E)$, we have $E \in \mathcal{L}_\mathbb{R}$.

(v) $\implies$ **(i)** Let $E \subseteq \mathbb{R}$ be such that there exists an F_σ-set $F \subseteq E$ with $\overset{*}{\lambda}(E \setminus F) = 0$. Since $E = F \cup (E \setminus F)$ with $F \in \mathcal{B}_\mathbb{R} \subset \mathcal{L}$ and $E \setminus F$ is a $\overset{*}{\lambda}$-null set, both $E \setminus F, F \in \mathcal{L}$, and hence $E \in \mathcal{L}$. ∎

4.2.3. Exercise: Let $E \subseteq \mathbb{R}$. Show that the following statements are equivalent:

(i) $E \in \mathcal{L}$.

(ii) $\overset{*}{\lambda}(I) = \overset{*}{\lambda}(E \cap I) + \overset{*}{\lambda}(E^c \cap I)$ for every interval I.

(iii) $E \cap [n, n+1) \in \mathcal{L}$ for every $n \in \mathbb{Z}$.

(iv) $\overset{*}{\lambda}(E \cap [n, n+1)) + \overset{*}{\lambda}(E^c \cap [n, n+1)) = 1$ for every $n \in \mathbb{Z}$.

•**4.2.4. Exercise:** Let $A \in \mathcal{L}$ and $x \in \mathbb{R}$. Using theorem 4.2.2, show that

(i) $A + x \in \mathcal{L}$, where $A + x := \{y + x \mid y \in A\}$.

(ii) $-A \in \mathcal{L}$, where $-A := \{-y \mid y \in A\}$.

4.2.5. Exercise: Let $E \in \mathcal{L}$ with $0 < \lambda(E) < \infty$, and let $0 \leq c < 1$. Show that there exists an open interval I such that $\lambda(E \cap I) > c\lambda(I)$.
(Hint: Either assume that the claim is not true and get a contradiction. Or use theorem 4.2.2(ii) to get an open set $U \supseteq E$ such that $\lambda(E) > \lambda(U) - (1 - c)\lambda(U)$, and use the fact that U is a countable union of disjoint open intervals.)

4.2.6. Note: Theorem 4.2.2 tells us the relation between $\mathcal{L}$, the class of Lebesgue measurable sets, and the topologically nice sets, e.g., open sets and closed sets. The property that for $E \in \mathcal{L}$ and $\epsilon > 0$, there exists an open set $G \supseteq E$ with $\lambda(G \setminus E) < \epsilon$ can be stated equivalently as:

$$\lambda(E) = \inf\{\lambda(U) \mid U \text{ open}, U \supseteq E\}.$$

This is called the **outer regularity** of λ. Other examples of outer regular measures on $\mathbb{R}$ (in fact any metric space) are given in the following exercise:

●**4.2.7. Exercise:** Let (X, d) be any metric space and let μ be a measure on $\mathcal{B}_X$, the σ-algebra generated by open subsets of X, called the σ-algebra of **Borel subsets** of X. The measure μ is called **outer regular** if $\forall\, E \in \mathcal{B}_X$,

$$\mu(E) \;=\; \inf\{\mu(U) \mid U \text{ open}, U \supseteq E\},$$
$$=\; \sup\{\mu(C) \mid C \text{ closed}, C \subseteq E\}. \tag{4.3}$$

  (i) If $\mu(X) < +\infty$, show that μ is outer regular iff for every $E \in \mathcal{B}_X$ and $\epsilon > 0$ given, there exist an open set U_ϵ and a closed set C_ϵ such that

$$U_\epsilon \supseteq E \supseteq C_\epsilon \ \text{ and } \ \mu(U_\epsilon - C_\epsilon) < \epsilon.$$

 (ii) For $A \subseteq X$, let

$$d(x, A) := \inf\{d(x, y) \mid y \in A\}.$$

Show that for every $A \subseteq X, x \longmapsto d(x, A)$ is a uniformly continuous function.
(Hint: $|d(x, A) - d(y, A)| \le d(x, y) \ \forall\, x, y$.)

(iii) Let $\mu(X) < +\infty$ and

$$\mathcal{S} := \{E \in \mathcal{B}_X \mid (4.3) \text{ holds for } E\}.$$

Show that $\mathcal{S}$ is a σ-algebra of subsets of X.

(iv) Let C be any closed set in X. Show that $C \in \mathcal{S}$.
(Hint: $C = \bigcap_{n=1}^{\infty}\{x \in X : d(x, C) < 1/n\}$.)

 (v) Show that μ is outer regular on $\mathcal{B}_X$.

Another topologically nice class of subsets of $\mathbb{R}$ is that of compact subsets of $\mathbb{R}$. It is natural to ask the question: does there exist a relation between $\mathcal{L}$ and the class of compact subsets of $\mathbb{R}$? Let K be any compact subset of $\mathbb{R}$. Since K is closed (and bounded), clearly $K \in \mathcal{B}_\mathbb{R} \subset \mathcal{L}$ and $\lambda(K) < +\infty$. It is natural to ask the question: can one obtain $\lambda(E)$ for a set $E \in \mathcal{B}_\mathbb{R}$, if $\lambda(E) < +\infty$, from the knowledge of $\lambda(K), K$ compact in $\mathbb{R}$? The answer is given by the next proposition.

4.2.8. Proposition: *Let $E \in \mathcal{L}$ with $0 < \lambda(E) < +\infty$ and let $\epsilon > 0$ be given. Then there exists a compact set $K \subseteq E$ such that $\lambda(E \setminus K) < \epsilon$.*

Proof: Let $E_n := E \cap [-n, n], n \ge 1$. Then $\{E_n\}_{n \ge 1}$ is an increasing sequence of sets such that $\bigcup_{n=1}^{\infty} E_n = E$. Since $\lambda(E) < +\infty$, we can choose n sufficiently large so that $\mu(E) - \lambda(E_n) < \epsilon/2$. Now, using theorem 4.2.2, we can find a closed set $K \subseteq E_n \subseteq [-n, n]$ such that $\lambda(E_n) - \lambda(K) < \epsilon/2$. Then K is compact, $K \subset E$ and $\lambda(E) - \lambda(K) < \epsilon$. ∎

4.2.9. Note: Let (X, d) and $\mathcal{B}_X$ be as in exercise 4.2.7. A measure μ on $\mathcal{B}_X$ is called **inner regular** if $\forall E \in \mathcal{B}_X$ with $0 < \mu(E) < \infty$, and $\forall \epsilon > 0$, $\exists$ a compact set K such that $\mu(E \setminus K) < \epsilon$. Exercise 4.2.7 and proposition 4.2.8 tell us that the Lebesgue measure is both inner and outer regular. Exercise 4.2.7 says that on a metric space (X, d) every finite measure is outer regular. If X is also complete and separable, then every finite measure is also inner regular (see lemma 9.2.5).

4.3. Properties of the Lebesgue measure with respect to the group structure on $\mathbb{R}$

On the set $\mathbb{R}$, we have the group structure given by the binary operation of the addition of two real numbers. We analyze the behavior of λ on $\mathcal{L}$ under the map $y \longmapsto y + x$, $y \in \mathbb{R}$ and $x \in \mathbb{R}$ fixed.

In exercise 4.2.4, we saw that $A + x$ is a Lebesgue measurable set whenever A is Lebesgue measurable and $x \in \mathbb{R}$. It is natural to ask the question: for $A \in \mathcal{L}$ and $x \in \mathbb{R}$, is $\lambda(A + x) = \lambda(A)$? The Lebesgue outer measure $\overset{*}{\lambda}$ obviously has the property that $\overset{*}{\lambda}(E + x) = \overset{*}{\lambda}(E)$ for every $E \subseteq \mathbb{R}$ and $x \in \mathbb{R}$. Next, suppose $E \in \mathcal{L}$. Then for every $A \subseteq X$ and $x \in \mathbb{R}$,

$$\overset{*}{\lambda}(A) = \overset{*}{\lambda}(A - x) = \overset{*}{\lambda}((A - x) \cap E) + \overset{*}{\lambda}((A - x) \cap E^c).$$

Since

$$(A - x) \cap E = (A \cap (E + x)) - x \text{ and } (A - x) \cap E^c = (A \cap (E + x)^c) - x,$$

we have

$$\overset{*}{\lambda}(A) = \overset{*}{\lambda}(A \cap (E + x)) + \overset{*}{\lambda}(A \cap (E + x)^c).$$

Thus $E + x \in \mathcal{L}$ and $\overset{*}{\lambda}(E + x) = \overset{*}{\lambda}(E)$, i.e., $\lambda(E + x) = \lambda(E)$. Hence we have proved the following:

4.3.1. Theorem (Translation invariance property): *Let $E \in \mathcal{L}$. Then $E + x \in \mathcal{L}$ for every $x \in \mathbb{R}$, and $\lambda(E + x) = \lambda(E)$.*

4.3.2. Exercise: Let $E \in \mathcal{B}_\mathbb{R}$. Show that $E + x \in \mathcal{B}_\mathbb{R}$ for every $x \in \mathbb{R}$.

4.3.3. Exercise: Let $E \in \mathcal{L}$ and $x \in \mathbb{R}$. Let

$$xE := \{xy \mid y \in E\} \text{ and } - E := \{-x \mid x \in E\}.$$

Show that $-E, xE \in \mathcal{L}$ for every $x \in E$. Compute $\lambda(xE)$ and $\lambda(-E)$ in terms of $\lambda(E)$.

Here is another property of the Lebesgue measure which utilizes its regularity properties.

*4.3.4.   Theorem (Steinhaus): *Let* $E, F \in \mathcal{L}$ *be such that* $\lambda(E) < +\infty, \lambda(F) < +\infty$. *Then* $x \longmapsto \lambda(E \cap (F + x)), x \in \mathbb{R}$, *is a continuous map.*

Proof: First suppose that E, F are intervals. Without loss of generality we may assume that $E = (a, b)$ and $F = (c, d)$. Suppose $a \leq c < d \leq b$. Then

$$(E \cap (F + x)) = \begin{cases} \emptyset & \text{if} \quad x \leq a - d, \\ (a, d + x) & \text{if} \quad a - d \leq x \leq a - c, \\ (c + x, d + x) & \text{if} \quad a - c \leq x \leq b - d, \\ (c + x, b) & \text{if} \quad b - d \leq x \leq b - c, \\ \emptyset & \text{if} \quad b - c \leq x. \end{cases}$$

Clearly, $x \longmapsto \lambda(E \cap F + x)$ is continuous. Similarly, it is easy to see that $x \longmapsto \lambda(E \cap (F + x))$ is continuous in other cases also when E, F are intervals with $\lambda(E) < +\infty$, $\lambda(F) < +\infty$.

Next, let E and F be open subsets of $\mathbb{R}$ with $\lambda(E) < +\infty, \lambda(F) < +\infty$. We can express $E = \bigcup_{n=1}^{\infty} I_n, F = \bigcup_{m=1}^{\infty} J_m$, where I_n, J_m are open intervals such that $I_j \cap I_k = \emptyset$ and $J_j \cap J_k = \emptyset$ for $j \neq k$. Note that $\lambda(I_m) < +\infty$ and $\lambda(J_n) < +\infty \ \forall \, n, m$. Thus

$$E \cap (F + x) = \left(\bigcup_{n=1}^{\infty} I_n \right) \cap \left(\bigcup_{m=1}^{\infty} (J_m + x) \right) = \bigcup_{n=1}^{\infty} \bigcup_{m=1}^{\infty} (I_n \cap (J_m + x)).$$

Hence

$$\lambda(E \cap (F + x)) = \sum_{n,m=1}^{\infty} \lambda(I_n \cap (J_m + x)).$$

In fact, the series on the right hand side of the above equality converges uniformly by Weierstrass' M-test because for every n and m,

$$\lambda(I_n \cap (J_m + x)) \leq \lambda(I_n) \text{ and } \sum_{n=1}^{\infty} \lambda(I_n) = \lambda(E) < +\infty.$$

Since each $\lambda(I_n \cap (J_m + x))$ is continuous, $\lambda(E \cap (F + x))$ is continuous as a function of x, for any open sets E, F with $\lambda(E) < +\infty$ and $\lambda(F) < +\infty$.

Finally, let E, F be arbitrary sets in $\mathcal{L}$ with $\lambda(E) < +\infty$ and $\lambda(F) < +\infty$. Let $\epsilon > 0$ be arbitrary. We can choose (by theorem 4.2.2) open sets U, V such that $E \subseteq V, F \subseteq U$ and

$$\lambda(V - E) < \epsilon/2, \quad \lambda(U - F) < \epsilon/2.$$

Now $\forall \, x \in \mathbb{R}$,

$$V \cap (x + U) \subseteq (x + (U - F)) \cup (V - E) \cup ((x + F) \cap E)$$

and

$$(x + F) \cap E \subseteq ((x + U) \cap V) \cup (U - F) \cup (V - E).$$

Thus

$$|\lambda(V \cap (x + U)) - \lambda((x + F) \cap F)| \leq \lambda(U - F) + \lambda(V - E) < \epsilon.$$

Since $\lambda(V \cap (x + U))$ is continuous as a function of x, for $x \in \mathbb{R}$ fixed, we can find a $\delta > 0$ such that

$$|x - y| < \delta \text{ implies } |\lambda(V \cap (x + U)) - \lambda(V \cap (y + U))| < \epsilon.$$

But then for y with $|x - y| < \delta$, we have

$$
\begin{aligned}
|\lambda(E \cap (x + F)) &- \lambda(E \cap (y + F))| \\
&\leq |\lambda(V \cap (x + U)) - \lambda(E \cap (x + F))| \\
&\quad + |\lambda(V \cap (x + U)) - \lambda(V \cap (y + U))| \\
&\quad + |\lambda(V \cap (y + U)) - \lambda(E \cap (y + F))| \\
&\leq 3\epsilon.
\end{aligned}
$$

This proves the continuity of the map $x \longmapsto \lambda(E \cap (F + x))$ for $E, F \in \mathcal{L}$ with $\lambda(E) < +\infty, \lambda(F) < +\infty$. $\blacksquare$

*4.3.5. Corollary: *Let $E \in \mathcal{L}$ be such that $0 < \lambda(E) < \infty$. Then there exists $\alpha > 0$ such that*

$$[-\alpha, +\alpha] \subset E - E := \{x - y \mid x, y \in E\}.$$

Proof: Since $0 < \lambda(E) < \infty$, the set $E \neq \emptyset$, and hence $0 \in E - E$. Since $\lambda(E \cap (x + E)) > 0$ for $x = 0$, by the continuity of the map

$$x \longmapsto \lambda(E \cap (E + x)),$$

there exists $\alpha > 0$ such that for every $y \in [-\alpha, +\alpha]$, $\lambda(E \cap (E + y)) > 0$. But then $E \cap (E + y) \neq \emptyset$ for every $y \in [-\alpha, \alpha]$. Thus $y \in E - E$ for every $y \in [-\alpha, \alpha]$. $\blacksquare$

*4.3.6. Exercise: Let $E \in \mathcal{L}$ with $\lambda(E) < +\infty$. Show that the function $x \longmapsto \lambda(E \bigtriangleup (E + x))$ is continuous on $\mathbb{R}$.

*4.3.7. Exercise: Prove corollary 4.3.5 as follows:

(i) If E is an open interval or includes an open interval, the claim is obvious.

(ii) In general, use exercise 4.2.5 to show that there exists a bounded open interval I such that $\lambda(E \cap I) > 3\lambda(I)/4$.

(iii) Let $\alpha = \lambda(I)/2$. Show that for every $x \in [-\alpha, +\alpha]$, $I \cup (I + x)$ is an interval with

$$\lambda(I \cup (I + x)) \leq 3\lambda(I)/2$$

and
$$(E \cap I) \cup [(E \cap I) + x] \subseteq (I \cup (I + x)).$$

(iv) For $x \in [-\alpha, +\alpha]$, if $(E \cap I) \cap ((E \cap I) + x) = \emptyset$, show that (ii) above will be contradicted. Deduce that $(E \cap I) \cap ((E \cap I) + x) \neq \emptyset$ for $x \in [-\alpha, +\alpha]$, and hence $[-\alpha, +\alpha] \subset E - E$.

*4.3.8. Exercise: Let $f : \mathbb{R} \longrightarrow \mathbb{R}$ be a measurable map such that $f(x + y) = f(x) + f(y) \ \forall \ x, y \in \mathbb{R}$. Prove the following statements:

(i) $f(rx) = rf(x), \ \forall \ x \in \mathbb{R}$ and $r \in \mathbb{Q}$.

(ii) For every $\epsilon > 0$, $\lambda(f^{-1}(0, \epsilon)) > 0$.
     (Hint: Use (i).)

(iii) Show that f is continuous at $0 \in \mathbb{R}$.
      (Hint: Use corollary 4.3.5.)

(iv) Show that f is continuous everywhere and deduce that $f(x) = xf(1)$ $\forall \ x \in \mathbb{R}$.

4.4. Uniqueness of the Lebesgue measure

We saw in section 4.1 that Lebesgue measure is the unique extension of the length function from the class $\mathcal{I}$ of intervals to $\mathcal{B}_{\mathbb{R}}$, the σ-algebra of Borel subsets of $\mathbb{R}$. This gave us a measure λ on $\mathcal{B}_{\mathbb{R}}$ with the following properties:

(i) For every nonempty open set U, $\lambda(U) > 0$.

(ii) For every compact set K, $\lambda(K) < +\infty$.

(iii) For every $E \in \mathcal{B}_{\mathbb{R}}$,
$$\begin{aligned} \lambda(E) &= \inf\{\lambda(U) \mid U \text{ open}, U \supseteq E\}, \\ &= \sup\{\lambda(C) \mid C \subseteq E, C \text{ closed}\}. \end{aligned}$$

If $\lambda(E) < +\infty$, then we also have
$$\lambda(E) = \sup\{\lambda(K) \mid K \subseteq E, K \text{ compact}\}.$$

(iv) For every $E \in \mathcal{B}_{\mathbb{R}}$ and $x \in \mathbb{R}$, $E + x \in \mathcal{B}_{\mathbb{R}}$ and $\lambda(E + x) = \lambda(E)$.

Thus the Lebesgue measure is a translation invariant σ-finite regular measure on $\mathcal{B}_{\mathbb{R}}$. The question arises: are there other σ-finite measures on $\mathcal{B}_{\mathbb{R}}$ with these properties? Obviously, if $c > 0$ then $c\lambda$ defined by $(c\lambda)(E) := c\lambda(E), E \in \mathcal{B}_{\mathbb{R}}$, is also a σ-finite measure and is translation invariant. Suppose μ is any σ-finite measure on $\mathcal{B}_{\mathbb{R}}$ such that μ is also translation invariant and $0 < c := \mu(0, 1] < +\infty$. Then by the translation invariance and countable additivity of μ,

$$\mu(m, n] = c(n - m) \text{ for every } m, n \in \mathbb{Z}, n \geq m.$$

Thus $\forall\, m, n \in \mathbb{Z}$ with $n \geq m$,

$$\mu(m, n] = c\lambda(m, n].$$

Hence $\mu(I) = c\lambda(I)$ if $I \in \tilde{\mathcal{I}}$ has integral endpoints. Using again translation invariance and countable additivity, we get

$$\mu(0, 1/n] = \mu(0, 1]/n = c/n = c\lambda(0, 1/n].$$

Using these two properties again, we get

$$\mu(0, m/n] = c\lambda(0, m/n] \text{ for every } m \geq 1.$$

In fact, if $I = (m/k, n/k]$, where $m, n \in \mathbb{Z}$ and $k \in \mathbb{N}$, then

$$\mu(I) = \mu(0, (n - m)/k] = c\lambda(0, (n - m)/k] = c\lambda(I).$$

Thus $\mu(I) = c\lambda(I)$ for every $I \in \tilde{\mathcal{I}}$ with rational endpoints. Finally, let I be any finite interval, $I = (a, b]$. Then we can choose sequences of rationals $\{r_n\}_{n \geq 1}$ and $\{s_n\}_{n \geq 1}$ such that $\{r_n\}_{n \geq 1}$ increases to a and s_n decreases to b with $r_n < s_n \ \forall\, n$. Noting that $\mu(J) < +\infty$ for every finite interval, by theorem 3.6.3,

$$\mu(a, b] = \lim_{n \to \infty} \mu(r_n, s_n] = c \lim_{n \to \infty} \lambda(r_n, r_m] = c\lambda(I).$$

Also, $\forall\, b \in \mathbb{R}$ we have

$$\begin{aligned}
\mu(\{b\}) &= \mu(\{1\}) \\
&= \lim_{n \to \infty} \mu(\,1 - 1/n, 1 + 1/n\,] \\
&= \lim_{n \to \infty} c\lambda(\,1 - 1/n, 1 + 1/n\,] = 0.
\end{aligned}$$

Hence μ and λ are σ-finite measures with $\mu(I) = \lambda(I)$ for every $I \in \tilde{\mathcal{I}}$. Now, using theorems 3.3.3 and 3.10.8, $\mu(E) = c\lambda(E)$ for every $E \in \mathcal{B}_{\mathbb{R}}$. We note that the condition $0 < \mu(0, 1] < \infty$ will automatically hold if $\mu(V) > 0$ for every nonempty open set U and $\mu(K) < +\infty$ for every compact set K. Thus we have proved the following:

4.4.1. Theorem: *Let μ be a measure on $\mathcal{B}_{\mathbb{R}}$ such that*

   (i) $\mu(U) > 0$ *for every nonempty open set $U \subseteq \mathbb{R}$.*

   (ii) $\mu(K) < +\infty$ *for every compact set $K \subset \mathbb{R}$.*

   (iii) $\mu(E + x) = \mu(E), \ \forall\, E \in \mathcal{B}_{\mathbb{R}} \text{ and } \ \forall\, x \in \mathbb{R}.$

Then there exists a positive real number c such that $\mu(E) = c\lambda(E)$ $\forall\, E \in \mathcal{B}_{\mathbb{R}}$.

4.4.2. Note: In fact the above theorem has a far-reaching generalization to abstract 'topological groups'. Let us recall that the set of real numbers $\mathbb{R}$ is a group under the binary operation $+$, the addition of real numbers.

Also, there is a topology on $\mathbb{R}$ which 'respects' the group structure, i.e., the maps $(t,s) \longmapsto t + s$ and $t \longrightarrow -t$ from $\mathbb{R} \times \mathbb{R} \longrightarrow \mathbb{R}$ and $\mathbb{R} \longrightarrow \mathbb{R}$, respectively, are continuous when $\mathbb{R} \times \mathbb{R}$ is given the product topology. In an abstract setting, if G is a set with a binary operation '$\cdot$' and a topology $\mathcal{T}$ such that $(G, \cdot)$ is a group and the maps $G \times G \longrightarrow G, (g,h) \longmapsto g.h$ and $G \longrightarrow G, g \longmapsto g^{-1}$ are continuous with respect to the product topology on $G \times G$, one calls G a **topological group.** Given a topological group, let $\mathcal{B}_G$ denote the σ-algebra generated by open subsets of G, called the σ-algebra of Borel subsets of G. The question arises: does there exist a σ-finite measure μ on G such that it has the properties as given in theorem 4.4.1? A celebrated theorem due to A. Haar states that such a measure exists and is unique up to a multiplicative (positive) constant if G is locally-compact. Such a measure is called a (right) **Haar measure** on G. Theorem 4.4.1 then states that for the topological group $\mathbb{R}$, the Lebesgue measure λ is a Haar measure. Consider the group $(\mathbb{R} \setminus \{0\}, \cdot)$, where $\mathbb{R} \setminus \{0\} = \{t \in \mathbb{R} | t \neq 0\}$ and '$\cdot$' is the usual multiplication of real numbers. Let $\mathbb{R} \setminus \{0\}$ be given the subspace topology from $\mathbb{R}$. It is easy to show that $\mathbb{R} \setminus \{0\}$ is a topological group and, $\forall E \in \mathcal{B}_{\mathbb{R} \setminus \{0\}}$,

$$\mu(E) := \int_E \frac{1}{|x|} d\lambda(x) \tag{4.4}$$

is a Haar measure on $\mathbb{R} \setminus \{0\}$. (For a meaning of the right hand side of equation (4.4), see Chapter 5.)

We close this section by proving a result, theorem 4.4.5, which has many important applications in measure theory. Recall that given a covering of an interval $[a, b]$ by open sets, we can choose a finite number of them, still covering $[a, b]$. This is the well-known **Heine-Borel theorem**. The theorem we want to prove essentially says that given a set $E \subseteq \mathbb{R}$ with $\overset{*}{\lambda}(E) < +\infty$ and a cover of E by intervals of 'arbitrary small Lebesgue measure', one can almost cover E by a finite number of pairwise disjoint intervals from the given cover. This is made precise below.

4.4.3. Definition: Let $E \subseteq \mathbb{R}$, and let $\mathcal{G}$ be a collection of intervals of positive length. We say $\mathcal{G}$ is a **Vitali cover** of E if for every $\epsilon > 0$ and any $x \in E$, there exists an interval $I \in \mathcal{G}$ such that $x \in I$ and $\lambda(I) < \epsilon$.

4.4.4. Example: Let $\{r_n\}_{n \geq 1}$ be an enumeration of the rationals in $[a, b]$. Let $\mathcal{G} := \{[r_n - 1/k, r_n + 1/k] \mid n = 1, 2, \ldots; k = 1, 2, \ldots\}$. Then $\mathcal{G}$ is a Vitali covering of $[a, b]$.

4.4.5. Theorem (Vitali's covering): *Let* $E \subseteq \mathbb{R}$ *be such that* $\overset{*}{\lambda}(E) < +\infty$, *and let* $\mathcal{G}$ *be a Vitali cover of* E. *Then, given* $\epsilon > 0$, *there exists a finite* *pairwise disjoint collection* $\{I_1, \ldots, I_N\}$ *of intervals in* $\mathcal{G}$ *such that*

$$\overset{*}{\lambda}\left(E \setminus \left(\bigcup_{n=1}^{N} I_n\right)\right) < \epsilon.$$

Proof (Banach): Without loss of generality we may assume that all the intervals in $\mathcal{G}$ are closed. Since $\overset{*}{\lambda}(E) < +\infty$, using theorem 4.2.2 we can find an open set $U \supseteq E$ such that $\lambda(U) < +\infty$. Let $\mathcal{G}_0 = \{I \in \mathcal{G} \mid I \subseteq U\}$. Obviously, $\mathcal{G}_0$ is also a Vitali cover of E. Let $I_1 \in \mathcal{G}_0$ be arbitrary. If $E \subseteq I_2$, then we are through. If not, suppose $I_1, I_2, \ldots, I_n \in \mathcal{G}_0$ have been selected such that they are pairwise disjoint. If $E \subseteq \bigcup_{k=1}^{n} I_k$, then again we are through. If not, $\exists\, x \in E \setminus (\bigcup_{k=1}^{n} I_k)$. Since $\bigcup_{k=1}^{n} I_k$ is a closed set, the distance between x and $\bigcup_{k=1}^{n} I_k$, say η_x, is positive. Thus we can choose $I_{n+1} \in \mathcal{G}_0$ such that $x \in I_{n+1}$ and $\lambda(I_{n+1}) < \eta_x/2$. Then $I_{n+1} \cap I_k = \emptyset$ for $k = 1, 2, \ldots, n$. In fact, we can select I_{n+1} with the additional property that $\lambda(I_{n+1}) > \alpha_n/2$, where

$$\alpha_n := \sup\{\lambda(I) \mid I \in \mathcal{G}_0, I \cap I_k = \emptyset \text{ for } k = 1, 2, \ldots, n\}.$$

By induction, we have a sequence $\{I_n\}_{n \geq 1}$ of pairwise disjoint intervals from $\mathcal{G}_0$ such that $\lambda(I_{n+1}) > \alpha_n/2$ for every $n \geq 1$. Since each $I_n \subseteq U$,

$$\sum_{n=1}^{\infty} \lambda(I_n) \leq \lambda(U) < +\infty.$$

Thus $\lambda(I_n) \longrightarrow 0$ as $n \to \infty$. We claim that $\overset{*}{\lambda}(E \setminus (\bigcup_{k=1}^{\infty} I_k)) = 0$. For this, let $x \in E \setminus \bigcup_{k=1}^{\infty} I_k$. Then $x \in E \setminus \bigcup_{k=1}^{n} I_k \;\forall\, n$. Let $N \in \mathbb{N}$ be fixed. Once again, since $x \notin \bigcup_{n=1}^{N} I_k$ as shown above, we can choose $I \in \mathcal{G}_0$ such that $I \cap I_k = \emptyset$ for $k = 1, 2, \ldots, N$ and $x \in I$. Since $\lambda(I_n) \longrightarrow 0$ as $n \longrightarrow \infty$ and $\alpha_n < 2\lambda(I_n)$, there exists some integer n such that $\alpha_n < \lambda(I)$. But then $I \cap I_n \neq \emptyset$. Let n_0 be the smallest integer such that $I \cap I_{n_0} \neq \emptyset$. Clearly $n_0 > N$. Since $I \cap I_{n_0} \neq \emptyset$ and $x \in I$, the distance of x from the midpoint of I_{n_0}, say x_{n_0}, is at most $\lambda(I) + \lambda(I_{n_0})/2$. Note that

$$\lambda(I) + \lambda(I_{n_0})/2 < \alpha_{n_0 - 1} + \lambda(I_{n_0})/2 < 5\lambda(I_{n_0})/2.$$

Let J_{n_0} denote the closed interval with midpoint x_{n_0} and $\lambda(J_{n_0}) = 5\lambda(I_{n_0})$. Then $x \in J_{n_0}$. Thus $\forall\, x \in \bigcup_{k=1}^{N} I_k$, $\exists\, n > N$ such that $x \in J_n$ with $\lambda(J_n) = 5\lambda(I_n)$. Hence

$$\overset{*}{\lambda}\left(E \setminus \bigcup_{n=1}^{N} I_n\right) \leq \sum_{n=N+1}^{\infty} \lambda(J_n) \leq 5 \sum_{n=N+1}^{\infty} \lambda(I_n).$$

Since this holds for every N,

$$\overset{*}{\lambda} \left(E \setminus \bigcup_{n=1}^{\infty} I_n \right) = \lim_{N \to \infty} \overset{*}{\lambda} \left(E \setminus \bigcup_{n=1}^{N} I_n \right) = 0. \blacksquare$$

4.4.6. Exercise: Let $E \subseteq \mathbb{R}$, and let $\mathcal{G}$ be a Vitali cover of E. Show that, given $\epsilon > 0$, there exists a countable family $\{I_n\}_{n \geq 1}$ of pairwise disjoint sets from $\mathcal{G}$ such that $\overset{*}{\lambda}(E \setminus \bigcup_{n=1}^{\infty} I_n) < \epsilon$.
(Hint: λ is σ-finite.)

We give next an application of the Vitali covering theorem. More applications are given in Chapter 6.

4.4.7. Proposition: *Let $\{I_\alpha \mid \alpha \in J\}$ be any arbitrary collection of intervals of positive length. Then $E := \bigcup_{\alpha \in J} I_\alpha$ is Lebesgue measurable.*

Proof: Assume without loss of generality that $\overset{*}{\lambda}(E) < +\infty$. Let

$$\mathcal{G} := \{ I \subseteq \mathbb{R} \mid I \text{ is bounded and } I \subseteq I_\alpha \text{ for some } \alpha \}.$$

Then $\mathcal{G}$ is a Vitali covering of E. By theorem 4.4.5, $\exists$ a sequence $\{I_{\alpha_i}\}_{i \geq 1}$ of pairwise disjoint intervals such that $\overset{*}{\lambda} \left(E \setminus \bigcup_{i=1}^{\infty} I_{\alpha_i} \right) = 0$. Thus

$$E = \left(E \setminus \bigcup_{i=1}^{\infty} I_{\alpha_i} \right) \cup \left(\bigcup_{i=1}^{\infty} I_{\alpha_i} \right),$$

and hence $E \in \mathcal{L}$. $\blacksquare$

4.5. *Cardinalities of the σ-algebras $\mathcal{L}$ and $\mathcal{B}_\mathbb{R}$

As a special case of corollary 3.11.3, we have $\mathcal{L} = \mathcal{B}_\mathbb{R} \cup \mathcal{N}$, where

$$\mathcal{N} := \{ N \subseteq \mathbb{R} \mid N \subseteq E \in \mathcal{B}_\mathbb{R}, \lambda(E) = 0 \}.$$

Thus $\mathcal{B}_\mathbb{R} \subseteq \mathcal{L} \subseteq \mathcal{P}(\mathbb{R})$. The question arises: are there sets in $\mathcal{L}$ which are not in $\mathcal{B}_\mathbb{R}$, i.e., is $\mathcal{B}_\mathbb{R}$ a proper subclass of $\mathcal{L}$? First of all, we note that a set $A \subset \mathbb{R}$ is a null set as per definition 1.2.8 iff $A \in \mathcal{N}$. Thus the Cantor ternary set $C \in \mathcal{N} \subset \mathcal{L}$. If $E \subseteq C$, then $\overset{*}{\lambda}(E) = 0$ and hence $E \in \mathcal{L}$. In other words, $\mathcal{P}(C) \subseteq \mathcal{L}$. Thus the cardinality of $\mathcal{L}$ is at least $2^\mathfrak{c}$ (here $\mathfrak{c}$ denotes the cardinality of the real line, also called the **cardinality of the continuum**). Since $\mathcal{L} \subseteq \mathcal{P}(\mathbb{R})$, we get the cardinality of $\mathcal{L}$ to be $2^\mathfrak{c}$. On the other hand, $\mathcal{B}_\mathbb{R}$ is the σ-algebra generated by all open intervals of $\mathbb{R}$ with rational endpoints (exercise 3.9.8). What is the cardinality of $\mathcal{B}_\mathbb{R}$? To answer this, we give below a description of the algebra and the σ-algebra generated by a class of subsets of a set X.

Let X be any nonempty set with at least two points and let $\mathcal{C}$ be any class of subsets of X such that $X \in \mathcal{C}$. Let

$$\tilde{\mathcal{C}} := \{A \subseteq X \mid A \ \text{ or } \ A^c \in \mathcal{C}\}$$

and

$$\mathcal{C}^* := \left\{ E \subseteq X \ \middle| \ \text{for some } n \geq 1, E = \bigcup_{i=1}^{n} A_i, \ \text{ where each } \ A_i \in \tilde{\mathcal{C}} \right\}.$$

Then we have the following:

4.5.1. Theorem: *Let $\mathcal{C}$ be any class of subsets of a set X such that $X \in \mathcal{C}$. Let $\mathcal{C}_1 := \mathcal{C}^*$ and for every $n \geq 1$, let $\mathcal{C}_{n+1} := \mathcal{C}_n^*$. Let $\mathcal{F} := \bigcup_{n=1}^{\infty} \mathcal{C}_n$. Then $\mathcal{F}$ is an algebra of subsets of X containing $\mathcal{C}$. In fact $\mathcal{F} = \mathcal{F}(\mathcal{C})$, the algebra generated by $\mathcal{C}$.*

Proof: Clearly, $\mathcal{C}_n \subseteq \mathcal{C}_{n+1}$ for every n. Hence $\mathcal{C} \subseteq \mathcal{F} = \bigcup_{n=1}^{\infty} \mathcal{C}_n$. Next, if $E \in \mathcal{C}_n$ for some n, then clearly $E^c \in \mathcal{C}_{n+1}$. Thus for $E \in \mathcal{F}$, $E^c \in \mathcal{F}$. Also, if $E_1, \ldots, E_m \in \mathcal{C}_n$ for some n, then $\bigcup_{i=1}^{m} E_i \in \mathcal{C}_{n+1}$. Thus for $E_1, E_2, \ldots, E_m \in \mathcal{F}$, we can assume without loss of generality that for every $1 \leq i \leq m$, $E_i \in \mathcal{C}_n$ for some n, and hence $\bigcup_{i=1}^{m} E_i \in \mathcal{C}_{n+1} \subseteq \mathcal{F}$. This proves that $\mathcal{F}$ is an algebra. To show that $\mathcal{F} = \mathcal{F}(\mathcal{C})$, let $\mathcal{A}$ be any algebra of subsets of X such that $\mathcal{C} \subseteq \mathcal{A}$. Then clearly $\mathcal{C}_n \subseteq \mathcal{A}$ for every n, and hence $\mathcal{F} \subseteq \mathcal{A}$. ∎

The corresponding result for σ-algebras is the following: For any family $\mathcal{C}$ of subsets of a set X, let

$$\mathcal{C}^* := \left\{ \bigcup_{i=1}^{\infty} E_i \ \middle| \ \text{for every } i, \text{ either } E_i \in \mathcal{C} \text{ or } E_i^c \in \mathcal{C} \right\}.$$

Let Ω denote the first uncountable ordinal number. Let $\mathcal{C}_0 := \mathcal{C} \cup \{X\}$, and let α be any ordinal number, $0 < \alpha < \Omega$. We use transfinite induction to define $\mathcal{C}_\alpha$ as follows: Suppose for every $\beta < \alpha$, $\mathcal{C}_\beta$ has been defined. Define

$$\mathcal{C}_\alpha := \left(\bigcup_{0 \leq \beta < \alpha} \mathcal{C}_\beta \right)^*.$$

Then we have the following:

4.5.2. Theorem: *Let $\mathcal{C}$ be any family of subsets of a set X, and for every ordinal number $0 \leq \alpha < \Omega$, let $\mathcal{C}_\alpha$ be defined as above. Then $\mathcal{S} := \bigcup_{0 \leq \alpha < \Omega} \mathcal{C}_\alpha$ is a σ-algebra of subsets of X. In fact, $\mathcal{S} = \mathcal{S}(\mathcal{C})$, the σ-algebra generated by $\mathcal{C}$.*

Proof: Clearly, if $\alpha < \beta < \Omega$ then $\mathcal{C}_\alpha \subseteq \mathcal{C}_\alpha^* \subseteq \mathcal{C}_\beta$ and, for $A \in \mathcal{C}_\alpha$, $A^c \in \mathcal{C}_\alpha^*$, and hence $A^c \in \mathcal{C}_\beta$ for every $\beta > \alpha$. Thus $A \in \mathcal{S}$ would imply that $A^c \in \mathcal{S}$. Next, let $A_i \in \mathcal{C}_{\alpha_i}$ for $i = 1, 2, \ldots$. Then

$$\bigcup_{i=1}^{\infty} A_i \in \left(\bigcup_{i=1}^{\infty} \mathcal{C}_{\alpha_i} \right)^* \subseteq \mathcal{C}_\beta$$

for every β such that $\beta > \alpha_n$ for every n. Hence $A_i \in \mathcal{S}, i = 1, 2, \ldots$, would imply that, $\bigcup_{i=1} A_i \in \mathcal{S}$. Finally, $\emptyset = X^c \in \mathcal{C}_1 \subset \mathcal{S}$ and hence $X \in \mathcal{S}$. This proves that $\mathcal{S}$ is a σ-algebra. Let $\mathcal{B}$ be any σ-algebra of subsets of X such that $\mathcal{B} \supseteq \mathcal{C}$. Then clearly $\mathcal{B} \supseteq \mathcal{C}_0^*$. Further, if $\mathcal{C}_\alpha \subseteq \mathcal{B}$, then $\mathcal{C}_\alpha^* \subseteq \mathcal{B}$ and hence $\mathcal{C}_\beta \subseteq \mathcal{B}$ for every $\beta < \Omega$. Thus $\mathcal{S} \subseteq \mathcal{B}$, showing that $\mathcal{S} = \mathcal{S}(\mathcal{C})$. ∎

4.5.3. Corollary: *The σ-algebra $\mathcal{B}_\mathbb{R}$ of Borel subsets of $\mathbb{R}$ has cardinality $\mathfrak{c}$, that of the continuum.*

Proof: Since each singleton set $\{x\}$ is a closed set, $\{x\} \in \mathcal{B}_\mathbb{R}$. Thus $\mathcal{B}_\mathbb{R}$ has cardinality at least $\mathfrak{c}$. On the other hand, let $\mathcal{C}$ denote the class of all open intervals in $\mathbb{R}$ with rational endpoints. Then by exercise 3.9.8, $\mathcal{S}(\mathcal{C}) = \mathcal{B}_\mathbb{R}$. By theorem 4.5.2,

$$\mathcal{S}(\mathcal{C}) = \bigcup_{0 \leq \beta < \Omega} \mathcal{C}_\beta.$$

Note that $\mathcal{C}_0$ has countably infinite elements, i.e., $\mathcal{C}_0$ has cardinality $\aleph_0$ (read as **aleph nought**) and to construct an element of $\mathcal{C}_0^*$ we have to choose $\aleph_0$ elements with each element having two choices, i.e., either it is in $\mathcal{C}_0$ or its complement is in $\mathcal{C}_0$. Thus $\mathcal{C}_0^* = \mathcal{C}_1$ will have at most $2^{\aleph_0} < \mathfrak{c}$ elements. Now assume that each $\mathcal{C}_\alpha$ has cardinality at most $\mathfrak{c}$ for $\alpha < \beta$. Then

$$\mathcal{C}_\beta = \left(\bigcup_{1 \leq \alpha < \beta} \mathcal{C}_\alpha \right)^*.$$

Clearly, $\{\alpha \mid \alpha < \beta\}$ has cardinality at most $\aleph_0$ and hence $\bigcup_{1 \leq \alpha < \beta} \mathcal{C}_\alpha$ has cardinality at most $\mathfrak{c}.\aleph_0 = \mathfrak{c}$. Thus $\mathcal{C}_\beta$ will have cardinality at most $\mathfrak{c}$. By transfinite induction, each $\mathcal{C}_\beta, \beta < \Omega$, has cardinality at most $\mathfrak{c}$. Hence $\mathcal{S}(\mathcal{C}) = \bigcup_{1 \leq \beta < \Omega} \mathcal{C}_\beta$ will have cardinality at most $\mathfrak{c}.\mathfrak{c} = \mathfrak{c}$, proving that $\mathcal{B}_\mathbb{R} = \mathcal{S}(\mathcal{C})$ has cardinality exactly $\mathfrak{c}$ elements. ∎

4.5.4. Note: As stated in the beginning of this section, the class $\mathcal{L}$ of all Lebesgue measurable sets has cardinality $2^\mathfrak{c}$. We showed just now that the cardinality of $\mathcal{B}_\mathbb{R}$ is $\mathfrak{c}$. Since $2^\mathfrak{c} > \mathfrak{c}$, there exist sets which are Lebesgue measurable but are not Borel sets. The actual construction of such sets is not easy. One such class of sets is called analytic sets. An **analytic set** is a set which can be represented as a continuous image of a Borel set. For a detailed discussion on analytic sets, see Srivastava [38], Parthasarathy [29].

4.6. Nonmeasurable subsets of $\mathbb{R}$

We showed in section 4.5 that $\mathcal{L}$, the class of all Lebesgue measurable subsets of $\mathbb{R}$, has $2^{\mathfrak{c}}$ elements, i.e., the same as the number of elements in $\mathcal{P}(\mathbb{R})$. The natural question arises: is $\mathcal{L} = \mathcal{P}(\mathbb{R})$? We saw in 3.4 that if we assume the continuum hypothesis, it is not possible to define a countably additive set function μ on $\mathcal{P}(\mathbb{R})$ such that $\mu(\{x\}) = 0 \;\; \forall \; x \in \mathbb{R}$. In particular, if we assume the continuum hypothesis, we cannot extend λ to all subsets of $\mathbb{R}$. Hence $\mathcal{L} \neq \mathcal{P}(\mathbb{R})$. What can be said if one does not assume the continuum hypothesis? To answer this question, one can either try to construct a set $E \subset \mathbb{R}$ such that $E \notin \mathcal{L}$, or, assuming that such a set exists, try to see whether one can reach a contradiction. G. Vitali (1905), F. Bernstein (1908), H. Rademacher (1916) and others constructed such sets assuming the 'axiom of choice' (see appendix B). The example of Vitali used the translation invariance property of the Lebesgue measure, and that of Bernstein used the regularity properties of the Lebesgue measure. Rademacher proved that every set of positive outer Lebesgue measure includes a Lebesgue nonmeasurable set. Even today, more and more nonmeasurable sets with additional properties are being constructed. For example, one can construct nonmeasurable subsets A of $\mathbb{R}$ such that $\overset{*}{\lambda}(A \cap I) = \overset{*}{\lambda}(I)$ for every interval $I \subset \mathbb{R}$. Of course, all these constructions are under the assumption of the 'axiom of choice'. Lebesgue himself did not accept such constructions. In 1970, R. Solovay [37] proved that if one includes the statement "all subsets of $\mathbb{R}$ are Lebesgue measurable" as an axiom in set theory, then it is consistent with the other axioms of set theory if the axiom of choice is not assumed. We give below the construction (due to Vitali) of a nonmeasurable set, assuming the axiom of choice.

4.6.1. Example (Vitali): Define a relation on $[0,1]$ as follows: for $x, y \in [0,1]$, we say x is related to y, written as $x \sim y$, if $x - y$ is a rational. One checks that $\sim$ is an equivalence relation on $[0,1]$. Let $\{E_\alpha\}_{\alpha \in I}$ denote the set of equivalence classes of elements of $[0,1]$. Using the axiom of choice, we choose exactly one element $x_\alpha \in E_\alpha$ for every $\alpha \in I$ and construct the set $E := \{x_\alpha | \alpha \in I\}$. Let $r_1, r_2, \ldots, r_n, \ldots$ denote an enumeration of the rationals in $[-1, 1]$. Let

$$E_n := r_n + E, \; n = 1, 2, \ldots .$$

It is easy to check that $E_n \cap E_m = \emptyset$ for $n \neq m$ and $E_n \subseteq [-1, 2]$ for every n. If $x \in [0, 1]$, then $x \in E_\alpha$ for some $\alpha \in I$, and hence $x \sim x_\alpha, x_\alpha \in E$. But then $x - x_\alpha$ is a rational and $-1 \leq x - x_\alpha \leq 1$. Hence $x \in E_n$ for some n. Thus

$$[0, 1] \subseteq \bigcup_{n=1}^{\infty} E_n \subseteq [-1, 2].$$

Now, suppose $E \in \mathcal{L}$. Then $E_n \in \mathcal{L}$ for every n, and $\lambda(E_n) = \lambda(E)$. On one hand, $\lambda(E) > 0$, in which case $\lambda(E_n) = \lambda(E) > 0$ for every n. But then by the countable additivity of λ,

$$\infty = \sum_{n=1}^{\infty} \lambda(E_n) = \lambda\left(\bigcup_{n=1}^{\infty} E_n\right) \leq 3,$$

which is absurd. On the other hand, if $\lambda(E) = 0$, then $\lambda(E_n) = 0 \; \forall\, n$ and hence

$$1 = \lambda([0,1]) \leq \sum_{n=1}^{\infty} \lambda(E_n) = 0,$$

again not possible. Hence E is not Lebesgue measurable.

4.6.2. Exercise: Using the axiom of choice, choose one element from each of the sets $x + \mathbb{Q}$, where $x \in \mathbb{R}$ and $\mathbb{Q}$ is the set of rationals in $\mathbb{R}$, and construct the set E. Show that E is not Lebesgue measurable using the following steps:

    (i) Assume that E is Lebesgue measurable. Show that for some $r \in \mathbb{Q}$, $\lambda(E + r) > 0$.

    (ii) Use corollary 4.3.5 to show that $(E - E) \cap \mathbb{Q} \neq \emptyset$, and hence the definition of E is contradicted.

4.6.3. Note: As shown in section 4.1, we can extend the notion of length from the class of intervals to a class $\mathcal{L}$ of Lebesgue measurable sets which includes all topologically nice sets and which is invariant under the group operations. We also saw that unless some extra hypothesis/axiom is assumed in set theory, it is not possible to show the existence of nonmeasurable sets. So, the question arises: can one extend the Lebesgue measure beyond the class of Lebesgue measurable sets, preserving all its properties? The answer is: yes, it is possible. The interested reader may refer to Kakutani and Oxtoby [19], or Hewitt and Ross [17].

4.7. The Lebesgue-Stieltjes measure

In the previous sections we have seen how the general extension theory, as developed in chapter 3, can be applied to the particular situation when the semi-algebra is that of intervals and the set function is the length function. More generally, if we consider the semi-algebra $\tilde{\mathcal{I}}$ of left-open right-closed intervals in $\mathbb{R}$ and consider $F : \mathbb{R} \longrightarrow \mathbb{R}$ as a monotonically increasing right continuous function, then we can construct a countably additive set function μ_F on the semi-algebra $\tilde{\mathcal{I}}$, as in proposition 3.5.1. Using theorem 3.3.3 and theorem 3.10.8, we can construct a complete measure μ_F on a σ-algebra of subsets of $\mathbb{R}$ which includes $\mathcal{B}_{\mathbb{R}}$. This measure μ_F is called the **Lebesgue-Stieltjes measure** induced by the function F. Note that μ_F has the property that $\mu_F(a, b] < +\infty \quad \forall \, a, b \in \mathbb{R}, a < b$. Conversely, given a measure μ on $\mathcal{B}_\mathbb{R}$ such that $\mu(a, b] < +\infty \; \forall \, a, b \in \mathbb{R}, a < b$, we can restrict it to $\tilde{\mathcal{I}}$ and, using proposition 3.5.3, define a monotonically increasing right continuous function $F : \mathbb{R} \longrightarrow \mathbb{R}$ such that the unique Lebesgue-Stieltjes measure μ_F induced by F is nothing but μ (by the uniqueness of the extension). Thus measures μ on $\mathcal{B}_\mathbb{R}$ which have the property that $\mu(a, b] < +\infty \; \forall \, a < b$ can be looked upon as a Lebesgue-Stieltjes measure μ_F for some F. We point out that it is possible to find different $F_1, F_2 :$ $\mathbb{R} \longrightarrow \mathbb{R}$ such that both are monotonically increasing and right continuous and $\mu_{F_1} = \mu_{F_2}$. If μ is finite measure, i.e., $\mu(\mathbb{R}) < +\infty$, then it is easy to see that $F(x) := \mu(-\infty, x], x \in \mathbb{R}$, is a monotonically increasing right continuous function such that $\mu = \mu_F$. This F is called **the distribution function** of μ. When $\mu(\mathbb{R}) = 1$, μ is called a **probability** and its distribution function F, which is monotonically increasing and is right continuous with $\lim\limits_{x \to \infty} [F(x) - F(-x)] = \mu_F(\mathbb{R}) = 1$, is called a **probability distribution function.**

Chapter 5

Integration

Let us recall that our aim is to define the notion of integral for a class of functions on $\mathbb{R}$ so as to extend the class of Riemann integrable functions. Of course, we expect the new notion of integral to be linear and behave reasonably well with respect to limiting operations. As we saw in section 2.1, in order to do this, our idea is to enlarge the class of building blocks. For Riemann integrable functions, the building blocks were step functions, i.e., functions which are representable as $\sum_{i=1}^n a_i \chi_{I_i}(x)$, where the a_i's are real numbers and the intervals $I_1, I_2, \ldots, I_n$ form a partition of $[a, b]$, the domain of the function. For our new integral, we consider functions of the type $s = \sum_{i=1}^n a_i \chi_{A_i}$, where n is a positive integer, the a_i's are real numbers and the A_i's are pairwise disjoint sets such that $\bigcup_{i=1}^n A_i = \mathbb{R}$. Further, we demand that $A_i \in \mathcal{L}$ for every i, i.e., the A_i's are sets for which the notion of length has been defined. Since we expect our new integral to be linear and to be an extension of the Riemann integral, we should define the integral of s to be $\int s\,d\lambda := \sum_{i=1}^n a_i \lambda(A_i)$. However, $\lambda(A_i)$ could be $+\infty$ for some i. To avoid unpleasant situations (e.g., $\infty - \infty$), we start with functions $s = \sum_{i=1}^n a_i \chi_{A_i}$, where $a_i \geq 0$ for each i. In fact, we can allow $a_i = +\infty$ for every i. Since the definition and properties of the new integral are not going to depend on the fact that the A_i's are subsets of $\mathbb{R}$, but only on the fact that they are sets for which the notion of 'length' has been defined, we shall proceed with the process of integration when $\mathbb{R}$ is replaced by any set X, $\mathcal{L}$ is replaced by a σ-algebra $\mathcal{S}$ of subsets of X, and λ by a σ-finite measure μ on $\mathcal{S}$. In section 5.1 we shall define the integral for the class of functions of the type $s = \sum_{i=1}^n a_i \chi_{A_i}$, which serve as building blocks for our integral. Then, keeping in mind the limiting property that the integral should have, we will extend it to a larger class of functions in section 5.2. The class of functions for which this integral can be defined will be discussed in sections 5.3 and 5.4.

For the rest of the chapter, unless stated otherwise, we shall work on a fixed σ-finite measure space $(X, \mathcal{S}, \mu)$. We shall further assume that $(X, \mathcal{S}, \mu)$ is a complete measure space.

5.1. Integral of nonnegative simple measurable functions

5.1.1. Definition: Let $s : X \longrightarrow [0, \infty]$ be defined by

$$s(x) = \sum_{i=1}^{n} a_i \chi_{A_i}(x), \quad x \in X,$$

where n is some positive integer; $a_1, a_2, \ldots, a_n$ are nonnegative extended real numbers; $A_i \in \mathcal{S}$ for every i; $A_i \cap A_j = \emptyset$ for $i \neq j$; and $\bigcup_{i=1}^{n} A_i = X$. Such a function s is called a **nonnegative simple measurable function** on $(X, \mathcal{S})$ and $\sum_{i=1}^{n} a_i \chi_{A_i}(x)$ is called a **representation** of s. We say $\sum_{i=1}^{n} a_i \chi_{A_i}$ is the **standard representation** of s if $a_1, a_2, \ldots, a_n$ are all distinct. We denote by $\mathbb{L}_0^+$ the class of all nonnegative simple measurable functions on $(X, \mathcal{S})$.

Note that $s \in \mathbb{L}_0^+$ iff s takes only a finite number of distinct values, say $a_1, a_2, \ldots, a_n$, the value a_i being taken on the set $A_i \in \mathcal{S}$, $i = 1, 2, \ldots, n$. And in that case its standard representation is $\sum_{i=1}^{n} a_i \chi_{A_i}$. Also note that the class $\mathbb{L}_0^+$ depends only upon the set X and the σ-algebra $\mathcal{S}$; the measure μ plays no part in the definition of functions in $\mathbb{L}_0^+$.

5.1.2. Examples:

(i) Clearly, if $s(x) \equiv c$ for some $c \in [0, +\infty]$, then $s \in \mathbb{L}_0^+$.

(ii) For $A \subseteq X$, consider $\chi_A : X \longrightarrow [0, +\infty]$, the indicator function of the set A, i.e., $\chi_A(x) = 1$ if $x \in A$ and $\chi_A(x) = 0$ if $x \notin A$. Then $\chi_A \in \mathbb{L}_0^+$ iff $A \in \mathcal{S}$, for $\chi_A = a\chi_A + b\chi_{A^c}$ with $a = 1$ and $b = 0$.

(iii) Let $A, B \in \mathcal{S}$. Then $s = \chi_A \chi_B \in \mathbb{L}_0^+$, since $s = \chi_{A \cap B}$.

(iv) Let $A, B \in \mathcal{S}$. If $A \cap B = \emptyset$, then clearly $\chi_A + \chi_B = \chi_{A \cup B} \in \mathbb{L}_0^+$.

5.1.3. Exercise: Let $A, B \in \mathcal{S}$. Express the functions $|\chi_A - \chi_B|$ and $\chi_A + \chi_B - \chi_{A \cap B}$ as indicator functions of sets in $\mathcal{S}$ and hence deduce that they belong to $\mathbb{L}_0^+$.

5.1.4. Definition: For $s \in \mathbb{L}_0^+$ with a representation $s = \sum_{i=1}^n a_i \chi_{A_i}$, we define $\int s(x) d\mu(x)$, the **integral** of s with respect to μ, by

$$\int s(x) d\mu(x) := \sum_{i=1}^n a_i \mu(A_i).$$

The integral $\int s(x) d\mu(x)$ is also denoted by $\int s d\mu$.

Before we proceed further, we should check that $\int s(x) d\mu(x)$ is well-defined, i.e., if

$$s = \sum_{i=1}^n a_i \chi_{A_i} = \sum_{j=1}^m b_j \chi_{B_j},$$

where $\{A_1, \dots, A_n\}$ and $\{B_1, \dots, B_m\}$ are partitions of X by elements of $\mathcal{S}$, then

$$\sum_{i=1}^n a_i \mu(A_i) = \sum_{j=1}^m b_j \mu(B_j).$$

For this, we note that we can write

$$s = \sum_{i=1}^n a_i \sum_{j=1}^m \chi_{A_i \cap B_j} = \sum_{j=1}^m b_j \sum_{i=1}^n \chi_{A_i \cap B_j}.$$

Thus if $A_i \cap B_j \neq \emptyset$, then $a_i = b_j$. Hence, using finite additivity of μ,

$$\sum_{i=1}^n a_i \mu(A_i) = \sum_{i=1}^n a_i \sum_{j=1}^m \mu(A_i \cap B_j) = \sum_{j=1}^m b_j \sum_{i=1}^n \mu(A_i \cap B_j) = \sum_{j=1}^m b_j \mu(B_j),$$

Thus $\int s(x) d\mu(x)$ is independent of the representation $s(x) = \sum_{i=1}^n a_i \chi_{A_i}$. The properties of $\int s d\mu$, for $s \in \mathbb{L}_0^+$, are given by the next proposition.

5.1.5. Proposition: *For $s, s_1, s_2 \in \mathbb{L}_0^+$ and $\alpha \in \mathbb{R}$ with $\alpha \geq 0$, the following hold:*

(i) $0 \leq \int s d\mu \leq +\infty$.

(ii) $\alpha s \in \mathbb{L}_0^+$ *and*

$$\int (\alpha s) d\mu = \alpha \int s d\mu.$$

(iii) $s_1 + s_2 \in \mathbb{L}_0^+$ *and*

$$\int (s_1 + s_2) d\mu = \int s_1 d\mu + \int s_2 d\mu.$$

(iv) *For $E \in \mathcal{S}$ we have $s\chi_E \in \mathbb{L}_0^+$, and the set function*

$$E \longmapsto \nu(E) := \int s\chi_E d\mu$$

is a measure on $\mathcal{S}$. Further, $\nu(E) = 0$ whenever $\mu(E) = 0, E \in \mathcal{S}$.

Proof: Statements (i) and (ii) are obvious. For (iii), let

$$s_1 = \sum_{i=1}^{n} a_i \chi_{A_i} \text{ and } s_2 = \sum_{j=1}^{m} b_j \chi_{B_j}.$$

Then we can write

$$s_1 = \sum_{i=1}^{n}\sum_{j=1}^{m} a_i \chi_{A_i \cap B_j} \text{ and } s_2 = \sum_{i=1}^{n}\sum_{i=1}^{m} b_j \chi_{A_i \cap B_j}.$$

Thus

$$s_1 + s_2 = \sum_{i=1}^{n}\sum_{j=1}^{m}(a_i + b_j)\chi_{A_i \cap B_j}.$$

Hence $s_1 + s_2 \in \mathbb{L}_0^+$ and, using these representations, clearly

$$\int (s_1 + s_2)d\mu = \int s_1 d\mu + \int s_2 d\mu.$$

This proves (iii). To prove (iv), let $s = \sum_{i=1}^n a_i \chi_{A_i}$. Then for $E \in \mathcal{S}$,

$$s\chi_E = \sum_{i=1}^{n} a_i \chi_{A_i \cap E} + a\chi_{E^c}, \text{ where } a = 0.$$

Hence $s\chi_E \in \mathbb{L}^+$ and

$$\nu(E) := \int s\chi_E d\mu = \sum_{i=1}^{n} a_i \mu(E \cap A_i).$$

Using this, it is easy to check that ν is a measure. Clearly $\mu(E) = 0$ implies that $\nu(E) = 0$. ∎

•**5.1.6. Exercise:** Let $s_1, s_2 \in \mathbb{L}_0^+$. Prove the following:

(i) If $s_1 \geq s_2$, then $\int s_1 d\mu \geq \int s_2 d\mu$.

(ii) Let $\forall\, x \in X$,

$(s_1 \vee s_2)(x) := \max\{s_1(x), s_2(x)\}$ and $(s_1 \wedge s_2)(x) := \min\{s_1(x), s_2(x)\}$.

Then $s_1 \wedge s_2$ and $s_1 \vee s_2 \in \mathbb{L}_0^+$ with

$$\int (s_1 \wedge s_2)d\mu \leq \int s_i d\mu \leq \int (s_1 \vee s_2)d\mu, \; i = 1, 2.$$

(iii) Express the functions $\chi_A \wedge \chi_B$ and $\chi_A \vee \chi_B$, for $A, B \in \mathcal{S}$, in terms of the functions χ_A and χ_B.

5.1.7. Exercise: Let $X = (0, 1]$, $\mathcal{S} = \mathcal{B}_{(0,1]}$, the σ-algebra of Borel subsets of $(0, 1]$ and $\mu = \lambda$, the Lebesgue measure restricted to $\mathcal{S}$. For $x \in (0, 1]$, if x has non-terminating dyadic expansion $x = \sum_{n=1}^{\infty} x_n/2^n$ (as in exercise 3.3.4), let

$$f_i(x) := \begin{cases} +1 & \text{if } x_i = 1, \\ -1 & \text{if } x_i = 0, \end{cases} \quad i = 1, 2, \ldots.$$

Show that for every i, there exists simple function $s_i \in \mathbb{L}_0^+$ such that $f_i = s_i - 1$. Compute $\int s_i d\lambda$.

• **5.1.8. Exercise:**

(i) Let $s : X \longrightarrow \mathbb{R}^*$ be any nonnegative function such that the range of s is a finite set. Show that $s \in \mathbb{L}_0^+$ iff $s^{-1}\{t\} \in \mathcal{S}$ for every $t \in \mathbb{R}^*$.

(ii) For $s_1, s_2 \in \mathbb{L}_0^+$ show that $\{x \mid s_1(x) \geq s_2(x)\} \in \mathcal{S}$. Can you say that the sets $\{x \in X \mid s_1(x) > s_2(x)\}, \{x \in X \mid s_1(x) \leq s_2(x)\}$ and $\{x \in X \mid s_1(x) = s_2(x)\}$ are also elements of $\mathcal{S}$?

5.1.9. Exercise: Let $s_1, s_2 \in \mathbb{L}_0^+$ be real valued and $s_1 \geq s_2$. Let $\phi = s_1 - s_2$. Show that $\phi \in \mathbb{L}_0^+$. Can you say that

$$\int \phi d\mu = \int s_1 d\mu - \int s_2 d\mu?$$

5.1.10. Proposition: *Let $s \in \mathbb{L}_0^+$. Then the following hold:*

(i) *If $\{s_n\}_{n \geq 1}$ is any increasing sequence in $\mathbb{L}_0^+$ such that $\lim_{n \to \infty} s_n(x) = s(x), x \in X$, then*

$$\int s d\mu = \lim_{n \to \infty} \int s_n d\mu.$$

(ii) $\int s d\mu = \sup \left\{ \int s' d\mu \mid 0 \leq s' \leq s, s' \in \mathbb{L}_0^+ \right\}.$

Proof : (i) Since $0 \leq s_n \leq s$, by exercise 5.1.6 for every n we have

$$\int s_n d\mu \leq \int s d\mu.$$

Hence

$$\limsup_{n \to \infty} \int s_n d\mu \leq \int s d\mu. \tag{5.1}$$

Let $0 < c < 1$ be arbitrary and let

$$B_n := \{x \in X \mid s_n(x) \geq cs(x)\}.$$

Then $B_n \in \mathcal{S}$ (exercise 5.1.8) and $B_n \subseteq B_{n+1}$ $\forall\, n$ with $\bigcup_{n=1}^{\infty} B_n = X$. Thus by proposition 5.1.5 (iv) and theorem 3.6.3, we have

$$
\begin{aligned}
c \int s(x)d\mu(x) &= \lim_{n\to\infty} \int_{B_n} c\, s(x)d\mu(x) \\
&\leq \liminf_{n\to\infty} \int_{B_n} s_n(x)d\mu(x) \\
&\leq \liminf_{n\to\infty} \int s_n(x)d\mu(x).
\end{aligned}
$$

Since this holds $\forall\, c$ with $0 < c < 1$, we have

$$
\int s(x)d\mu(x) \;\leq\; \liminf_{n\to\infty} \int s_n(x)d\mu(x). \tag{5.2}
$$

From (5.1) and (5.2) we get

$$
\int s d\mu = \lim_{n\to\infty} \int s_n d\mu.
$$

This proves (i). The proof of (ii) is obvious. ∎

•**5.1.11. Exercise:** Let $\{s_n\}_{n\geq 1}$ and $\{s'_n\}_{n\geq 1}$ be sequences in $\mathbb{L}_0^+$ such that for each $x \in X$, both $\{s_n(x)\}_{n\geq 1}$ and $\{s'_n(x)\}_{n\geq 1}$ are increasing and $\lim_{n\to\infty} s_n(x) = \lim_{n\to\infty} s'_n(x)$. Show that

$$
\lim_{n\to\infty} \int s_n d\mu = \lim_{n\to\infty} \int s'_n d\mu.
$$

(Hint: Apply exercise 5.1.6 and proposition 5.1.10 to $\{s_n \wedge s'_m\}_n$ for all fixed m to deduce that $\int s'_m d\mu \leq \lim_{n\to\infty} \int s_n d\mu$.)

5.1.12. Exercise: Show that in general $\mathbb{L}_0^+$ need not be closed under limiting operations. For example, consider the Lebesgue measure space $(\mathbb{R}, \mathcal{L}, \lambda)$ and construct a sequence $\{s_n\}_{n\geq 1}$ in $\mathbb{L}_0^+$ such that $\lim_{n\to\infty} s_n(x) = f(x)$ exists but $f \notin \mathbb{L}_0^+$.

5.2. Integral of nonnegative measurable functions

Having defined the integral for functions $s \in \mathbb{L}_0^+$, i.e., nonnegative simple measurable functions, we would like to extend it to a larger class. Let us recall that, given a Riemann integrable function $f : [a, b] \longrightarrow \mathbb{R}$, in section 2.1 we constructed a sequence $\{f_n\}_{n\geq 1}$ of step functions such that $\{f_n(x)\}_{n\geq 1}$

increases to $f(x) \forall x \in [a, b]$ and $\int_a^b f(x)dx = \lim_{n \to \infty} \int_a^b f_n(x)dx$. In the extended integral, step functions are replaced by nonnegative simple measurable functions, whose integral is already defined. Let $f : X \longrightarrow \mathbb{R}^*$ be a function such that there exists a sequence $\{s_n\}_{n \geq 1}$ of nonnegative simple measurable functions increasing to f. Then one can define $\int f d\mu := \lim_{n \to \infty} \int s_n d\mu$. This motivates the following definition.

5.2.1. Definition:

(i) A nonnegative function $f : X \longrightarrow \mathbb{R}^*$ is said to be **$\mathcal{S}$-measurable** if there exists an increasing sequence of functions $\{s_n\}_{n \geq 1}$ in $\mathbb{L}_0^+$ such that $f(x) = \lim_{n \to \infty} s_n(x) \ \forall \ x \in X$.

If the underlying σ-algebra is clear from the context, an $\mathcal{S}$-measurable function is also called measurable. We denote the set of all nonnegative measurable functions by $\mathbb{L}^+$.

(ii) For a function $f \in \mathbb{L}^+$, we define the **integral** of f with respect to μ by

$$\int f(x)d\mu(x) := \lim_{n \to \infty} \int s_n(x)d\mu(x).$$

It follows from exercise 5.1.11 that for $f \in \mathbb{L}^+$, $\int f d\mu$ is well-defined. Clearly, $\mathbb{L}_0^+ \subseteq \mathbb{L}^+$ and $\int s d\mu$ for an element $s \in \mathbb{L}_0^+$ is the same as $\int s d\mu$, for s as an element of $\mathbb{L}^+$. The next proposition gives a characterization of functions in $\mathbb{L}^+$ and the integrals of its elements. Another (intrinsic) characterization of $\mathbb{L}^+$ will be given in the next section.

5.2.2. Proposition: *Let $f : X \longrightarrow \mathbb{R}^*$ be a non-negative function. Then the following hold:*

(i) *$f \in \mathbb{L}^+$ iff there exist functions $s_n \in \mathbb{L}_0^+, n \geq 1$, such that $0 \leq s_n \leq f \ \forall \ n$ and $f(x) = \lim_{n \to \infty} s_n(x) \ \forall \ x \in X$.*

(ii) *If $f \in \mathbb{L}^+$ and $s \in \mathbb{L}_0^+$ is such that $0 \leq s \leq f$, then $\int s d\mu \leq \int f d\mu$ and*

$$\int f d\mu = \sup \left\{ \int s d\mu \ \middle| \ 0 \leq s \leq f, \ s \in \mathbb{L}_0^+ \right\}.$$

Proof: (i) Let $f \in \mathbb{L}^+$. By definition, there exists a sequence $\{s_n\}_{n \geq 1}$ in $\mathbb{L}_0^+$ such that $\{s_n(x)\}_{n \geq 1}$ increases to $f(x) \ \forall \ x \in X$. Hence the direct implication holds. Conversely, let there exist a sequence $\{s_n\}_{n \geq 1}$ in $\mathbb{L}_0^+$ such that $0 \leq s_n \leq f \ \forall \ n$ and $f(x) = \lim_{n \to \infty} s_n(x) \ \forall \ x \in X$. Put

$$s_n'(x) := \max\{s_1(x), \cdots, s_n(x)\}, \ x \in X.$$

Then $s'_n \in \mathbb{L}_0^+, 0 \leq s'_n \leq f$ and $\{s'_n(x)\}_{n\geq 1}$ increases to $f(x)$ $\forall\, x \in X$. This proves (i).

(ii) Let $f \in \mathbb{L}^+$, and let $\{s_n\}_{n\geq 1}$ be a sequence in $\mathbb{L}_0^+$ such that $\{s_n\}_{n\geq 1}$ increases to $f(x)$ $\forall\, x$ and

$$\int f d\mu = \lim_{n\to\infty} \int s_n d\mu.$$

Let

$$\beta := \sup\left\{ \int s d\mu \,\bigg|\, 0 \leq s \leq f, s \in \mathbb{L}_0^+ \right\}$$

and let $s \in \mathbb{L}_0^+$ be such that $0 \leq s \leq f$. Let

$$B_n := \{x \in X \mid s(x) \leq s_n(x)\}, \quad n \geq 1.$$

Then $B_n \in \mathcal{S}$ (by exercise 5.1.8) and $\forall\, n, B_n \subseteq B_{n+1}$ with $\bigcup_{n=1}^{\infty} B_n = X$. Thus by proposition 5.1.5 (iv) and theorem 3.6.3, we have

$$\int s d\mu = \lim_{n\to\infty} \int_{B_n} s d\mu \leq \lim_{n\to\infty} \int s_n d\mu = \int f d\mu.$$

Further, since this holds $\forall\, s \in \mathbb{L}_0^+$ with $0 \leq s \leq f$, we have

$$\beta \leq \int f d\mu.$$

Conversely, if $\int f d\mu = +\infty$, then $\forall\, N > 0$, we can choose n_0 such that $\int s_{n_0} d\mu > N$. Since $0 \leq s_{n_0} \leq f$, we have $\beta > N$, $\forall\, N$. Thus

$$\beta = +\infty = \int f d\mu.$$

In case $\int f d\mu < +\infty$ and $\epsilon > 0$ is given, we can choose n_0 such that

$$\int f d\mu - \int s_{n_0} d\mu < \epsilon,$$

i.e.,

$$\int f d\mu \leq \int s_{n_0} d\mu + \epsilon < \beta + \epsilon.$$

Since this holds $\forall\, \epsilon > 0$, we have

$$\int f d\mu \leq \beta. \quad \blacksquare$$

5.2.3. Exercise: Let $f \in \mathbb{L}^+$ and let $\{s_n\}_{n\geq 1}$ be in $\mathbb{L}_0^+$ and such that $\{s_n(x)\}_{n\geq 1}$ is decreasing and $\forall\, x \in X$, $\lim_{n\to\infty} s_n(x) = f(x)$. Can you conclude that

$$\int f d\mu = \lim_{n\to\infty} \int s_n d\mu?$$

5.2.4. Definition: Let $(X, \mathcal{S}, \mu)$ be a measure space and $Y \in \mathcal{S}$. We say a property P holds **almost everywhere** on Y with respect to the measure μ if the set $E = \{x \in Y \mid P \text{ does not hold at } x\} \in \mathcal{S}$ and $\mu(E) = 0$. We write this as P **for a.e.** $x(\mu)$ or P **for a.e.** $(\mu)x \in Y$. If the set Y and μ are clear from the context, we shall simply write P **a.e.** For example if $f : X \longrightarrow \mathbb{R}$ is a function, then $f(x) = 0$ for a.e. $x(\mu)$ means that $E = \{x \in X \mid f(x) \neq 0\} \in \mathcal{S}$ and $\mu(E) = 0$.

5.2.5. Exercise: Let $f \in \mathbb{L}^+$. Show that

$$\int f d\mu = \sup \left\{ \int s d\mu \,\middle|\, 0 \leq s(x) \leq f(x) \text{ for a.e. } x(\mu), s \in \mathbb{L}_0^+ \right\}.$$

We describe next the properties of $\int f d\mu$, for $f \in \mathbb{L}^+$.

5.2.6. Proposition: *Let $f, f_1, f_2 \in \mathbb{L}^+$. Then the following hold:*

(i) *$\int f d\mu \geq 0$ and for $f_1 \geq f_2$*

$$\int f_1 d\mu \geq \int f_2 \, d\mu.$$

(ii) *For $\alpha, \beta \geq 0$ we have $(\alpha f_1 + \beta f_2) \in \mathbb{L}^+$ and*

$$\int (\alpha f_1 + \beta f_2) d\mu = \alpha \int f_1 d\mu + \beta \int f_2 d\mu.$$

(iii) *For every $E \in \mathcal{S}$ we have $\chi_E f \in \mathbb{L}^+$. If*

$$\nu(E) := \int \chi_E f d\mu, \ E \in \mathcal{S},$$

then ν is a measure on $\mathcal{S}$ and $\nu(E) = 0$ whenever $\mu(E) = 0$.
The integral $\int f \chi_E d\mu$ is also denoted by $\int_E f d\mu$ and is called the **integral of f over E**.

(iv) *If $f_1(x) = f_2(x)$ for a.e. $x(\mu)$, then*

$$\int f_1 d\mu = \int f_2 d\mu.$$

Proof: (i) Let $f \in \mathbb{L}^+$. Clearly by the definition of the integral, $\int f d\mu \geq 0$. For $f_1, f_2 \in \mathbb{L}^+$, if $f_1 \leq f_2$, then using proposition 5.2.2(ii) and exercise 5.1.6.(i) it follows that $\int f_1 d\mu \leq \int f_2 d\mu$.

(ii) Let $f_1, f_2 \in \mathbb{L}^+$, and let $\alpha, \beta \in \mathbb{R}$ be nonnegative. Let $\{s_n^1\}_{n \geq 1}$ and $\{s_n^2\}_{n \geq 1}$ be increasing sequences in $\mathbb{L}_0^+$ such that $\forall \, x \in X$,

$$\lim_{n \to \infty} s_n^i(x) = f_i(x), i = 1, 2.$$

Then $\{s_n^1 + s_n^2\}_{n\geq 1}$ is an increasing sequence in $\mathbb{L}_0^+$ and

$$\lim_{n\to\infty} (\alpha s_n^1 + \beta s_n^2)(x) = \alpha f_1(x) + \beta f_2(x), \quad \forall\, x \in X.$$

Thus by exercise 5.1.11 and proposition 5.1.5,

$$
\begin{aligned}
\int (\alpha f_1 + \beta f_2) d\mu &= \lim_{n\to\infty} \int (\alpha s_n^1 + \beta s_n^2) d\mu \\
&= \alpha \lim_{n\to\infty} \int s_n^1 d\mu + \beta \lim_{n\to\infty} \int s_n^2 d\mu \\
&= \alpha \int f_1 d\mu + \beta \int f_2 d\mu.
\end{aligned}
$$

(iii) Let $f \in \mathbb{L}^+$ and $E \in \mathcal{S}$. Let $\{s_n\}_{n\geq 1}$ be an increasing sequence in $\mathbb{L}_0^+$ such that $f(x) = \lim_{n\to\infty} s_n(x) \ \forall\, x \in X$. Then clearly, $\{s_n \chi_E\}_{n\geq 1}$ is an increasing sequence in $\mathbb{L}_0^+$ and

$$(f\chi_E)(x) = \lim_{n\to\infty} (s_n \chi_E)(x), \quad \forall\, x \in X.$$

Hence $f\chi_E \in \mathbb{L}^+$ and, by exercise 5.1.11,

$$\int f\chi_E \, d\mu = \lim_{n\to\infty} \int s_n \chi_E \, d\mu.$$

Further, if $\mu(E) = 0$, then it follows from the above equality and proposition 5.1.5 that

$$\nu(E) := \int_E f\, d\mu = \int f\chi_E \, d\mu = 0.$$

To prove that ν is countably additive, we first show that ν is countably subadditive. Let $\{E_n\}_{n\geq 1}$ be a sequence in $\mathcal{S}$ and $E := \bigcup_{n=1}^{\infty} E_n$. Let $\{s_n\}_{n\geq 1}$ be an increasing sequence in $\mathbb{L}_0^+$ such that $f(x) = \lim_{n\to\infty} s_n(x) \ \forall\, x \in X$. Then, using proposition 5.1.5 (iv) and proposition 5.2.2 (ii), we have

$$
\begin{aligned}
\int_E f\, d\mu &= \lim_{n\to\infty} \int_E s_n \, d\mu \\
&= \lim_{n\to\infty} \left(\sum_{i=1}^{\infty} \int_{E_i} s_n \, d\mu \right) \\
&\leq \lim_{n\to\infty} \left(\sum_{i=1}^{\infty} \int_{E_i} f\, d\mu \right) \\
&= \sum_{i=1}^{\infty} \int_{E_i} f\, d\mu.
\end{aligned}
$$

This proves that ν is countably subadditive. To prove that ν is a measure, we only have to show that it is finitely additive (see theorem 3.6.1). Let

$E_1, E_2, \ldots, E_m$ be pairwise disjoint sets in $\mathcal{S}$ and $E = \bigcup_{i=1}^{m} E_i$. Then, again using proposition 5.1.5 (iv),

$$
\begin{aligned}
\int_E f d\mu &= \lim_{n \to \infty} \left(\int_E s_n d\mu \right) \\
&= \lim_{n \to \infty} \left(\sum_{i=1}^{m} \int_{E_i} s_n d\mu \right) \\
&= \sum_{i=1}^{m} \left(\lim_{n \to \infty} \int_{E_i} s d\mu \right) \\
&= \sum_{i=1}^{m} \int_{E_i} f d\mu.
\end{aligned}
$$

This proves (iii). The proof of (iv) is easy and is left as an exercise. ∎

Since the class $\mathbb{L}_0^+$ is not closed under limiting operations (exercise 5.1.12), we defined the class $\mathbb{L}^+$ by taking limits of sequences in $\mathbb{L}_0^+$. Naturally, we expect $\mathbb{L}^+$ to be closed under limits. The next theorem discusses this and the behavior of $\int f d\mu$ under increasing limits, extending proposition 5.1.10 to functions in $\mathbb{L}^+$.

5.2.7. Theorem (Monotone convergence): *Let $\{f_n\}_{n \geq 1}$ be an increasing sequence of functions in $\mathbb{L}^+$, and $f(x) := \lim_{n \to \infty} f_n(x), x \in X$. Then $f \in \mathbb{L}^+$ and*

$$
\int f d\mu = \lim_{n \to \infty} \int f_n d\mu.
$$

Proof: Since $f_n \in \mathbb{L}^+$, there exists a sequence $\{s_j^n\}_{j \geq 1}$ of functions in $\mathbb{L}_0^+$ such that $\{s_j^n(x)\}_{j \geq 1}$ increases to $f_n(x) \ \forall \ x$. We represent it as an array (see Figure 14). In each row functions are increasing from left to right, and in the last column the functions are increasing from bottom to top. For $n = 1, 2, \ldots$, define

$$
g_n(x) := \max\{s_n^1(x), s_n^2(x), \ldots, s_n^n(x)\}.
$$

By exercise 5.1.6(ii), $g_n \in \mathbb{L}_0^+$, and for every $x \in X$, $\{g_n(x)\}_{n \geq 1}$ is an increasing sequence in $\mathbb{R}^*$. Let

$$
g(x) := \lim_{n \to \infty} g_n(x).
$$

Then by definition $g \in \mathbb{L}^+$. Since $\{f_n\}_{n \geq 1}$ is increasing and

$$
s_n^j \leq f_j \leq f \text{ for all } n \text{ and for all } j,
$$

$$f$$

$$\cdots \quad \cdots \quad \cdots \quad \cdots \quad \cdots \quad \cdots \quad \cdots \qquad \uparrow$$

$$s_1^n \quad s_2^n \quad \cdots \quad s_j^n \quad \cdots \quad s_n^n \quad \cdots \quad \rightarrow \quad f_n$$

$$\cdots \quad \cdots \quad \cdots \quad \cdots \qquad\qquad \cdots \quad \cdots \qquad\qquad \cdots$$

$$s_1^j \quad s_2^j \quad \cdots \quad s_j^j \quad \cdots \quad s_n^j \quad \cdots \quad \rightarrow \quad f_j$$

$$\cdots \quad \cdots \quad \cdots \quad \cdots \qquad\qquad \cdots \quad \cdots \qquad\qquad \cdots$$

$$s_1^2 \quad s_2^2 \quad \cdots \quad s_j^2 \quad \cdots \quad s_n^2 \quad \cdots \quad \rightarrow \quad f_2$$

$$s_1^1 \quad s_2^1 \quad \cdots \quad s_j^1 \quad \cdots \quad s_n^1 \quad \cdots \quad \rightarrow \quad f_1$$

$$g_1 \quad g_2 \quad \cdots \quad g_j \quad \cdots \quad g_n \quad \cdots \quad \rightarrow \quad g$$

Figure 14: Definition of g_n

we have

$$g_n = \max_{1 \le j \le n} \{s_n^j\} \le f_n \le f.$$

Hence $g \le f$. Also,

$$s_n^j \le g_n \le g \text{ whenever } j \le n \text{ and } n \ge 1.$$

Thus, letting $n \longrightarrow \infty$, we have $f_j \le g$, $\forall\, j \ge 1$. Hence $f \le g$, proving that $f = g \in \mathbb{L}^+$. Also, by definition

$$\int g d\mu = \lim_{n \to \infty} \int g_n d\mu.$$

Since for every n

$$g_n \le f_n \le f,$$

we get

$$\lim_{n \to \infty} \int g_n d\mu \le \lim_{n \to \infty} \int f_n d\mu \le \int f d\mu.$$

Hence

$$\int f d\mu = \int g d\mu = \lim_{n \to \infty} \int g_n d\mu \le \lim_{n \to \infty} \int f_n d\mu \le \int f d\mu,$$

proving the theorem. ■

5.2.8. Remark: If $\{f_n\}_{n\geq1}$ is a sequence in $\mathbb{L}^+$ decreasing to a function $f \in \mathbb{L}^+$, then the equality $\int f d\mu = \lim_{n\to\infty} \int f_n d\mu$ need not hold. For example, let $X = \mathbb{R}$, $\mathcal{S} = \mathcal{L}$ and $\mu = \lambda$, the Lebesgue measure. Let $f_n = \chi_{[n,\infty)}$. Then $f_n \in \mathbb{L}_0^+ \subseteq \mathbb{L}^+$, and $\{f_n\}_{n\geq1}$ decreases to $f \equiv 0$. Clearly, $\int f_n d\lambda = +\infty$ for every n and $\int f d\lambda = 0$. In fact, at this stage it is not clear whether $f \in \mathbb{L}^+$ whenever $\{f_n\}_{n\geq1}$ decreases to f, with each $f_n \in \mathbb{L}^+$. That this is true will be shown as a consequence of the characterization of $\mathbb{L}^+$ proved in the next section (see corollary 5.3.15).

5.2.9. Exercise: Let $\{f_n\}_{n\geq1}$ be an increasing sequence of functions in $\mathbb{L}^+$ such that $f(x) := \lim_{n\to\infty} f_n(x)$ exists for a.e. $x(\mu)$. Show that $f \in \mathbb{L}^+$ and

$$\int f d\mu = \lim_{n\to\infty} \int f_n d\mu,$$

where $f(x)$ is defined as an arbitrary constant for all those x for which $\lim_{n\to\infty} f_n(x)$ does not converge.

5.2.10. Exercise: Let $\mu(X) < \infty$, and let $f \in \mathbb{L}^+$ be a bounded function. Let $P := \{E_1, E_2, \ldots, E_n\}$ be such that $\bigcup_{i=1}^{n} E_i = X$, $E_i \cap E_j = \emptyset$ for $i \neq j$ and $E_i \in \mathcal{S}\ \forall\ i$. Such a P is called a **measurable partition** of X. Given a measurable partition $P = \{E_1, \ldots, E_n\}$, define

$$M_i := \sup\{f(x) \,|\, x \in E_i\}\ \text{ and }\ m_i := \inf\{f(x) \,|\, x \in E_i\}.$$

Let

$$\Phi_P := \sum_{i=1}^{n} m_i \chi_{E_i}\ \text{ and }\ \Psi_P := \sum_{i=1}^{n} M_i \chi_{E_i}.$$

Prove the following:

(i) For every partition P, show that $\Phi_P, \Psi_P \in \mathbb{L}_0^+$ and $\Phi_P \leq f \leq \Psi_P$.

(ii) $\int f d\mu\ =\ \sup\left\{\int \Phi_P d\mu \,|\, P \text{ is a measurable partition of } X\right\},$
$=\ \inf\left\{\int \Psi_P d\mu \,|\, P \text{ is a measurable partition of } X\right\}.$
(This gives an equivalent way of defining $\int f d\mu$, in a way similar to that for the Riemann integral.)

(iii) Let

$$\alpha = \sup\left\{\int_0 s d\mu \,|\, s \in \mathbb{L}_0^+,\ s \leq f\right\}\ \text{ and }\ \beta = \inf\left\{\int s d\mu \,|\, s \in \mathbb{L}_0^+,\ f \leq s\right\}.$$

Show that

$$\alpha = \sup\left\{\int \Phi_p d\mu \,|\, P \text{ is a measurable partition of } X\right\}$$

and

$$\beta = \inf \left\{ \int \Psi_p d\mu \mid P \text{ is a measurable partition of } X \right\}.$$

(iv) Deduce that $f \in \mathbb{L}^+$ implies $\alpha = \int f d\mu = \beta$.

5.2.11. Note: Exercise 5.2.10 tells us that for $f \in \mathbb{L}^+$, in defining $\int f d\mu$ it is enough to consider approximations of f from below, as the approximations from above will also give the same value for $\int f d\mu$. This is because $f \in \mathbb{L}^+$, i.e., f is nonnegative measurable. The converse is also true, i.e., if $\alpha = \beta$, for $f : X \to [0, \infty]$, then $f \in \mathbb{L}^+$. To see this, first note that

$$\alpha = \beta < M(\mu(X)) < \infty,$$

where M is such that $|f(x)| \le M \ \forall \ x \in X$. Thus for every n we can choose functions $\phi_n, \psi_n \in \mathbb{L}_0^+$ such that

$$\phi_n \le f \le \psi_n \text{ and } \int (\psi_n - \phi_n) d\mu < \frac{1}{n}.$$

Let $\phi := \sup \phi_n$ and $\psi := \inf \psi_n$. Then $\phi, \psi \in \mathbb{L}^+$ (see corollary 5.3.13) and $\forall \ n$,

$$\int (\psi - \phi) d\mu \le \int (\psi_n - \phi_n) d\mu < \frac{1}{n}.$$

Thus

$$\int (\psi - \phi) d\mu = 0$$

and by proposition 5.3.3, $\psi = \phi = f$ a.e. μ. Hence $f \in \mathbb{L}^+$.

5.3. Intrinsic characterization of nonnegative measurable functions

Recall, $f \in \mathbb{L}^+$ means $f : X \longrightarrow \mathbb{R}^*$ is a nonnegative function with the property that there exists a sequence $\{s_n\}_{n \ge 1}$ of functions in $\mathbb{L}_0^+$ such that $\{s_n(x)\}_{n \ge 1}$ increases to $f(x)$ for every $x \in X$. Note that the measure μ plays no part in the definition of the functions in $\mathbb{L}^+$. It is only to define the integral of functions $f \in \mathbb{L}^+$ that we need the measure μ. We want to characterize the functions in $\mathbb{L}^+$ intrinsically. Consider the particular case when $f = \chi_A$ for $A \subseteq X$. Then $A = \{x \in X \mid \chi_A(x) = 1\} = f^{-1}\{1\}, A^c = f^{-1}\{0\}$ and $f^{-1}\{t\} = \emptyset \ \forall \ t \in \mathbb{R}^*, t \ne 0, 1$. Thus

$$f = \chi_A \in \mathbb{L}_0^+ \text{ iff } \chi_A^{-1}\{t\} \in \mathcal{S} \ \forall t \in \mathbb{R}^*.$$

Since any function $s : X \longrightarrow \mathbb{R}$ which takes only finitely many values can be written as $\sum_{i=1}^{n} a_i \chi_{A_i}$, where $\{A_1, \dots, A_n\}$ is a partition of X, we have the following proposition:

5.3.1. Proposition: *Let $s : X \longrightarrow \mathbb{R}^*$ be such that s takes only finitely many distinct nonnegative values. Then the following are equivalent:*

  (i) $s \in \mathbb{L}^+$ *(and hence $s \in \mathbb{L}_0^+$).*

  (ii) $s^{-1}\{t\} \in \mathcal{S} \ \forall \, t \in \mathbb{R}^*.$

  (iii) $s^{-1}[t, \infty] \in \mathcal{S} \ \forall \, t \in \mathbb{R}^*.$

  (iv) $s^{-1}(I) \in \mathcal{S}$ *for every interval I in $\mathbb{R}^*$.*

Proof: Let the distinct values of s be $a_1, a_2, \ldots, a_n$ and $A_i := s^{-1}\{a_i\}$. Then $s = \sum_{i=1}^{n} a_i \chi_{A_i}$, where $\bigcup_{i=1}^{n} A_i = X$ and $A_i \cap A_j = \emptyset$ for $i \neq j$.

(i) $\Longleftrightarrow$ **(ii):** Since $s \in \mathbb{L}^+$, let $\{s_n\}_{n \geq 1}$ be a sequence in $\mathbb{L}_0^+$ such that $\{s_n(x)\}_{n \geq 1}$ increases to $s(x)$ for every x. Then for $a_i \in \mathbb{R}$,

$$A_i := s^{-1}\{a_i\} = \bigcap_{m=1}^{\infty} \bigcup_{r=1}^{\infty} \bigcap_{n=r}^{\infty} \{x \mid s_n(x) > a_i - 1/m\}$$

and hence $A_i \in \mathcal{S}$. Thus $s^{-1}(t) \in \mathcal{S}$ if $t = a_i$. If $t \in \mathbb{R}$ and $t \neq a_i$ for any i, then clearly $s^{-1}(t) = \emptyset \in \mathcal{S}$. Also, $s^{-1}\{-\infty\} = \emptyset \in \mathcal{S}$. Finally, if $t = +\infty$, then

$$s^{-1}\{+\infty\} = \bigcap_{n=1}^{\infty} \bigcap_{m=n}^{\infty} (s_m^{-1}[n, +\infty]).$$

Thus $s^{-1}\{+\infty\} \in \mathcal{S}$. Hence (ii) is proved. Conversely, if (ii) holds then clearly $s \in \mathbb{L}_0^+ \subseteq \mathbb{L}^+$.

(ii) $\Longrightarrow$ **(iii):** For $t \in \mathbb{R}, s^{-1}[t, \infty] = \bigcup A_i$, where the union is over only those i's such that $a_i \in [t, \infty]$. Hence $s^{-1}[t, \infty] \in \mathcal{S}$ for every $t \in \mathbb{R}^*$. This proves that (ii) $\Longrightarrow$ (iii).

    The implication (iii) $\Longrightarrow$ (iv) is an application of the 'σ-algebra technique', and the implication (iv) $\Longrightarrow$ (i) is easy to verify. ∎

    In view of the above proposition it is natural to ask the following question: does proposition 5.3.1 remain true if $s \in \mathbb{L}_0^+$ is replaced by any $f \in \mathbb{L}^+$? The answer is yes, as proved in the next proposition.

5.3.2. Proposition: *Let $f : X \longrightarrow \mathbb{R}^*$ be a nonnegative function. Then the following are equivalent:*

  (i) $f \in \mathbb{L}^+.$

  (ii) $f^{-1}(c, +\infty] \in \mathcal{S}$ *for every $c \in \mathbb{R}$.*

  (iii) $f^{-1}[c, +\infty] \in \mathcal{S}$ *for every $c \in \mathbb{R}$.*

  (iv) $f^{-1}[-\infty, c) \in \mathcal{S}$ *for every $c \in \mathbb{R}$.*

  (v) $f^{-1}[-\infty, c] \in \mathcal{S}$ *for every $c \in \mathbb{R}$.*

(vi) $f^{-1}\{+\infty\}, f^-\{-\infty\}$ *and* $f^{-1}(E) \in \mathcal{S}$ *for every* $E \in \mathcal{B}_{\mathbb{R}}$.

Proof: We shall prove the following implications:

$$(i) \implies (ii) \iff (iii) \iff (iv) \iff (v) \implies (vi) \implies (i).$$

(i) $\implies$ **(ii):** Since $f \in \mathbb{L}^+$, there exists a sequence $\{s_n\}_{n\geq 1}$ of functions in $\mathbb{L}_0^+$ such that $\forall\, x \in X, \{s_n(x)\}_{n\geq 1}$ increases to $f(x)$. Now, for $c \in \mathbb{R}$

$$
\begin{aligned}
f^{-1}(c, +\infty] &= \{x : f(x) > c\} \\
&= \bigcup_{n=1}^{\infty} \{x : s_n(x) > c\} = \bigcup_{n=1}^{\infty} \left(s_n^{-1}(\,c, \infty]\right).
\end{aligned}
$$

By proposition 5.3.1,

$$s_n^{-1}(c, \infty] = \left(s_n^{-1}[c, \infty] \setminus s_n^{-1}\{c\}\right) \in \mathcal{S}.$$

Thus $f^{-1}(c, +\infty] \in \mathcal{S}$.

(ii) $\iff$ **(iii):** Note that $\forall\, c \in \mathbb{R}$,

$$[c, +\infty] = \bigcap_{n=1}^{\infty} (c - 1/n, +\infty\,] \quad \text{and} \quad (c, +\infty\,] = \bigcup_{n=1}^{\infty} [c + 1/n, \infty].$$

Thus

$$f^{-1}[c, +\infty] = \bigcap_{n=1}^{\infty} f^{-1}(c - 1/n, +\infty\,]$$

and

$$f^{-1}(c, +\infty\,] = \bigcup_{n=1}^{\infty} f^{-1}[c + 1/n, +\infty].$$

From these identities, the implications (ii) $\iff$ (iii) follow.

(iii) $\iff$ **(iv):** Since

$$(c, +\infty\,] = \mathbb{R}^* \setminus [-\infty, c] \quad \text{and} \quad [-\infty, c\,) = \mathbb{R}^* \setminus [c, +\infty],$$

we have

$$f^{-1}(c, +\infty] = X \setminus f^{-1}[-\infty, c] \quad \text{and} \quad f^{-1}[-\infty, c) = X \setminus f^{-1}[c, +\infty].$$

From this the required implications follow.

(iv) $\iff$ **(v):** This is similar to the proofs of the implications (ii) $\iff$ (iii) and is left as an exercise.

(v) $\implies$ **(vi):** Note that

$$\{+\infty\} = \bigcap_{n=1}^{\infty} (n, +\infty\,] \quad \text{and} \quad \{-\infty\} = \bigcap_{n=1}^{\infty} [\,-\infty, -n).$$

Hence

$$f^{-1}(\{+\infty\}) = \bigcap_{n=1}^{\infty} f^{-1}(n, +\infty] \in \mathcal{S} \quad \text{and} \quad f^{-1}\{-\infty\} = \bigcap_{n=1}^{\infty} f^{-1}[-\infty, -n] \in \mathcal{S}.$$

Let

$$\mathcal{B} := \{E \in \mathcal{B}_\mathbb{R} \,|\, f^{-1}(E) \in \mathcal{S}\}.$$

By (v) (and hence using (ii) and (iii)), it is easy to show that $I \in \mathcal{B}$ whenever $I \subseteq \mathbb{R}$ is an interval and $\mathcal{B}$ is a σ-algebra of subsets of $\mathbb{R}$. Hence $\mathcal{B} = \mathcal{B}_\mathbb{R}$, proving (vi).

(vi) $\implies$ (i): Let $f : X \longrightarrow \mathbb{R}^*$ be a nonnegative function such that (vi) holds. Since f is nonnegative, the range of f is a subset of $[0, +\infty]$. For every n, consider the partition of $[0, +\infty]$ given by

$$[0, +\infty] = \left(\bigcup_{k=1}^{n2^n} [(k-1)/2^n, k/2^n) \right) \bigcup [n, +\infty].$$

Then we get a partition of X, the domain of f, given by

$$X = f^{-1}[0, +\infty] = \left(\bigcup_{k=1}^{n2^n} f^{-1}[(k-1)/2^n, k/2^n) \right) \bigcup f^{-1}[n, +\infty].$$

For $1 \le k \le n2^n$, let

$$X_k^n := f^{-1}[(k-1)/2^n, k/2^n) \quad \text{and} \quad X_\infty^n := f^{-1}[n, +\infty].$$

For every $n = 1, 2, \ldots$ and $1 \le k \le n2^n$, by (vi) we have that $X_k^n \in \mathcal{S}$ and $X_\infty^n \in \mathcal{S}$. For every $n \ge 1$, we define function s_n on X by

$$s_n := \sum_{n=1}^{n2^n} \frac{k-1}{2^n} \chi_{X_k^n} + n \chi_{X_\infty^n}.$$

Clearly, $s_n \in \mathbb{L}_0^+$, and it is easy to check that for every n,

$$s_n(x) \le s_{n+1}(x), \quad \forall \, x \in X.$$

For any $x \in X$, if $f(x) = +\infty$, then $x \in X_\infty^n$ for every n, and hence $s_n(x) = n$. Thus $\lim_{n\to\infty} s_n(x) = f(x)$. Also, if $f(x) < +\infty$, then for every n, $x \in X_k^n$ for some k, $1 \le k \le 2^n$. Thus

$$s_n(x) = (k-1)/2^n.$$

Since $f(x) \in [(k-1)/2^n, k/2^n)$, we have $s_n(x) \le f(x)$ and

$$f(x) - s_n(x) < 1/2^n.$$

In other words, $\lim_{n\to\infty} s_n(x) = f(x)$. This proves that $f \in \mathbb{L}^+$. ∎

The statements (ii) to (vi) of proposition 5.3.2 describe the elements of $\mathbb{L}^+$ intrinsically. This proposition is used very often to check the measurability of nonnegative functions. Once again we emphasize the fact that for a nonnegative function $f : X \longrightarrow \mathbb{R}^*$ to be measurable, i.e., for f to be in $\mathbb{L}^+$, the measure μ plays no part. As is clear from the above proposition, it is only the σ-algebra S of subsets of X that is important (see also exercise 5.3.27). The notion of measurability is similar to the concept of continuity for topological spaces. As an immediate application of proposition 5.3.2, we have the following:

5.3.3. Proposition: *Let $f \in \mathbb{L}^+$ and $E \in S$ be such that $\int_E f d\mu = 0$. Then $f(x) = 0$ for a.e. $(\mu)x \in E$.*

Proof: Let $X_0 := \{x \in X \mid f(x) > 0\}$, and $\forall \, n \neq 1$, let $X_n := \{x \in X \mid f(x) \geq 1/n\}$. Then by proposition 5.3.2, $X_n \in S$ and hence $E_n := E \cap X_n \in S$ for $n = 0, 1, 2, \ldots$. Since $E_0 = \bigcup_{n=1}^{\infty} E_n$, if $\mu(E_0) > 0$ then $\mu(E_n) > 0$ for some n_0, and we will have

$$\int_E f(x) d\mu(x) \geq \int_{E_{n_0}} f(x) d\mu(x) \geq \mu(E_{n_0})/n_0 > 0,$$

which is not true. Hence $\mu(E_0) = 0$, i.e., $f(x) = 0$ a.e. $(\mu)x \in E$. $\blacksquare$

•**5.3.4. Exercise:**

(i) Let $f \in \mathbb{L}^+$ and $E \in S$ be such that $f(x) > 0$ for every $x \in E$ and $\mu(E) > 0$. Show that $\int_E f d\mu > 0$.

(ii) Let $f, g \in \mathbb{L}^+$ be such that

$$\int f d\mu = \int g d\mu < +\infty \quad \text{and} \quad \int_E f d\mu = \int_E g d\mu, \, \forall \, E \in S.$$

Show that $f(x) = g(x)$ a.e. $(x)\mu$.

(iii) Let f, g be nonnegative measurable functions on $(\mathbb{R}, \mathcal{L})$ such that

$$\int_a^b f d\mu = \int_a^b g d\mu < +\infty \quad \text{for every} \, a < b$$

show that then

$$\int_E f d\mu = \int_E g d\mu, \, \forall \, E \in \mathcal{L},$$

and deduce that $f(x) = g(x)$ a.e. $(x)\lambda$.

Next, we extend the concept of measurability of nonnegative functions to functions $f : X \longrightarrow \mathbb{R}^*$ which are not necessarily nonnegative. For this we consider f^+ and f^-, the **positive** and **negative part** of the function f respectively, defined as follows:

$$f^+(x) := \begin{cases} f(x) & \text{if } f(x) \geq 0, \\ 0 & \text{if } f(x) < 0, \end{cases}$$

and

$$f^-(x) := \begin{cases} 0 & \text{if } f(x) \geq 0, \\ -f(x) & \text{if } f(x) \leq 0. \end{cases}$$

Clearly, f^+ and f^- are nonnegative functions on X with

$$f = f^+ - f^- \text{ and } |f| = f^+ + f^-.$$

Since we would like functions to have the property that their sums and differences are also measurable, we are motivated to make the following definition:

5.3.5. Definition: Let $(X, \mathcal{S})$ be a measurable space.

(i) A function $f : X \longrightarrow \mathbb{R}^*$ is said to be $\mathcal{S}$-**measurable** if both f^+ and f^- are $\mathcal{S}$-measurable.

    We denote by $\mathbb{L}$ the class of all $\mathcal{S}$-measurable functions on X. If the underlying σ-algebra is clear from the context, we call a $\mathcal{S}$-measurable function to be measurable.

(ii) If $f \in \mathbb{L}$ is such that both $f^+, f^- \in \mathbb{L}_0^+$, we call f a **simple measurable function**.

    We denote the class of all simple measurable functions by $\mathbb{L}_0$. Note that $s \in \mathbb{L}_0$ iff both $s^+, s^- \in \mathbb{L}_0^+$.

5.3.6. Proposition: *Let $(X, \mathcal{S})$ be a measurable space and $f : X \to \mathbb{R}^*$ be any function. Then following statements are equivalent:*

  (i) *f is $\mathcal{S}$-measurable.*

  (ii) *There exists a sequence $\{s_n\}_{n \geq 1}$ of real valued functions on X such that $\forall\, n, s_n^+$ and s_n^- are both nonnegative simple measurable functions on $(X, \mathcal{S})$ and $\lim_{n \to \infty} s_n(x) = f(x) \; \forall\, x \in X$.*

  (iii) *f satisfies any one (and hence all) of the statements (ii) to (vi) of proposition 5.3.2.*

Proof: We ask the reader to extrapolate the proof of proposition 5.3.2 to prove the required claim. ∎

•**5.3.7. Exercise:** Let $f : X \longrightarrow \mathbb{R}^*$ be a bounded measurable function. Then there exists a sequence $\{s_n\}_{n \geq 1}$ of simple measurable functions such that $\{s_n\}_{n \geq 1}$ converges uniformly to f.

(Hint: If $0 \leq f(x) \leq M \ \forall \ x$, then $|s_n(x) - f(x)| < 1/2^n \ \forall \ n \geq n_0$, where $n_0 \geq M$ and the s_n's are as in proposition 5.3.2.)

•**5.3.8. Exercise:** Let $f : X \longrightarrow \mathbb{R}^*$ be a nonnegative measurable function. Show that there exist sequences of nonnegative simple functions $\{s_n\}_{n \geq 1}$ and $\{\tilde{s}_n\}_{n \geq 1}$ such that

$$0 \leq \cdots \leq s_n(n) \leq s_{n+1}(x) \leq \cdots \leq f(x) \leq \cdots \leq \tilde{s}_{n+1}(x) \leq \tilde{s}_n(x) \cdots$$

and $\lim\limits_{n \to \infty} s_n(x) = f(x) = \lim\limits_{n \to \infty} \tilde{s}_n(x) \ \forall \ x \in X$.

5.3.9. Examples:

(i) Let $f : X \longrightarrow \mathbb{R}^*$ be a constant function, $f(x) = \alpha \ \forall x \in X$. Then f is measurable $\forall c \in \mathbb{R}$, since

$$\{x \in X \mid f(x) > c\} = \begin{cases} \emptyset & \text{if } c \leq \alpha, \\ X & \text{if } c > \alpha. \end{cases}$$

(ii) Let $f : X \to \mathbb{R}^*$ be measurable, and $\alpha \in \mathbb{R}$. Then αf is also measurable, since

$$\{x \in X \mid \alpha(x) > c\} = \begin{cases} \{x \in X \mid f(x) < c/\alpha\} & \text{if } \alpha > 0, \\ X & \text{if } \alpha = 0, c \leq 0, \\ \emptyset & \text{if } \alpha = 0, c > 0, \\ \{x \in X \mid f(x) < c/\alpha\} & \text{if } \alpha < 0. \end{cases}$$

(iii) Let X be a topological space and $\mathcal{S}$ be the σ-algebra of Borel subsets of X, i.e., the σ-algebra generated by the open sets. Let $f : X \longrightarrow \mathbb{R}$ be any continuous function. Then f is $\mathcal{S}$-measurable. To see this, we first note that by continuity of f, $f^{-1}(U)$ is open whenever $U \subseteq \mathbb{R}$ is open, and $f^{-1}(U) \in y\mathcal{B}_X$. Thus, if

$$\mathcal{S} := \{E \subseteq \mathbb{R} \mid f^{-1}(E) \in \mathcal{B}_X\},$$

then every open subset of $\mathbb{R}$ belongs to $\mathcal{S}$. Further, it is easy to check that $\mathcal{S}$ is a σ-algebra of subsets of X. Hence by definition, $\mathcal{B}_X \subseteq \mathcal{S}$, i.e., $f^{-1}(E) \in \mathcal{B}_X \ \forall \ E \in \mathcal{B}_{\mathbb{R}}$, proving that f is measurable with respect to $\mathcal{B}_X$.

We next describe some more properties of measurable functions.

5.3.10. Proposition: *Let f, g be measurable functions. Then each of the sets $\{x \in X \mid f(x) > g(x)\}, \{x \in X \mid \{f(x) \leq g(x)\}, \{x \in X \mid f(x) < g(x)\}, \{x \in X \mid f(x) \geq g(x)\}$ and $\{x \in X \mid f(x) = g(x)\} \in \mathcal{S}$.*

Proof: Since f, g are measurable, $\forall \ c \in \mathbb{R}$, the sets $\{x \in X \mid f(x) > c\}$, $\{x \in X \mid g(x) > c\} \in \mathcal{S}$. Note that for $x \in X$, $f(x) > g(x)$ iff there exists a rational r such that $f(x) > r > g(x)$. Hence

$$
\begin{aligned}
\{x \in X \mid f(x) > g(x)\} &= \bigcup_{r \in \mathbb{Q}} \{x \in X \mid f(x) > r > g(x)\} \\
&= \bigcup_{r \in \mathbb{Q}} (\{x \in X \mid f(x) > r\} \cap \{x \in X \mid r > g(x)\}).
\end{aligned}
$$

Since f, g are measurable, $\{x \in X \mid f(x) > r\}, \{x \in X \mid r > g(x)\} \in \mathcal{S}$ for every r. Thus the right side in the above equality, being a countable union of sets from $\mathcal{S}$, implies that $\{x \in X \mid f(x) > g(x)\} \in \mathcal{S}$. Interchanging f and g, we get $\{x \in X \mid f(x) < g(x)\} \in \mathcal{S}$. Taking complements, we have $\{x \in X \mid f(x) \geq g(x)\}, \{x \in X \mid f(x) \leq g(x)\} \in \mathcal{S}$. Finally,

$$\{x \in X \mid f(x) = g(x)\} = \{x \in X \mid f(x) \geq g(x)\} \cap \{x \in X \mid f(x) \leq g(X)\}$$

implies that $\{x \in X \mid f(x) = g(x)\} \in \mathcal{S}$. ■

5.3.11. Proposition: *Let $f, g : X \to \mathbb{R}^*$ be measurable functions and let $\beta \in \mathbb{R}^*$ be arbitrary. Let*

$$A := \{x \in X \mid f(x) = +\infty, g(X) = -\infty\} \cup \{x \in X \mid f(x) = -\infty, g(x) = +\infty\}.$$

Define $\forall\, x \in X$

$$
(f + g)(x) := \begin{cases} f(x) + g(x) & \text{if } x \notin A, \\ \beta & \text{if } x \in A. \end{cases}
$$

Then $f + g : X \to \mathbb{R}^*$ is a well-defined measurable function.

Proof: Clearly $f + g$ is well-defined and $A \in \mathcal{S}$. For any $c \in \mathbb{R}$,

$$
\{x \in X \mid (f + g)(x) > c\} \cap A = \begin{cases} A & \text{if } \beta > c, \\ \emptyset & \text{if } \beta \leq c. \end{cases}
$$

Thus $\{x \in X \mid (f + g)(x) > c\} \cap A \in \mathcal{S}$. Also by examples 5.3.9 (i), (ii),

$$\{x \in X \mid (f + g)(x) > c\} \cap A^c = \{x \in X \mid f(x) > c - g(x)\} \cap A^c \in \mathcal{S}.$$

Hence $\{x \in X \mid (f + g)(x) > c\} \in \mathcal{S}$. ■

5.3.12. Proposition: *Let $f : X \longrightarrow \mathbb{R}^*$ be measurable and let $\Phi : \mathbb{R}^* \longrightarrow \mathbb{R}^*$ be such that $\mathbb{R} \cap \{x \in \mathbb{R}^* \mid \Phi(x) \geq \alpha\} \in \mathcal{B}_{\mathbb{R}}, \, \forall\, \alpha \in \mathbb{R}$. Then $\Phi \circ f$ is also measurable.*

Proof: Let $\alpha \in \mathbb{R}$. Let

$$A_+ := \{x \in \mathbb{R}^* \mid \Phi(x) \geq \alpha\} \cap \{+\infty\} \quad \text{and} \quad A_- := \{x \in \mathbb{R}^* \mid \Phi(x) \geq \alpha\} \cap \{-\infty\}.$$

Since f is measurable, it is easy to check that both $f^{-1}(A_+)$ and $f^{-1}(A_)\in\mathcal{S}$. Further

$$(\Phi\circ f)^{-1}[\alpha,+\infty]$$
$$= f^{-1}(\Phi^{-1}[\alpha,+\infty])$$
$$= f^{-1}[(\{x\in\mathbb{R}^*\mid\Phi(x)\geq\alpha\}\cap\mathbb{R})\cup A_+\cup A_-]$$
$$= f^{-1}(\{x\in\mathbb{R}^*\mid\Phi(x)\geq\alpha\}\cap\mathbb{R})\cup f^{-1}(A_+)\cup f^{-1}(A_-).$$

Now it follows from the given hypothesis and the above observations that $(\Phi\circ f)^{-1}[\alpha,+\infty]\in\mathcal{S}$. Hence by proposition 5.3.6, $(\Phi\circ f)$ is measurable. ∎

•5.3.13. Exercise: Let f and $g:X\longrightarrow\mathbb{R}^*$ be measurable functions, p and $\alpha\in\mathbb{R}$ with $p>1$, and let m be any positive integer. Use proposition 5.3.12 to prove the following:

(i) $f+\alpha$ is a measurable function.

(ii) Let β and $\gamma\in\mathbb{R}^*$ be arbitrary. Define for $x\in\mathbb{R}$,

$$f^m(x):=\begin{cases}(f(x))^m & \text{if } f(x)\in\mathbb{R}, \\ \beta & \text{if } f(x)=+\infty, \\ \gamma & \text{if } f(x)=-\infty.\end{cases}$$

Then f^m is a measurable function.

(iii) Let $|f|^p$ be defined similarly to f^m, where p is a nonnegative real number. Then $|f|^p$ is a measurable function.

(iv) Let $\beta,\gamma,\delta\in\mathbb{R}^*$ be arbitrary. Define for $x\in\mathbb{R}$,

$$(1/f)(x):=\begin{cases}1/f(x) & \text{if } f(x)\notin\{0,+\infty,-\infty\}, \\ \beta & \text{if } f(x)=0, \\ \gamma & \text{if } f(x)=-\infty, \\ \delta & \text{if } f(x)=+\infty.\end{cases}$$

Then $1/f$ is a measurable function.

(v) Let $\beta\in\mathbb{R}^*$ be arbitrary and A be as in proposition 5.3.11. Define for $x\in\mathbb{R}$,

$$(fg)(x):=\begin{cases}f(x)g(x) & \text{if } x\notin A, \\ \beta & \text{if } x\in A.\end{cases}$$

Then fg is a measurable function.

5.3.14. Proposition: *Let $f_n:X\longrightarrow\mathbb{R}^*,n=1,2,\ldots,$ be measurable functions. Then each of the functions $\sup_n f_n$, $\inf_n f_n$, $\limsup_{n\to\infty} f_n$ and $\liminf_{n\to\infty} f_n$ is a measurable function. In particular, if $\{f_n\}_{n\geq 1}$ converges to f, then f is a measurable function.*

Proof: Let $\alpha \in \mathbb{R}$. Then

$$(\sup_n f_n)^{-1}[-\infty, \alpha] = \{x \in X \mid \sup_n f_n(x) \leq \alpha\}$$

$$= \bigcap_{n=1}^{\infty} \{x \in X \mid f_n(x) \leq \alpha\}$$

and

$$(\inf_n f_n)^{-1}[\alpha, +\infty] = \{x \in X \mid \inf_n f_n(x) \geq \alpha\}$$

$$= \bigcap_{n=1}^{\infty} \{x \in X \mid f_n(x) \geq \alpha\}.$$

Since each f_n is measurable, by proposition 5.3.6 $\{x \in X \mid f_n(x) \leq \alpha\}, \{x \in X \mid f_n(x) \geq \alpha\} \in \mathcal{S}$. Thus the above equalities show that $\inf_n f_n$ and $\sup_n f_n$ are measurable. Using this, clearly $\limsup_{n \to \infty} f_n$, $\liminf_{n \to \infty} f_n$ are measurable. ■

5.3.15. Corollary: *Let $\{f_n\}_{n \geq 1}$ be a sequence in $\mathbb{L}^+$. Then each of the functions $\sup_n f_n, \inf_n f_n, \limsup_{n \to \infty} f_n$ and $\liminf_{n \to \infty} f_n$ is in $\mathbb{L}^+$. In particular, if $\lim_{n \to \infty} f_n =: f$ exists, then $f \in \mathbb{L}^+$.*

Proof: Since $f_n \in \mathbb{L}^+ \subseteq \mathbb{L}$, by the above proposition each of $\sup_n f_n$, $\inf_n f_n$, $\limsup_{n \to \infty} f_n, \liminf_{n \to \infty} f_n$ and f is in $\mathbb{L}$. Further, since all of them are nonnegative, it follows that they are in $\mathbb{L}^+$. ■

●**5.3.16. Exercise:**

(i) Let $f : X \to \mathbb{R}^*$ be $\mathcal{S}$-measurable. Show that $|f|$ is also $\mathcal{S}$-measurable. Give an example to show that the converse need not be true.

(ii) Let $(X, \mathcal{S})$ be a measurable space such that for every function $f : X \longrightarrow \mathbb{R}$, f is $\mathcal{S}$-measurable iff $|f|$ is $\mathcal{S}$-measurable. Show that $\mathcal{S} = \mathcal{P}(X)$.

5.3.17. Exercise: Let $f_n \in \mathbb{L}$, $n = 1, 2, \ldots$. Show that the sets $\{x \in X \mid \{f_n(x)\}_n \text{ is convergent}\}$ and $\{x \in X \mid \{f_n(x)\}_{n \geq 1} \text{is Cauchy}\}$ belong to $\mathcal{S}$.

Recall that in theorem 5.2.7 we analyzed the limit of $\int f_n d\mu$ for an increasing sequence of nonnegative measurable functions. We analyze next the behavior of $\int f_n d\mu$ when $\{f_n\}_{n \geq 1}$ is not necessarily an increasing sequence of nonnegative measurable functions.

5.3.18. Theorem (Fatou's lemma): *Let* $\{f_n\}_{n\geq 1}$ *be a sequence of nonnegative measurable functions. Then*

$$\int \left(\liminf_{n\to\infty} f_n\right) d\mu \;\leq\; \liminf_{n\to\infty} \int f_n d\mu.$$

Proof: By definition,

$$\liminf_{n\to\infty} f_n := \sup_{n\geq 1}\{\inf_{k\geq n} f_k\}.$$

We have already shown in corollary 5.3.15 that $\liminf_{n\to\infty} f_n \in \mathbb{L}^+$. Further, $\{\inf_{k\geq n} f_k\}_{n\geq 1}$ is an increasing sequence in $\mathbb{L}^+$, converging to $\liminf_{n\to\infty} f_n$. Thus by the monotone convergence theorem (5.2.7), we have

$$\int \left(\liminf_{n\to\infty} f_n\right) d\mu \;=\; \lim_{n\to\infty} \int \left(\inf_{k\geq n} f_k\right) d\mu. \qquad (5.3)$$

Also, $(\inf_{k\geq n} f_k) \leq f_n \; \forall\, n$. Using proposition 5.2.6, we have

$$\int \left(\inf_{k\geq n} f_k\right) d\mu \;\leq\; \int f_n d\mu \;\; \forall\, n.$$

Hence

$$\lim_{n\to\infty} \int \left(\inf_{k\geq n} f_k\right) \;\leq\; \liminf_{n\to\infty} \int f_n d\mu. \qquad (5.4)$$

The required inequality follows from (5.3) and (5.4). ∎

5.3.19. Exercise:

(i) Give an example to show that strict inequality can occur in Fatou's lemma.

(ii) Let $\{f_n\}_{n\geq 1}$ be a sequence of functions in $\mathbb{L}^+$ and let $\sum_{n=1}^{\infty} f_n(x) =: f(x), x \in X$. Show that $f \in \mathbb{L}^+$ and

$$\int f d\mu \;=\; \sum_{n=1}^{\infty} \int f_n d\mu.$$

5.3.20. Exercise: Show that each of the functions $f : \mathbb{R} \longrightarrow \mathbb{R}$ defined below is $\mathcal{L}$-measurable, and compute $\int f d\lambda$:

(i) $f(x) := \begin{cases} 0 & \text{if } x \leq 0, \\ 1/x & \text{if } x > 0. \end{cases}$

(ii) $f(x) := \chi_{\mathbb{Q}}(x)$, the indicator function of $\mathbb{Q}$, the set of rationals.

(iii) $f(x) := \begin{cases} 0 & \text{if} \quad x > 1 \text{ or } x < 0 \text{ or } x \in [0,1] \text{ and } x \text{ is rational,} \\ n & \text{if} \quad x \text{ is an irrational, } 0 < x < 1 \text{ and in the decimal} \\ & \text{expansion of } x, \text{ the first nonzero entry is at the} \\ & (n+1)^{\text{th}} \text{ place.} \end{cases}$

5.3.21. Exercise: Let $f, g \in \mathbb{L}^+$ with $f \geq g$. Show that $(f - g) \in \mathbb{L}^+$ and $\int f d\mu \geq \int g d\mu$. Can you conclude that

$$\int (f - g) d\mu = \int f d\mu - \int g d\mu?$$

5.3.22. Exercise: Let $f, f_n \in \mathbb{L}^+$, $n = 1, 2, \ldots$, be such that $0 \leq f_n \leq f$. If $\lim_{n \to \infty} f_n(x) = f(x)$, can you deduce that

$$\int f d\mu = \lim_{n \to \infty} \int f_n d\mu?$$

5.3.23. Exercise: Let $f \in \mathbb{L}$. For $x \in X$ and $n \geq 1$, define

$$f_n(x) := \begin{cases} f(x) & \text{if} \quad |f(x)| \leq n, \\ n & \text{if} \quad f(x) > n, \\ -n & \text{if} \quad f(x) < -n. \end{cases}$$

Prove the following:

(i) $f_n \in \mathbb{L}$ and $|f_n(x)| \leq n \ \forall \, n$ and $\forall \, x \in X$.

(ii) $\lim_{n \to \infty} f_n(x) = f(x) \ \forall \, x \in X$.

(iii) $|f_n(x)| := \min\{|f_n(x)|, n\} := (|f| \wedge n)(x)$ is an element of $\mathbb{L}^+$ and

$$\lim_{n \to \infty} \int |f_n| d\mu = \int |f| d\mu.$$

5.3.24. Note: For $f \in \mathbb{L}$, the sequence $\{f_n\}_{n \geq 1}$ as defined in exercise 5.3.23 is called the **truncation sequence** of f. The truncation sequence is useful in proving results about functions in the class $\mathbb{L}$. See for example, proposition 5.4.6.

5.3.25. Exercise: Let $f \in \mathbb{L}$ and

$$\nu(E) := \mu\{x \in X \mid f(x) \in E\}, \ E \in \mathcal{B}_{\mathbb{R}}.$$

Show that ν is a measure on $(\mathbb{R}, \mathcal{B}_{\mathbb{R}})$. Further, if $g : \mathbb{R} \longrightarrow \mathbb{R}$ is any nonnegative $\mathcal{B}_{\mathbb{R}}$-measurable function, i.e., $g^{-1}(A) \in \mathcal{B}_{\mathbb{R}} \ \forall \, A \in \mathcal{B}_{\mathbb{R}}$, then $g \circ f \in \mathbb{L}$ and

$$\int g \, d\nu = \int (g \circ f) \, d\mu.$$

The measure ν is usually denoted by μf^{-1} and is called the **distribution** of the measurable function f.

5.3.26. Exercise: Let $f \in \mathbb{L}^+$ be a bounded function, say $f(x) \le N \ \forall \, x \in X$ and for some $N \in \mathbb{N}$. Show that

$$\int f \, d\mu = \lim_{n \to \infty} \sum_{k=1}^{N2^n} \frac{k-1}{2^n} \, \mu \left\{ x \mid \frac{k-1}{2^n} \le f(x) < \frac{k}{2^n} \right\}. \qquad (5.5)$$

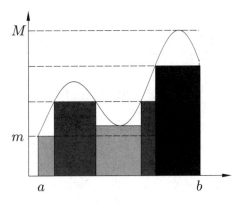

Figure 15: Area below the curve $y = f(x)$ from inside

Note that here $\forall \, n \in \mathbb{N}$ we are taking the partition $\{0, 1/2^n, 2/2^n, \dots, N\}$ of the range of f and using it to induce the measurable partition P_n of the domain $|X|$ of f, given by

$$\{X_k^n \mid 1 \le k \le N2^n\}, \quad \text{where } X_k^n := f^{-1}[(k-1)/2^n, k/2^n).$$

Using this partition P_n, we form the sums on the right hand side of (5.5), approximating the area below the curve $y = f(x)$ from 'inside' (Figure 15). Thus in our integral we use partitions of the range, whereas in Riemann integration we use partitions of the domain. In the words of H. Lebesgue, the situation is similar to the problem of finding the total amount in a cash box containing say n coins, the ith coin being of denomination $\alpha_i, 1 \le i \le n$. One method of finding the total amount in the box is to add the value of each coin, i.e., the sum $\sum_{i=1}^{n} \alpha_i$. The other method is to separate out coins of similar denominations. If there are k_j coins of denominations α_j, then the total amount is $\sum_j k_j \alpha_j$.

• **5.3.27. Exercise:** Let $(X, \mathcal{S}, \mu)$ be a measure space and let $(X, \bar{\mathcal{S}}, \bar{\mu})$ be its completion (see theorem 3.11.8). Let $\overline{f} : X \longrightarrow \mathbb{R}$ be an $\bar{\mathcal{S}}$-measurable function. Show that there exists an $\mathcal{S}$-measurable function $f : X \longrightarrow \mathbb{R}$ such that $\overline{f}(x) = f(x)$ for a.e. $x(\mu)$.

(Hint: Use theorem 3.11.8 and proposition 5.3.6.)

5.3.28. Proposition: *Let $(X, \mathcal{S})$ be a measurable space and let $f : X \longrightarrow \mathbb{R}^*$ be $\mathcal{S}$-measurable. Let μ be a measure on $(X, \mathcal{S})$. Let $g : X \longrightarrow \mathbb{R}^*$ be such that $\{x \in X \mid f(x) \neq g(x)\}$ is a μ-null set. If $(X, \mathcal{S}, \mu)$ is a complete measure space, then g is also $\mathcal{S}$-measurable.*

Proof: To prove that g is $\mathcal{S}$-measurable we have to show that $\forall\, t \in \mathbb{R}$, $g^{-1}[t, \infty] \in \mathcal{S}$ (see proposition 5.3.6). Let

$$N := \{x \in X \mid f(x) \neq g(x)\}.$$

By the given hypothesis, N is a μ-null set, i.e., $N \subseteq A \in \mathcal{S}$ with $\mu(A) = 0$. But then $\mu^*(N) = 0$, and since $(X, \mathcal{S}, \mu)$ is complete, $N \in \mathcal{S}$. Further, by the same reasoning, if $E \subset N$, then $E \in \mathcal{S}$. Now for $t \in \mathbb{R}$ fixed,

$$g^{-1}[t, \infty] = (g^{-1}[t, \infty] \cap N) \cup (g^{-1}[t, \infty] \cap N^c).$$

Since $g^{-1}[t, \infty] \cap N \subseteq N$, we have $g^{-1}[t, \infty] \cap N \in \mathcal{S}$. Also, since f is also $\mathcal{S}$-measurable,

$$g^{-1}[t, \infty] \cap N^c = f^{-1}[t, \infty] \cap N^c \in \mathcal{S}.$$

Hence $g^{-1}[t, \infty] \in \mathcal{S}$. ∎

5.3.29. Exercise: Let $(X, \mathcal{S}, \mu)$ be a complete measure space and $\{f_n\}_{n \geq 1}$ be a sequence of $\mathcal{S}$-measurable functions on X. Let f be a function on X such that $f(x) = \lim_{n \to \infty} f_n(x)$ for a.e. $x(\mu)$. Show that f is $\mathcal{S}$-measurable.

5.4. Integrable functions

Given a measure space $(X, \mathcal{S}, \mu)$ in section 5.3, we defined $\int f d\mu$, the integral for functions $f \in \mathbb{L}^+$, i.e., $f : X \longrightarrow \mathbb{R}^*$, f nonnegative measurable. If f is measurable, but not necessarily nonnegative, we can write $f = f^+ - f^-$. Since both f^+ and f^- are nonnegative measurable, $\int f^+ d\mu$ and $\int f^- d\mu$ are defined. Thus it is reasonable (as the integral is expected to be linear) to define the integral of f to be $\int f d\mu := \int f^+ d\mu - \int f^- d\mu$. The problem can arise in the case $\int f^- d\mu = \int f^+ d\mu = +\infty$. To overcome this difficulty, we introduce the following definition:

5.4.1. Definition: A measurable function $f : X \longrightarrow \mathbb{R}^*$ is said to be μ-**integrable** if both $\int f^+ d\mu$ and $\int f^- d\mu$ are finite, and in that case we define the **integral** of f to be

$$\int f d\mu := \int f^+ d\mu - \int f^- d\mu.$$

We denote by $L_1(X, \mathcal{S}, \mu)$ (or simply by $L_1(X)$ or $L_1(\mu)$) the space of all μ-integrable functions on X.

•5.4.2. Exercise: For $f \in \mathbb{L}$, prove the following:

(i) $f \in L_1(\mu)$ iff $|f| \in L_1(\mu)$. Further, in either case

$$\left| \int f d\mu \right| \leq \int |f| d\mu.$$

(ii) If $f \in L_1(\mu)$, then $|f(x)| < +\infty$ for a.e. $x(\mu)$.

The properties of the space $L_1(X, \mathcal{S}, \mu)$ and of the map $f \longmapsto \int f d\mu$, $f \in L_1(X, \mathcal{S}, \mu)$, are given in the next proposition.

5.4.3. Proposition: *For $f, g \in \mathbb{L}$ and $a, b \in \mathbb{R}$, the following hold:*

(i) *If $|f(x)| \leq g(x)$ for a.e. $x(\mu)$ and $g \in L_1(\mu)$, then $f \in L_1(\mu)$.*

(ii) *If $f(x) = g(x)$ for a.e. $x(\mu)$ and $f \in L_1(\mu)$, then $g \in L_1(\mu)$ and*

$$\int f d\mu = \int g d\mu.$$

(iii) *If $f \in L_1(\mu)$, then $af \in L_1(\mu)$ and*

$$\int (af) d\mu = a \int f d\mu.$$

(iv) *If f and $g \in L_1(\mu)$, then $f + g \in L_1(\mu)$ and*

$$\int (f + g) d\mu = \int f d\mu + \int g d\mu.$$

(v) *If $f, g \in L_1(\mu)$, then $(af + bg) \in L_1(\mu)$ and*

$$\int (af + bg) d\mu = a \int f d\mu + b \int g d\mu.$$

Proof: (i) Since $|f(x)| \leq g(x)$ for a.e. $x(\mu)$, it is easy to check that

$$f^+(x) \leq |g(x)| \text{ for a.e. } x(\mu) \text{ and } f^-(x) \leq |g(x)| \text{ for a.e. } x(\mu).$$

Hence

$$\int f^+ d\mu \leq \int |g| d\mu < +\infty \text{ and } \int f^- d\mu \leq \int |g| d\mu < +\infty.$$

Thus $f \in L_1(\mu)$.

(ii) Since $f(x) = g(x)$ for a.e. $x(\mu)$, it is easy to see that

$$f^+(x) = g^+(x) \text{ for a.e. } x(\mu) \text{ and } f^-(x) = g^-(x) \text{ a.e. } x(\mu).$$

Using proposition 5.2.6,

$$\int g^+ d\mu = \int f^+ d\mu < +\infty \text{ and } \int g^- d\mu = \int f^- d\mu < +\infty.$$

Thus $g \in L_1(\mu)$ and

$$\int g d\mu = \int f d\mu.$$

(iii) is easy and is left as an exercise. To prove (iv), let $f_1, f_2 \in L_1(\mu)$. We note that $|f_1 + f_2| \le |f_1| + |f_2|$, and hence, by proposition 5.2.6(i),

$$\int |f_1 + f_2| d\mu \le \int |f_1| d\mu + \int |f_2| d\mu < +\infty.$$

Thus $(f_1 + f_2) \in L_1(\mu)$ by exercise 5.4.2. Also

$$(f_1 + f_2)^+ - (f_1 + f_2)^- = f_1 + f_2 = f_1^+ + f_2^+ - f_1^- - f_2^-.$$

By exercise 5.4.2, all the functions involved are finite a.e. (μ). Thus

$$(f_1 + f_2)^+ + f_1^- + f_2^- = f_1^+ + f_2^+ + (f_1 + f_2)^- \text{ a.e. } (\mu).$$

Since both sides of the above equality represent nonnegative measurable function, using proposition 5.2.6 we have

$$\int (f_1 + f_2)^+ d\mu + \int f_1^- d\mu + \int f_2^- d\mu = \int f_1^+ d\mu + \int f_2^+ d\mu + \int (f_1 + f_2)^- d\mu.$$

Since all the terms in the above equality are finite, we get

$$\begin{aligned}
\int (f_1 + f_2) d\mu &= \int (f_1 + f_2)^+ d\mu - \int (f_1 + f_2)^- d\mu \\
&= \int f_1^+ d\mu - \int f_1^- d\mu + \int f_2^+ d\mu - \int f_2^- d\mu \\
&= \int f_1 d\mu + \int f_2 d\mu.
\end{aligned}$$

This proves (iv). The proof of (v) follows from (iii) and (iv). ∎

●**5.4.4. Exercise:**

(i) Let $\mu(X) < +\infty$ and let $f \in \mathbb{L}$ be such that $|f(x)| \le M$ for a.e. $x(\mu)$ and for some M. Show that $f \in L_1(\mu)$.

(ii) Let $f \in L_1(\mu)$ and $E \in \mathcal{S}$. Show that $\chi_E f \in L_1(\mu)$, where

$$\int_E f d\mu := \int \chi_E f d\mu.$$

Further, if $E, F \in \mathcal{S}$ are disjoint sets, show that

$$\int_{E \cup F} f d\mu = \int_E f d\mu + \int_F f d\mu.$$

(iii) Let $f \in L_1(\mu)$ and $E_i \in \mathcal{S}, i \geq 1$, be such that $E_i \cap E_j = \emptyset$ for $i \neq j$. Show that the series $\sum_{i=1}^{\infty} \int_{E_i} f d\mu$ is absolutely convergent, and if $E := \bigcup_{i=1}^{\infty} E_i$, then

$$\sum_{i=1}^{\infty} \int_{E_i} f d\mu = \int_E f d\mu.$$

•5.4.5. Exercise:

(i) For every $\epsilon > 0$ and $f \in L_1(\mu)$, show that

$$\mu \{ x \in X \mid |f(x)| \geq \epsilon \} \leq \frac{1}{\epsilon} \int |f| d\mu < \infty.$$

This is called **Chebyshev's inequality**.

(ii) Let $f \in L_1(\mu)$, and let there exist $M > 0$ such that

$$\left| \frac{1}{\mu(E)} \int_E f d\mu \right| \leq M$$

for every $E \in \mathcal{S}$ with $0 < \mu(E) < \infty$. Show that $|f(x)| \leq M$ for a.e. $x(\mu)$.

5.4.6. Proposition: *Let* $f \in L_1(\mu)$. *For every* $E \in \mathcal{S}$, *let*

$$\nu(E) := \int \chi_E |f| d\mu \quad and \quad \tilde{\nu}(E) := \int \chi_E f d\mu.$$

Then the following hold:

  (i) *If* $\mu(E) = 0$, *then* $\tilde{\nu}(E) = 0$.
  (ii) *If* $\mu(E) = 0$, *then* $\nu(E) = 0$.
  (iii) $\lim_{\mu(E) \to 0} \nu(E) = 0$, *i.e., given any* $\epsilon > 0$, *there exists* $\delta > 0$ *such that* $\nu(E) < \epsilon$ *whenever, for* $E \in \mathcal{S}, \mu(E) < \delta$.
  (iv) *If* $\tilde{\nu}(E) = 0 \ \forall \ E$, *then* $f(x) = 0$ *for a.e.* $x(\mu)$ *on* E.

Proof: (i) and (ii) are easy, and are left as exercises.

To prove (iii), let us first assume that $f \in L_1(\mu)$ is also bounded, say $|f(x)| \leq M \ \forall \ x \in X$. Then for a given $\epsilon > 0$, any $0 < \delta < \epsilon/M$ will satisfy the required claim. For the general case, we consider $f_n := |f| \wedge n$ (as defined in exercise 5.3.23). Then it follows from the monotone convergence theorem that

$$\int |f| d\mu = \lim_{n \to 0} \int f_n d\mu.$$

Thus, given $\epsilon > 0$, we can choose n_0 such that

$$\int (|f| - f_{n_0}) d\mu \ < \ \epsilon/2.$$

Thus $\forall\, E \in \mathcal{S}$,

$$
\begin{aligned}
\nu(E) \ &= \ \int \chi_E |f| \, d\mu \\
&= \ \int \chi_E (|f| - f_{n_0}) \, d\mu + \int \chi_E f_{n_0} \, d\mu \\
&\leq \ \int (|f| - f_{n_0}) \, d\mu + n_0 \, \mu(E) \\
&\leq \ \epsilon/2 + n_0 \, \mu(E).
\end{aligned}
$$

If we choose δ such that $n_0 \delta < \epsilon/2$, then for $\mu(E) < \delta$ we will have $\nu(E) < \epsilon$. This proves (iii).

To prove (iv), let $X^+ = \{x \in X \mid f(x) \geq 0\}$. Then, by the given hypothesis, $\forall\, E \in \mathcal{S}$,

$$\int_E f^+ \, d\mu \ = \ \int_{E \cap X^+} f \, d\mu \ = \ 0,$$

and hence by proposition 5.3.3, $f^+(x) = 0$ for a.e. $x(\mu)$. Similarly, $f^-(x) = 0$ for a.e. $x(\mu)$. Thus for $A := \{x : f^+(x) \neq 0\}$ and $B = \{x : f^-(x) \neq 0\}$, we have $\mu(A) = \mu(B) = 0$. Since $\{x | f(x) \neq 0\} \subseteq A \cup B$, we have $\mu(\{x | f(x) \neq 0\}) = 0$, i.e., $f(x) = 0$ for a.e. $x(\mu)$. ∎

5.4.7. Remark: It is easy to see that (iii) in the above proposition implies (ii). In fact (ii) also implies (iii). To see this, suppose (iii) does not hold. Then there exist an $\epsilon > 0$ and sets $E_n \in \mathcal{S}$, $n \geq 1$, such that $\mu(E_n) < 2^{-n}$ but $\nu(E_n) \geq \epsilon$. Let $A_n = \bigcup_{k=n}^{\infty} E_k$. Then $\{A_n\}_{n \geq 1}$ is a decreasing sequence in $\mathcal{S}$ and $\mu(A_n) \leq \mu(E_n) \leq 2^{-n}$. Thus by theorem 3.6.3,

$$\mu \left(\bigcap_{n=1}^{\infty} A_n \right) = \lim_{n \to \infty} \mu(A_n) = 0.$$

On the other hand, $\mu(A_n) \geq \mu(E_n) \geq \epsilon$, $\forall\, \epsilon$, contradicting (ii).

•**5.4.8. Exercise:** Let λ be the Lebesgue measure on $\mathbb{R}$, and let $f \in L_1(\mathbb{R}, \mathcal{L}, \lambda)$ be such that

$$\int_{(-\infty, x)} f(t) d\lambda(t) = 0, \ \ \forall\, x \in \mathbb{R}.$$

Show that $f(x) = 0$ for a.e. $(\lambda) x \in \mathbb{R}$.

We prove next the most frequently used theorem which allows us to interchange the operations of integration and limits.

5.4.9. Theorem (Lebesgue's dominated convergence theorem): *Let* $\{f_n\}_{n\geq 1}$ *be a sequence of measurable functions and let* $g \in L_1(\mu)$ *be such that* $\forall n, |f_n(x)| \leq g(x)$ *for a.e.* $x(\mu)$. *Let* $\{f_n(x)\}_{n\geq 1}$ *converge to* $f(x)$ *for a.e.* $x(\mu)$. *Then the following hold:*

(i) $f \in L_1(\mu)$.

(ii) $\int f\,d\mu = \lim_{n\to\infty} \int f_n\,d\mu$.

(iii) $\lim_{n\to\infty} \int |f_n - f|\,d\mu = 0$.

Proof: Let us first suppose that $|f_n(x)| \leq g(x)$ and $f(x) = \lim_{n\to\infty} f_n(x)$ for every $x \in X$. Clearly, since $|f_n(x)| \leq g(x)\ \forall\ x, f_n \in L_1(\mu)$ for every n. Also $|f(x)| \leq g(x)\ \forall\ x \in X$ and hence $f \in L_1(\mu)$. We only have to show that $\int f d\mu = \lim_{n\to\infty} \int f_n d\mu$. (Since the only tools available to us are the monotone convergence theorem - which obviously we cannot use here - and Fatou's lemma (theorem 5.3.18), we should try to get a sequence of nonnegative functions). For this, we consider the sequence $\{g - f_n\}_{n\geq 1}$. Clearly, $g - f_n \in \mathbb{L}^+$ for every n, and by Fatou's lemma,

$$\liminf_{n\to\infty} \int (g - f_n)d\mu \ \geq\ \int (\lim_{n\to\infty}(g - f_n))d\mu = \int (g - f)d\mu.$$

Thus

$$\limsup_{n\to\infty} \int f_n d\mu \ \leq\ \int f d\mu. \tag{5.6}$$

Similarly, $\{g + f_n\}_{n\geq 1}$ is a sequence in $\mathbb{L}^+$, and by Fatou's lemma again,

$$\liminf_{n\to\infty} \int (g + f_n)d\mu \geq \int (g + f)d\mu.$$

Thus

$$\liminf_{n\to\infty} \int f_n d\mu \ \geq\ \int f d\mu. \tag{5.7}$$

The inequalities (5.6) and (5.7) together imply that

$$\int f d\mu \ =\ \lim_{n\to\infty} \int f_n d\mu.$$

To prove the theorem in the general case, we put

$$N := \{x \in X \mid |f_n(x)| > g(x)\ \text{for some}\ n\} \cup \{x \in X \mid f(x) \neq \lim_{n\to\infty} f_n(x)\}.$$

Then $N \in \mathcal{S}$ and $\mu(N) = 0$. Since $f_n \in \mathbb{L}$ and $\lim_{n\to\infty} f_n(x) = f(x)$ for a.e. $x(\mu)$, by exercise 5.3.29, $f \in \mathbb{L}$. Further, by our earlier case applied to the sequence $\{\chi_{N^c} f_n\}_{n\geq 1}$, we have

$$\int_{N^c} f d\mu \ =\ \lim_{n\to\infty} \int_{N^c} f_n d\mu.$$

Also

$$\int_N f d\mu = \int_N f_n d\mu = 0, \ \forall \, n.$$

Thus by exercise 5.4.4, we have

$$\int f d\mu = \lim_{n \to \infty} \int f_n d\mu.$$

This proves (ii).

Finally, (iii) follows from (ii) and the fact that $\forall \, n, \ |f_n - f| \le 2g$. ∎

We state another version of this theorem, which is applicable to series of functions.

5.4.10. Corollary: *Let $\{f_n\}_{n \ge 1}$ be a sequence of functions in $L_1(\mu)$ such that $\sum_{n=1}^{\infty} \int |f_n| d\mu < +\infty$. Then $f(x) := \sum_{n=1}^{\infty} f_n(x)$ exists for a.e. $x(\mu)$, $f \in L_1(\mu)$ and*

$$\int f d\mu = \sum_{n=1}^{\infty} \int f_n d\mu.$$

Proof: Let $\Phi(x) := \sum_{n=1}^{\infty} |f_n(x)|, \ x \in X$. Then by the monotone convergence theorem (5.2.7), $\Phi \in \mathbb{L}^+$ and

$$\int \Phi(x) d\mu = \lim_{k \to \infty} \sum_{n=1}^{k} \left(\int |f_n| d\mu \right) = \sum_{n=1}^{\infty} \left(\int |f_n| d\mu \right) < +\infty.$$

Hence $\Phi \in L_1(\mu)$ and, by exercise 5.4.2, $|\Phi(x)| < +\infty$ for a.e. $x(\mu)$. Thus $\sum_{n=1}^{\infty} |f_n(x)| < +\infty$ for a.e. $x(\mu)$. Let $f(x) := \sum_{n=1}^{\infty} f_n(x)$ if the right hand side is finite, and $f(x) := 0$ otherwise. Clearly, $f \in \mathbb{L}$ and $|f(x)| \le \Phi(x)$ for a.e. $x(\mu)$. Thus $f \in L_1(\mu)$. Since

$$\left| \sum_{k=1}^{n} f_k(x) \right| \le \Phi(x)$$

for every n and for a.e. $x(\mu)$, by the dominated convergence theorem (5.4.9),

$$\sum_{n=1}^{\infty} \left(\int f_n d\mu \right) = \lim_{n \to \infty} \left(\int \left(\sum_{1}^{n} f_n \right) d\mu \right) = \int f d\mu. \ ∎$$

An extension of the Lebesgue dominated convergence theorem is given in the next exercise.

5.4.11. Exercise: Let $I \subseteq \mathbb{R}$ be an interval and $\forall \, t \in I$, let $f_t \in \mathbb{L}$. Let $g \in L_1(\mu)$ be such that $\forall \, t, |f_t(x)| \le g(x)$ for a.e. $x(\mu)$. Let $t_0 \in \mathbb{R}^*$ be any accumulation point of I and let $f(x) := \lim_{t \to t_0} f_t(x)$ exist for a.e. $x(\mu)$. Then $f \in L_1(\mu)$ and

$$\int f d\mu = \lim_{t \to t_0} \int f_t(x) d\mu(x).$$

Further, if $\forall\, x$ the function $t \longmapsto f_t(x)$ is continuous, then so is the function $h(t) := \int f_t(x)\, d\mu,\ t \in I$.

(Hint: Apply theorem 5.4.9 to every sequence $t_n \to t_0$.)

As an application of the dominated convergence theorem, we exhibit the possibility of interchanging the order of integration and differentiation in the next theorem.

5.4.12. Theorem: *Let $f_t \in L_1(\mu)$ for every $t \in (a,b) \subseteq \mathbb{R}$. Let $t_0 \in (a,b)$ be such that for a.e. $x(\mu), t \longmapsto f_t(x)$ is differentiable in a neighborhood U of t_0 and there exists a function $g \in L_1(\mu)$ such that $\left| \dfrac{df_t}{dt}(x) \right| \leq g(x)$ for a.e. $x(\mu)$ and for every $t \in U$. Then $\phi(t) := \int f_t(x) d\mu(x)$ is differentiable at t_0 and*

$$\phi'(t_0) = \int \left(\left[\frac{df_t}{dt}(x) \right]_{t_0} \right) d\mu(x).$$

Proof: To show that ϕ is differentiable, let us consider, for $t \neq t_0$,

$$\frac{\phi(t) - \phi(t_0)}{t - t_0} = \int \left(\frac{f_t(x) - f_{t_0}(x)}{t - t_0} \right) d\mu(x).$$

Since

$$\lim_{t \to t_0} \left(\frac{f_t(x) - f_{t_0}(x)}{t - t_0} \right) = \left[\frac{df_t}{dt}(x) \right]_{t=t_0} \quad \text{for a.e. } x(\mu),$$

to be able to apply the dominated convergence theorem and deduce the required claim, we only have to show that for all t in a neighborhood of $t_0, t \neq t_0$, the inequalities

$$\left| \frac{f_t(x) - f_{t_0}(x)}{t - t_0} \right| \leq \tilde{g}(x) \quad \text{for a.e. } x(\mu) \tag{5.8}$$

holds for some $\tilde{g} \in L_1(\mu)$. By the given hypothesis, since $f_t(x)$ is differentiable in a neighborhood U of t_0, by the mean value theorem for derivatives, we have for all fixed $t \in U$,

$$\frac{f_t(x) - f_{t_0}(x)}{t - t_0} = \left[\frac{df_t}{dt}(x) \right]_{t=c}$$

for some real number c between t and t_0. Hence (5.8) holds, for all $t \in U$ if we take $\tilde{g} = g$, the function given by the hypothesis. This completes the proof. ∎

We shall see some more applications of the dominated convergence theorem in the remaining sections. In the next section we look at some special properties of $L_1(X, \mathcal{S}, \mu)$ in the particular case when $X = \mathbb{R}$, $\mathcal{S} = \mathcal{L}$, the σ-algebra of Lebesgue measurable sets, and $\mu = \lambda$, the Lebesgue measure.

The next exercise gives yet another variation of the dominated convergence theorem.

•**5.4.13. Exercise:** Let $\{f_n\}_{n \geq 1}$ and $\{g_n\}_{n \geq 1}$ be sequences of measurable functions such that $|f_n| \leq g_n \ \forall \ n$. Let f and g be measurable functions such that $\lim_{n \to \infty} f_n(x) = f(x)$ for a.e. $x(\mu)$ and $\lim_{n \to \infty} g_n(x) = g(x)$ for a.e. $x(\mu)$. If

$$\lim_{n \to \infty} \int g_n \, d\mu = \int g \, d\mu < +\infty,$$

show that

$$\lim_{n \to \infty} \int f_n \, d\mu = \int f \, d\mu.$$

(Hint: Apply Fatou's lemma to $(g_n - f_n)$ and $(g_n + f_n)$.)

5.4.14. Exercise: Let $\{f_n\}_{n \geq 0}$ be a sequence in $L_1(X, \mathcal{S}, \mu)$. Show that $\left\{ \int |f_n| d\mu \right\}_{n \geq 1}$ converges to $\int |f_0| d\mu$ iff $\left\{ \int |f_n - f_0| d\mu \right\}_{n \geq 1}$ converges to zero. (Hint: Use exercise 5.4.13.)

The following is a variation of the dominated convergence theorem for finite measure spaces.

5.4.15. Theorem (Bounded convergence): *Let $(X, \mathcal{S}, \mu)$ be a finite measure space and $f, f_1, f_2, \ldots$ be measurable functions. Suppose there exists $M > 0$ such that $|f_n(x)| \leq M$ a.e. $x(\mu)$ and $f_n(x) \to f(x)$ a.e. $x(\mu)$. Then $f, f_n \in L_1(X, \mathcal{S}, \mu)$ and*

$$\int f \, d\mu = \lim_{n \to \infty} \int f_n d\mu.$$

Proof: Let $g(x) = M \ \forall \ x \in X$. Then $g \in L_1(X, \mathcal{S}, \mu)$, and the claim follows from theorem 5.4.9. ∎

5.4.16. Exercise: Let $(X, \mathcal{S}, \mu)$ be a finite measure space and $\{f_n\}_{n \geq 1}$ be a sequence in $L_1(\mu)$ such that $f_n \to f$ uniformly. Show that $f \in L_1(\mu)$ and

$$\lim_{n \to \infty} \int |f_n - f| \, d\mu = 0.$$

Can the condition of $\mu(X) < +\infty$ be dropped?

5.4.17. Notes:

(1) The monotone convergence theorem and the dominated convergence theorem (along with its variations and versions) are the most important theorems used for the interchange of integrals and limits.

(2) **Simple function technique:** This is an important technique (similar to the σ-algebra technique) used very often to prove results about integrable and nonnegative measurable functions. Suppose we want to show that a certain claim $(*)$ holds for all integrable functions. Then technique is the following:

(i) Show that $(*)$ holds for nonnegative simple measurable functions.

(ii) Show that $(*)$ holds for nonnegative measurable / integrable functions by approximating them by nonnegative simple measurable functions and using (i).

(iii) Show that $(*)$ holds for integrable functions f, by using (ii) and the fact that for $f \in L_1$, $f = f^+ - f^-$ and both $f^+, f^- \in L_1$.

We give below an illustration of this technique (see also theorem 5.6.2).

5.4.18. Proposition: *Let $(X, \mathcal{S}, \mu)$ be a σ-finite measure space and $f \in L_1(X, \mathcal{S}, \mu)$ be nonnegative. For every $E \in \mathcal{S}$, let*

$$\nu(E) := \int_E f d\mu.$$

Then ν is a finite measure on $\mathcal{S}$. Further, $fg \in L_1(X, \mathcal{S}, \mu)$ for every $g \in L_1(X, \mathcal{S}, \nu)$, and

$$\int f d\nu = \int fg d\mu.$$

Proof: Since f is nonnegative and $\int f d\mu < +\infty$, it follows from proposition 5.2.6(iii) that ν is a finite measure on $\mathcal{S}$. Let $g \in L_1(X, \mathcal{S}, \nu)$. If $g = \chi_E$, for $E \in \mathcal{S}$, then $\nu(E) < +\infty$ and

$$\int \chi_E d\nu = \nu(E) = \int_E f d\mu = \int \chi_E f d\mu.$$

Hence $\chi_E f$ is μ-integrable, and the required equality holds. By linearity of the integrals, it follows that the required claim holds for nonnegative simple measurable functions. If $g \in L_1(X, \mathcal{S}, \nu)$ is nonnegative, by the definition of measurability, there exists a sequence $\{g_n\}_{n\geq 1}$ of nonnegative simple functions increasing to f. Since $g_n \leq f \ \forall n$, we have $g_n \in L_1(\nu)$ by proposition 5.4.3(i), and hence

$$\int g_n d\nu = \int g_n f d\mu.$$

Since $\{g_n f\}_{n \geq 1}$ is a sequence of nonnegative measurable functions increasing to gf, by the monotone convergence theorem,

$$\int g d\nu = \lim_{n \to \infty} \int g_n d\nu$$

$$= \lim_{n \to \infty} \int g_n f d\mu = \int g f d\mu.$$

Thus the required claim holds for nonnegative functions $g \in L_1(X, \mathcal{S}, \nu)$. For general $g \in L_1(X, \mathcal{S}, \nu)$, $g = g^+ - g^-$ implies $g^+, g^- \in L_1(X, \mathcal{S}, \nu)$. Thus the required claim holds for g^+, g^- and hence for g. ∎

5.4.19. Exercise: Let $(X, \mathcal{S})$ be a measurable space and $f : X \longrightarrow \mathbb{R}$ be $\mathcal{S}$-measurable. Prove the following:

(i) $\mathcal{S}_0 := \{f^{-1}(E) \mid E \in \mathcal{B}_{\mathbb{R}}\}$ is the σ-algebra of subsets of X, and $\mathcal{S}_0 \subseteq \mathcal{S}$.

(ii) If $\phi : \mathbb{R} \longrightarrow \mathbb{R}$ is Borel measurable, i.e., $\phi^{-1}(E) \in \mathcal{B}_{\mathbb{R}} \ \forall \ E \in \mathcal{B}_{\mathbb{R}}$, then $\phi \circ f$ is an $\mathcal{S}_0$-measurable function on X.

(iii) If $\psi : X \longrightarrow \mathbb{R}$ is any $\mathcal{S}_0$-measurable function, then there exists a Borel measurable function $\phi : \mathbb{R} \longrightarrow \mathbb{R}$ such that $\psi = \phi \circ f$.
(Hint: Use the simple function technique and note that if ψ is a simple $\mathcal{S}_0$-measurable function, then $\psi = \sum_{i=1}^{n} a_n \chi_{f^{-1}(E_i)}$ for some positive integer n, $a_i \in \mathbb{R}$ for each i, and $E_i \in \mathcal{B}_{\mathbb{R}}$. Thus $\psi = (\sum_{i=1}^{n} a_i \chi_{E_i}) \circ f$.)

5.4.20. Exercise: Let $\{f_n\}_{n \geq 1}$ be a decreasing sequence of nonnegative functions in $L_1(\mu)$ such that $f_n(x) \to f(x)$. Show that

$$\lim_{x \to \infty} \int f_n d\mu = 0 \ \text{ iff } \ f(x) = 0 \ \text{ a.e. } \ x(\mu).$$

5.4.21. Exercise: Let μ, ν be as in proposition 5.4.18. Let $\mathcal{S}_\nu$ denote the σ-algebra of all ν^*-measurable subsets of X. Prove the following:

(i) $\mathcal{S} \subseteq \mathcal{S}_\nu$.
(Hint: Use the theorem 3.8.4.)

(ii) There exist examples such that $\mathcal{S}$ is a proper subclass of $\mathcal{S}_\nu$. Show that $\mathcal{S} = \mathcal{S}_\nu$ if $\mu^*\{x \in X \mid f(x) = 0\} = 0$.

5.5. The Lebesgue integral and its relation with the Riemann integral

In this section we analyze the integral, as constructed in the previous section, for the particular situation when $X = \mathbb{R}$, $\mathcal{S} = \mathcal{L}$ (the σ-algebra of Lebesgue measurable sets) and $\mu = \lambda$, the Lebesgue measure. The space $L_1(\mathbb{R}, \mathcal{L}, \lambda)$, also denoted by $L_1(\mathbb{R})$ or $L_1(\lambda)$, is called the space of **Lebesgue integrable** functions on $\mathbb{R}$, and $\int f d\lambda$ is called the **Lebesgue integral** of f. For any set $E \in \mathcal{L}$, we write $L_1(E)$ for the space of integrable functions on the measure space $(E, \mathcal{L} \cap E, \lambda)$, where λ is restricted to $\mathcal{L} \cap E$. In the special case when $E = [a, b]$, we would like to show that the new notion of integral for $f \in L_1[a, b]$ indeed extends the notion of Riemann integral. To be precise, we have the following theorem:

5.5.1. Theorem: *Let* $f : [a, b] \longrightarrow \mathbb{R}$ *be a Riemann integrable function. Then* $f \in L_1[a, b]$ *and*

$$\int f d\lambda = \int_a^b f(x)dx.$$

Proof: Since f is bounded and $\lambda([a, b]) < +\infty$, by exercise 5.4.4 $f \in L_1[a, b]$ if f is measurable. To show that f is measurable and $\int f d\lambda = \int_a^b f(x)dx$, we go back to the motivation for the Lebesgue integral (as in section 2.1). Since f is Riemann integrable, using theorem 1.1.5, we can choose a sequence $\{P_n\}_{n \geq 1}$ of partitions of $[a, b]$ such that $\forall\, n, P_{n+1}$ is a refinement of P_n, $\|P_n\| \longrightarrow 0$ as $n \longrightarrow \infty$ and

$$\int_a^b f(x)dx = \lim_{n \to \infty} L(P_n, f) = \lim_{n \to \infty} U(P_n, f).$$

Let $P_n = \{a = x_0 < x_1 < \cdots < x_{k_n} = b\}$. and for every $1 \leq i \leq k_n$, let

$$m_i := \inf \{f(x) \,|\, x_{i-1} \leq x \leq x_i\} \quad \text{and} \quad M_i := \sup \{f(x) \,|\, x_{i-1} \leq x \leq x_i\}.$$

For every $n \geq 1$, and $x \in [a, b]$, let

$$\Psi_n(x) := \sum_{i=1}^n m_i \, \chi_{[x_{i-1}, x_i)}(x)$$

and

$$\Phi_n(x) := \sum_{i=1}^n M_i \, \chi_{[x_{i-1}, x_i)}(x).$$

Then $\forall\, n$ we have $\Psi_n, \Phi_n \in L_1([a, b])$ with

$$\int \Psi_n d\lambda = L(P_n, f) \quad \text{and} \quad \int \Phi_n d\lambda = U(P_n, f).$$

Further,

$$\Psi_n(x) \leq f(x) \leq \Phi_n(x)$$

for $x \in (a, b)$. Since $\forall\, n, P_{n+1}$ is a refinement of P_n, it is easy to see that $\{\Psi_n\}_{n \geq 1}$ is an increasing sequence and $\{\Phi_n\}_{n \geq 1}$ is a decreasing sequence.

Thus the sequence $\{\Phi_n - \Psi_n\}_{n\geq 1}$ is a sequence of nonnegative simple measurable functions, and, by Fatou's lemma (5.3.18),

$$
\begin{aligned}
\int \liminf_{n\to\infty}(\Phi_n - \Psi_n)d\lambda &\leq \liminf_{n\to\infty}\left(\int(\Phi_n - \Psi_n)d\lambda\right) \\
&= \liminf_{n\to\infty}\int \Phi_n d\lambda - \limsup_{n\to\infty}\int \psi_n d\lambda \\
&= \liminf_{n\to\infty} U(P_n, f) - \limsup_{n\to\infty} L(P_n, f) \\
&= 0.
\end{aligned}
$$

Thus by proposition 5.3.3

$$
\liminf_{n\to\infty}\Phi_n(x) = \limsup_{n\to\infty}\Psi_n(x) \text{ for a.e. } x(\lambda).
$$

Since $\Psi_n(x) \leq f(x) \leq \Phi_n(x)$ for $x \in (a,b)$ and both $\{\Phi_n(x)\}_{n\geq 1}$ and $\{\Psi_n(x)\}_{n\geq 1}$, being bounded monotone sequences, are convergent, we have

$$
f(x) = \lim_{n\to\infty}\Phi_n(x) = \lim_{n\to\infty}\Psi_n(x) \text{ for a.e. } x(\lambda).
$$

Hence f is measurable by exercise 5.3.29. Further, since $f \leq \Phi_n \ \forall\, n$ and $\Phi_n \in L_1(\lambda)$, it follows from proposition 5.4.3(i) that $f \in L_1[a,b]$. Now using the dominated convergence theorem for the sequence $\{\Psi_n\}_{n\geq 1}$, we get

$$
\lim_{n\to\infty}\int \Psi_n d\lambda = \int f d\lambda.
$$

Hence

$$
\int_a^b f(x)dx = \lim_{n\to\infty} L(P_n, f) = \lim_{n\to\infty}\int \Psi_n d\lambda = \int f d\lambda.
$$

This proves the theorem. ■

5.5.2. Remark: In fact, the proof of the above theorem includes a proof of the following: If $f \in \mathcal{R}[a,b]$, then f is continuous a.e. $x(\lambda)$. This is because $f(x) = \lim_{n\to\infty}\Psi_n(x) = \lim_{n\to\infty}\Phi_n(x)$ a.e. $x(\lambda)$. Thus if we put

$$
E := \{x \in [a,b] \mid f(x) = \lim_{n\to\infty}\Phi_n(x) = \lim_{n\to\infty}\Psi_n(x)\},
$$

then E is a Lebesgue measurable set and $\lambda([a,b] \setminus E) = 0$. For $x \in E$, given an arbitrary $\epsilon > 0$, we can choose n_0 such that

$$
\Psi_{n_0}(x) - \Phi_{n_0}(x) < \epsilon. \tag{5.9}
$$

Further, if x is not a point in any partition P_n, then we can choose $\delta > 0$ such that whenever $y \in [a,b]$ and $|x - y| < \delta$, then y belongs to the same subinterval of the partition P_{n_0} to which x belongs. Thus by (5.9), $|f(x) - f(y)| < \epsilon$, showing that x is a point of continuity of f. Thus the set of discontinuity points of f forms a subset of $([a,b]) \setminus E) \cup P$, where P is the set of partition points of $P_n, n = 1, 2, \ldots$. Hence f is continuous almost everywhere. We had proved this and its converse in chapter 1. Another proof of the converse is given in the next exercise.

5.5.3. Exercise: Let $f : [a, b] \longrightarrow \mathbb{R}$ be bounded and continuous for a.e. $x(\lambda)$.

(i) Let $\{P_n\}_{n \geq 1}$ be any sequence of partitions of $[a, b]$ such that each P_{n+1} is a refinement of P_n and $\|P_n\| \longrightarrow 0$ as $n \to \infty$. Let Φ_n, Ψ_n be as constructed in theorem 5.5.1. Let $x \in (a, b)$ be a point of continuity of f. Show that

$$\lim_{n \to \infty} \Phi_n(x) = f(x) = \lim_{n \to \infty} \Psi_n(x).$$

(ii) Using (i) and the dominated convergence theorem, deduce that $f \in L_1([a, b])$ and

$$\int f d\lambda = \lim_{n \to \infty} \int \Phi_n d\mu = \lim_{n \to \infty} \int \Psi_n d\mu.$$

(iii) Show that $f \in \mathcal{R}[a, b]$ and

$$\int f d\lambda = \int_a^b f(x) dx.$$

•**5.5.4. Exercise:** Let $f : [0, 1] \longrightarrow [0, \infty)$ be Riemann integrable on $[\epsilon, 1]$ for all $\epsilon > 0$. Show that $f \in L_1[0, 1]$ iff $\lim_{\epsilon \to 0} \int_\epsilon^1 f(x) dx$ exists, and in that case

$$\int f(x) d\lambda(x) = \lim_{\epsilon \to 0} \int_\epsilon^1 f(x) dx.$$

5.5.5. Exercise: Let $f(x) = 1/x^p$ if $0 < x \leq 1$, and $f(0) = 0$. Find necessary and sufficient condition on p such that $f \in L_1[0, 1]$. Compute $\int_0^1 f(x) d\lambda(x)$ in that case.
(Hint: Use exercise 5.5.4.)

5.5.6. Exercise (Mean value property): Let $f : [a, b] \longrightarrow \mathbb{R}$ be a continuous function and let $E \subseteq [a, b], E \in \mathcal{L}$, be such that $\lambda(E) > 0$. Show that there exists a real number α such that

$$\int_E f(x) \lambda(x) = \alpha \lambda(E).$$

5.5.7. Exercise: Let $f \in L_1(\mathbb{R})$, and let $g : \mathbb{R} \longrightarrow \mathbb{R}$ be a measurable function such that $\alpha \leq g(x) \leq \beta$ for a.e. $x(\lambda)$. Show that $fg \in L_1(\mathbb{R})$ and there exists $\gamma \in [\alpha, \beta]$ such that

$$\int |f| g d\lambda = \gamma \int |f| d\lambda.$$

5.5.8. Exercise: Let $f \in L_1(\mathbb{R}, \mathcal{L}, \lambda)$ and let $a \in \mathbb{R}$ be fixed. Define

$$
F(x) := \begin{cases} \int_{[a,x]} f(t)\, d\lambda(t) & \text{for } x \geq a, \\[2ex] \int_{[x,a]} f(t) d\lambda(t) & \text{for } x \geq a. \end{cases}
$$

Show that F is continuous.

(Hint: Without loss of generality take $f \geq 0$ and show that F is continuous from the left and right. In fact, using proposition 5.4.3 and proposition 5.4.6, you can deduce that F is actually uniformly continuous.)

5.5.9. Exercise: Let $f \in L_1(\mathbb{R}, \mathcal{L}, \lambda)$ and let $c \in \mathbb{R}$ be a point of continuity of f. Show that

$$
\lim_{n \to \infty} n \int_{[c, c+1/n]} f(x)\, d\lambda(x) = f(c).
$$

5.5.10. Note: We showed in theorem 5.5.1 that for a Riemann integrable function $f : [a, b] \longrightarrow \mathbb{R}$, f is also Lebesgue integrable and the two integrals are equal. A similar result can be proved for functions $f : [a, b] \longrightarrow \mathbb{R}$ which are Riemann-Stieltjes integrable with respect to $F : [a, b] \longrightarrow \mathbb{R}$, where F is monotonically increasing and right continuous. One can show that such a function f is $\mathcal{L}_F \cap [a, b]$, measurable and the Riemann-Stieltjes integral of f is the same as the integral $\int f d\mu_F$, where $\mathcal{L}_F$ is the σ-algebra of μ_F^*-measurable sets.

5.5.11. Exercise (Arzela's theorem): Prove theorem 1.4.6 using theorem 5.4.9 and theorem 5.5.1.

5.5.12. Exercise:

(i) Let $f : [a, b] \longrightarrow \mathbb{R}$ be any constant function. Show that $f \in L_1[a, b]$.

(ii) Let $f : [a, b] \longrightarrow \mathbb{R}$ be any bounded measurable function. Show that $f \in L_1[a, b]$.

(iii) Let $f : [a, b] \longrightarrow \mathbb{R}$ be any continuous function. Show that $f \in L_1[a, b]$.

5.5.13. Exercise: Let $f \in L_1(\mathbb{R})$ be such that $\int_K f d\lambda = 0$ for every compact set $K \subseteq \mathbb{R}$. Show that $f(x) = 0$ for a.e. $x(\lambda)$.

5.5.14. Exercise: Let $\{f_n\}_{n \geq 1}$ be a decreasing sequence of nonnegative functions in $C(a, b)$ and let $f_1 \in L_1(a, b)$. If $\sum_{n=1}^{\infty} (-1)^{n-1} f_n \in C(a, b)$, show that

$$\int_a^b \left(\sum_{n=1}^{\infty} (-1)^{n-1} f_n(x) \right) dx = \sum_{n=1}^{\infty} \left((-1)^{n-1} \left(\int_a^b f_n(x) dx \right) \right).$$

(Hint: For every n, $\sum_{k=1}^{n} (-1)^k f_k \leq f \in L_1(a,b)$).

5.5.15. Exercise: Give examples to show that analogues of the monotone convergence theorem and the dominated convergence theorem do not hold for the Riemann integral.

5.5.16. Exercise: Let $f \in L_1(\mathbb{R})$ and, $\forall\, t \in [0, \infty)$,

$$g(t) = \sup \left\{ \int |f(x+y) - f(x)|\, d\mu(x) \,\middle|\, -t \leq y \leq t \right\}.$$

Show that g is continuous at $t = 0$.

(Hint: Use the simple function technique).

5.6. $L_1[a,b]$ as completion of $\mathcal{R}[a,b]$

Recall that, in section 1.4, we saw that $\mathcal{R}[a,b]$ is not a complete metric space under the L_1-metric $\tilde{d}(f,g) := \int_a^b |\tilde{f}(x) - \tilde{g}(x)| dx$, for $f, g \in \mathcal{R}[a,b]$. Since every metric space has a completion, the question arises: what is the completion of $\mathcal{R}[a,b]$ under this metric? The reader might have seen the abstract construction of the completion of a metric space. We shall show that for $\mathcal{R}[a,b]$ this completion is nothing but $L_1[a,b]$. Thus $L_1[a,b]$ is the concrete realization of the completion of $\mathcal{R}[a,b]$. We shall first show that $L_1[a,b]$ is a complete metric space, and then show that $\mathcal{R}[a,b]$ is dense in $L_1[a,b]$.

For $f, g \in L_1[a,b]$ we say f is **equivalent** to g, and write $f \sim g$, if the set $\{x \in [a,b] \mid f(x) \neq g(x)\}$ has Lebesgue measure zero. It is easy to see that the relation $\sim$ is an equivalence relation on $L_1[a,b]$. We denote the set of equivalence classes again by $L_1[a,b]$. In other words, we identify two functions f, g with each other if $f \sim g$. Thus for $g, f \in L_1[a,b]$, $f = g$ iff $f(x) = g(x)$ for a.e. $x(\lambda)$, as functions. For $f \in L_1[a,b]$, we define

$$\|f\|_1 := \int |f(x)| d\lambda(x).$$

Clearly $\|f\|_1$ is well-defined, and it is easy to check that the function $f \longmapsto \|f\|_1, f \in L_1[a,b]$, has the following properties:

  (i) $\|f\|_1 \geq 0 \quad \forall\, f \in L_1[a,b]$.

  (ii) $\|f\|_1 = 0$ iff $f = 0$.

  (iii) $\|af\|_1 = |a|\, \|f\|_1 \ \forall\, a \in \mathbb{R}$ and $f \in L_1[a,b]$.

(iv) $\|f + g\|_1 \le \|f\|_1 + \|g\|_1 \; \forall \; f, g \in L_1[a,b]$.

The function $\| \cdot \|_1$ is called a **norm** on $L_1[a,b]$. (Geometrically it is the distance of the 'vector' $f \in L_1[a,b]$ from the 'vector' $0 \in L_1[a,b]$.) For $f, g \in L_1[a,b]$, if we define

$$d(f,g) := \|f - g\|_1,$$

then d is a metric on $L_1[a,b]$. This was the reason that it was called the L_1**-metric** in section 1.4. The most important property of this metric is given by the next theorem.

5.6.1. Theorem (Riesz-Fischer): $L_1[a,b]$ *is a complete metric space in the L_1-metric.*

Proof: Let $\{f_n\}_{n \ge 1}$ be a Cauchy sequence in $L_1[a,b]$. We have to show that there exists some $f \in L_1[a,b]$ such that $\|f_n - f\|_1 \to 0$ as $n \to \infty$. Since $\{f_n\}_{n \ge 1}$ is Cauchy, it is enough to find a subsequence $\{f_{n_k}\}_{n \ge 1}$ and $f \in L_1[a,b]$ such that $\|f_{n_k} - f\|_1 \to 0$ as $k \to \infty$. Let us first try to find a subsequence $\{f_{n_k}\}_{k \ge 1}$ and $f \in L_1[a,b]$ such that $f_{n_k}(x) \to f(x)$ for a.e. $x(\lambda)$, as $k \to \infty$. Since for every n_k,

$$f_{n_k}(x) = f_{n_1}(x) + \sum_{j=1}^{k-1} [f_{n_{j+1}}(x) - f_{n_j}(x)],$$

we should find $\{f_{n_k}\}_{k \ge 1}$ such that

$$f_{n_1}(x) + \sum_{j=1}^{\infty} (f_{n_{j+1}}(x) - f_{n_j}(x)) < +\infty.$$

For this we note that, by corollary 5.4.10, the function

$$f(x) := f_{n_1}(x) + \sum_{j=1}^{\infty} (f_{n_{j+1}}(x) - f_{n_j}(x))$$

will be defined for a.e. $x(\lambda)$ with the property that $f \in L_1[a,b]$ and

$$\int f(x)d\lambda(x) = \int f_{n_1}(x)d\lambda(x) + \sum_{j=1}^{\infty} \int [f_{n_{j+1}}(x) - f_{n_j}(x)] \, d\lambda(x),$$

provided

$$\|f_{n_1}\|_1 + \sum_{j=1}^{\infty} \|f_{n_{j+1}} - f_{n_j}\|_1 < +\infty. \tag{5.10}$$

Thus to prove the required claim, we want to construct a subsequence $\{f_{n_k}\}_{k \ge 1}$ of the sequence $\{f_n\}_{n \ge 1}$ such that (5.10) holds. This can be achieved using the fact that $\{f_n\}_{n\geq 1}$ is Cauchy as follows: given $\epsilon = 1/2$, we choose n_1 such that

$$\|f_n - f_{n_1}\|_1 < 1/2, \quad \forall\, n \geq n_1.$$

Suppose $n_1 < n_2 < \ldots < n_{j-1}$ have been chosen. We choose $n_j > n_{j-1}$ such that

$$\|f_n - f_{n_j}\|_1 < 1/2^j, \quad \forall\, n \geq n_j.$$

Then by induction we have the sequence $\{f_{n_k}\}_{k\geq 1}$, and

$$\|f_{n_1}\|_1 + \sum_{j=1}^{\infty} \|f_{n_{j+1}} - f_{n_j}\|_1 < \|f_{n_1}\|_1 + \sum_{j=1}^{\infty} \frac{1}{2^j} < +\infty.$$

Hence by corollary 5.4.10, we will have a subsequence $\{f_{n_k}\}_{k\geq 1}$ of $\{f_n\}_{n\geq 1}$ and $f \in L_1[a,b]$ such that

$$f(x) := f_{n_1}(x) + \sum_{j=1}^{\infty} (f_{n_{j+1}}(x) - f_{n_j}(x)) \quad \text{for a.e. } x(\lambda)$$

exists. Further, $f \in L_1[a,b]$ and

$$\int f(x)d\lambda(x) = \int f_{n_1}(x)d\lambda(x) + \sum_{j=1}^{\infty} \int (f_{n_{j+1}}(x) - f_{n_j}(x))\, d\lambda(x).$$

But then, for a.e. $x(\lambda)$,

$$f(x) - f_{n_j}(x) = \sum_{k=j+1}^{\infty} (f_{n_{k+1}}(x) - f_{n_k}(x)).$$

Thus for every $j \geq 1$,

$$\|f - f_{n_j}\|_1 \leq \sum_{k=j+1}^{\infty} \|f_{n_{k+1}} - f_{n_k}\|_1 < \sum_{k=j+1}^{\infty} 1/2^k = 1/2^j.$$

Hence $\|f - f_{n_j}\|_1 \longrightarrow 0$ as $j \longrightarrow \infty$. ∎

We prove next that $C[a,b]$, the space of continuous function on $[a,b]$, (and hence $\mathcal{R}[a,b]$) is dense in $L_1[a,b]$.

5.6.2. Theorem: *The space $C[a,b]$ is a dense subset of $L_1[a,b]$.*

Proof: First note that if $g \in C[a,b]$, then g is bounded and by exercise 5.5.12 (iii), it is a measurable function. Hence $g \in L_1[a,b]$ by exercise 5.5.12. Thus $C[a,b] \subseteq L_1[a,b]$. To show that $C[a,b]$ is dense in $L_1[a,b]$ we use the 'simple function technique' as outlined in note 5.4.17(ii).

Let $f \in L_1[a,b]$. Given $\epsilon > 0$, we have to find a function $g \in C[a,b]$ such that $\|f - g\|_1 < \epsilon$. Since for $f \in L_1[a,b]$ we have $f = f^+ - f^-$ and both $f^+, f^- \in L_1[a,b]$, it is enough to prove the theorem for $f \in L_1[a,b]$ with

$f \geq 0$. So we may assume f is nonnegative measurable and $\int f d\lambda < +\infty$. By definition, we can choose a sequence $\{s_n\}_{n\geq 1}$ of nonnegative simple measurable functions such that $\{s_n\}_{n\geq 1}$ increases to f and

$$\lim_{n\to\infty} \int s_n d\lambda = \int f d\lambda.$$

Note that each $s_n \in L_1[a,b]$, and we can choose n_0 such that $\|s_{n_0} - f\|_1 < \epsilon$. (This shows that simple measurable functions in $L_1[a,b]$ are dense in it.) Thus it is enough to prove the theorem for $f \in L_1[a,b]$, a nonnegative simple measurable function. Since any such function is of the form $\sum_{i=1}^{n} a_i \chi_{A_i}$, where $a_i \in \mathbb{R}, A_i \in \mathcal{L}$ with $\bigcup_{i=1}^{n} A_i = [a,b]$ and $A_i \cap A_j = \emptyset$ for $i \neq j$, it is enough to prove the theorem for $f = \chi_A$ for $A \in \mathcal{L}$ with $A \subseteq [a,b]$. Now by theorem 4.2.1, we can choose a set $F \subseteq [a,b]$ such that F is a finite disjoint union of intervals and $\lambda(A \triangle F) < \epsilon$. Thus

$$\|\chi_A - \chi_F\|_1 = \lambda(A \triangle F) < \epsilon.$$

Let $F = \bigcup_{i=1}^{n} I_i$, where the I_i are intervals with $I_i \subset [a,b]$ and $I_i \cap I_j = \emptyset$ for $i \neq j$. Then

$$\chi_F = \sum_{i=1}^{m} \chi_{I_i}.$$

To complete the proof, we only have to show that given $I \subset [a,b]$, there exists a continuous function g on $[a,b]$ such that $\|\chi_I - g\|_1 < \epsilon$. This is easy. For example, if $I = (c,d), a < c < d < b$, consider g having the graph as given in Figure 16 below:

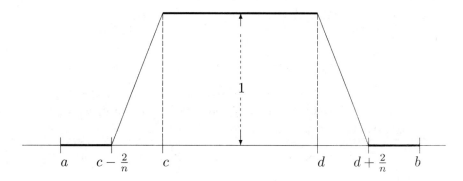

Figure 16: The function g

Then $\|\chi_I - g\|_1 = 1/n$. Thus for n sufficiently large, $\|\chi_I - g\|_1 < \epsilon$. ∎

Since $C[a,b] \subseteq \mathcal{R}[a,b]$, theorems 5.6.1 and 5.6.2 together prove the following theorem:

5.6.3. Theorem: $L_1[a, b]$ *is the completion of* $\mathcal{R}[a, b]$.

5.6.4. Notes:

(i) In the proof of theorem 5.6.1, we didn't use anywhere the fact that the functions are defined on an interval. One can define $\| \cdot \|_1$ for functions defined on $(E, \mathcal{L} \cap E, \lambda)$, where $E \in \mathcal{L}$ is arbitrary, and the proof of theorem 5.6.1 will show that $L_1(E) := L_1(E, \mathcal{L} \cap E, \lambda)$ is also a complete metric space under the metric

$$\|f - g\|_1 := \int_E |f(x) - g(x)| d\lambda(x).$$

A closer look will show that the metric d makes sense on $L_1(X, \mathcal{S}, \mu)$, where $(X, \mathcal{S}, \mu)$ is any complete measure space and we identify functions which agree for a.e. (μ). Further, theorem 5.6.1 also remains true for $L_1(X, \mathcal{S}, \mu)$.

(ii) Parts of the proof of theorem 5.6.2 also exhibit the following facts which are of independent interest. Let $f \in L_1[a, b]$ and $\epsilon > 0$ be given. Then there exists a simple function Φ such that $\|f - \Phi\|_1 < \epsilon$ and a step function h such that $\|f - h\|_1 < \epsilon$. Thus simple functions in $L_1[a, b]$ are dense in it.

•**5.6.5. Exercise:** Let $f \in L_1(\mathbb{R})$ and let $\epsilon > 0$ be given. Prove the following:

   (i) There exists a positive integer n such that

$$\|f - \chi_{[-n,n]} f\|_1 < \epsilon.$$

   (ii) There exists a continuous function g on $\mathbb{R}$ such that g is zero outside some finite interval and $\|f \chi_{[-n,n]} - g\|_1 < \epsilon$.

   (iii) For $f : \mathbb{R} \longrightarrow \mathbb{R}$, let

$$\text{supp } (f) := \text{ closure } \{x \in \mathbb{R} \mid f(x) \neq 0\}.$$

   The set $\text{supp}(f)$ is called the **support** of f and is the smallest closed subset of $\mathbb{R}$ outside which f vanishes. Let the space of continuous functions on $\mathbb{R}$ be denoted by $C(\mathbb{R})$ and let

$$C_c(\mathbb{R}) := \{f : \mathbb{R} \longrightarrow \mathbb{R} \mid f \in C(\mathbb{R}) \text{ and } \text{supp}(f) \text{ is compact}\}.$$

   Then $C_c(\mathbb{R})$ is a dense subset of $L_1(\mathbb{R})$.

• **5.6.6. Exercise:** Let $f \in L_1(\mathbb{R})$ and $\tilde{f}(x) := f(-x) \; \forall \; x \in \mathbb{R}$. Prove the following:

   (i) $\int \tilde{f}(x) d\lambda(x) = \int f(x) d\lambda(x)$.

   (ii) $fg \in L_1(\mathbb{R})$ for any bounded measurable function $g : \mathbb{R} \to \mathbb{R}$.

Dense subspaces of $L_1(\mathbb{R})$ are very useful in proving results about L_1-functions. As an application of exercise 5.6.5 we have the following:

•**5.6.7. Exercise:** Let $f \in L_1(\mathbb{R})$ and for every $h, k \in \mathbb{R}$, let

$$f_h(x) := f(x + h) \quad \text{and} \quad \phi(x) := f(kx + h), x \in \mathbb{R}.$$

Prove the following:

(i) $f_h, \phi \in L_1(\mathbb{R})$ with

$$\int \phi(x) d\lambda(x) = |k| \int f(x) d\lambda(x) \text{ and } \int f_h(x) d\lambda(x) = \int f(x) d\lambda(x).$$

(ii) For every $h \in \mathbb{R}$, $f_h \in L_1(\mathbb{R})$ and $\lim_{h \to 0} \|f_h - f\|_1 = 0$.
(Hint : Use exercise 5.6.5 to get a function $g \in C_c(\mathbb{R})$ with $\|g - f\|_1 < \epsilon$, and note that $\|g_h - g\|_1 < 2(b - a + 1)$ when $\text{supp}(g) \subseteq [a, b]$ and $|h|$ is sufficiently small.)

(iii) The function $h \longmapsto \|f_h\|_1$ is continuous.

5.6.8. Exercise (Riemann-Lebesgue lemma): Let $f \in L_1(\mathbb{R})$, and let $g : \mathbb{R} \longrightarrow \mathbb{R}$ be any bounded measurable function such that $g(x+p) - g(x) = 0$ for every $x \in \mathbb{R}$ and $p \in \mathbb{R}$ fixed. Show that $\forall t \neq 0$,

$$\left| \int f(x)g(tx)dx \right| \leq M \|f_{p/t} - f\|_1,$$

where $M = \sup |g(x)|/2$. Hence deduce (using exercise 5.6.7) that

$$\lim_{|t| \to \infty} \int f(x)g(tx)dx = 0.$$

(In the special case when $f \in L_1[0, 2\pi]$ and $g(x) = \cos x$ or $\sin x$, we have

$$\lim_{n \to \infty} \int_0^{2\pi} f(x) \cos nx dx = 0 = \lim_{n \to \infty} \int_0^{2\pi} f(x) \sin nx dx.$$

This finds applications in the theory of Fourier series.)

5.7. Another dense subspace of $L_1[a, b]$

While proving theorem 5.6.2 we also showed that, given $f \in L_1[a, b]$, f can be approximated by a function χ_F, where F is a finite disjoint union of intervals in $[a, b]$. We then approximated, for every interval $I \subset [a, b]$, the function χ_I, by a polygonal continuous function to get an approximation of f by continuous functions in the L_1-metric. One can ask the question: If $I \subseteq [a, b]$ is an interval and $\epsilon > 0$ is given, can we find a function Φ on $[a, b]$ which is infinitely differentiable and is such that $\|\chi_I - \Phi\|_1 < \epsilon$? If this is possible, then we can construct an approximation of $f \in L_1[a, b]$ by infinitely differentiable functions. To do this we need functions Φ with the following properties: given $c, d \in \mathbb{R}$ and $c < d$,

   (i) $\Phi(x) = 1$ for $x \geq d$ and $\Phi(x) = 0$ for $x \leq c$.

   (ii) $0 \leq \Phi(x) \leq 1$ and $\Phi \in C^\infty(\mathbb{R})$.

Here, $C^\infty(\mathbb{R})$ denotes the set of **infinitely differentiable** functions on $\mathbb{R}$.

   In other words, we want functions which interpolate between the value 0 at c and the value 1 at d in a smooth (infinitely differentiable) way. We give below the construction of such functions.

5.7.1. Lemma: *For any real number $\alpha > 0$, let*

$$\Phi(x) := \begin{cases} \exp\left(-\dfrac{\alpha}{x}\right) & \text{if } x > 0, \\ 0 & \text{if } x \leq 0, \end{cases}$$

and

$$\Psi(x) := \begin{cases} \exp\left(\dfrac{\alpha}{x}\right) & \text{if } x < 0, \\ 0 & \text{if } x \geq 0. \end{cases}$$

Then the functions $\Phi, \Psi \in C^\infty(\mathbb{R})$.

Proof: We first note that Φ is a continuous function and it is enough to prove the lemma for $\alpha = 1$. For $x > 0$, $\Phi'(x) = \exp(-1/x)/x^2$. In fact, $\forall\, n \geq 0$ and $x > 0$,

$$\Phi^{(n)} = P_n\left(1/x\right)\exp\left(-1/x\right),$$

where P_n is a polynomial of degree $2n$. This can easily be proved by induction. We next show that $\Phi^{(n)}(0) = 0\ \forall n$. Clearly, if $n = 0$, it is true.

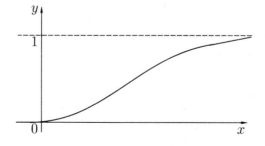

Figure 17 : The function $\Phi(x)$

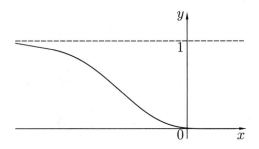

Figure 18 : The function $\Psi(x)$

Assume $\Phi^{(n-1)}(0) = 0$. Then for $x > 0$,

$$\lim_{x \to 0} \left(\frac{\Phi^{(n-1)}(x) - \Phi^{(n-1)}(0)}{x} \right) = \lim_{x \to 0} \left[P_{n-1}(1/x) exp(-1/x) \right] 1/x$$

$$= \lim_{t \to \infty} \left[t P_{n-1}(t) exp(-t) \right] = 0.$$

The last equality holds because for $t > 0$ and t large, $exp(t)$ dominates t^n for any $n \geq 0$. This proves that $\Phi \in C^\infty(\mathbb{R})$. Similarly, $\Psi \in C^\infty(\mathbb{R})$. ∎

5.7.2. Corollary: *Let c and d be real numbers such that $c < d$. Let*

$$f_{c,d}(x) := \begin{cases} exp(-1/(x-c)(d-x)) & \text{if } c < x < d, \\ 0 & \text{otherwise.} \end{cases}$$

Then $f_{c,d} \in C^\infty(\mathbb{R})$.

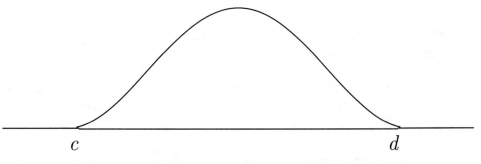

c $\qquad\qquad\qquad\qquad\qquad\qquad\qquad$ d

Figure 19 : The function $f_{c,d}$

Proof: Let

$$f_c(x) := \begin{cases} exp(-1/(x-c)) & \text{if } x > c, \\ 0 & \text{if } x \leq c \end{cases}$$

and

$$f_d(x) := \begin{cases} exp(-1/(d-x)) & \text{if } x < d, \\ 0 & \text{if } x \geq d. \end{cases}$$

By lemma 5.7.1, both f_c and f_d are in $C^\infty(\mathbb{R})$, and $f_{c,d}(x) = f_c(x)f_d(x)$ for every $x \in \mathbb{R}$. Thus $f_{c,d} \in C^\infty(\mathbb{R})$. ■

5.7.3. Corollary: *Let $c < d$ and $f_{c,d}$ be as in corollary 5.7.2. Let*

$$\eta_{c,d}(x) = \int_{-\infty}^{x} f_{c,d}(t)dt, \quad x \in \mathbb{R}.$$

Then $\eta_{c,d} \in C^\infty(\mathbb{R})$, $\eta_{c,d}(x) = 0$ for $x \leq c$ and $\eta_{c,d}(x) > 0$ $\forall \, x > c$. Let $\delta_{c,d} = \eta_{c,d}/M$, where $M := \int_c^d f_{c,d}(t)dt$. Then $\delta_{c,d} \in C^\infty(\mathbb{R})$, $0 \leq \delta_{c,d} \leq 1$, with $\delta_{c,d}(x) = 0$ for $x \leq c$ and $\delta_{c,d}(x) = 1$ for $x \geq d$.

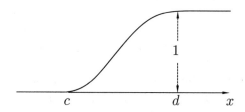

Figure 20 : The function $\delta_{c,d}$

Proof: Clearly, $\eta_{c,d} \in C^\infty(\mathbb{R})$ and for $x \leq c$, $\eta_{cd}(x) = 0$. For $x > c$, since $f_{c,d}(t) > 0$ for every t,

$$\eta_{c,d}(x) := \int_c^x f_{c,d}(t)dt > 0.$$

Let $M := \int_c^d f_{c,d}(t)dt$ and $\delta_{c,d} := \eta_{c,d}/M$. Then the function $\delta_{c,d}$ clearly has the required properties. ■

5.7.4. Corollary: *For real numbers c and d with $c < d$ there exists a function $\pi_{c,d} \in C^\infty(\mathbb{R})$ such that $0 \leq \pi_{c,d} \leq 1$, $\pi_{c,d}(x) = 0$ for $x \geq d$, and $\pi_{c,d}(x) = 1$ for $x \leq c$.*

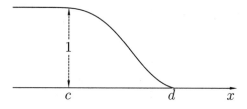

Figure 21 : The function $\pi_{c,d}$

Proof: Let $\pi_{c,d} := 1 - \delta_{c,d}$. Then $\pi_{c,d}$ has the required properties. ■

5.7.5. Corollary: *Let* $a < b$ *and* $\epsilon > 0$ *be such that* $a + \epsilon < b - \epsilon$. *Then there exists a function* $\Phi_\epsilon \in C^\infty(\mathbb{R})$ *with the following properties:*

   (i) $0 \leq \Phi_\epsilon(x) \leq 1 \ \forall \ x \in \mathbb{R}$.

   (ii) $\Phi_\epsilon(x) = 1 \ \forall \ x \in (a + \epsilon, b - \epsilon)$.

   (iii) $\Phi_\epsilon(x) = 0 \ \forall \ x \notin (a, b)$.

Proof: Let $c := a + \epsilon$ and $d := b - \epsilon$. Define $\Phi_\epsilon : \mathbb{R} \longrightarrow \mathbb{R}$ by

$$\Phi_\epsilon(x) := \begin{cases} 0 & \text{if} \ x \notin (a, b), \\ 1 & \text{if} \ x \in (c, d), \\ \delta_{a,c} & \text{if} \ x \in (a, c) \\ \pi_{d,b} & \text{if} \ x \in (d, b), \end{cases}$$

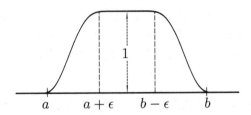

Figure 22 : The function Φ_ϵ

where $\delta_{a,c}$ and $\pi_{b,d}$ are as given by corollaries 5.7.3 and 5.7.4. Then $\Phi_\epsilon \in C^\infty(\mathbb{R})$ and has the required properties. ∎

5.7.6. Theorem: *The space* $C^\infty[a, b]$ *of infinitely differentiable functions on* $[a, b]$ *is a dense subset of* $L_1[a, b]$.

Proof: As remarked in the beginning of the section, we only have to prove that $\ \forall \ \epsilon > 0$ and $(c, d) \subseteq (a, b)$, $\ \exists \ \tilde{\Phi} \in C^\infty[a, b]$ such that

$$\| \chi_{(c,d)} - \tilde{\Phi} \|_1 < \epsilon.$$

Choose an integer $n \geq 1$ such that

$$c + 2/n < d - 2/n \ \text{ and } \ 4/n < \epsilon.$$

Now consider $\Phi \in C^\infty(\mathbb{R})$, as given by corollary 5.7.5 with the properties $0 \leq \Phi(x) \leq 1$, $\Phi(x) = 1$ for $x \in (c + 2/n, d - 2/n)$ and $\Phi(x) = 0$ for $x \notin (c + 1/n, d - 1/n)$. Consider $\tilde{\Phi}$, the restriction of Φ to $[a, b]$. Then $\tilde{\Phi} \in C^\infty[a, b]$ and

$$\| \chi_{(c,d)} - \tilde{\Phi} \|_1 = \int_{c+\frac{1}{n}}^{c+\frac{2}{n}} \tilde{\Phi}(x) \, d\lambda(x) + \int_{d-\frac{2}{n}}^{d-\frac{1}{n}} \tilde{\Phi}(x) \, d\lambda(x) \leq 4/n < \epsilon. \ \blacksquare$$

5.7.7. Exercise: Let $C_c^\infty(\mathbb{R}) := \{f \in C^\infty(\mathbb{R}) \mid \text{supp}(f) \text{ is compact}\}$. Show that $C_c^\infty(\mathbb{R})$ is dense in $L_1(\mathbb{R})$.

(Hint: $\lim\limits_{n\to\infty} \| \chi_{[-n,n]} f - f \|_1 = 0$.)

5.8. Improper Riemann integral and its relation with the Lebesgue integral

Let us recall that the Riemann integral is defined only for bounded functions over bounded intervals. The notion of Riemann integral for functions which are either not bounded or are defined over unbounded intervals can be developed as follows. Let $I = [a, \infty)$ be an infinite interval and let $f : I \longrightarrow \mathbb{R}$ be a bounded function. Let $\{b_n\}_{n\geq 1}$ be any sequence of real numbers such that $b_{n+1} > b_n > a$ for every n and $\lim_{n\to\infty} b_n = \infty$. Let $I_n := [a, b_n]$. Further, suppose that $f \in \mathcal{R}[I_n] \ \forall \ n$ and that the sequence $\{\int_a^{b_n} f(x)dx\}_{n\geq 1}$ is convergent, say to α. If α is independent of the sequence $\{b_n\}_{n\geq 1}$, then we can define the integral of f over I to be α, denoted by $\int_I f(x)dx$ (also denoted by $\int_a^\infty f(x)dx$), and call it the **improper Riemann integral** of f over the interval I. Let us look at some examples.

5.8.1. Example: Consider the function $f : [0, \infty) \longrightarrow \mathbb{R}$ defined by

$$f(x) := (-1)^n/n \ \text{ if } \ n - 1 \leq x < n, n = 1, 2, \ldots .$$

Clearly, f is bounded and is Riemann integrable on every closed bounded subinterval of $[0, \infty)$. Let us take $I_m = [0, m], m = 1, 2, \ldots$. Then

$$\int_{I_m} f(x)dx = \sum_{n=1}^{m} (-1)^n/n,$$

and the limit

$$\lim_{n\to\infty} \int_{I_n} f(x)dx = \sum_{n=1}^{\infty} (-1)^n/n = -\ln 2$$

exists. In fact, it is easy to see that

$$\lim_{b\to\infty} \int_0^b f(x)dx = -\ln 2.$$

Thus the improper Riemann integral $\int_0^\infty f(x)dx$ exists. However, it is easy to see that $f \notin L_1[0, \infty)$. For example, if it were so, then by the dominated convergence theorem, since $\chi_{[0,n]} f \in L_1[0, \infty) \ \forall \ n$ and $|\chi_{[0,n]} f| \leq |f|$, we will have

$$\int |f|d\lambda(x) = \lim_{n\to\infty} \int |\chi_{[0,n]} f|d\lambda(x) = \sum_{n=1}^{\infty} 1/n = +\infty.$$

The second situation can arise when we have a function $f : [a, b] \to \mathbb{R}$ which is not bounded, but f is bounded and is Riemann integrable on $[c, b]$ for every $c > a$ and $\lim_{c \to a} \int_c^b f(x)dx$ exists. In that case, $\lim_{c \to a} \int_c^b f(x)dx$ is called the **improper Riemann integral** of f over $[a, b]$ and is denoted by $\int_a^b f(x)dx$.

5.8.2. Example: Let $f : (0, 1] \longrightarrow \mathbb{R}$ be defined by $f(x) = 1/\sqrt{x}$. Then, for every $c > 0, f \in \mathcal{R}[c, 1]$ and

$$\int_c^1 \frac{1}{\sqrt{x}} dx = 2(1 - c^{1/2}).$$

Thus

$$\lim_{c \to 0} \int_c^1 \frac{1}{\sqrt{x}} dx = 2.$$

Hence the improper integral of f on $[0, 1]$ exists and

$$\int_0^1 \frac{1}{\sqrt{x}} dx = 2.$$

The improper Riemann integrals in other situations, for example when f is defined on say $(-\infty, b]$ or when f is defined on $[a, b)$ and is not bounded but is Riemann integrable on $[a, c]$ for every $c < b$, can be defined similarly. We leave the following simple properties of improper Riemann integrals for the reader to verify.

5.8.3. Exercise:

(i) Let $\int_a^\infty f_i dx$ exist for $i = 1, 2$. Show that $\forall \, \alpha, \beta \in \mathbb{R}$, $\int_a^\infty (\alpha f_1 \pm \beta f_2)dx$ exists and is equal to $\alpha \int_a^\infty f_1 dx \pm \beta \int_a^0 f_2 dx$.

(ii) Let $f : [a, \infty) \longrightarrow \mathbb{R}$ be such that $f \in \mathcal{R}[c, d]$ $\forall \, a \leq c < d < \infty$. Show that the improper Riemann integral $\int_a^\infty f(x)dx$ exists iff $\forall \, \epsilon > 0$, $\exists \, N$ such that for every $c, d \geq N, \int_c^d f(x)dx < \epsilon$.

(iii) Using (ii), show that for a function $f : [a, \infty) \longrightarrow \mathbb{R}$, if $f \in \mathcal{R}[a, b]$ $\forall \, b > a$ and if $\int_a^\infty |f(x)|dx < +\infty$ (in which case one says that the **improper integral exists absolutely**), then $\int_a^\infty f(x)dx$ also exists.

(iv) Using (ii) above, show that the improper Riemann integral $\int_0^\infty \sin x / x dx$ exists (see also theorem 5.9.1), but $\int_0^\infty |\sin x / x| dx = +\infty$, i.e., the improper integral of $\sin x / x$ does not exist absolutely.

As we saw in example 5.8.2 and exercise 5.8.3(iv), for a function f its improper Riemann integral can exist, even though it is not Lebesgue integrable.

Conversely, even if a function is Lebesgue integrable on bounded intervals, its improper Riemann integrable need not exist. The exact relation is given by the following theorem:

5.8.4. Theorem: *Let $f : [a, \infty) \longrightarrow \mathbb{R}$ be such that $f \in \mathcal{R}[I]$ for every closed bounded interval $I \subset [a, \infty)$. Then f is Lebesgue integrable iff the improper Riemann integral $\int_a^\infty |f(x)| dx$ exists.*

Proof: Let f be Lebesgue integrable. To show that the improper integral $\int_a^\infty |f(x)| dx$ exists, let $\{a_n\}_{n \geq 1}$ be any sequence of real numbers such that $\lim_{n \to \infty} a_n = \infty$. Let $f_n = \chi_{[a, a_n]} f$. Then each $f_n \in \mathcal{R}[a, a_n]$ with $|f_n| \leq |f|$ and $f_n(x) \to f(x)$ for every $x \in [a, \infty)$. Thus by the dominated convergence theorem

$$\lim_{n \to \infty} \int |f_n(x)| d\lambda(x) = \int_{[a, \infty)} |f| d\lambda(x).$$

On the other hand, by theorem 5.5.1,

$$\int |f_n(x)| d\lambda(x) = \int_a^{a_n} |f(x)| dx.$$

Thus

$$\lim_{n \to \infty} \int_a^{a_n} |f_n(x)| dx = \int_{[a, \infty)} |f(x)| d\lambda(x).$$

Hence $\int_a^\infty |f(x)| dx$ exists. Conversely, suppose $\lim_{b \to \infty} \int_a^b |f(x)| dx$ exists. Let $\{a_n\}_{n \geq 1}$ be any increasing sequence such that $\lim_{n \to \infty} a_n = \infty$. Let

$$g_n := \chi_{[a, a_n]} |f|, n = 1, 2, \dots .$$

Then $\{g_n\}_{n \geq 1}$ is an increasing sequence of nonnegative measurable functions and, by the monotone convergence theorem,

$$\int_{[a, \infty)} |f| d\lambda(x) = \lim_{n \to \infty} \int_{[a, a_n]} |f| d\lambda(x).$$

As $g_n \in \mathcal{R}[a, a_n]$, again by theorem 5.5.1,

$$\int_{[a, a_n]} |f| d\lambda(x) = \int_a^{a_n} |f| dx.$$

Since $\int_a^\infty |f| dx < +\infty$, we have

$$\begin{aligned} \int |f| d\lambda(x) &= \lim_{n \to \infty} \int_{[a, a_n]} |f| d\lambda(x) \\ &= \lim_{n \to \infty} \int_a^{a_n} |f| dx = \int_a^\infty |f| dx < +\infty. \quad \blacksquare \end{aligned}$$

•5.8.5. Exercise:

(i) Let $f(t) = 1/1 + t^2$, $t > 0$. Show that the improper Riemann integral $\int_0^\infty f(t)dt$ exists. Compute its value also. Does $f \in L_1(0, \infty)$?

(ii) Let

$$g(t) = \frac{1 + (1 + t)e^{-t}}{1 + t^2}, \quad t > 0.$$

Show that $g \in L_1[0, \infty)$.

(Hint: $(1 + t)e^{-t} \to 0$ as $t \to \infty$).

5.8.6. Remark: As we have seen in theorem 5.5.1, the theory of Lebesgue integration extends the theory of Riemann integration and does not include the theory of improper Riemann integration, as shown in example 5.8.1. The reason is that Lebesgue integration is absolute integration, i.e., f is Lebesgue integrable iff $|f|$ is integrable. On the other hand, as seen in exercise 5.8.5, for $f(x) = \sin x/x$, $0 < x < \infty$, the improper integral $\int_0^\infty f(x)dx$ exists, but the improper integral $\int_0^\infty |f(x)|dx$ does not exist. Another way of observing this difference is that for a Lebesgue integrable function f,

$$\int_E f d\mu = \sum_{n=1}^\infty \int_{E_n} f d\mu, \tag{5.11}$$

whenever $E = \bigcup_{n=1}^\infty E_n$, where E and the E_n's are measurable sets with $E_n \cap E_m = \emptyset$, for $n \neq m$. However, this property is not true for improper Riemann integration, even when E and all the E_n's are intervals. To see this, recall that the series $\sum_{n=1}^\infty (-1)^n/n$ is convergent but is not absolutely convergent. Thus, given any $\alpha \in \mathbb{R}$, $\alpha \neq -\ln 2$, we can have a rearrangement of $\sum_{n=1}^\infty (-1)^n/n$ such that the rearranged series converges to α. Let the corresponding rearrangement of the intervals $\{[n-1, n)\}_{n \geq 1}$ be denoted by $\{E_n\}_{n \geq 1}$. Let

$$f(x) := (-1)^n/n \text{ for } x \in [n-1, n), n = 1, 2, \ldots.$$

We saw in example 5.8.1 that $\int_0^\infty f(x)dx$ exists. However,

$$-\ell n 2 = \int_{[0,\infty)} f(x)dx \neq \sum_{n=1}^\infty \int_{E_n} f(x)dx = \alpha,$$

even though $[0, \infty) = \bigcup_{n=1}^\infty E_n$, where each E_n is an interval and $E_n \cap E_m = \emptyset$ for $n \neq m$. This example shows that any theory of integration in which every improper Riemann integrable function is also integrable, cannot have the property $\int_E f = \sum_{n=1}^\infty \int_{E_n} f$, whenever $E = \bigcup_{n=1}^\infty E_n$ where E_n's are pairwise disjoint measurable sets. Thus one cannot hope to have a theory of integration which extends both the theory of improper Riemann integration and Lebesgue integration. Suppose we drop the demand of the property in (5.11) and ask the question: can one develop a theory of integration in which every bounded function on finite intervals is integrable and every improper Riemann integrable function is also integrable? Such theories are possible: **Perron integral, Denjoy integral, Kurzweil-Henstock integral, gauge integral, generalized Riemann integral.** All of these integrals are equivalent. For more details see Bartle [3], DePree and Swartz [11], McLeod [25] and Saks [35].

5.9. Calculation of some improper Riemann integrals

As applications of the Lebesgue dominated convergence theorem and theorem 5.5.1 we calculate the improper integral $\int_0^\infty \frac{\sin x}{x} dx$, which exists (exercise 5.8.3). Normally, the calculation of this integral is done as an application of the residue theorem in complex analysis.

5.9.1. Theorem: $\displaystyle\int_0^\infty \frac{\sin x}{x} dx = \pi/2.$

Proof: Since the required integral exists, by the dominated convergence theorem we have

$$\int_0^\infty \frac{\sin x}{x} dx = \lim_{n\to\infty} \int_0^n \frac{\sin x}{x} dx.$$

Let

$$f_n(t) := \int_0^n e^{-xt} \frac{\sin x}{x} dx \ \forall \ t \geq 0 \text{ and } n = 1, 2, \ldots.$$

Then

$$\int_0^\infty \frac{\sin x}{x} dx = \lim_{n\to\infty} f_n(0).$$

To compute $f_n(0)$, we note that $\forall \ t \geq 0$ and every $x > 0$, $\dfrac{d}{dt}\left(e^{-xt}\dfrac{\sin x}{x}\right)$ exists and

$$\left| \frac{d}{dt}\left(e^{-xt}\frac{\sin x}{x}\right) \right| = |e^{-xt}\sin x| < e^{-xt}.$$

Since $e^{-xt} \in L_1[0, n]$ for every $t \geq 0$, $f_n(t)$ is differentiable $\forall \ t \geq 0$, by theorem 5.4.12, and

$$f_n'(t) = -\int_0^n e^{-xt} \sin x dx.$$

It is easy to see that $f_n'(t) \in \mathcal{R}[0, n]$ and hence, by the fundamental theorem of calculus,

$$\int_0^n f_n'(t) dt = f_n(n) - f_n(0).$$

Also for every n

$$|f_n(n)| \leq \frac{1}{n} \int_0^n e^{-nx} dx \leq \frac{1}{n} \ \forall \, n.$$

Thus, $\lim_{n\to\infty} f_n(n) = 0$, and we have

$$\lim_{n\to\infty} f_n(0) = \lim_{n\to\infty} \left[-\int_0^n f_n'(t) dt \right].$$

Integrating twice by parts, we get

$$-f_n'(t) = \int_0^n e^{-xt} \sin x dx = \frac{1 - e^{-nt}(t \sin n + \cos n)}{1 + t^2}.$$

Thus $-\chi_{[0,n]}(t) f_n'(t)$ converges to $1/(1 + t^2)$ as $n \to \infty$, and

$$\left| \chi_{[0,n]}(t) f_n'(t) \right| \leq \frac{1 + e^{-t}(1 + t)}{1 + t^2} := g(t).$$

By exercise 5.8.5, $g \in L_1[0, \infty)$. Thus, using the dominated convergence theorem, we have

$$\lim_{n\to\infty} \int_0^n -f_n'(t) dt = \int_0^\infty \frac{1}{1 + t^2} dt = \pi/2.$$

Hence

$$\int_0^\infty \frac{\sin x}{x} dx = \lim_{n\to\infty} f_n(0) = \lim_{n\to\infty} \int_0^n f_n'(t) dt = \pi/2. \ \blacksquare$$

5.9.2. Exercise: Let $f(t, x) = x^{t-1} e^{-x}$, for every $t > 0$ and $x \geq 0$. Prove the following:

(i) Show that for all fixed t as a function of x, $f \in L_1[1, \infty)$ and hence the improper Riemann integral

$$\Gamma(t) := \int_0^\infty f(t, x) dx$$

exits. The function $\Gamma(t)$ is called the **Gamma function**.

(ii) Show that $\Gamma(1) = 1$ and $\Gamma(t + 1) = t\Gamma(t) \ \forall \, t > 0$.

(iii) The function $\Gamma(t)$ has derivatives of all orders, and

$$\Gamma^{(n)}(t) = \int_0^\infty x^{t-1} e^{-x} (\ln x)^n dx.$$

Chapter 6

Fundamental theorem of calculus for the Lebesgue integral

We recall that one of the aims of extending the notion of Riemann integral was to make the fundamental theorem of the integral calculus valid, i.e., to find the relation between the pair of functions f and F defined on an interval $[a, b]$ such that the relation

$$F(t) - F(s) = \int_s^t f(x) d\lambda(x). \tag{6.1}$$

holds for every $a \le s < t \le b$. To analyze the above relation, we fix $f \in L_1[a, b]$ and consider the function

$$F(x) := \int_a^x f(t) d\lambda(t), \ \ x \in [a, b].$$

The function F is called the **indefinite integral** of f.

Note that F and f satisfy the relation (6.1). We analyze the properties of F in the next section.

6.1. Absolutely continuous functions

We had already shown in exercise 5.5.8 that F, the indefinite integral of $f \in L_1[a, b]$, is a uniformly continuous function. In fact, it has the following property which is stronger than uniform continuity:

6.1.1. Theorem: *For every $\epsilon > 0$, $\exists \, \delta > 0$ such that for mutually disjoint subintervals (a_k, b_k), $k = 1, 2, \ldots n$, of $[a, b]$*

$$\sum_{k=1}^{n}(b_k - a_k) < \delta \ \text{implies} \ \sum_{k=1}^{n}|F(b_k) - F(a_k)| < \epsilon.$$

Proof: This follows from proposition 5.4.6(iii) with $\mu = \lambda$. ∎

In view of the above theorem, we introduce the following definition:

6.1.2. Definition: Let $g : [a, b] \longrightarrow \mathbb{R}$. We say g is **absolutely continuous** if $\forall \ \epsilon > 0$, $\exists \ \delta > 0$ such that for any finite collection of mutually disjoint subintervals (a_i, b_i), $1 \leq i \leq n$, of (a, b)

$$\sum_{i=1}^{n}(b_i - a_i) < \delta \ \text{implies} \ \sum_{i=1}^{n}|\, g(b_i) - g(a_i)\,| < \epsilon.$$

6.1.3. Example: In view of theorem 6.1.1, for $f \in L_1[a, b]$, the function $F(x) := \int_a^x f(t)dt$, $x \in [a, b]$, is absolutely continuous. The fact that essentially these are the only examples of absolutely continuous functions is the claim of the fundamental theorem of calculus (theorem 6.3.6).

Let us analyze absolutely continuous functions. We keep in mind that in order to prove the fundamental theorem of calculus, we have to analyze the differentiability of $F(x)$. Before proceeding further, the reader is advised to recall functions of bounded variation (see appendix F).

6.1.4. Theorem: *Let $g : [a, b] \longrightarrow \mathbb{R}$ be an absolutely continuous function. Then g has bounded variation.*

Proof: By the absolute continuity of g, given $\epsilon = 1$, we can find a $\delta > 0$ such that

$$\sum_{i=1}^{n}|\, g(b_i) - g(a_i)\,| < 1,$$

whenever (a_i, b_i), $i = 1, 2, \ldots n$, are pairwise disjoint subintervals of $[a, b]$ with $\sum_{i=1}^{n}(b_i - a_i) < \delta$. But then for any subinterval $[c, d]$ of $[a, b]$ with $(d - c) < \delta$, clearly $V_c^d(g) \leq 1$, where $V_c^d(g)$ denotes the variation of g on the interval $[c, d]$. Let $P = \{a = x_0 < x_1 < \ldots < x_k = b\}$ be any partition of $[a, b]$ such that $\|P\| < \delta$. Then

$$V_a^b(g) = \sum_{i=1}^{k} V_{x_{i-1}}^{x_i}(g) \leq k,$$

i.e., the function g has bounded variation. ∎

6.1.5. Corollary: *For $f \in L_1[a, b]$, let*

$$F(x) := \int_a^x f(t) d\lambda(t), \, x \in [a, b].$$

Then F is a difference of two monotonically increasing functions on $[a, b]$.

Proof: Since F is absolutely continuous, it is of bounded variation, and every function of bounded variation is a difference of two monotonically increasing functions (see Appendix F.2). ∎

In view of the above corollary, one asks the question: if $g : [a, b] \longrightarrow \mathbb{R}$ is a monotonically increasing function, what kind of differentiability properties can g have? Recall that a monotone function can have only a countable number of points of discontinuity. Thus a monotone function is continuous a.e. (λ). One wonders: Is a monotone function also differentiable a.e. (λ)? The answer is yes, and is the content of Lebesgue's theorem (6.2.1), proved in the next section.

•**6.1.6. Exercise:** Let $f \in L_1[a, b]$, and let F be the infinite integral of f. Show that

$$V_a^b(F) = \int_a^b |f(t)| \, d\lambda(t).$$

•**6.1.7. Exercise:**

(i) Let $g : [a, b] \longrightarrow \mathbb{R}$ be a **Lipschitz function**, i.e., there exists some $M > 0$ such that

$$|g(x) - g(y)| \leq M |x - y| \, \forall \, x, y \in [a, b].$$

Show that g is absolutely continuous.

(ii) Let $g : [a, b] \longrightarrow \mathbb{R}$ be differentiable with bounded derivative. Show that g is Lipschitz and hence is an absolutely continuous function.

(iii) Let $f, g : [a, b] \longrightarrow \mathbb{R}$ be absolutely continuous functions. What can you say about the functions $f + g, f - g, \alpha f$, and fg, where $\alpha \in \mathbb{R}$?

6.1.8. Exercise: Let $f : [a, b] \longrightarrow \mathbb{R}$ be an absolutely continuous function. For $x \in [a, b]$, and let $h(x) := V_a^x(f)$. Prove the following:

  (i) The function h is absolutely continuous.

  (ii) The functions $h(x)$ and $h(x) - f(x)$ are both (monotonically increasing) absolutely continuous. Hence $f = h - (h - f)$ gives a representation of an absolutely continuous function as a difference of two monotonically increasing absolutely continuous functions.

6.1.9. Proposition:*Let* $g : [a, b] \longrightarrow \mathbb{R}$ *be an absolutely continuous function. Then the following hold:*

(i) *If* $N \subset [a, b]$ *is a null set, then* $g(N)$ *is also a null set.*

(ii) *If* $E \subseteq [a, b]$ *be Lebesgue measurable, then* $g(E)$ *is also Lebesgue measurable.*

Proof: (i) Let $\epsilon > 0$ be given. Since g is absolutely continuous, we can choose $\delta > 0$ such that whenever $(a_k, b_k), 1 \le k \le n$, are disjoint subintervals of $[a, b]$, then

$$\sum_{k=1}^{n} (b_k - a_k) < \delta \text{ implies } \sum_{k=1}^{n} |g(b_k) - g(a_k)| < \epsilon.$$

Next, N being a null set, we can find intervals $I_k = [x_k, y_k], k \ge 1$, such that

$$N \subseteq \bigcup_{k=1}^{\infty} [x_k, y_k] \subseteq [a, b] \text{ and } \sum_{k=1}^{\infty} (y_k - x_k) < \delta.$$

Since g is continuous, there exist points $a_k, b_k \in [x_k, y_k]$ such that $g(a_k) = m_k$ and $g(b_k) = M_k$, where

$$m_k := \min\{g(x) \,|\, x \in [x_k, y_k]\} \text{ and } M_k := \max\{g(x) \,|\, x \in [x_k, y_k]\}.$$

Then

$$g([x_k, y_k]) \subseteq [m_k, M_k] = [g(a_k), g(b_k)].$$

Thus

$$g(N) \subseteq \bigcup_{k=1}^{\infty} g[x_k, y_k] \subseteq \bigcup_{k=1}^{\infty} [g(a_k), g(b_k)].$$

Since $\forall n$,

$$\sum_{k=1}^{n} |b_k - a_k| \le \sum_{k=1}^{n} (y_k - x_k) < \delta,$$

we have

$$\sum_{k=1}^{n} |g(b_k) - g(a_k)| < \epsilon.$$

Hence

$$g(N) \subseteq \bigcup_{k=1}^{\infty} [g(a_k), g(b_k)] \text{ with } \sum_{k=1}^{\infty} |g(b_k) - g(a_k)| < \epsilon,$$

i.e., $g(N)$ is a null set. This proves (i).

To prove (ii), let $E \subset [a, b]$ be Lebesgue measurable. Using theorem 4.2.2(v), we can find an F_σ-set F and a null set N such that $E = F \cup N$. Then $g(E) = g(F) \cup g(N)$. Since $F \subseteq [a, b]$ is an F_σ-set, it is a countable union of closed subsets of $[a, b]$, say C_n. Then each C_n is a compact set and, g being continuous, $g(C_n)$ is compact. Hence $g(F) = \bigcup_{n=1}^{\infty} g(C_n)$ is Lebesgue measurable. The set $g(N)$ is Lebesgue measurable by (i). Thus $g(E) = g(F) \cup g(N)$ is Lebesgue measurable. ∎

6.1.10. Exercise: Let $f(x) := x^2 \sin^2(1/x)$ for $x \neq 0$, $f(0) := 0$, and let $g(x) := \sqrt{x}$ for $x \geq 0$. Show that

   (i) f is absolutely continuous.
       (Hint: Use exercise 6.1.7.)

   (ii) g is absolutely continuous.
        (Hint: $g(x) = \int_0^x \dfrac{1}{2\sqrt{t}} dt$.)

   (iii) $g \circ f$ is not absolutely continuous.
         (Hint: $V_0^1(g \circ f) = +\infty$.)

●**6.1.11. Exercise:** Let $g : [a, b] \longrightarrow [c, d]$ be absolutely continuous and monotone, and let $f : [c, d] \longrightarrow \mathbb{R}$ be absolutely continuous. Show that $f \circ g$ is also absolutely continuous.

●**6.1.12. Exercise:** Let $g : [a, b] \longrightarrow [c, d]$ be absolutely continuous. Let $f \in L_1[c, d]$ be bounded and F be the indefinite integral of f. Show that $F \circ g$ is also absolutely continuous.

6.1.13. Exercise: Let $f(x) := x \sin(1/x)$ for $x \in (0, 1]$, and $f(0) := 0$. Let $g(x) := \sqrt{x}$ for $0 \leq x \leq 1/2$, and define g linearly on $[1/2, 1]$. Show that both f and g are not absolutely continuous.

6.1.14. Exercise: Show that a function f is absolutely continuous iff both f^+ and f^- are absolutely continuous.

6.2. Differentiability of monotone functions

In this section all the a.e. statements are with respect to the Lebesgue measure λ on $\mathbb{R}$. The aim of this section is to prove the following theorem:

6.2.1. Theorem (Lebesgue - Young): *Let $f : [a, b] \longrightarrow \mathbb{R}$ be a monotone function. Then f is differentiable a.e.*

The proof of the theorem is long, and we shall make preparations for it. Recall that, to analyze the continuity of a function at a point quantitatively, in chapter 1 we introduced the concept of oscillation of the function at a point. Similarly, to analyze the differentiability of a function at a point quantitatively, we consider what are called the Dini derivatives of f.

6.2.2. Definition: Let $\Phi : [a, b] \longrightarrow \mathbb{R}$. Then for any $c \in [a, b)$, we define

$$\liminf_{h \downarrow c} \Phi(x) := \sup \left\{ \inf\{\Phi(h) \,|\, c < h \leq c + \delta\} \,|\, \delta > 0, \, c + \delta < b \right\}$$

and

$$\limsup_{h \downarrow c} \Phi(x) := \inf \left\{ \sup\{\Phi(h) \,|\, c < h \leq c + \delta\} \,|\, \delta > 0, \, c + \delta < b \right\}.$$

For any $c \in (a, b]$, we define

$$\liminf_{h \uparrow c} \Phi(x) := \sup \left\{ \inf\{\Phi(h) \,|\, c - \delta \leq h < c\} \,|\, \delta > 0, \, a < c - \delta \right\}$$

and

$$\limsup_{h \uparrow c} \Phi(x) := \inf \left\{ \sup\{\Phi(h) \,|\, c - \delta \leq h < c\} \,|\, \delta > 0, \, a < c - \delta \right\}.$$

The quantities $\liminf\limits_{h \downarrow c} \Phi(x), \limsup\limits_{h \downarrow c} \Phi(x), \liminf\limits_{h \uparrow c} \Phi(x)$ and $\limsup\limits_{h \uparrow c} \Phi(x)$ exist as extended real numbers and are called, respectively, the **lower right limit, upper right limit, lower left limit** and **upper left limit** of Φ at c.

6.2.3. Definition: Let $f : [a, b] \longrightarrow \mathbb{R}$. For any $c \in [a, b)$, we define

$$(D_+ f)(c) := \liminf_{h \downarrow 0} \left[\frac{f(c + h) - f(c)}{h} \right]$$

and

$$(D^+ f)(c) := \limsup_{h \downarrow 0} \left[\frac{f(c + h) - f(c)}{h} \right].$$

For $c \in (a, b]$, we define

$$(D_- f)(c) := \liminf_{h \uparrow 0} \left[\frac{f(c + h) - f(c)}{h} \right]$$

and

$$(D^- f)(c) := \limsup_{h \uparrow 0} \left[\frac{f(c + h) - f(c)}{h} \right].$$

The extended real numbers $(D_+ f)(c), (D^+ f)(c), (D_- f)(c)$ and $(D^- f)(c)$ are called, respectively, the **lower right derivative, upper right derivative, lower left derivative** and **upper left derivative** of f at c. (These are also known as **Dini derivatives** of f at c.) If all of them are equal, we call it **the derivative** of f at c and denote it by $f'(c)$. Note that in our definition $f'(c)$ is an extended real number.

6.2.4. Examples:

(i) Let $f(x) := x^{1/3}, x \in \mathbb{R}$. Then

$$D_+ f(0) = D^+ f(0) = D_- f(0) = D^- f(0) = +\infty.$$

(ii) Let $f(x) := |x|, x \in \mathbb{R}$. Then

$$(D_+ f)(0) = (D^+ f)(0) = 1 \ \text{ and } \ (D_- f)(0) = (D^- f)(0) = -1.$$

(iii) Let

$$f(x) := \begin{cases} 0 & \text{if} \quad x \in \mathbb{Q} \cap [0,1], \\ 1 & \text{if} \quad x \notin \mathbb{Q} \cap [0,1]. \end{cases}$$

Here $\mathbb{Q}$ denotes the set of rationals. Clearly, for any $x \in [0,1]$, if $x \in \mathbb{Q}$, then

$$D_+ f(x) = 0, \ D^+ f(x) = +\infty, \ D_- f(x) = -\infty \ \text{ and } \ D^- f(x) = 0.$$

If $x \in [0,1]$ but $x \notin \mathbb{Q}$, then

$$D_+ f(x) = -\infty, \ (D^+ f)(x) = 0, \ (D_- f)(x) = 0 \ \text{ and } \ (D^- f)(x) = \infty.$$

(iv) **The Lebesgue singular function:** Let C denote the Cantor ternary set as constructed in example 1.2.13. For $x \in C$, let $x = \sum_{n=1}^{\infty} a_n/3^n$ denote the ternary representation of x, i.e., the representation in base 3, where all the a_i's are either 0 or 2. Let

$$\Phi(x) := \sum_{n=1}^{\infty} a_n/2^{n+1} \text{ whenever } x \in C \text{ and } x = \sum_{n=1}^{\infty} a_n/3^n.$$

Note that if $y = \sum_{n=1}^{\infty} a_n/2^{n+1}$ then $y \in [0,1]$. Let I_k^n, $1 \leq k \leq 2^n$, denote the open intervals removed at the nth stage in the construction of the Cantor set C. If $I_k^n = (a,b)$, say, then

$$a = \sum_{k=1}^{n-1} a_k/3^k + \sum_{k=n+1}^{\infty} 2/3^k \ \text{ and } \ b = \sum_{k=1}^{n-1} a_k/3^k + 2/3^n.$$

Thus

$$\Phi(a) = \sum_{k=1}^{n-1} a_k/2^{k+1} + \sum_{k=n+1}^{\infty} 1/2^k = \sum_{k=1}^{n-1} a_k/2^{k+1} + 1/2^n = \Phi(b).$$

We define a function $f : [0,1] \longrightarrow [0,1]$ as follows:

$$f(x) := \begin{cases} \Phi(x) & \text{if } x \in F, \\ \Phi(a) & \text{if } x \in I_k^n := (a,b) \text{ for some } n, 1 \leq k \leq 2^{n-1}. \end{cases}$$

The function f is called the **Lebesgue singular function**.

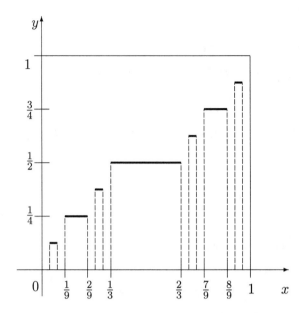

Figure 23 : Part of the graph of f

(For a more geometric description of f, see exercise 6.2.5.) Note that f is constant on each interval I_k^n. If $x, y \in C$ with $x < y$ and are not the end points of any I_k^n, then the ternary representations of x and y must be of the form $x = \sum_{i=1}^{\infty} a_i/3^i$ and $y = \sum_{i=1}^{\infty} b_i/3^i$, where for some n we have $a_i = b_i, 1 \le i \le n$, and $b_{n+1} = 2, a_{n+1} = 0$. But then $\Phi(x) < \Phi(y)$, and hence $f(x) < f(y)$. Finally, if $0 \le x < y \le 1$ with either x or $y \notin C$, it is easy to check that $f(x) < f(y)$. Thus f is monotonically increasing on $[0, 1]$.

Also $f(C) = [0, 1]$. Clearly, f is continuous on each I_k^n. To show that f is continuous everywhere, let $x \in C$ and let

$$N_n := \{y \in [0, 1] \mid |x - y| < 1/3^n\}.$$

If $y \in C \cap N_n$, then the first n terms in the ternary representation of x and y must be identical. But then $f(x)$ and $f(y)$ will have binary representation having identical first n terms, and hence $|f(x) - f(y)| < 1/2^n$. If $y \in N_n \setminus C$, then there exists $z \in C$ which is an end point of some I_k^n, and hence $f(y) = f(z)$. Thus $\forall\ y \in N_n$ we have $|f(x) - f(y)| < 1/2^n\ \forall\ n$, proving the continuity of f everywhere.

Clearly $\forall\ x \in I_k^n, f$ is differentiable at x and $f'(x) = 0$. Thus $f'(x) = 0\ \forall\ x \in (0, 1] \setminus C$, i.e., $f'(x) = 0$ for a.e. $x \in [a, b]$. We show that f is not absolutely continuous. For this, let us extend f to $\mathbb{R}$ by defining

$$f(x) := 0 \text{ if } x < 0 \text{ and } f(x) := 1 \text{ if } x > 1.$$

Since C is a null set, given $\epsilon > 0$, we can find pairwise disjoint intervals $\{(a_k, b_k)\}_{k \geq 1}$ such that

$$C \subset \bigcup_{k=1}^{\infty} (a_k, b_k) \quad \text{and} \quad \sum_{k=1}^{\infty} (b_k - a_k) < \epsilon.$$

Since $0, 1 \in C$, without loss of generality, let $0 \in (a_1, b_1)$ and $1 \in (a_2, b_2)$ with $a_1 < 0 < b_1 \leq a_3 < b_3 \leq \cdots \leq a_2 < 1 < b_2$. Since f is monotonically increasing, for every $n \geq 1$ we have

$$1 = f(1) - f(0) = f(b_2) - f(a_1) \geq \sum_{k=1}^{n} [f(b_k) - f(a_k)].$$

Hence

$$\sum_{k=1}^{\infty} [f(b_k) - f(a_k)] = \delta \leq 1.$$

On the other hand, $f(b_k) - f(a_k) \neq 0 \ \forall \ k$, for otherwise $f(x) = 0 \ \forall \ x$. Thus

$$0 < \sum_{k=1}^{\infty} [f(a_k) - f(b_k)] < 1,$$

and we can find N such that

$$\sum_{k=1}^{N} [f(b_k) - f(a_k)] > \delta/2.$$

This shows that f is not absolutely continuous on $\mathbb{R}$, and hence not on $[0, 1]$.

Finally, we compute $(D^+ f)(x), (D_+ f)(x), (D^- f)(x)$ and $(D_- f)(x)$ when $x \in C$. Let $x \in C$ be such that x is the left endpoint of one of the open intervals that had been removed from $[0,1]$ to construct C. Then clearly $(D^+ f)(x) = (D_+ f)(x) = 0$. Let us calculate $(D_- f)(x)$ at such a point. Since x is the left endpoint of some I_k^n, let

$$x = \sum_{i=1}^{k+1} a_i/3^i + 1/3^k$$

for some $n, 1 \leq k \leq 2^n$ and $a_i \in \{0, 2\} \ \forall \ i$. Thus for all sufficiently small h, say,

$$1/3^{m+1} < h < 1/3^m, \ m > k, \quad \text{implies} \quad 1/2^{m+1} < f(x) - f(x - h) < 1/2^m.$$

Thus

$$3^m/2^{m+1} < \frac{f(x) - f(x - h)}{h} < 3^{m+1}/2^{m+2}.$$

Hence $(D_- f)(x) = +\infty = (D^- f)(x)$. Similarly, one can check that if x is the right endpoint of one of the open intervals removed, then

$$(D^- f)(x) = (D_- f)(x) = 0 \text{ and } (D^+ f)(x) = (D_+ f)(x) = +\infty.$$

Finally, if x is not an endpoint of the open intervals which are removed, then $x = \sum_{k=1}^{\infty} a_k/3^k$, where $a_k \in \{0,2\}$ and $a_k \neq 0$ for infinitely many k's. Let $x_n := \sum_{k=1}^{n} a_k/3^k$, $n = 1, 2, \ldots$. Then $\{x_n\}_{n \geq 1}$ is a sequence of right endpoints of open intervals removed, and $\{x_n\}_{n \geq 1}$ increases to x. Since

$$f(x) - f(x_n) = \sum_{k=n+1}^{\infty} a_k/2^{k+1},$$

we have

$$\frac{f(x) - f(x_n)}{x - x_n} = \frac{\displaystyle\sum_{k=n+1}^{\infty} a_k/2^{k+1}}{\displaystyle\sum_{k=n+1}^{\infty} a_k/3^k}$$

$$\geq \frac{1}{2^{N+1}} \left(\sum_{k=N}^{\infty} 1/3^k \right)$$

$$= 3^{N-1}/2^N,$$

where N is the smallest of all the integers $k \geq n$ such that $a_k \neq 0$. Since $N \to \infty$ when $n \to \infty$, we get

$$\lim_{n \to \infty} \frac{f(x) - f(x_n)}{x - x_n} = +\infty.$$

Hence $(D^- f)(x) = +\infty$. A similar argument shows that $(D^+ f)(x) = +\infty$.

6.2.5. Exercise: Let f be the Lebesgue singular function as defined in example 6.2.4(iv). Show that

(i) $f(x) = (2k-1)/2^n$ if $x \in I_k^n$, for every $n = 1, 2, \ldots$ and $1 \leq k \leq 2^{n-1}$.

(ii) Define $f_n : [0,1] \longrightarrow [0,1]$ $\forall$ $n = 1, 2, \ldots$, continuously by

$$f_n(x) := \begin{cases} 0 & \text{if } x = 0, \\ 1 & \text{if } x = 1, \\ (2k-1)/m & \text{if } x \in I_k^m, \quad 1 \leq k \leq 2^{m-1}, 1 \leq m \leq n, \\ \text{linearly on} \quad [0,1] \setminus \left(\bigcup_{m=1}^{n} (\bigcup_{k=1}^{2^{m-1}} I_k^m) \right). \end{cases}$$

Show that $\{f_n\}_{n \geq 1}$ converges uniformly to f.

(iii) Using the fact that $f(C) = [0,1]$ and proposition 6.1.9, deduce that f is not absolutely continuous.

The next proposition follows easily from the definitions of the Dini derivatives.

6.2.6. Proposition: *Let $f : (a,b) \longrightarrow \mathbb{R}$. Then*

(i) $D^+f(x) \geq D_+f(x)$ *and* $D^-f(x) \geq D_-f(x)$.

(ii) f *is differentiable at* $x \in (a,b)$ *iff all the Dini derivatives exist, are finite and are equal.*

Proof: Exercise. ∎

6.2.7. Exercise: Give an example of a function $f : (a,b) \to \mathbb{R}$ such that f is discontinuous at $x_0 \in (a,b)$, but all the Dini derivatives exist and are equal.

6.2.8. Exercise: Let $f : (a,b) \longrightarrow \mathbb{R}$. Let $S := \{x \in (a,b) | f$ is differentiable at $x\}$ and

$$
\begin{aligned}
A &:= \{x \in (a,b) \,|\, D_-f(x) < D^+f(x)\}, \\
B &:= \{x \in (a,b) \,|\, D_+f(x) < D^-f(x)\}, \\
C &:= \{x \in (a,b) \,|\, D_+f(x) = +\infty\}, \\
D &:= \{x \in (a,b) \,|\, D_-f(x) = +\infty\}.
\end{aligned}
$$

Show that $(a,b) \setminus (A \cup B \cup C \cup D) \subseteq S$.

We are now ready to prove theorem 6.2.1.

Proof of Theorem 6.2.1: Without loss of generality we may assume that f is monotonically increasing, for otherwise we can consider $-f$. Let

$$
\begin{aligned}
E &:= \{x \in (a,b) \,|\, D^+f(x) > D_-f(x)\}, \\
F &:= \{x \in (a,b) \,|\, D_+f(x) < D^-f(x)\}, \\
G &:= \{x \in (a,b) \,|\, (f')(x) = +\infty\}.
\end{aligned}
$$

To show that f is differentiable a.e., in view of proposition 6.2.6 it is enough to show that the sets E, F and G are all null sets. We first show that G is a null set. If $x \in G$, then $\forall \beta > 0$, $\exists$ arbitrarily small $h > 0$ such that $[x, x+h] \subset (a,b)$ and

$$ f(x+h) - f(x) > \beta h. $$

Thus for $\beta > 0$ fixed, the collection

$$ \{[x, x+h] \,|\, x \in G \text{ and } f(x+h) - f(x) > \beta h, h > 0\} $$

is a Vitali covering of G. By theorem 4.4.5, there exists a sequence $\{x_n\}_{n \geq 1}$ in (a,b) such that

$$ \overset{*}{\lambda} \left(G \cap \left(\bigcup_{n=1}^{\infty} [x_n, x_n + h_n] \right)^c \right) = 0. $$

Thus

$$\lambda(G) \;\le\; \sum_{n=1}^{\infty} \lambda[x_n, x_n + h_n]$$

$$= \sum_{n=1}^{\infty} h_n$$

$$\le \; \frac{f(x + h_n) - f(x)}{\beta}$$

$$\le \; \frac{f(b) - f(c)}{\beta}.$$

Since this holds $\forall \, \beta > 0$, we have $\lambda(G) = 0$.

We prove next that $\lambda(E) = 0$. First note that

$$E \;=\; \{x \in (a, b) \mid D^+ f(x) > D_- f(x)\}$$

$$= \bigcup_{r,s \in \mathbb{Q}, r < s} \{x \in (a, b) \mid D^+ f(x) > r > s > D_- f(x)\}.$$

Thus to show that E is a null set, it is enough to show that $\forall \, r, s \in \mathbb{Q}$ with $r < s$ we have $\lambda^*(E_{r,s}) = 0$, where

$$E_{r,s} := \{x \in (a, b) \mid D^+ f(x) > r > s > D_- f(x)\}.$$

Since $\lambda^*(E_{r,s}) < (b - a) < +\infty \;\; \forall \, r, s \in \mathbb{Q}$, given $\epsilon > 0$ we can find an open set $H \supseteq E_{r,s}$ such that

$$\overset{*}{\lambda}(H) < \overset{*}{\lambda}(E_{r,s}) + \epsilon.$$

Also for every $x \in E_{r,s}$, since $D_- f(x) < s$, we can choose an arbitrarily small real number $h > 0$ such that

$$[x - h, x] \subset H \quad \text{and} \quad f(x) - f(x - h) < sh.$$

Thus the collection

$$\{[x - h, x] \mid x \in E_{r,s}, h > 0 \;\; \text{and} \;\; f(x) - f(x - h) < sh\}$$

forms a Vitali covering of $E_{r,s}$. By theorem 4.4.5, we can choose pairwise disjoint intervals $[x_1 - h_1, x_1], \dots, [x_n - h_n, x_n]$ such that for every k

$$f(x_k) - f(x_k - h_k) < sh_k,$$

and

$$\overset{*}{\lambda}\left(E_{r,s} \setminus \left(\bigcup_{k=1}^{n} [x_k - h_k, x_k] \right) \right) < \epsilon.$$

Thus

$$\overset{*}{\lambda}\left(E_{r,s} \cap \left(\bigcup_{k=1}^{n} [x_k - h_k, x_k] \right) \right) > \overset{*}{\lambda}(E_{r,s}) - \epsilon. \qquad (6.2)$$

Further,

$$\sum_{k=1}^{n} [f(x_k) - f(x_k - h_k)] \ < \ s\sum_{k=1}^{n} h_k$$
$$\le \ s\lambda(H)$$
$$< \ s\left(\overset{*}{\lambda}(E_{r,s}) + \epsilon\right). \qquad (6.3)$$

Again, for each $y \in (\bigcup_{k=1}^{n}(x_k - h_k, x_k)) \cap E_{r,s}$, since $D^+f(y) > r$, we can find $z > 0$ arbitrarily small such that $(y, y + z) \subset (x_k - h_k, x_k)$ for some k and

$$f(y + z) - f(y) > rz.$$

Once again, the collection of intervals

$$\left\{ (y, y + z) \mid y \in (\bigcup_{k=1}^{n}(x_k - h_k, x_k)) \cap E_{r,s}, \ z > 0 \text{ and } f(y + z) - f(y) > rz \right\}$$

forms a Vitali covering of the set $(\bigcup_{k=1}^{n}(x_k - h_k, x_k)) \cap E_{r,s}$. Thus by theorem 4.4.5, we can find pairwise disjoint intervals $(y_i, y_i + z_i), 1 \le i \le m$, such that

$$f(y_i + z_i) - f(y_i) > rz_i$$

and

$$\overset{*}{\lambda}\left\{ \left[\left(\bigcup_{k=1}^{n}(x_k - h_k, x_k)\right) \cap E_{r,s}\right] \setminus \left(\bigcup_{i=1}^{m}(y_i, y_i + z_i)\right) \right\} < \epsilon.$$

Thus

$$\overset{*}{\lambda}\left[E_{r,s} \cap \left(\bigcup_{k=1}^{n}(x_k - h_k, x_k)\right) \cap \left(\bigcup_{i=1}^{m}(y_i, y_i + z_i)\right) \right]$$
$$> \overset{*}{\lambda}\left(E_{r,s} \cap \left(\bigcup_{k=1}^{n}(x_k - h_k, x_k)\right)\right) - \epsilon. \qquad (6.4)$$

We note that for every i, $J_i := (y_i, y_i + z_i) \subset (x_k - h_k, x_k) := I_k$ for some k. Thus for every fixed k, since the intervals $(y_i, y_i + z_i), 1 < i \le m$, are pairwise disjoint and f is increasing, we have

$$\sum_{i: J_i \subset I_k} (f(y_i + z_i) - f(y_i)) \le (f(x_k) - f(x_k - h_k)).$$

Therefore,

$$\sum_{k=1}^{n}(f(x_k) - f(x_k - h_k)) \geq \sum_{i=1}^{m}(f(y_i + z_i) - f(y_i))$$

$$\geq r\sum_{i=1}^{m}z_i$$

$$= r\lambda\left(\bigcup_{i=1}^{m}(y_i, y_i + z_i)\right)$$

$$\geq r\overset{*}{\lambda}\left[E_{r,s} \cap \left(\bigcup_{k=1}^{m}(x_k - h_k, x_k)\right)\right.$$

$$\left.\cap\left(\bigcup_{i=1}^{n}(y_i, y_i + z_i)\right)\right].$$

Using (6.4), we get

$$\sum_{k=1}^{n}(f(x_k) - f(x_k - h_k))$$

$$> \left[\overset{*}{\lambda}\left(E_{r,s} \cap \left(\bigcup_{k=1}^{n}(x_k - h_k, x_k)\right)\right) - \epsilon\right]. \qquad (6.5)$$

From (6.2), (6.3) and (6.5) we have

$$s(\overset{*}{\lambda}(E_{r,s}) + \epsilon) > r\left[\overset{*}{\lambda}\left(E_{r,s} \cap \left(\bigcup_{k=1}^{n}(x_k - h_k, x_k)\right)\right) - \epsilon\right]$$

$$> r\left[\overset{*}{\lambda}(E_{r,s}) - 2\epsilon\right].$$

Since $\epsilon > 0$ is arbitrary, we have

$$s(\overset{*}{\lambda}(E_{r,s})) \geq r(\overset{*}{\lambda}(E_{r,s})).$$

Because $r > s$, the above inequality implies that $\overset{*}{\lambda}(E_{r,s}) = 0$. This completes the proof that E is a null set. The proof that F is a null set is similar. This completes the proof of the theorem. ∎

We next analyze measurability and integrability of the derivative function.

6.2.9. Theorem: *Let* $f : [a, b] \longrightarrow \mathbb{R}$ *be a monotonically increasing function. Then* $f' \in L_1[a, b]$ *and*

$$\int_{a}^{b} f'd\lambda \leq f(b) - f(a).$$

Proof: First note that, being monotonically increasing, f is a measurable function. By theorem 6.2.1, $f'(x)$ exists for a.e. x. Let

$$g_n(x) := \left[\frac{f(x + (1/n)) - f(x)}{1/n}\right], \quad x \in [a, b].$$

Here, $f(x) \equiv f(b)$ for $x > b$. Each g_n is a measurable function, and $g_n(x) \to f'(x)$ for a.e. $x \in [a, b]$. Thus $f'(x)$, which is defined a.e., is a measurable function (with arbitrary values on the null set where it is not defined). Since f is monotonically increasing, $\{g_n\}_{n\geq 1}$ is a sequence of nonnegative measurable functions. By Fatou's lemma, we have

$$
\begin{aligned}
\int_a^b f'(x)d\lambda(x) &\leq \liminf_{n\to\infty} \int_a^b g_n(x)d\lambda(x) \\
&= \liminf_{n\to\infty} \left[n\int_a^b f(x + \frac{1}{n})d\lambda(x) - n\int_a^b f(x)d\lambda(x)\right] \\
&= \liminf_{n\to\infty} \left[n\int_{a+1/n}^{b+1/n} f(x)d\lambda(x) - n\int_a^b f(x)d\lambda(x)\right] \\
&= \liminf_{n\to\infty} \left[n\int_b^{b+1/n} f(x)dx - n\int_a^{a+1/n} f(x)d\lambda(x)\right] \\
&= f(b) - \limsup_{n\to\infty} \left[n\int_a^{a+1/n} f(x)d\lambda(x)\right] \\
&\leq f(b) - \limsup_{n\to\infty} \left[n\left(\frac{f(a)}{n}\right)\right] = f(b) - f(a). \quad \blacksquare
\end{aligned}
$$

6.2.10. Remark: The inequality $\displaystyle\int_a^b f'(x)\,d\lambda(x) \leq f(b) - f(a)$ can be strict. For example, take f to be the Lebesgue singular function, as in example 6.2.4(iv).

In the next section we shall prove that the inequality in theorem 6.2.9 becomes an equality iff f is absolutely continuous (see theorems 6.3.1 and 6.3.2). We conclude this section with an application of theorem 6.2.1 to differentiation of a series of nondecreasing functions.

6.2.11. Theorem (Fubini): *Let $\{f_n\}_{n\geq 1}$ be a sequence of real-valued nondecreasing functions on $[a, b]$ such that $\sum_{n=1}^{\infty} f_n(x) := f(x)$ exists for every $x \in [a, b]$. Then f is differentiable for a.e. $x \in [a, b]$, and, for a.e. $x \in [a, b]$,*

$$f'(x) = \sum_{n=1}^{\infty} f_n'(x).$$

Proof: Without loss of generality, we may assume that $f_n(x) \geq 0$ $\forall\, n$ and $\forall\, x$. Since each f_n is nondecreasing, it is differentiable for a.e. x, by theorem 6.2.1, and $f_n'(x) \geq 0$, whenever it exists. Let

$$E_n := \{x \in [a,b] \mid f_n'(x) \text{ does not exist}\} \text{ and } E = \bigcup_{n=1}^{\infty} E_n.$$

Then E is a null set and $\forall\, x \in [a,b] \setminus E$, $\left\{\sum_{k=1}^{n} f_k'(x)\right\}_{n \geq 1}$ is a nondecreasing sequence. Further,

$$\sum_{k=1}^{n} \frac{f_k(x+h) - f_k(x)}{h} \leq \lim_{n \to \infty} \sum_{k=1}^{n} \frac{f_k(x+h) - f_k(x)}{h}$$
$$= \frac{f(x+h) - f(x)}{h}.$$

Since f also is a nondecreasing function, by theorem 6.2.1 again, $f'(x)$ exists for all $x \notin F \subset [a,b]$, where F is a null set. Thus $\forall\, x \in [a,b] \setminus (E \cup F)$, we have

$$\sum_{k=1}^{n} f_k'(x) = \lim_{h \to 0} \sum_{k=1}^{n} \frac{f_k(x+h) - f_k(x)}{h}$$
$$\leq \lim_{h \to 0} \frac{f(x+h) - f(x)}{h}$$
$$= f'(x).$$

Hence $\left\{\sum_{k=1}^{n} f_k'(x)\right\}_{n \geq 1}$ is a nondecreasing sequence and is bounded above by $f'(x)$, $x \in [a,b] \setminus (E \cup F)$. Thus $\sum_{k=1}^{\infty} f_k'(x)$ is convergent for a.e. x. To complete the proof we have to show that $\sum_{k=1}^{\infty} f_k'(x) = f'(x)$ for a.e. $x \in [a,b]$. For this, it is enough to show that there is a subsequence of $\left\{\sum_{k=1}^{n} f_k'(x)\right\}_{n \geq 1}$ which converges to $f'(x)$ for a.e. x. To prove this, we shall show that there exist positive integers $n_1 < n_2 < n_3 < \cdots < n_k \ldots$ such that $\sum_{k=1}^{\infty} \left[f'(x) - \sum_{j=1}^{n_k} f_j'(x)\right]$ is convergent for a.e. $x \in [a,b]$, for then its general term will converge to zero. We note that for every $x \in [a,b]$ and every choice of positive integers $n_1 < n_2 < \cdots < n_k < \cdots$,

$$f'(x) - \sum_{j=1}^{n_k} f_j'(x) = \left[f(x) - \sum_{j=1}^{n_k} f_j(x)\right]'$$

and

$$f(x) - \sum_{j=1}^{n_k} f_j(x) = \sum_{j=n_k+1}^{\infty} f_j(x).$$

Since $f_n(x) \geq 0 \ \forall \ n$ and $\forall \ x$, $\left\{ \sum_{j=n_k+1}^{\infty} f_j(x) \right\}_{k \geq 1}$ is a sequence of nonde-

creasing functions. Thus, whenever the series $\sum_{k=1}^{\infty} \left(\sum_{j=n_k+1}^{\infty} f_j \right)$ converges
pointwise, then, by above argument, the corresponding series of deriva-
tives will converge a.e. x. Thus we only have to choose $\{n_k\}_{k \geq 1}$ such that
$\forall \ x \in [a, b]$, $\sum_{k=1}^{\infty} \left(\sum_{j=n_k+1}^{\infty} f_j(x) \right) < +\infty$. Since

$$\sum_{j=n_k+1}^{\infty} f_j(x) \leq \sum_{j=n_k+1}^{\infty} f_j(b),$$

we only have to choose $\{n_k\}_{k \geq 1}$ such that $\sum_{k=1}^{\infty} \left[\sum_{j=n_k+1}^{\infty} f_j(b) \right] < +\infty$.
But that is possible, since $f(b) = \sum_{j=1}^{\infty} f_j(b)$ and we can choose $\{n_k\}_{k \geq 1}$
with

$$\sum_{j=n_k+1}^{\infty} f_j(b) = f(b) - \sum_{j=1}^{n_k} f(b) < \frac{1}{2^k}.$$

Then

$$\sum_{k=1}^{\infty} \left[\sum_{j=n_k+1}^{\infty} f_j(b) \right] \leq \sum_{k=1}^{\infty} \frac{1}{2^k} < +\infty.$$

This completes the proof. ∎

•**6.2.12. Exercise:** Let $f : [0, 1] \longrightarrow [0, 1]$ be the Lebesgue singular function as constructed in example 6.2.4(iv). Extend f to $\mathbb{R}$ by $f(x) = 0$ if $x < 0$
and $f(x) = 1$ if $x > 1$. Let $\{r_n \mid n = 1, 2, \dots\}$ be any enumeration of the
rationals. Define

$$\Phi(x) := \sum_{n=1}^{\infty} \frac{f(2^n(x - r_n))}{2^n}, \quad x \in \mathbb{R}.$$

Show that Φ is a well-defined, continuous, strictly increasing function on $\mathbb{R}$.
Further, $\Phi'(x) = 0$ for a.e. x.
(Hint: Use theorem 6.2.11.)

6.3. Fundamental theorem of calculus and its applications

As in section 6.2, in this section also all a.e. statements are with respect to
the Lebesgue measure λ on $\mathbb{R}$.

6.3.1. Theorem (Fundamental theorem of calculus-I): *Let $f \in L_1[a, b]$
and $F(x) := \int_a^x f(t) \, d\lambda(t)$, $x \in [a, b]$. Then F is absolutely continuous and
is differentiable, with $F'(x) = f(x)$ for a.e. $x \in [a, b]$.*

Proof: That F is absolutely continuous has already been proved in theorem 6.1.1. Since $f = f^+ - f^-$ and both $f^+, f^- \in L_1[a,b]$, we have

$$
\begin{aligned}
F(x) &= \int_a^x f^+(t)d\lambda(t) - \int_a^x f^-(t)d\lambda(t) \\
&:= F_1(x) - F_2(x).
\end{aligned}
$$

Both $F_1(x)$ and $F_2(x)$ are nonnegative and monotonically increasing (and also absolutely continuous). Thus to show that F is differentiable for a.e. x and $F'(x) = f(x)$, it is enough to show that each of F_1 and F_2 have this property. For in that case we will have

$$
F'(x) = F_1'(x) - F_2'(x) = f^+(x) - f^-(x) = f(x).
$$

So, we assume, without loss of generality, that $f \geq 0$. Then F is monotonically increasing, and by theorem 6.2.1, F is differentiable for a.e. $x \in [a,b]$. We only have to identify its derivative. First assume that f is bounded also, i.e., $0 \leq f(x) \leq M \;\forall\, x \in [a,b]$ and for some M. Let

$$
F_n(x) := \frac{F(x + (1/n)) - F(x)}{1/n}, \quad a < x < b.
$$

Then each F_n is a measurable function (in fact continuous) and $F_n(x)$ converges to $F'(x)$ for a.e. $x \in [a,b]$. Further, $\forall\, n$,

$$
|F_n(x)| = \left| n \int_x^{x+1/n} f(t)d\lambda(t) \right| \leq M, \quad x \in [a,b].
$$

Hence by Lebesgue's dominated convergence theorem, $\forall\, c \in (a,b)$,

$$
\begin{aligned}
\int_a^c F'(t)d\lambda(t) &= \lim_{n\to\infty} \int_a^c F_n(t)d\lambda(t) \\
&= \lim_{n\to\infty} \left[n \int_a^c F(t+1/n)d\lambda(t) - n \int_a^c F(t)d\lambda(t) \right] \\
&= \lim_{n\to\infty} \left[n \int_{a+1/n}^{c+1/n} F(t)d\lambda(t) - n \int_a^c F(t)d\lambda(t) \right] \\
&= \lim_{n\to\infty} n \left[\int_c^{c+1/n} F(t)d\lambda(t) - \int_a^{a+1/n} F(t)d\lambda(t) \right]. \quad (6.6)
\end{aligned}
$$

Since F is a nonnegative monotonically increasing function, we have

$$
F(c) \leq n \int_c^{c+1/n} F(t)d\lambda(t) \leq F(c+1/n)
$$

and

$$
F(a) \leq n \int_a^{a+1/n} F(t)d\lambda(t) \leq F(a+1/n).
$$

Using these and the fact that F is continuous (in fact absolutely continuous), we get

$$\lim_{n\to\infty} n \left[\int_c^{c+1/n} F(t)d\lambda(t) - \int_a^{a+1/n} F(t)d\lambda(t) \right] = F(c)$$

$$= \int_a^c f(t)d\lambda(t). \ (6.7)$$

From (6.5) and (6.7), we get $\forall\, c \in (a,b)$,

$$\int_a^c F'(t)d\lambda(t) = \int_a^c f(t)d\lambda(t).$$

Since this holds for every $a < c < b$, by exercise 5.4.8, we have

$$f'(t) = F(t) \ \text{ for a.e. } \ t \in [a,b].$$

This proves the theorem in the particular case when f is bounded.

In the general case, we 'truncate f' (see note 5.3.24) as follows: define $\forall\, n = 1, 2, \ldots$

$$f_n(x) := \begin{cases} f(x) & \text{if } f(x) \le n, \\ n & \text{if } f(x) > n. \end{cases}$$

Then $\{f_n\}_{n\geq 1}$ is a sequence of bounded measurable functions such that $\{f_n(x)\}_{n\geq 1}$ increases to $f(x)$ for every $x \in [a,b]$. For every $n \geq 1$, let

$$G_n(x) := \int_a^x (f - f_n)(t)d\lambda(t), \ \ x \in [a,b].$$

Then each G_n is an absolutely continuous, monotonically increasing function, and hence $G'_n(x) \geq 0$ for a.e. $x \in [a,b]$. Further,

$$F(x) = G_n(x) + \int_a^x f_n(t)d\lambda(t), \ \ x \in [a,b].$$

Thus $F'(x)$ exists for a.e. $x \in [a,b]$ and, by the earlier case,

$$F'(x) = G'_n(x) + f_n(x) \ \text{ for a.e. } \ x \in [a,b] \ \text{ and } \ \forall\, n.$$

Hence $F'(x) \geq f_n(x)$ for every n and for a.e. $x \in [a,b]$. Thus

$$F'(x) \geq f(x) \ \text{ for a.e. } \ x \in [a,b].$$

On the other hand, by theorem 6.2.9,

$$\int_a^b F'(x)d\lambda(x) \leq F(b) = \int_a^b f(x)d\lambda(x).$$

Thus

$$\int_a^b \left[F'(x) - f(x) \right] d\lambda(x) = 0.$$

Since $F'(x) - f(x) \geq 0$ for a.e. $x \in [a,b]$, this implies that $F'(x) = f(x)$ for a.e. $x \in [a,b]$. ∎

As an application of theorem 6.3.1, we have the following theorem.

6.3.2. Theorem: *Let $f \in L_1[a, b]$. Then there exists a set $E \subseteq [a, b]$ such that $\lambda([a, b] \setminus E) = 0$ and $\forall \, x \in E$*

$$\lim_{h \to 0} \frac{1}{h} \int_0^h |f(x + t) - f(x)| \, d\lambda(t) = 0.$$

(Elements of E are called the **Lebesgue points** of f in $[a, b]$.)

Proof: For every $\xi \in \mathbb{R}$ fixed, consider

$$F(y) := \int_a^y |f(t) - \xi| \, d\lambda(t), \quad y \in [a, b].$$

By the fundamental theorem of calculus (6.3.1), F is differentiable for a.e. $y \in [a, b]$, and for such y,

$$|f(y) - \xi| = F'(y) \quad = \quad \lim_{h \to 0} \frac{1}{h} \int_y^{y+h} |f(t) - \xi| \, d\lambda(t)$$

$$= \quad \lim_{h \to 0} \frac{1}{h} \int_0^h |f(y + t) - \xi| \, d\lambda(t). \quad (6.8)$$

Let E_ξ denote the set of points $y \in [a, b]$ such that (6.8) holds. Then $\lambda([a, b] \setminus E_\xi) = 0$. Let

$$E := \bigcap_{\xi \in \mathbb{Q}} E_\xi.$$

Clearly,

$$0 \leq \lambda([a, b] \setminus E) \leq \sum_{\xi \in \mathbb{Q}} \lambda([a, b] \setminus E_\xi) = 0.$$

We shall show that $\forall \, x \in E$, the required property holds. Fix any $x \in [a, b]$ and let $\epsilon > 0$ be arbitrary. Choose a rational ξ such that $|f(x) - \xi| \leq \epsilon$. If $x \in E$, then $x \in E_\xi$ and

$$|f(x) - \xi| = \lim_{h \to 0} \frac{1}{h} \int_0^h |f(x + t) - \xi| \, d\lambda(t).$$

Let us choose $\delta > 0$ such that $\forall \, 0 < |h| < \delta$,

$$\left| \frac{1}{h} \int_0^h |f(x + t) - \xi| \, d\lambda(t) - |f(x) - \xi| \right| < \epsilon/2.$$

Then

$$\left| \frac{1}{h} \int_0^h |f(x + t) - \xi| \, d\lambda(t) \right| \leq |f(x) - \xi| + \epsilon/2 \leq \epsilon.$$

Finally,

$$\left| \frac{1}{h} \int_0^h |f(t+x) - f(x)| \, d\lambda(t) \right| \leq \left| \frac{1}{h} \int_0^h |f(x+t) - \xi| \, d\lambda(t) \right|$$

$$+ \left| \frac{1}{h} \int_0^h |f(x) - \xi| \, d\lambda(t) \right|$$

$$< \quad \epsilon + |f(x) - \xi| \quad < \quad 2\epsilon. \quad \blacksquare$$

6.3.3. Note: Let $f \in L_1[a,b]$ and let $t \in \mathbb{R}$. Then it follows from exercise 5.5.9 that every continuity point of f is also a Lebesgue point of f.

Theorem 6.3.1 gives one part of the fundamental theorem of calculus: for a function $f \in L_1[a,b]$, its indefinite (Lebesgue) integral $F(x) := \int_a^x f(t)d\lambda(t)$ is differentiable a.e. $x \in [a,b]$, and at these points $F'(x) = f(x)$. Next we look at the converse question: when is a function $F : [a,b] \longrightarrow \mathbb{R}$ the indefinite integral of its derivative? If we recall the example of the Lebesgue singular function, it is not enough to assume that F is continuous, is differentiable a.e. and $F \in L_1[a,b]$. Some additional property of F is needed to conclude that it is the indefinite integral of its derivative. The extra property should be absolute continuity, for if F is an indefinite integral, then it is going to be so. The precise statement is as follows:

6.3.4.   Theorem (Fundamental theorem of calculus-II): *Let* $F :$ $[a,b] \longrightarrow \mathbb{R}$ *be an absolutely continuous function. Then* $F'(x)$ *exists for a.e.* $x \in [a,b]$, *with* $F' \in L_1[a,b]$ *and*

$$F(y) - F(x) = \int_x^y F'(t)d\lambda(t), \quad \forall \, a \leq x < y \leq b.$$

For the proof we need the following lemma, which is another application of the Vitali covering theorem (4.4.5).

6.3.5. Lemma: *Let* $\phi : [a,b] \longrightarrow \mathbb{R}$ *be an absolutely continuous function such that* $\phi'(x) = 0$ *for a.e.* $x \in [a,b]$. *Then* ϕ *is a constant function.*

Proof: We shall show that $\forall \, c \in (a,b]$, $\phi(c) = \phi(a)$. Let

$$E := \{x \in (a,c) \mid \phi'(x) = 0\}.$$

By the given hypothesis, $\lambda(E) = c - a$. Let $\eta > 0$ be given. For every $x \in E$, we can find an arbitrarily small $h > 0$ such that

$$[x, x+h] \subset (a,c) \quad \text{and} \quad |\phi(x+h) - \phi(x)| < \eta h.$$

Thus the collection of intervals

$$\{[x, x+h] \mid x \in (a, c),\ h > 0,\ |\phi(x+h) - \phi(x)| < \eta h\}$$

forms a Vitali covering of E. By theorem 4.4.5, given any $\delta > 0$, there exist pairwise disjoint intervals $[x_i, x_i + h_i], i = 1, 2, \ldots, n$, such that

$$\bigcup_{i=1}^{n}[x_i, x_i + h_i] \subset (a, c) \quad \text{with} \quad |\phi(x_i + h_i) - \phi(x_i)| < \eta h_i$$

for every $1 \le i \le n$ and

$$\lambda\left(E \setminus \bigcup_{i=1}^{n}[x_i, x_i + h_i]\right) < \delta.$$

Without loss of generality, let

$$x_0 + h_0 := a < x_1 < x_1 + h_1 < x_2 < x_2 + h_2 < \cdots < x_n + h_n < c := x_{n+1}.$$

Then

$$
\begin{aligned}
\sum_{k=0}^{n}[x_{k+1} - (x_k + h_k)] &= c - \sum_{k=1}^{n}[x_k + h_k - x_k] - a \\
&= \lambda(E) - \lambda\left(\bigcup_{k=1}^{n}[x_k, x_k + h_k]\right) \\
&= \lambda\left(E \setminus \bigcup_{k=1}^{n}[x_k, x_k + h_k]\right) < \delta. \qquad (6.9)
\end{aligned}
$$

Also,

$$
\begin{aligned}
|\phi(c) - \phi(a)| &= |\phi(x_{n+1}) - \phi(x_0 + h_0)| \\
&= |\sum_{k=0}^{n}[\phi(x_{k+1}) - \phi(x_k + h_k)] \\
&\qquad + \sum_{k=1}^{n}[\phi(x_k + h_k) - \phi(x_k)]| \\
&\le \sum_{k=0}^{n}|\phi(x_{k+1}) - \phi(x_k + h_k)| \\
&\qquad + \sum_{k=1}^{n}|\phi(x_k + h_k) - \phi(x_k)|. \qquad (6.10)
\end{aligned}
$$

Let $\epsilon > 0$ be arbitrary. We choose and fix $\delta > 0$ given by the absolute continuity property of ϕ. Then for this δ we have, by (6.9),

$$\sum_{k=0}^{n}|\phi(x_k) - \phi(x_k + h_k)| < \epsilon.$$

Thus from (6.10), we have

$$|\phi(c) - \phi(a)| \leq \epsilon + \sum_{k=1}^{n} \eta h_i \leq \epsilon + \eta(b-a).$$

Since $\eta > 0$ and $\epsilon > 0$ are arbitrary, we have $\phi(c) = \phi(a)$.

(Lemma 6.3.5 can also be deduced from proposition 4.1.3 and proposition 6.1.9 as follows: Let $E = \{x \in (a,b) | f'(x) = 0\}$. By proposition 4.1.3 with $\alpha = 0$, $\lambda(\phi(E)) = 0$. Also, $\overset{*}{\lambda}(\phi[a,b]) = 0$, i.e., the range of ϕ is a singleton.) ∎

Proof of Theorem 6.3.4: Since $F : [a,b] \longrightarrow \mathbb{R}$ is absolutely continuous, by theorem 6.1.4, F is a function of bounded variation and hence $F(x) = F_1(x) - F_2(x)$, where F_1 and F_2 are monotonically increasing functions on $[a,b]$. But then, by theorem 6.2.1, $F'(x)$ exists with $F'(x) = F_1'(x) - F_2'(x)$ for a.e. x. Further, by theorem 6.2.9, $F_1', F_2' \in L_1[a,b]$ and

$$F_1(x) \leq \int_a^x F_1'(t)d\lambda(t), \ F_2(x) \leq \int_a^x F_2'(t)d\lambda(t).$$

Thus $F' \in L_1[a,b]$. Let

$$G(x) := \int_a^x F'(t)d\lambda(t), \quad x \in [a,b].$$

Then $G(x)$ is absolutely continuous, is differentiable for a.e. $x \in [a,b]$, and $G'(x) = F'(x)$ for a.e. $x \in [a,b]$ (by theorem 6.3.1). Now by lemma 6.3.5, $G(x) = F(x) \ \forall x$. ∎

Theorems 6.2.1 and 6.3.4 can be combined together as follows:

6.3.6. Theorem (Fundamental theorem of calculus): *Let $F : [a,b] \longrightarrow \mathbb{R}$. Then the following statements are equivalent:*

(i) *F is absolutely continuous.*

(ii) *$F(x) = \int_a^x f(t)d\lambda(t) \ \forall x \in [a,b]$ and for some $f \in L_1[a,b]$.*

(iii) *$F(x)$ is differentiable for a.e. $x \in [a,b]$, with $F' \in L_1[a,b]$ and*

$$F(x) = \int_a^x F'(t)d\lambda(t) \ \forall x \in [a,b].$$

In fact, the above theorem can be extended to functions defined on $\mathbb{R}$ as follows: Suppose $F : \mathbb{R} \longrightarrow \mathbb{R}$ is such that

$$F(x) = \int_{-\infty}^x f(t)d\lambda(t),$$

for some $f \in L_1(\mathbb{R})$ and every $x \in \mathbb{R}$. Then clearly $\forall\, a > 0$,

$$F(x) = \int_{-a}^{x} f(t)d\lambda(t) + F(-a), \quad x \in [-a, a].$$

Thus F is absolutely continuous on $[-a, a]$ $\forall\, a > 0$. Further, it is easy to check that $\lim_{a \to \infty} V_{-a}^{a}(F)$ is finite. One writes

$$V_{-\infty}^{+\infty}(F) := \lim_{a \to \infty} V_{-a}^{a}(F),$$

called the **variation** of F on $\mathbb{R}$. In fact,

$$V_{-\infty}^{+\infty}(F) \leq \int_{-\infty}^{+\infty} |f(x)|d\lambda(x).$$

Finally, an application of the dominated convergence theorem shows that $\lim_{x \to -\infty} F(x) = 0$. Conversely, suppose $F : \mathbb{R} \longrightarrow \mathbb{R}$ is such that F is absolutely continuous on $[-a, a]$ $\forall\, a > 0$ with finite variation on $\mathbb{R}$, and $\lim_{x \to -\infty} F(x) = 0$. Then, clearly, $F'(x)$ exists for a.e. $x \in \mathbb{R}$, and by the monotone convergence theorem, we have

$$\int_{-\infty}^{+\infty} |F'(t)|d\lambda(t) = \lim_{n \to \infty} \int_{-n}^{+n} |F'(t)|d\lambda(t).$$

Since by exercise 6.1.6,

$$\int_{-n}^{+n} |F'(t)|d\lambda(t) = V_{-n}^{n}(F) < V_{-\infty}^{+\infty}(F) \ \forall\, n,$$

we have

$$\int_{-\infty}^{+\infty} |F'(t)|d\lambda(t) < +\infty.$$

Thus $F' \in L_1(\mathbb{R})$, and by the Lebesgue's dominated convergence theorem, we have

$$\lim_{a \to \infty} \int_{-a}^{x} F'(t)d\lambda(t) = \int_{-\infty}^{x} F'(t)d\lambda(t).$$

Since $\forall\, a > 0$ and $x > -a$,

$$F(x) = F(-a) + \int_{-a}^{x} F'(t)d\lambda(t),$$

we have

$$\begin{aligned}
F(x) &= \lim_{a \to \infty} F(-a) + \lim_{a \to \infty} \int_{-a}^{x} F'(t)d\lambda(t) \\
&= \int_{-\infty}^{x} F'(t)d\lambda(t).
\end{aligned}$$

Thus we have proved the following theorem:

6.3.7. **Theorem:** *Let $F : \mathbb{R} \longrightarrow \mathbb{R}$. Then the following statements are equivalent:*

(i) *F is differentiable for a.e. $x \in \mathbb{R}$ with $F' \in L_1(\mathbb{R})$ and*

$$F(x) = \int_{-\infty}^{x} F'(t)d\lambda(t), \quad x \in \mathbb{R}.$$

(ii) *F is absolutely continuous on $[-a, a]$ $\forall\, a > 0$ with $\displaystyle\lim_{x \to \infty} F(-x) = 0$, and F has finite variation on $\mathbb{R}$.*

As an application of the fundamental theorem of calculus we have the following.

6.3.8. **Corollary:** *Let f , $g \in L_1[a, b]$. Let*

$$F(x) := \int_{a}^{x} f(t)d\lambda(t) + \alpha \quad and \quad G(t) := \int_{a}^{x} g(t)d\lambda(t) + \beta,$$

where $\alpha, \beta \in \mathbb{R}$ and $x \in [a, b]$. Then

$$\int_{a}^{b} (Gf)(t)d\lambda(t) = [G(b)F(b) - G(a)F(a)] - \int_{a}^{b} (Fg)(t)d\lambda(t).$$

Proof: First note that since F and G are absolutely continuous, it follows from exercise 6.1.7 that FG is absolutely continuous, and thus FG is differentiable for a.e. x. Further, by theorem 6.3.1,

$$(FG)(x) = (Fg)(x) + (fG)(x) \text{ for a.e. } x.$$

Now by theorem 6.3.4,

$$
\begin{aligned}
F(b)G(b) - F(a)G(a) &= \int_{a}^{b} (FG)'(t)d\lambda(t) \\
&= \int_{a}^{b} (Fg)(t)d\lambda(t) + \int_{a}^{b} (fG)(t)d\lambda(t). \blacksquare
\end{aligned}
$$

6.3.9. **Corollary (Integration by parts):** *Let F, $G : [a, b] \to \mathbb{R}$ be absolutely continuous functions. Then*

$$F(b)G(b) - F(a)G(a) = \int_{a}^{b} (F'G)(t)d\lambda(t) + \int_{a}^{b} (FG')(t)d\lambda(t).$$

Proof: Take $f = F'$ and $g = G'$ in corollary 6.3.8. $\blacksquare$

In view of theorem 6.3.7, and corollary 6.3.9, we have the following.

6.3.10. Corollary (Extended integration by parts): *Let* f, $g : \mathbb{R} \longrightarrow \mathbb{R}$ *be such that both are absolutely continuous on* $[-a, a]$ *for every* $a > 0$, $\lim_{x \to \infty} f(-x) = 0 = \lim_{x \to \infty} g(-x)$, *and both* f, g *have finite variation on* $\mathbb{R}$. *Then*

$$\int_{\mathbb{R}} f(t)g'(t)\, d\lambda(t) + \int_{\mathbb{R}} f'(t)g(t)\, d\lambda(t)$$

$$= \left(\int_{\mathbb{R}} f'(t)d\lambda(t) \right) \left(\int_{\mathbb{R}} g'(t)d\lambda(t) \right)$$

$$= \left(\lim_{x \to \infty} f(x) \right) \left(\lim_{x \to \infty} g(x) \right). \blacksquare$$

As another application of the fundamental theorem of calculus, we look at the extension of the integration by substitution formula from the Riemann integral to the Lebesgue integral. The integration by substitution for Riemann integration is as follows (see also exercise 6.3.20).

6.3.11. Theorem (Change of variable for Riemann integration): *Let* $f : [c, d] \longrightarrow \mathbb{R}$ *and* $\phi : [a, b] \longrightarrow [c, d]$ *be such that both have continuous derivatives. Then*

$$\int_a^b (f \circ \phi)(x)\phi'(x)dx = \int_{\phi(a)}^{\phi(b)} f(y)dy.$$

Proof: Let

$$F(x) := \int_a^x f(t)dt, \quad a \le x \le b.$$

Then $(F \circ \phi)$ is differentiable and, by the chain rule,

$$(F \circ \phi)'(x) = (F' \circ \phi)(x)\phi(x) = (f \circ \phi)(x)\phi'(x).$$

Thus by the fundamental theorem of calculus (6.3.6),

$$
\begin{aligned}
\int_a^b (f \circ \phi)(x)\phi'(x)dx &= \int_a^b (F \circ \phi)'(x)dx \\
&= (F \circ \phi)(b) - (F \circ \phi)(a) \\
&= \int_{\phi(a)}^{\phi(b)} F'(y)dy \\
&= \int_{\phi(a)}^{\phi(b)} f(y)dy. \blacksquare
\end{aligned}
$$

An immediate extension of theorem 6.3.11 is the following.

6.3.12. Theorem: *Let* $\phi : [a, b] \longrightarrow [c, d]$ *be absolutely continuous. Let* $f : [c, d] \longrightarrow \mathbb{R}$ *be a continuous function and* F *its indefinite integral. Then*

(i) $(F \circ \phi)$ *is differentiable a.e. on* $[a, b]$, *and*

$$(F \circ \phi)'(x) = (f \circ \phi)(x)\phi'(x)$$

whenever $x \in [a, b]$ *is such that* $\phi'(x)$ *exists.*

(ii) $\displaystyle\int_{\phi(a)}^{\phi(b)} f(y) dy = \int_a^b f(\phi(x))\phi'(x) dx.$

Proof: Since $F \circ \phi$ is absolutely continuous, it is differentiable a.e. (by theorem 6.3.6 and exercise 6.1.12). In fact, $F'(y) = f(y) \; \forall \, y \in [c, d]$. Thus whenever $\phi'(x)$ exists and is finite, we have

$$(F \circ \phi)'(x) = (F' \circ \phi)(x)\phi'(x) = (f \circ \phi)(x)\phi'(x).$$

Further, by theorem 6.3.6,

$$
\begin{aligned}
\int_a^b (f \circ \phi')(t)\phi(t) dt &= \int_a^b (F \circ \phi)'(x) dx \\
&= (F \circ \phi)(b) - (F \circ \phi)(a) \\
&= F(\phi(b)) - F(\phi(a)) \\
&= \int_{\phi(a)}^{\phi(b)} f(y) dy. \quad \blacksquare
\end{aligned}
$$

6.3.13. Corollary: *Let* $\phi : [a, b] \to [c, d]$ *be a monotonically increasing, absolutely continuous function and* $f : [c, d] \to \mathbb{R}$ *a bounded measurable function. Then* $(f \circ \phi)\phi'$ *is integrable on* $[a, b]$, *and*

$$\int_{\phi(c)}^{\phi(b)} f(y) dy = \int_a^b (f \circ \phi)(x)\phi'(x) dx. \tag{6.11}$$

Proof: Since f is bounded measurable and ϕ is absolutely continuous (thus $\phi' \in L_1[a, b]$), it follows that $(f \circ \phi)\phi' \in L_1[a, b]$. To show that (6.11) holds for every bounded measurable function, we proceed as follows: Firstly, note that it is enough to prove that (6.11) holds when f is a nonnegative bounded measurable function.

Step 1: Suppose (6.11) holds for a sequence $\{f_n\}_{n\geq 1}$ of functions on $[c, d]$ such that $\{f_n\}_{n\geq 1}$ is uniformly bounded and $f_n(x) \to f(x)$, $x \in [c, d]$. Then (6.11) holds for f.

To see this, let $|f_n(x)| \leq K \quad \forall \; x \in [c,d]$ and $n = 1,2,\ldots$. Then by Lebesgue's dominated convergence theorem,

$$
\begin{aligned}
\int_{\phi(a)}^{\phi(b)} f(y)dy &= \lim_{n\to\infty} \int_{\phi(a)}^{\phi(b)} f_n(y)dy \\
&= \lim_{n\to\infty} \int_a^b (f_n \circ \phi)(x)\phi'(x)dx \\
&= \int_a^b (f \circ \phi)(x)\phi'(x)dx.
\end{aligned}
$$

Step 2: Let I be any subinterval of $[c,d]$. Then (6.11) holds for $f = \chi_I$.

For this, we show that χ_I is the pointwise limit of a uniformly bounded sequence of continuous functions. The required claim will then follow from theorem 6.3.11 and step 1. For example, suppose $I = (\alpha,\beta) \subset [c,d]$. Consider the functions $f_n : [c,d] \longrightarrow \mathbb{R}$ as shown in Figure 24, given below. Then $|f_n(x)| \leq 1 \; \forall \, x \in [c,d]$ and $\forall \, n$. Further, $f_n(x) \to \chi_I(x) \; \forall \, x$.

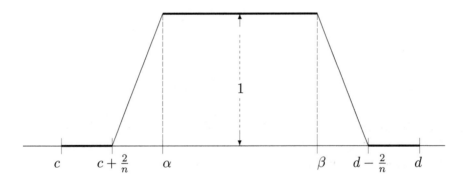

Figure 24 : The function f_n

Step 3: Using step 2, it is easy to check that (6.11) holds whenever f is a step function, i.e., $f = \sum_{i=1}^{n} a_i\chi_{I_i}$, where $I_i \subset [c,d]$, $1 \leq i \leq n$, are pairwise disjoint open intervals with $\bigcup_{i=1}^{n} I_i = [c,d]$ and $a_i \in \mathbb{R} \; \forall \, i$.

Step 4: Equation (6.11) holds for $f = \chi_U$ and χ_F, where $U \subset [c,d]$ is an open set and $F \subseteq [c,d]$ is any closed set.

To see this we note that U, being an open set in $\mathbb{R}$, is a union of countably many pairwise disjoint open intervals, say $\{I_i\}_{i\geq1}$. Then by step 3, (6.11) holds for each $f_n := \sum_{i=1}^{n} \chi_{I_i}$. Note that, for every $n \geq 1$, $|f_n(x)| \leq 1$ $\forall \, x \in [c,d]$ and $f_n(x) \to X_U(x)$ as $n \to \infty$. Thus by step 2, (6.11) holds for

$f = X_U$ also. Since $\{1 - f_n\}_{n \geq 1}$ converges to χ_{U^c}, (6.11) holds for $f = \chi_F$ also, where $F \subseteq [c, d]$ is any closed set.

Step 5: Let $E \subseteq [c, d]$ be any Lebesgue measurable set. Then (6.11) holds for $f = \chi_E$.

For this, we note that since E is measurable, by theorem 4.2.2, we can choose a closed set F_n and an open set G_n for every $n \geq 1$ such that

$$F_n \subseteq E \subseteq G_n \quad \text{and} \quad \lambda(G_n \setminus F_n) < 1/n.$$

Let

$$F := \bigcup_{n=1}^{\infty} F_n \quad \text{and} \quad G := \bigcap_{n=1}^{\infty} G_n.$$

Then $\lambda(G \setminus F) = 0$ and $F \subseteq E \subseteq G$. Thus

$$\chi_F \leq \chi_E \leq \chi_G \quad \text{and} \quad \chi_F(x) = \chi_E(x) = \chi_G(x) \text{ for a.e. } x \in [c, d].$$

Hence

$$\int_{\phi(a)}^{\phi(b)} \chi_F(y)dy = \int_{\phi(a)}^{\phi(b)} \chi_E(y)dy = \int_{\phi(a)}^{\phi(b)} \chi_G(y)dy.$$

Since χ_F and χ_G are pointwise limits of $\{\chi_{\bigcup_{k=1}^n F_k}\}_{n \geq 1}$ and $\{\chi_{\bigcup_{k=1}^n G_k}\}_{n \geq 1}$ and those sequences are uniformly bounded, by steps 1 and 4 we have

$$\int_{\phi(a)}^{\phi(b)} \chi_F(y)dy = \int_a^b (\chi_F \circ \phi)(x)\phi'(x)dx$$

and

$$\int_{\phi(a)}^{\phi(b)} \chi_G(y)dy = \int_a^b (\chi_G \circ \phi)(x)\phi'(x)dx.$$

The function ϕ is monotonically increasing, $\phi'(x) \geq 0$ whenever it exists. Thus the above equalities give us

$$(\chi_F \circ \phi)(x)\phi'(x) = (\chi_G \circ \phi)(x)\phi'(x) \quad \text{for a.e. } x \in [a, b].$$

Since

$$(\chi_F \circ \phi)(x)\phi'(x) \leq (\chi_E \circ \phi)(x)\phi'(x) \leq (\chi_G \circ \phi)(x)\phi'(x) \quad \text{for a.e.} x \in [a, b],$$

these functions are all equal for a.e. $x \in [a, b]$. Hence

$$\begin{aligned}
\int_{\phi(a)}^{\phi(b)} \chi_E(y)dy &= \int_{\phi(a)}^{\phi(b)} \chi_F(y)dy \\
&= \int_a^b (\chi_F \circ \phi)(x)\phi'(x)dx \\
&= \int_a^b (\chi_E \circ \phi)(x)\phi'(x)dx.
\end{aligned}$$

Thus (6.11) holds for $f = \chi_E$.

Step 6: The equation (6.11) holds for any bounded measurable function f.

This follows from step 5, using step 1 and the 'simple function technique'. We leave the details as an exercise. ∎

We note that in the proof of the theorem 6.3.11, there are two key steps:

(i) *Chain rule:* If F and ϕ are differentiable at x, then $F \circ \phi$ is differentiable at x and $(F \circ \phi)'(x) = (F' \circ \phi)(x)\phi'(x)$.

(ii) *Fundamental theorem of calculus,* which gives

$$\int_a^b (f \circ \phi)(x)\phi'(x)dx = \int_{\phi(a)}^{\phi(b)} f(y)dy.$$

In order to extend this theorem to functions $f \in L_1[a, b]$, we have to first answer the following question: let $\phi : [a, b] \longrightarrow [c, d]$ and let $F : [c, d] \longrightarrow \mathbb{R}$. When can we say $(F \circ \phi)$ is differentiable and

$$(F \circ \phi)'(x) = (F \circ \phi)'(x)\phi'(x) \text{ for a.e. } x \in [a, b]?$$

And whenever equation in (i) holds, we should try to apply the fundamental theorem of calculus (theorem 6.3.6) to deduce the corresponding change of variable formula for $f \in L_1[a, b]$. Even if both $\phi : [a, b] \longrightarrow [c, d]$ and $F : [c, d] \longrightarrow \mathbb{R}$ are differentiable for a.e. $x \in [a, b]$ and further $(F \circ \phi)(x)$ is also differentiable for a.e. $x \in [a, b]$, the relation $(F \circ \phi)'(x) = F(\phi(x))\phi'(x)$ need not hold for a.e. $x \in [a, b]$, as the next example shows.

6.3.14. Example: Let $\phi : [0, 1] \longrightarrow \mathbb{R}$ be the strictly increasing, continuous function with $\phi'(x) = 0$ for a.e. $x \in [0, 1]$, as constructed in exercise 6.2.12, and let $F = \phi^{-1}$. Then F, being monotone, is differentiable a.e. (by theorem 6.2.1) and $(F \circ \phi)(x) = x \quad \forall x \in [a, b]$. Thus $(F \circ \phi)$ is differentiable everywhere and $(F \circ \phi)'(x) = 1 \quad \forall x \in [a, b]$, but $(F' \circ \phi)(x)\phi'(x) = 0$ for a.e. $x \in [0, 1]$.

A sufficient condition for the chain rule formula to hold is given by the following theorem.

6.3.15. Theorem (Chain rule): *Let $\phi : [a, b] \longrightarrow [c, d]$ and $F : [c, d] \longrightarrow \mathbb{R}$ be such that ϕ, F and $F \circ \phi$ are differentiable a.e. Let F be such that it maps null subsets of $[c, d]$ to null subsets of $\mathbb{R}$. Then*

$$(F \circ \phi)'(x) = (f \circ \phi)(x)\phi'(x) \quad \text{for a.e. } x \in [a, b],$$

where $f : [c, d] \longrightarrow \mathbb{R}$ is any function such that $F'(x) = f(x)$ for a.e. $x \in [c, d]$.

Proof: We first note that by the chain rule for differentiation, if F is differentiable at $\phi(x)$ for some $x \in [a, b]$ and ϕ is differentiable at x, then $(F \circ \phi)'(x) = F'(\phi(x))\phi'(x)$. We fix any function $f : [c, d] \to \mathbb{R}$ such that $F'(x) = f(x)$ for a.e. $x \in [c, d]$, and define

$$A := \{x \in [c, d] \mid F'(x) \text{ exists and } f(x) = F'(x)\}, \quad B := \phi^{-1}(A).$$

Then for a.e. $x \in B$, ϕ is differentiable at x (because ϕ is differentiable a.e. on $[a, b]$), and since $\phi(x) \in A$, the function F is differentiable at $\phi(x)$ with $F'(\phi(x)) = f(\phi(x))$. Thus the required claim holds for a.e. $x \in B$. Let $C := [a, b] \setminus B$. We shall show that the required claim also holds for a.e. $x \in C$. Let

$$D := \{x \in C \mid (F \circ \phi) \text{ and } \phi \text{ are both differentiable at } x\}.$$

Since $x \in C \setminus D$ means either $F \circ \phi$ is not differentiable at x or ϕ is not differentiable at x, we have, by the given hypothesis, $\overset{*}{\lambda}(C \setminus D) = 0$. Thus to complete the proof we only have to show that for a.e. $x \in D$, $(F \circ \phi)'(x) = (f \circ \phi)(x)\phi'(x)$. We note that

$$\phi(D) \subseteq \phi(C) = [c, d] \setminus \phi(B) = [c, d] \setminus A$$

and $\overset{*}{\lambda}([c, d] \setminus A) = 0$, by the given hypothesis. Thus $\overset{*}{\lambda}(\phi(D)) = 0$, and by theorem 4.1.6 we have $\phi'(x) = 0$ for a.e. $x \in D$. Also, by the given property of F, $\overset{*}{\lambda}(F(\phi(D)) = 0$, and once again by theorem 4.1.6,

$$(F \circ \phi)'(x) = 0 \text{ for a.e. } x \in D.$$

Hence

$$(F \circ \phi)'(x) = 0 = (f \circ \phi)(x)\phi(x) \text{ for a.e. } x \in D.$$

This completes the proof. ∎

Next we analyze the validity of theorem 6.3.11 for the Lebesgue integral, i.e., given $\phi : [a, b] \longrightarrow [c, d]$ and $f : [c, d] \longrightarrow \mathbb{R}$, when can we say that $\forall \, \alpha, \beta \in [a, b]$

$$\int_\alpha^\beta (f \circ \phi)(x)\phi'(x)d\lambda(x) = \int_{\phi(\alpha)}^{\phi(\beta)} f(x)d\lambda(x)?$$

Clearly, $\phi'(x)$ should exist for a.e. $x \in [a, b]$, f should be integrable and $(f \circ \phi)(x)\phi'(x)$ should be integrable on $[a, b]$ for both sides of the above formula to make sense. Are these conditions also sufficient? Let us suppose $(f \circ \phi)(x)\phi'(x) \in L_1[a, b]$ and the above formula holds. Let

$$F(x) := \int_c^x f(t)d\lambda(t), \ x \in [c, d].$$

Then by the fundamental theorem of calculus, F is absolutely continuous, $F'(x) = f(x)$ for a.e. $x \in [c, d]$, and for a.e. $y \in [a, b]$,

$$F(\phi(y)) - F(\phi(a)) = \int_{\phi(a)}^{\phi(y)} f(x) d\lambda(x) = \int_a^y (f \circ \phi)(x) \phi'(x) d\lambda(x).$$

Thus $(F \circ \phi)$ is absolutely continuous. Conversely, let us suppose $\phi'(x)$ exists for a.e. x, f is integrable and $F \circ \phi$ is absolutely continuous. Then by theorem 6.3.15,

$$(F \circ \phi)'(x) = (f \circ \phi)(x) \phi'(x) \text{ for a.e. } x \in [a, b].$$

Also by the fundamental theorem of calculus, we have $(f \circ \phi) \phi' \in L_1[a, b]$ and $\forall\, \alpha, \beta \in [a, b]$

$$
\begin{aligned}
\int_{\phi(\alpha)}^{\phi(\beta)} f d\lambda &= F(\phi(\beta)) - F(\phi(\alpha)) \\
&= \int_\alpha^\beta (F \circ \phi)'(x) d\lambda(x) \\
&= \int_\alpha^\beta (f \circ \phi)(x) \phi'(x) d\lambda(x).
\end{aligned}
$$

Thus we have proved the following theorem.

6.3.16. Theorem (Integration by substitution): *Let* $\phi : [a, b] \longrightarrow [c, d]$ *be differentiable a.e. and* $F : [c, d] \longrightarrow \mathbb{R}$ *be absolutely continuous. Then the following are equivalent:*

(i) $F \circ \phi$ *is absolutely continuous.*

(ii) *Let* $f : [c, d] \longrightarrow \mathbb{R}$ *be such that* $f(x) = F'(x)$ *for a.e.* $x \in [c, d]$. *Then* $(f \circ \phi) \phi' \in L_1[a, b]$ *and* $\forall\, \alpha, \beta \in [a, b]$

$$\int_{\phi(\alpha)}^{\phi(\beta)} f(x) dx = \int_\alpha^\beta (f \circ \phi)(x) \phi'(x) d\lambda(x).$$

6.3.17. Corollary: *Let* $\phi : [a, b] \longrightarrow [c, d]$ *be absolutely continuous and* $f \in L_1[c, d]$. *If* ϕ *is monotone, then* $\forall\, \alpha, \beta \in [a, b]$

$$\int_{\phi(\alpha)}^{\phi(\beta)} f(x) d\lambda(x) = \int_\alpha^\beta (f \circ \phi)(x) \phi'(x) d\lambda(x).$$

Proof: Let

$$F(x) := \int_c^x f(y) d\lambda(y), \ \ x \in [c, d].$$

Then F is absolutely continuous and, by exercise 6.1.11, $F \circ \phi$ is also absolutely continuous. Now, the conclusion follows from theorem 6.2.1 and theorem 6.3.16. ∎

6.3.18. Corollary: *Let* $\phi : [a, b] \longrightarrow [c, d]$ *be absolutely continuous and* $f : [c, d] \longrightarrow \mathbb{R}$ *be bounded and measurable. Then* $\forall \alpha, \beta \in [a, b]$

$$\int_{\phi(\alpha)}^{\phi(\beta)} f(x) d\lambda(x) = \int_{\alpha}^{\beta} (f \circ \phi)(x) \phi'(x) dx.$$

Proof: Let

$$F(x) = \int_{c}^{x} f(y) d\lambda(y), \; x \in [c, d].$$

Since f is bounded, F is well-defined, absolutely continuous, and $F'(x) = f(x)$ a.e. $x \in [c, d]$. By exercise 6.1.12, $F \circ \phi$ is absolutely continuous. The conclusion now follows from theorem 6.3.15. ∎

6.3.19. Exercise: Let $\phi : [a, b] \longrightarrow [c, d]$ be absolutely continuous and $f \in L_1[c, d]$ be such that $(f \circ \phi)\phi' \in L_1[a, b]$. Show that $\forall \alpha, \beta \in [a, b]$

$$\int_{\alpha}^{\beta} (f \circ \phi)(x) \phi'(x) d\lambda(x) = \int_{\phi(\alpha)}^{\phi(\beta)} f(x) d\lambda(x).$$

(Hint: Approximate f by bounded measurable functions on $[c, d]$ and use corollary 6.3.18, along with Lebesgue's dominated convergence theorem.)

6.3.20. Exercise: Prove exercise 6.3.19 via the following steps:

(i) Show that the conclusion holds when f is the characteristic function of an interval.

(ii) Approximate $f \in L_1[c, d]$ by step functions (see note 5.6.4 (ii)) and use (i) together with Lebesgue's dominated convergence theorem to prove the required conclusion.

6.3.21. Exercise (Change of variable formula for Riemann integration): Let $h : [c, d] \to \mathbb{R}$ be Riemann integrable and $g(x) := \int_{a}^{x} h(t) dt$, $x \in [c, d]$. Let $f : g[c, d] \to \mathbb{R}$ be Riemann integrable. Then, using exercise 6.3.19, deduce that

$$\int_{g(c)}^{g(d)} f(x) dx = \int_{c}^{d} f[g(t)] h(t) dt.$$

(Compare this with theorem 6.3.11.)

6.3.22 Note: The proofs of the chain rule and integration by substitution as given above are based on Serrin and Varberg [36].

Chapter 7

Measure and integration on product spaces

7.1. Introduction

In chapter 4, we saw that the intuitive notion of length, originally defined for intervals in $\mathbb{R}$, was extended to the class of Lebesgue measurable sets which included not only the intervals and all the topologically nice subsets of $\mathbb{R}$, but also $\mathcal{B}_{\mathbb{R}}$ – the σ-algebra of Borel subsets of $\mathbb{R}$. In a similar manner, one would like to extend the notion of area in $\mathbb{R}^2$ (volume in $\mathbb{R}^3$, and so on) to a larger class of subsets which includes $\mathcal{B}_{\mathbb{R}^2}$ ($\mathcal{B}_{\mathbb{R}^3}$) – the σ-algebra generated by open subsets of $\mathbb{R}^2$ ($\mathbb{R}^3$). In the abstract setting, given measure spaces $(X, \mathcal{A}, \mu)$ and $(Y, \mathcal{B}, \nu)$, one would like to define a measure η on the σ-algebra generated by sets of the form $\{A \times B \,|\, A \in \mathcal{A},\ B \in \mathcal{B}\}$ in the 'natural' way: $\eta(A \times B) = \mu(A)\nu(B)$. We call this natural for, when $X = Y = \mathbb{R}, \mathcal{A} = \mathcal{B} = \mathcal{B}_{\mathbb{R}}$ and $\mu = \nu = \lambda$, the Lebesgue measure, then for intervals I and J, $\eta(I \times J) = \lambda(I)\lambda(J)$ is the area of the rectangle with sides the intervals I and J. Thus η will automatically be an extension of the notion of area in $\mathbb{R}^2$. We note that the collection $\mathcal{R} := \{A \times B \,|\, A \in \mathcal{A}, B \in \mathcal{B}\}$ is only a semi-algebra of subsets of $A \times B$ in general. (See example 3.2.3(v) and exercise 3.2.5(iii).) Let $\mathcal{A} \otimes \mathcal{B}$ denote the σ-algebra of subsets of $X \times Y$ generated by $\mathcal{R}$.

7.1.1. Definition: Let $(X, \mathcal{A})$ and $(Y, \mathcal{B})$ be measurable spaces. A subset $E \subseteq X \times Y$ is called a **measurable rectangle** if $E = A \times B$ for some $A \in \mathcal{A}$

and $B \in \mathcal{B}$. We denote by $\mathcal{R}$ the class of all measurable rectangles. The σ-algebra of subsets of $X \times Y$ generated by the semi-algebra $\mathcal{R}$ is called the **product σ-algebra** and is denoted by $\mathcal{A} \otimes \mathcal{B}$.

7.1.2. Proposition: *Let $p_X : X \times Y \longrightarrow X$ and $p_Y : X \times Y \longrightarrow Y$ be defined by*
$$p_X(x,y) = x \quad and \quad p_Y(x,y) = y,$$
$\forall\, x \in X, y \in Y$. *Then the following hold:*

(i) *The maps p_X and p_Y are measurable, i.e., $\forall\, A \in \mathcal{A}, B \in \mathcal{B}$ we have $p_X^{-1}(A) \in \mathcal{A} \otimes \mathcal{B}$ and $p_Y^{-1}(B) \in \mathcal{A} \otimes \mathcal{B}$.*

(ii) *The σ-algebra $\mathcal{A} \otimes \mathcal{B}$ is the smallest σ-algebra of subsets of $X \times Y$ such that (i) holds.*

Proof: Let $A \in \mathcal{A}$ and $B \in \mathcal{B}$. Then
$$p_X^{-1}(A) = A \times Y \in \mathcal{R} \quad and \quad p_Y^{-1}(B) = X \times B \in \mathcal{R}.$$
Hence (i) holds. To prove (ii), let $\mathcal{S}$ be any σ-algebra of subsets of $X \times Y$ such that p_X and p_Y are both $\mathcal{S}$-measurable. We show that $\mathcal{S} \subseteq \mathcal{A} \otimes \mathcal{B}$. Let $A \in \mathcal{A}$ and $B \in \mathcal{B}$. Then $A \times Y = p_X^{-1}(A) \in \mathcal{S}$ and $X \times B = p_Y^{-1}(B) \in \mathcal{S}$. Since
$$A \times B = (A \times Y) \cap (X \times B),$$
it follows that $\mathcal{R} \subseteq \mathcal{S}$. Hence $\mathcal{A} \otimes \mathcal{B} = \mathcal{S}(\mathcal{R}) \subseteq \mathcal{S}$, proving (ii). ∎

•**7.1.3. Exercise:** Let $(X, \mathcal{A})$ be a measurable space. Let $\alpha, \beta \in \mathbb{R}$ and $E \in \mathcal{A} \otimes \mathcal{B}_{\mathbb{R}}$. Show that $\{(x, t) \in X \times \mathbb{R} \,|\, (x, \alpha t + \beta) \in E\} \in \mathcal{A} \otimes \mathcal{B}_{\mathbb{R}}$.
(Hint: Use the σ-algebra technique.)

•**7.1.4. Exercise:** Let $E \in \mathcal{B}_{\mathbb{R}}$. Show that $\{(x, y) \in \mathbb{R}^2 \,|\, x + y \in E\}$ and $\{(x, y) \in \mathbb{R}^2 \,|\, x - y \in E\}$ are elements of $\mathcal{B}_{\mathbb{R}} \otimes \mathcal{B}_{\mathbb{R}}$.

7.1.5. Proposition: *Let X and Y be nonempty sets and let $\mathcal{C}, \mathcal{D}$ be families of subsets of X and Y, respectively. Let $\mathcal{C} \times \mathcal{D} := \{C \times D \,|\, C \in \mathcal{C}, D \in \mathcal{D}\}$. Then the following hold:*

(i) $\mathcal{S}(\mathcal{C} \times \mathcal{D}) \subseteq \mathcal{S}(\mathcal{C}) \otimes \mathcal{S}(\mathcal{D})$.

(ii) *Let $\mathcal{C}$ and $\mathcal{D}$ have the property that there exist increasing sequences $\{C_i\}_{i \geq 1}$ and $\{D_i\}_{i \geq 1}$ in $\mathcal{C}$ and $\mathcal{D}$ respectively such that*
$$\bigcup_{i=1}^{\infty} C_i = X \quad and \quad \bigcup_{i=1}^{\infty} D_i = Y.$$
Then
$$\mathcal{S}(\mathcal{C} \times \mathcal{D}) = \mathcal{S}(\mathcal{C}) \otimes \mathcal{S}(\mathcal{D}).$$

Proof: Let $C \in \mathcal{C}$ and $D \in \mathcal{D}$. Since $\mathcal{C} \subseteq \mathcal{S}(\mathcal{C})$ and $\mathcal{D} \subseteq \mathcal{S}(\mathcal{D})$, we have

$$C \times D \in \mathcal{S}(\mathcal{C}) \times \mathcal{S}(\mathcal{D}) \subseteq \mathcal{S}(\mathcal{C}) \otimes \mathcal{S}(\mathcal{D}).$$

This implies that $\mathcal{C} \times \mathcal{D} \subseteq \mathcal{S}(\mathcal{C}) \otimes \mathcal{S}(\mathcal{D})$. Hence $\mathcal{S}(\mathcal{C} \times \mathcal{D}) \subseteq \mathcal{S}(\mathcal{C}) \otimes \mathcal{S}(\mathcal{D})$, proving (i). To prove (ii), we only have to show that $\mathcal{S}(\mathcal{C}) \otimes \mathcal{S}(\mathcal{D}) \subseteq \mathcal{S}(\mathcal{C} \times \mathcal{D})$. By proposition 7.1.2, $\mathcal{S}(\mathcal{C}) \otimes \mathcal{S}(\mathcal{D})$ is the smallest σ-algebra of subsets of $X \times Y$ with respect to which the projection maps p_X and p_Y are measurable. So to complete the proof, we show that p_X, p_Y are both $\mathcal{S}(\mathcal{C} \times \mathcal{D})$-measurable. Let $C \in \mathcal{C}$. Then

$$
\begin{aligned}
p_X^{-1}(C) &= C \times Y \\
&= C \times (\bigcup_{j=1}^{\infty} D_j) \\
&= \bigcup_{j=1}^{\infty} (C \times D_j).
\end{aligned}
$$

Since each $C \times D_j \in \mathcal{C} \times \mathcal{D} \subseteq \mathcal{S}(\mathcal{C} \times \mathcal{D})$, we have

$$p_X^{-1}(C) \in \mathcal{S}(\mathcal{C} \times \mathcal{D}) \quad \forall \, C \in \mathcal{C}.$$

Let

$$\mathcal{U} := \{E \in \mathcal{S}(\mathcal{C}) \mid p_X^{-1}(C) \in \mathcal{S}(\mathcal{C} \times \mathcal{D})\}.$$

Then by the above arguments

$$\mathcal{C} \subseteq \mathcal{U} \subseteq \mathcal{S}(\mathcal{C}).$$

It is easy to check that $\mathcal{U}$ is a σ-algebra of subsets of X. Hence $\mathcal{S}(\mathcal{C}) = \mathcal{U}$. Thus $p_X^{-1}(E) \in \mathcal{S}(\mathcal{C} \times \mathcal{D})$ for every $E \in \mathcal{S}(\mathcal{C})$, i.e., p_X is $\mathcal{S}(\mathcal{C} \times \mathcal{D})$-measurable. Similarly, p_Y is $\mathcal{S}(\mathcal{C} \times \mathcal{D})$-measurable. This completes the proof. ∎

•7.1.6. Exercise:

(i) Let X and Y be nonempty sets and $\mathcal{C}$, $\mathcal{D}$ be nonempty families of subsets of X and Y, respectively, as in proposition 7.1.5. Is it true that $\mathcal{S}(\mathcal{C} \times \mathcal{D}) = \mathcal{S}(\mathcal{C}) \otimes \mathcal{S}(\mathcal{D})$ in general? Check in the case when $\mathcal{C} = \{\emptyset\}$ and $\mathcal{D}$ is a σ-algebra of subsets of Y containing at least four elements.

(ii) Let $\mathcal{B}_{\mathbb{R}^2}$ denote the σ-algebra of Borel subsets of $\mathbb{R}^2$, i.e., the σ-algebra generated by the open subsets of $\mathbb{R}^2$. Show that

$$\mathcal{B}_{\mathbb{R}^2} = \mathcal{B}_{\mathbb{R}} \otimes \mathcal{B}_{\mathbb{R}}.$$

(Hint: Use proposition 7.1.5.)

7.2. Product of measure spaces

For the rest of the chapter, let $(X, \mathcal{A}, \mu)$ and $(Y, \mathcal{B}, \nu)$ be fixed measure spaces. Subsets of $X \times Y$ of the form $A \times B, A \in \mathcal{A}, B \in \mathcal{B}$, are called **measurable rectangles.** As before, let $\mathcal{R}$ denote the class of all measurable rectangles. The σ-algebra of subsets of $X \times Y$ generated by $\mathcal{R}$, denoted by $\mathcal{A} \otimes \mathcal{B}$, is called the **product σ-algebra.**

The problem we want to analyze in this section is the following: how can we construct a measure $\eta : \mathcal{A} \otimes \mathcal{B} \longrightarrow [0, +\infty]$ such that $\eta(A \times B) = \mu(A)\nu(B)$ for every $A \in \mathcal{A}, B \in \mathcal{B}$?

In fact, the property required of η for the elements of $\mathcal{R}$ suggests its definition on $\mathcal{R}$. Further, if we can show that η is countably additive on $\mathcal{R}$, then, observing that $\mathcal{R}$ is a semi-algebra, we can extend η, via the outer measure η^* (see theorem 3.10.8), to $\mathcal{A} \otimes \mathcal{B}$, the σ-algebra generated by $\mathcal{R}$. Further, this extension will be unique provided η is σ-finite on $\mathcal{R}$. These are the contents of our next theorem.

7.2.1. Theorem: *Let $\eta : \mathcal{R} \longrightarrow [0, \infty]$ be defined by*

$$\eta(A \times B) := \mu(A)\nu(B), \quad A \in \mathcal{A}, B \in \mathcal{B}.$$

Then η is a well-defined measure on $\mathcal{R}$. Further, if μ, ν are σ-finite, then there exists a unique measure $\tilde{\eta} : \mathcal{A} \otimes \mathcal{B} \to [0, +\infty]$ such that

$$\tilde{\eta}(A \times B) = \eta(A \times B) \text{ for every } A \times B \in \mathcal{R}.$$

Proof: Obviously, $\eta(\emptyset) = 0$. To show that η is countably additive, let $A \in \mathcal{A}, B \in \mathcal{B}$ be such that

$$A \times B = \bigcup_{n=1}^{\infty} (A_n \times B_n),$$

where each $A_n \in \mathcal{A}$ and each $B_n \in \mathcal{B}$, and $(A_n \times B_n) \cap (A_m \times B_m) = \emptyset$ for $n \neq m$. We have to show that

$$\eta(A \times B) = \sum_{n=1}^{\infty} \eta(A_n \times B_n).$$

For this, let $x \in A$ be fixed. Then for any $y \in B, (x, y) \in \bigcup_{n=1}^{\infty} (A_n \times B_n)$, and hence $y \in B_n$ provided $x \in A_n$. Thus $\forall\, x \in A$,

$$B = \bigcup_{n \in S} B_n, \quad \text{where } S := \{n \in \mathbb{N} \mid x \in A_n\}.$$

Further, for $m, n \in S$ we have $B_n \cap B_m = \emptyset$, for otherwise we would have $(A_n \times B_n) \cap (A_m \times B_m) \neq \emptyset$. Thus

$$\nu(B) = \sum_{n\in S} \nu(B_n).$$

Equivalently, for $x \in A$,

$$\chi_A(x)\nu(B) = \sum_{n\in S} \nu(B_n) = \sum_{n=1}^{\infty} \chi_{A_n}(x)\,\nu(B_n). \qquad (7.1)$$

If $x \notin A$, then $\chi_A(x)\nu(B) = 0$. Also for $x \notin A$, we have $x \notin A_n$ for every n, and thus $\chi_{A_n}(x)\nu(B_n) = 0 \ \forall\, n$. Thus equation (7.1) holds for $x \notin A$ also. Hence $\forall\, x \in X$,

$$\chi_A(x)\nu(B) = \sum_{n=1}^{\infty} \chi_{A_n}(x)\nu(B_n).$$

An application of the monotone convergence theorem gives us

$$
\begin{aligned}
\eta(A \times B) = \mu(A)\nu(B) &= \int \left(\sum_{n=1}^{\infty} \chi_{A_n}(x)\nu(B_n) \right) d\mu(x) \\
&= \sum_{n=1}^{\infty} \int \chi_{A_n}(x)\nu(B_n)d\mu(x) \\
&= \sum_{n=1}^{\infty} \mu(A_n)\nu(B_n) = \sum_{n=1}^{\infty} \eta(A_n \times B_n).
\end{aligned}
$$

This proves that η is a measure on $\mathcal{R}$. By theorem 3.10.8, η can be extended uniquely to a measure $\tilde{\eta}$ on the σ-algebra generated by $\mathcal{R}$ provided it is σ-finite. To complete the proof we show η is σ-finite when μ, ν are σ-finite. For this, let

$$X = \bigcup_{i=1}^{\infty} X_i, \quad Y = \bigcup_{j=1}^{\infty} Y_j$$

be such that $X_i \in \mathcal{A}, Y_j \in \mathcal{B}$, where the X_i's are pairwise disjoint and the Y_j's are pairwise disjoint, with $\mu(X_i) < +\infty$ and $\nu(Y_j) < +\infty \ \forall\, i, j$. Then

$$X \times Y = \bigcup_{i=1}^{\infty} \bigcup_{j=1}^{\infty} (X_i \times Y_j)$$

is a partition of $X \times Y$ by elements of $\mathcal{R}$ such that

$$\eta(X_i \times Y_j) = \mu(X_i)\nu(X_j) < +\infty.$$

Hence η is σ-finite. ∎

7.2.2. Definition: The measure $\tilde{\eta}$ on $\mathcal{A} \otimes \mathcal{B}$ given by theorem 7.2.1 is called the **product of the measures** μ and ν and is denoted by $\mu \times \nu$. The measure space $(X \times Y, \mathcal{A} \otimes \mathcal{B}, \mu \times \nu)$ is called the product of the measure space $(X, \mathcal{A}, \mu)$ and $(Y, \mathcal{B}, \nu)$, or just the **product measure space.**

We note that $\mu \times \nu$ is uniquely defined on $\mathcal{A} \times \mathcal{B}$ when μ, ν are σ-finite. So from now on we shall assume that μ and ν are σ-finite. As is clear, $\mu \times \nu$ is defined on $\mathcal{A} \otimes \mathcal{B}$ via the extension theorem 3.10.8, i.e., via the outer measure and so on. So, the natural question arises: how to compute $(\mu \times \nu)(E)$ for a general element $E \in \mathcal{A} \otimes \mathcal{B}$? Let us recall the computation (or rather the definition) of areas of planar regions that we met in the calculus: let $E \subseteq \mathbb{R}^2$ be a bounded region, say

$$E := \{(x, y) \in \mathbb{R}^2 \,|\, a \leq x \leq b,\, f(x) \leq y \leq g(x)\},$$

where $f(x)$ and $g(x)$ are continuous functions.

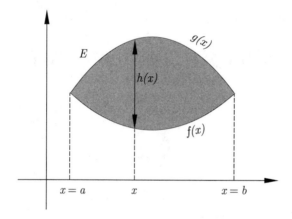

Figure 25

Then the area of E (see Figure 25) is defined by

$$\text{Area}(E) := \int_a^b (f(x) - g(x))dx.$$

If we write $h(x) := f(x) - g(x)$, then $h(x)$ is nothing but the length of the set $E_x := \{y \in \mathbb{R} \,|\, (x, y) \in E\}$, and an elementary result from multiple integrals tells us that

$$\text{Area}(E) := \int_a^b \lambda(E_x)dx.$$

The question arises: can we carry over this idea to find $(\mu \times \nu)(E)$ for $E \in \mathcal{A} \otimes \mathcal{B}$? Obviously, the following questions will have to be answered first:

(i) Given $E \in \mathcal{A} \otimes \mathcal{B}$ and $x \in X$, is $E_x \in \mathcal{B}$ (so that $\nu(E_x)$ makes sense)?

(ii) To integrate $\nu(E_x)$ with respect to μ, one has to answer the question: is the map $x \longmapsto \nu(E_x)$ measurable?

(iii) If (i) and (ii) make sense, can we compute $\eta(E)$ by

$$\eta(E) = \int_X \nu(E_x)d\mu(x)?$$

(iv) Can one interchange the roles of μ and ν in the above steps, i.e., is

$$\eta(E) = \int_Y \mu(E_y)d\nu(y) \text{ also?}$$

We shall answer these questions one by one.

7.2.3. Definition: Let $E \subseteq X \times Y, x \in X$ and $y \in Y$. Let

$$E_x := \{y \in Y \,|\, (x,y) \in E\} \quad \text{and} \quad E^y := \{x \in X \,|\, (x,y) \in E\}.$$

The set E_x is called the **section of E at x** (or **x-section** of E) and the set E^y is called the **section of E at y** (or **y-section** of E).

7.2.4. Examples:

(i) Let $E = A \times B$, where $A \in \mathcal{A}$ and $B \in \mathcal{B}$. Clearly, $E_x = B$ if $x \in A$ and $E_x = \emptyset$ if $x \notin A$. Similarly, $E^y = A$ if $y \in B$ and $E^y = \emptyset$ if $y \notin B$.

(ii) Let $(X, \mathcal{A})$ be a measurable space and let $A \in \mathcal{A}$. Let

$$E = \{(x,t) \in X \times \mathbb{R} \,|\, 0 \le t < \chi_A(x)\}.$$

It is easy to see that

$$E = (A \times [0,1)) \cup (A^c \times \{0\}).$$

Thus

$$E_x = \begin{cases} [0,1) & \text{if } x \in A, \\ \{0\} & \text{if } x \notin A. \end{cases}$$

Similarly,

$$E^y = \begin{cases} X & \text{if } y = 0, \\ A & \text{if } y \in (0,1), \\ \emptyset & \text{if } y \notin [0,1). \end{cases}$$

7.2.5. Proposition: *For $E, F, E_i \in \mathcal{A} \otimes \mathcal{B}$ and $i \in I$, any indexing set, the following hold $\forall x \in X, y \in Y$:*

(i) $(\bigcup_{i \in I} E_i)_x = \bigcup_{i \in I}(E_i)_x$ *and* $(\bigcup_{i \in I} E_i)^y = \bigcup_{i \in I}(E_i)^y$.

(ii) $(\bigcap_{i \in I} E_i)_x = \bigcap_{i \in I}(E_i)_x$ *and* $(\bigcap_{i \in I} E_i)^y = \bigcap_{i \in I}(E_i)^y$.

(iii) $(E \setminus F)_x = E_x \setminus F_x$ *and* $(E \setminus F)^y = E^y \setminus F^y$.

(iv) *If $E \subseteq F$, then $E_x \subseteq F_x$ and $E^y \subseteq F^y$.*

Proof: Exercise. ∎

Now we can answer the questions asked above.

7.2.6. Theorem: *Let $E \in \mathcal{A} \otimes \mathcal{B}$. Then the following hold:*

(i) $E_x \in \mathcal{B}$ *and* $E^y \in \mathcal{A}$ *for every* $x \in X, y \in Y$.

(ii) *The functions* $x \longmapsto \nu(E_x)$ *and* $y \longmapsto \mu(E^y)$ *are measurable functions on X and Y, respectively.*

(iii)
$$\int_X \nu(E_x) d\mu(x) = (\mu \times \nu)(E) = \int_Y \mu(E^y) d\nu(y).$$

Proof: The proof is a typical application of the 'σ-algebra-monotone class technique'. Let

$$\mathcal{S} := \{E \in \mathcal{A} \otimes \mathcal{B} \mid E_x \in \mathcal{B} \text{ and } E^y \in \mathcal{A} \ \forall \, x \in X, y \in Y\}.$$

It is easy to see that $\mathcal{S}$ is a σ-algebra and $A \times B \in \mathcal{S}$ whenever $A \in \mathcal{A}, B \in \mathcal{B}$. Thus $\mathcal{A} \times \mathcal{B} \subseteq \mathcal{S}$ and hence $\mathcal{S} = \mathcal{A} \otimes \mathcal{B}$. This proves (i).

To prove (ii) and (iii), let

$$\mathcal{P} := \{E \in \mathcal{A} \otimes \mathcal{B} \mid \text{ (ii) and (iii) hold}\}.$$

To prove the required statements, we have to show that $\mathcal{P} = \mathcal{A} \otimes \mathcal{B}$. For that we shall show that $\mathcal{P}$ is a monotone class, is closed under finite disjoint unions and includes $\mathcal{R} = \{A \times B \mid A \in \mathcal{A}, B \in \mathcal{B}\}$. Since $\mathcal{R}$ is a semi-algebra, using exercise 3.2.10(i), we will have $\mathcal{F}(\mathcal{R}) \subseteq \mathcal{P}$ and hence $\mathcal{M}(\mathcal{F}(\mathcal{R})) \subseteq \mathcal{P}$, where $\mathcal{F}(\mathcal{R})$ is the algebra generated by $\mathcal{R}$ and $\mathcal{M}(\mathcal{F}(\mathcal{R}))$ is the monotone class generated by $\mathcal{F}(\mathcal{R})$. By theorem 3.10.7, $\mathcal{M}(\mathcal{F}(\mathcal{R}))$ is the same as the σ-algebra generated by $\mathcal{F}(\mathcal{R})$, i.e., $\mathcal{A} \otimes \mathcal{B}$. Hence we will have $\mathcal{A} \otimes \mathcal{B} = \mathcal{P}$. We prove these claims one by one.

Let $E = A \times B \in \mathcal{R}$. Then by example 7.2.4 (i), we have

$$\begin{aligned} \nu(E_x) &= \nu(B)\chi_A(x) \quad \forall \, x \in X, \\ \mu(E^y) &= \mu(A)\chi_B(y) \quad \forall \, y \in Y. \end{aligned}$$

Clearly, $x \longmapsto \nu(E_x)$ and $y \longmapsto \mu(E^y)$ are measurable functions, and

$$\int_X \nu(E_x) d\mu(x) = \mu(A)\nu(B) = \int_Y \mu(E^y) d\nu(y).$$

Thus $\mathcal{R} \subseteq \mathcal{P}$.

Next, let $E_1, E_2 \in \mathcal{P}$ be such that $E_1 \cap E_2 = \emptyset$. Then $\forall \, x \in X$,

$$(E_1)_x \cap (E_2)_x = \emptyset \ \text{ and } \ (E_1 \cup E_2)_x = (E_1)_x \cup (E_2)_x.$$

Hence

$$\nu((E_1 \cup E_2)_x) = \nu((E_1)_x) + \nu((E_2)_x).$$

Thus by proposition 5.2.6(ii), $x \longmapsto \nu((E_1 \cup E_2)_x)$ is measurable and

$$
\begin{aligned}
\int_X \nu((E_1 \cup E_2)_x) d\mu(X) &= \int_X [\nu((E_1)_x) + \nu((E_2)_x)]\, d\mu(x) \\
&= (\mu \times \nu)(E_1) + (\mu \times \nu)(E_2) \\
&= (\mu \times \nu)(E_1 \cup E_2).
\end{aligned}
$$

Similarly, $y \longmapsto \mu((E_1 \cup E_2)^y)$ is measurable and

$$
\int_Y \mu((E_1 \cup E_2)^y) d\nu(y) = (\mu \times \nu)(E_1 \cup E_2).
$$

Hence $\mathcal{P}$ is closed under finite disjoint unions.

Finally, to show that $\mathcal{P}$ is a monotone class, let $E_n \in \mathcal{P}, n \geq 1$, be such that $E_n \subseteq E_{n+1} \ \forall n$ and $E = \bigcup_{n=1}^{\infty} E_n$. Then for every $n \geq 1$

$$(E_n)_x \subseteq (E_{n+1})_x \quad \text{and} \quad (E_n)^y \subseteq (E_{n+1})^y \ \forall x \in X \ \text{and} \ y \in Y.$$

Thus $\{\nu((E_n)_x)\}_{n \geq 1}$ and $\{\mu((E_n)^y)\}_{n \geq 1}$ are increasing sequences of nonnegative measurable functions. Using theorem 3.6.3(a)(i),

$$\lim_{n \to \infty} \nu((E_n)_x) = \nu(E_x) \quad \text{and} \quad \lim_{n \to \infty} \mu((E_n)^y) = \mu(E^y).$$

Thus by the monotone convergence theorem (5.2.7), $x \longmapsto \nu(E_x)$ and $y \longmapsto \mu(E^y)$ are nonnegative measurable functions with

$$
\left.
\begin{aligned}
\int_X \nu(E_x) d\mu(x) &= \lim_{n \to \infty} \int_X \nu((E_n)_x) d\mu(x), \\
\int_Y \mu(E^y) d\nu(y) &= \lim_{n \to \infty} \int_Y \mu((E_n)^y) d\nu(y).
\end{aligned}
\right\} \tag{7.2}
$$

Since $E_n \in \mathcal{P} \ \forall \, n \geq 1$, we have

$$\int_X \nu((E_n)_x) d\mu(x) = (\mu \times \nu)(E_n) = \int_Y \mu((E_n)^y) d\nu(y).$$

Thus using (7.2), we get

$$\int_X \nu(E_x) d\mu(x) = \lim_{n \to \infty} (\mu \times \nu)(E_n) = \int_Y \mu(E^y) d\nu(y).$$

Since $(\mu \times \nu)$ is countably additive, by theorem 3.6.3(a)(i),

$$\lim_{n \to \infty} (\mu \times \nu)(E_n) = (\mu \times \nu) \left(\bigcup_{n=1}^{\infty} E_n \right).$$

Hence for $n \geq 1$, if $E_n \in \mathcal{P}$ and $E_n \subseteq E_{n+1}$, then $\bigcup_{n=1}^{\infty} E_n \in \mathcal{P}$. Similarly, if $E_n \in \mathcal{P}$ and $E_n \supseteq E_{n+1} \ \forall n \geq 1$, to conclude that $\bigcap_{n=1}^{\infty} E_n \in \mathcal{P}$ we can try to argue as above. To deduce the relations

$$\lim_{n \to \infty} \nu((E_n)_x) = \nu(E_x), \quad \lim_{n \to \infty} \mu((E_n)^y) = \mu(E^y)$$

and

$$\lim_{n \to \infty} (\mu \times \nu)(E_n) = (\mu \times \nu)(E),$$

we need the extra condition that μ, ν are finite measures, for in that case $\mu \times \nu$ will be finite and we can apply theorem 3.6.3(a)(ii). Then the equalities similar to (7.2) will hold by an application of the dominated convergence theorem. Thus in the particular case when μ, ν are finite measures, the above arguments will prove that $\mathcal{P}$ is a monotone class and the conclusion of the theorem holds.

To prove the theorem in the general case, i.e., when μ and ν are σ-finite, let $X = \bigcup_{i=1}^{\infty} A_i$ and $Y = \bigcup_{j=1}^{\infty} B_j$, where $\forall\, i, j,\ A_i \in \mathcal{A}, B_j \in \mathcal{B}$ with $\mu(A_i) < +\infty$ and $\nu(B_j) < +\infty$. Then $(\mu \times \nu)(A_i \times B_j) < +\infty \ \forall\, i, j$. For $E \in \mathcal{A} \otimes \mathcal{B}$, by the earlier discussion, we have $\forall\, i, j$

$$\int_X \nu\big((E \cap (A_i \times B_j))_x\big)\, d\mu(x) = (\mu \times \nu)\big(E \cap (A_i \times B_j)\big)$$

$$= \int_Y \mu\big((E \cap (A_i \times B_j))^y\big)\, d\nu(y).$$

Thus

$$(\mu \times \nu)(E) = \sum_{i=1}^{\infty} \sum_{j=1}^{\infty} (\mu \times \nu)\big((A_i \times B_j) \cap E\big)$$

$$= \sum_{i=1}^{\infty} \sum_{j=1}^{\infty} \int_X \nu\big((E \cap (A_i \times B_j))_x\big)\, d\mu(x) \qquad (7.3)$$

$$= \sum_{i=1}^{\infty} \sum_{j=1}^{\infty} \int_Y \mu\big((E \cap (A_i \times B_j))^y\big)\, d\nu(y). \qquad (7.4)$$

Also,

$$(E \cap (A_i \times B_j))_x = E_x \cap B_j \text{ if } x \in A_i, \text{ and } \emptyset \text{ otherwise.}$$

Thus we have by the monotone convergence theorem,

$$\sum_{i=1}^{\infty} \sum_{j=1}^{\infty} \int_X \nu\big((E \cap (A_i \times B_j))_x\big)\, d\mu(x) = \sum_{j=1}^{\infty} \left(\sum_{i=1}^{\infty} \int_{A_i} \nu(E_x \cap B_j)\, d\mu(x) \right)$$

$$= \sum_{j=1}^{\infty} \int_X \nu(E_x \cap B_j)\, d\mu(x)$$

$$= \int_X \left(\sum_{j=1}^{\infty} \nu(E_x \cap B_j) \right) d\mu(x)$$

$$= \int_X \nu\big(E_x \cap (\cup_{j=1}^{\infty} B_j)\big)\, d\mu(x)$$

$$= \int_X \nu(E_x)\, d\mu(x). \qquad (7.5)$$

Similarly,

$$\sum_{i=1}^{\infty}\sum_{j=1}^{\infty}\int_Y \mu((E\cap(A_i\times B_j))^y)d\nu(y) = \int_Y \mu(E^y)d\nu(y). \quad (7.6)$$

Equations (7.3), (7.4), (7.5) and (7.6) complete the proof. ∎

7.2.7. Exercise: Let $(X,\mathcal{A},\mu)$ be a σ-finite measure space. For any non-negative function $f: X \longrightarrow \mathbb{R}$, let

$$E^*(f) := \{(x,t) \in X \times \mathbb{R} \mid 0 \le t \le f(x)\}$$

and

$$E_*(f) := \{(x,t) \in X \times \mathbb{R} \mid 0 \le t < f(x)\}.$$

Then the following hold:

(i) If $\{f_n\}_{n\ge 1}$ is an increasing sequence of nonnegative functions on X increasing to $f(x)$, show that $\{E_*(f_n)\}_{n\ge 1}$ is an increasing sequence of sets in $\mathcal{A}\otimes\mathcal{B}_{\mathbb{R}}$ with

$$\bigcup_{n=1}^{\infty} E_*(f_n) = E_*(f).$$

(ii) Using (i) and the 'simple function technique', show that $E_*(f) \in \mathcal{A}\otimes\mathcal{B}_{\mathbb{R}}$, whenever $f: X \longrightarrow \mathbb{R}$ is a nonnegative measurable function. Deduce that $E^*(f) \in \mathcal{A}\otimes\mathcal{B}_{\mathbb{R}}$.
(Hint: $E^*(f) = \bigcap_{n=1}^{\infty} E_*(f+1/n)$.)

(iii) Let $f: X \longrightarrow \mathbb{R}$ be a nonnegative function such that $E^*(f) \in \mathcal{A}\otimes\mathcal{B}_{\mathbb{R}}$. Using exercise 7.1.2 and the following equality

$$\begin{aligned} A \;&:=\; \{(x,t) \in X \times \mathbb{R} \mid f(x) > c, t > 0\} \\ &=\; \bigcup_{n=1}^{\infty}\{(x,t) \in X \times \mathbb{R} \mid (x,t/n+c) \in E^*(f), t > 0\}, \end{aligned}$$

show that $A \in \mathcal{A}\otimes\mathcal{B}_{\mathbb{R}}$, and deduce that f is measurable.

(iv) Let $f: X \longrightarrow \mathbb{R}$ be any measurable function. Show that $G(f) \in \mathcal{A}\otimes\mathcal{B}_{\mathbb{R}}$, where

$$G(f) := \{(x,t) \in X \times \mathbb{R} \mid f(x) = t\}.$$

The set $G(f)$ is called the **graph of the function.**

(v) Let $f \in L_1(X,\mathcal{A},\mu)$, where $\mu(X) < +\infty$. Show that

$$(\mu \times \nu)(E^*|f|) = \int |f|d\mu = (\mu \times \nu)(E_*|f|). \quad (7.7)$$

(Hint: First prove this for the case when f is bounded. For the general case, consider $f_n = |f| \wedge n$ and note that $\{E^*(f_n)\}_{n\ge 1}$ increases to $E^*|f|$.)

(vi) Extend (iv) to the case when μ is σ-finite.

The identity (7.7) shows that for nonnegative functions $\int f d\mu$ represents the area below the curve $y = f(x)$.

* 7.2.8. Exercise: Let X be any nonempty set and $\mathcal{P}(X)$ be its power set. Let $\mathcal{A} := \mathcal{P}(X) \otimes \mathcal{P}(X)$ and let $D := \{(x, y) \in X \times X \mid x = y\}$. Suppose $D \in \mathcal{A}$. Prove the following statements:

(i) There exist sets $A_i, B_i \in \mathcal{P}(X)$ such that D belongs to the σ-algebra generated by $(A_i \times B_i), i = 1, 2, \ldots$.
(Hint: See proposition 3.9.5.)

(ii) Let $\mathcal{B} = \mathcal{S}(\{A_i \mid i = 1, 2, \ldots\})$. Then card $(\mathcal{B}) \leq \mathfrak{c}$, by theorem 4.5.2. For every $x, y \in X, D_x \neq D_y$ if $x \neq y$ and $D_x \in \mathcal{B} \ \forall \ x \in X$. Deduce that card $(X) \leq \mathfrak{c}$.

(iii) If card $(X) > \mathfrak{c}$, then $D \notin \mathcal{P}(X) \otimes \mathcal{P}(X)$, even though $D_x \in \mathcal{P}(X)$ and $D^y \in \mathcal{P}(X), \ \forall \ x, y \in X$. Hence in general,

$$\mathcal{P}(X) \otimes \mathcal{P}(X) \neq \mathcal{P}(X \otimes X).$$

7.2.9. Remark: Given σ-finite measure spaces $(X, \mathcal{A}, \mu)$ and $(Y, \mathcal{B}, \nu)$, we showed in theorem 7.2.1 that $\mu \times \nu$ is the unique measure on $\mathcal{A} \otimes \mathcal{B}$ such that $(\mu \times \nu)(A \times B) = \mu(A)\nu(B)$. Note that the measure space $(X \times Y, \mathcal{A} \otimes \mathcal{B}, \mu \times \nu)$ need not be a complete measure space even if the measure spaces $(X, \mathcal{A}, \mu)$ and $(Y, \mathcal{B}, \nu)$ are complete. For example, if $A \subset X, A \notin \mathcal{A}$ and $\emptyset \neq B \in \mathcal{B}$ with $\mu(B) = 0$, then $(\mu \times \nu)^*(A \times B) = 0$, but $A \times B \notin \mathcal{A} \otimes \mathcal{B}$. In fact, theorem 7.2.1 itself gives a complete measure space $(X \times Y, \overline{\mathcal{A} \otimes \mathcal{B}}, \mu \times \nu)$, where $\overline{\mathcal{A} \otimes \mathcal{B}}$ is the σ-algebra of η^*-measurable subsets of $X \times Y$, η being as in theorem 7.2.1, and $\mu \times \nu$ is the restriction of η^* to $\overline{\mathcal{A} \otimes \mathcal{B}}$. The measure space $(X \times Y, \overline{\mathcal{A} \otimes \mathcal{B}}, \mu \times \nu)$ is nothing but the completion of the measure space $(X \times Y, \mathcal{A} \otimes \mathcal{B}, \mu \times \nu)$. It is easy to see that theorem 7.2.6 holds for $E \in \overline{\mathcal{A} \otimes \mathcal{B}}$ also, as claimed in the next exercise.

7.2.10. Exercise: Let $E \in \overline{\mathcal{A} \otimes \mathcal{B}}$. Then the functions $x \longmapsto \nu(E_x)$ and $y \longmapsto \mu(E^y)$ are measurable and

$$\int_X \nu(E_x) d\mu(x) = (\overline{\mu \times \nu})(E) = \int_Y \mu(E^y) d\nu(y).$$

(Hint: $E = F \cup N, F \in \mathcal{A} \otimes \mathcal{B}$ and $(\mu \times \nu)^*(N) = 0$ by theorem 3.11.8.)

7.2.11. Exercise: Let $E \in \mathcal{A} \otimes \mathcal{B}$ be such that $\mu(E^y) = 0$ for a.e. $(\nu)y \in Y$. Show that $\mu(E_x) = 0$ for a.e. $(\mu)x \in X$. What can you say about $(\mu \times \nu)(E)$?

7.3. Integration on product spaces: Fubini's theorems

Let $(X, \mathcal{A}, \mu)$ and $(Y, \mathcal{B}, \nu)$ be σ-finite measure spaces and $(X \times Y, \mathcal{A} \otimes \mathcal{B}, \mu \times \nu)$ the product measure space. Theorem 7.2.6 can be interpreted as follows: for every $E \in \mathcal{A} \otimes \mathcal{B}$,

$$\int_{X \times Y} \chi_E(x, y) d(\mu \times \nu)(x, y) = \int_X \left(\int_Y \chi_E(x, y) d\nu(y) \right) d\mu(x)$$
$$= \int_Y \left(\int_X \chi_E(x, y) d\mu(x) \right) d\nu(y).$$

This allows us to compute the integral of the function $\chi_E(x, y)$ by integrating one variable at a time. So, the natural question arises: does the above hold when χ_E is replaced by a nonnegative measurable function on $X \times Y$? The answer is yes, and is made precise in the next theorem.

7.3.1. Theorem (Fubini): *Let $f : X \times Y \longrightarrow \mathbb{R}$ be a nonnegative $\mathcal{A} \otimes \mathcal{B}$-measurable function. Then the following statements hold:*

(i) *For $x_0 \in X$ and $y_0 \in Y$ fixed, the functions $x \longmapsto f(x, y_0)$ and $y \longmapsto f(x_0, y)$ are measurable on X and Y, respectively.*

(ii) *The functions $y \longmapsto \int_X f(x, y) d\mu(x)$ and $x \longmapsto \int_Y f(x, y) d\nu(y)$ are well-defined nonnegative measurable functions on Y and X, respectively.*

(iii) $\int_X \left(\int_Y f(x, y) d\nu(y) \right) d\mu(x) = \int_Y \left(\int_X f(x, y) d\mu(x) \right) d\nu(y)$
$$= \int_{X \times Y} f(x, y) d(\mu \times \nu)(x, y).$$

Proof: The proof is yet another application of the 'simple function technique'.

When $f = \chi_E$ and $E \in \mathcal{A} \otimes \mathcal{B}$, the required claim is just theorem 7.2.6, as mentioned above. It is easy to see from this that the required claim holds when f is a nonnegative simple measurable function. In the general case, by theorem 5.3.2, let $\{s_n\}_{n \geq 1}$ be a sequence of nonnegative simple measurable functions on $X \times Y$ such that $\{s_n(x, y)\}_{n \geq 1}$ increases to $f(x, y)$, $\forall (x, y) \in X \times Y$. Then for $x \in X$ fixed, $\{s_n(x, .)\}_{n \geq 1}$ is a sequence of nonnegative simple measurable functions on Y such that $\{s_n(x, y)\}_{n \geq 1}$ increases to $f(x, y)$ for every $y \in Y$. Thus for $x \in X$ fixed, $y \longmapsto f(x, y)$ is a nonnegative measurable function on Y, and by the monotone convergence theorem,

$$\int_Y f(x, y) d\nu(y) = \lim_{n \to \infty} \int_Y s_n(x, y) d\nu(y). \tag{7.8}$$

Thus by the earlier case and corollary 5.3.15, $x \longmapsto \int_Y f(x, y) d\nu(y)$ is a nonnegative measurable function on X. Since $\{\int_Y s_n(., y) d\nu(y)\}_{n>1}$ is an increasing sequence of nonnegative measurable functions on X, by the monotone convergence theorem and (7.8),

$$\int_X \left(\int_Y f(x, y) d\nu(y) \right) d\mu(x) = \lim_{n \to \infty} \int_X \left(\int_Y s_n(x, y) d\nu(y) \right) d\mu(x).$$

By the earlier case,

$$\int_X \left(\int_Y s_n(x, y) d\nu(y) \right) d\mu(x) = \int_{X \times Y} s_n(x, y) d(\mu \times \nu).$$

By the monotone convergence theorem again, we have

$$\int_X \left(\int_Y f(x, y) d\nu(y) \right) d\mu(x) = \lim_{n \to \infty} \int_{X \times Y} s_n(x, y) d(\mu \times \nu)$$
$$= \int_{X \times Y} f(x, y) d(\mu \times \nu).$$

Similarly,

$$\int_Y \left(\int_X f(x, y) d\mu(x) \right) d\nu(y) = \int_{X \times Y} f(x, y) d(\mu \times \nu).$$

This completes the proof. ∎

•**7.3.2. Exercise:** Let $f : X \times Y \longrightarrow \mathbb{R}$ be $\mathcal{A} \otimes \mathcal{B}$-measurable. Show that the following statements are equivalent:

(i) $f \in L_1(\mu \times \nu) := L_1(X \times Y, \mathcal{A} \otimes \mathcal{B}, \mu \times \nu)$.

(ii) $\int_Y \left(\int_X |f(x, y)| \, d\mu(x) \right) d\nu(y) < +\infty.$

(iii) $\int_X \left(\int_Y |f(x, y)| d\nu(y) \right) d\mu(x) < +\infty.$

In view of theorem 7.3.1, it is natural to expect a similar result for $f \in L_1(\mu \times \nu)$, μ and ν being σ-finite measures. This is given by the following theorem.

7.3.3. Theorem (Fubini): *Let $f \in L_1(\mu \times \nu)$. Then the following statements are true:*

(i) *The functions $x \longmapsto f(x, y)$ and $y \longmapsto f(x, y)$ are integrable for a.e. $y(\nu)$ and for a.e. $x(\mu)$, respectively.*

(ii) *The functions*

$$y \longmapsto \int_X f(x, y) d\mu(x) \ \ and \ \ x \longmapsto \int_Y f(x, y) d\nu(y)$$

are defined for a.e. $y(\nu)$ and a.e. $x(\mu)$, and are ν, μ-integrable, respectively.

(iii) $\displaystyle\int_Y \left(\int_X f(x,y)d\mu(x) \right) d\nu(y) = \int_{X \times Y} f(x,y)\, d(\mu \times \nu)$

$$= \int_X \left(\int_Y f(x,y)d\nu(y) \right) d\mu(x).$$

Proof: Let f^+ and f^- denote the positive and negative parts of the function f. Since f^+ is nonnegative and integrable on $X \times Y$, by theorem 7.3.1,

$$\int_X \left(\int_Y f^+(x,y)d\nu(y) \right) d\mu(x) = \int_Y \left(\int_X f^+(x,y)d\mu(x) \right) d\nu(y)$$

$$= \int_{X \times Y} f^+(x,y)d(\mu \times \nu) \qquad (7.9)$$

$$\leq \int_{X \times Y} |f(x,y)|d(\mu \times \nu) < +\infty. \ (7.10)$$

Thus it follows from exercise 5.4.2(ii) that

$$\int_Y f^+(x,y)d\nu(y) \text{ exists for a.e. } x(\mu)$$

and

$$\int_X f^+(x,y)d\mu(x) \text{ exists for a.e. } y(\nu).$$

By a similar argument, we will have

$$\int_X \left(\int_Y f^-(x,y)d\nu(y) \right) d\mu(x) = \int_Y \left(\int_X f^-(x,y)d\mu(x) \right) d\nu(y) \ (7.11)$$

$$= \int_{X \times Y} f^-(x,y)d(\mu \times \nu) < +\infty. \ (7.12)$$

Thus once again it follows from exercise 5.4.2(ii) that

$$\int_Y f^-(x,y)d\nu(y) \text{ exists for a.e. } x(\mu)$$

and

$$\int_X f^-(x,y)d\mu(x) \text{ exists for a.e. } y(\nu).$$

Hence, for a.e. x the functions $y \longmapsto f^+(x,y), y \longmapsto f^-(x,y)$ are ν-integrable and for a.e. y the functions $x \longmapsto f^+(x,y), x \longmapsto f^-(x,y)$ are μ-integrable. Hence $y \longmapsto f(x,y)$ is ν-integrable for a.e. $x(\mu)$ and $y \longmapsto f(x,y)$ is μ-integrable for a.e. $y(\nu)$. Further, since $f \in L_1(\mu \times \nu)$, by definition

$$\int_{X \times Y} f(x,y)\, d(\mu \times \nu) = \int_{X \times Y} f^+(x,y)\, d(\mu \times \nu) - \int_{X \times Y} f^-(x,y)\, d(\mu \times \nu).$$

This, together with (7.9), (7.10), (7.11) and (7.12) gives

$$
\int_{X\times Y} f(x,y)d(\mu\times\nu) \;=\; \int_X \left(\int_Y f(x,y)d\nu(y)\right)d\mu(x)
$$
$$
= \int_Y \left(\int_X f(x,y)d\mu(x)\right)d\nu(y). \quad\blacksquare
$$

Theorem 7.3.1, exercise 7.3.2 and theorem 7.3.3 together give us the following theorem, which enables us to check the integrability of a function of two variables and compute its integral.

7.3.4. Theorem: *Let* $(X,\mathcal{A},\mu)$ *and* $(X,\mathcal{B},\nu)$ *be* σ-*finite measure spaces. Let* $f : X \times Y \longrightarrow \mathbb{R}$ *be an* $\mathcal{A}\otimes\mathcal{B}$-*measurable function such that* f *satisfies any one of the following statements:*

(i) f *is nonnegative.*

(ii) $f \in L_1(\mu\times\nu)$.

(iii) $\displaystyle\int_X \left(\int_Y |f(x,y)|d\nu(y)\right)d\mu(x) < +\infty.$

(iv) $\displaystyle\int_Y \left(\int_X |f(x,y)|d\mu(x)\right)d\nu(y) < +\infty.$

Then

$$
\int_{X\times Y} f(x,y)d(\mu\times\nu) \;=\; \int_X \left(\int_Y f(x,y)d\nu(y)\right)d\mu(x)
$$
$$
= \int_Y \left(\int_X f(x,y)d\mu(x)\right)d\nu(y),
$$

in the sense that all the integrals exist and are equal. $\blacksquare$

7.3.5. Exercise: Let $(X,\mathcal{A},\mu)$ and $(Y,\mathcal{B},\nu)$ be complete σ-finite measure spaces and let $(X\times Y, \overline{\mathcal{A}\otimes\mathcal{B}}, \mu\times\nu)$ be the completion of $(X\times Y, \mathcal{A}\otimes\mathcal{B}, \mu\times\nu)$. Let $f : X \times Y \longrightarrow \mathbb{R}$ be any nonnegative extended real valued $\overline{\mathcal{A}\otimes\mathcal{B}}$-measurable function. Show that:

(i) The function $x \longmapsto f(x,y)$ is $\mathcal{A}$-measurable for a.e. $y(\nu)$ and the function $y \longmapsto f(x,y)$ is $\mathcal{B}$-measurable for a.e. $x(\mu)$.

(ii) The function $y \longmapsto \int_X f(x,y)d\mu(x)$ is $\mathcal{B}$-measurable and the function $x \longmapsto \int_Y f(x,y)d\nu(y)$ is $\mathcal{A}$-measurable.

(iii) $\displaystyle\int_{X\times Y} f(x,y)d(\overline{\mu\times\nu}) \;=\; \int_X \left(\int_Y f(x,y)d\nu(y)\right)d\mu(x)$
$$
= \int_Y \left(\int_X f(x,y)d\mu(x)\right)d\nu(y).
$$

We give next some examples which illustrate the necessity of the conditions on μ, ν and f for the conclusions of theorem 7.3.4 to hold.

7.3.6. Example: Let $X = Y = [0,1]$ and $\mathcal{A} = \mathcal{B} = \mathcal{B}_{[0,1]}$, the σ-algebra of Borel subsets of $[0,1]$. Let μ be the Lebesgue measure on $\mathcal{A}$ and ν be the **counting measure** on $\mathcal{B}$, i.e., $\nu(E) :=$ number of elements in E if E is finite and $\nu(E) := +\infty$ otherwise. Let $D := \{(x,y) \,|\, x = y\}$. Let, for $n \geq 1$,

$$D_n := \bigcup_{j=1}^{n} (\, [(j-1)/n, j/n] \times [(j-1)/n, j/n] \,).$$

Then $D = \cap_{n=1}^{\infty} D_n$. Thus $D \in \mathcal{A} \otimes \mathcal{B}$. In fact, D is a closed subset of $[0,1] \times [0,1]$. Further,

$$\int_X \chi_D(x,y)d\mu(x) = 0 \ \ \forall\, y \in Y \quad \text{and} \quad \int_Y \chi_D(x,y)d\nu(y) = 1 \ \ \forall\, x \in X.$$

Hence

$$\int_Y \left(\int_X \chi_D(x,y)d\mu(x) \right) d\nu(y) = 0 \ \text{ and } \ \int_X \left(\int_Y \chi_D(x,y)d\nu(y) \right) d\mu(x) = 1.$$

This does not contradict theorem 7.3.1, since ν is not σ-finite.

7.3.7. Example: Let $X = Y = [0,1], \mathcal{A} = \mathcal{B} = \mathcal{B}_{[0,1]}$, and let $\mu = \nu$ be the Lebesgue measure on $[0,1]$. Let

$$f(x,y) := \begin{cases} \dfrac{x^2 - y^2}{(x^2 + y^2)^2} & \text{if} \quad (x,y) \neq (0,0), \\[2mm] 0 & \text{if} \quad x = y \text{ otherwise.} \end{cases}$$

Noting that for fixed x, $f(x,y)$ is a Riemann integrable function on $[0,1]$ and

$$\frac{\partial}{\partial y} \left(\frac{y}{x^2 + y^2} \right) = f(x,y),$$

we get

$$\int_0^1 f(x,y)d\nu(y) = 1/(1 + x^2).$$

Hence

$$\int_0^1 \left(\int_0^1 f(x,y)d\nu(y) \right) d\mu(x) = \pi/4$$

and

$$\int_0^1 \left(\int_0^1 f(x,y)d\mu(x) \right) d\nu(y) = -\int_0^1 \left(\int_0^1 (x,y)d\nu(y) \right) d\mu(x) = -\pi/4.$$

This does not contradict theorem 7.3.3, because $f \notin L_1(X \times Y)$. To see this, note that

$$\int_{[0,1] \times [0,1]} |f(x,y)| d(\mu \times \nu) = \int_0^1 \left(\int_0^1 |f(x,y)| d\nu(y) \right) d\mu(x)$$

$$\geq \int_0^1 \left(\int_0^x |f(x,y)| d\nu(y) \right) d\mu(x)$$

$$= \int_0^1 \frac{1}{x} \left(\int_0^{\pi/4} \cos 2\theta d\theta \right) d\mu(x)$$

$$= \int_0^1 \frac{1}{2x} d\mu(x) = +\infty.$$

7.3.8. Exercise: Let $X = Y = [-1,1], \mathcal{A} = \mathcal{B} = \mathcal{B}_{[-1,1]}$, and let $\mu = \nu$ be the Lebesgue measure on $[-1,1]$. Let

$$f(x,y) := \begin{cases} \dfrac{xy}{(x^2 + y^2)^2} & \text{if } (x,y) \neq (0,0), \\ 0 & \text{otherwise.} \end{cases}$$

Show that

$$\int_{-1}^1 \left(\int_{-1}^1 f(x,y) d\nu(y) \right) d\mu(x) = 0 = \int_{-1}^1 \left(\int_{-1}^1 f(x,y) d\mu(x) \right) d\nu(y).$$

Can you conclude that

$$\int_{-1}^1 \left(\int_{-1}^1 f(x,y) d\nu(y) \right) d\mu(x) = \int_{X \times Y} f(x,y) d(\mu \times \nu)(x,y)?$$

7.3.9. Exercise: Let $f \in L_1(X, \mathcal{A}, \mu)$ and $g \in L_1(Y, \mathcal{B}, \nu)$. Let

$$\phi(x,y) := f(x)g(y), \ x \in X \text{ and } y \in Y.$$

Show that $\phi \in L_1(X \times Y, \mathcal{A} \otimes \mathcal{B}, \mu \times \nu)$ and

$$\int_{X \times Y} \phi(x,y) d(\mu \times \nu) = \left(\int_X f d\mu \right) \left(\int_Y g d\nu \right).$$

7.3.10. Exercise: Let $f \in L_1(0,a)$ and let

$$g(x) := \int_x^a (f(t)/t) d\lambda(t), 0 < x \leq a.$$

Show that $g \in L_1(0,a)$, and compute $\int_0^a g(x) d\lambda(x)$.

7.3.11. Exercise: Let $(X, \mathcal{A}, \mu)$, and $(X, \mathcal{B}, \nu)$ be as in example 7.3.7. Define, for $x, y \in [0, 1]$,

$$f(x, y) := \begin{cases} 1 & \text{if } x \text{ is rational,} \\ 2y & \text{if } y \text{ is irrational.} \end{cases}$$

Compute

$$\int_0^1 \left(\int_0^1 f(x, y) d\nu(y) \right) d\mu(x) \text{ and } \int_0^1 \left(\int_0^1 f(x, y) d\mu(x) \right) d\nu(y).$$

Is f in $L_1(\mu \times \nu)$?

7.3.12. Exercise: Let $(X, \mathcal{A}, \mu)$ be as in example 7.3.7. Let $Y = [1, \infty), \mathcal{B} = \mathcal{L}_{\mathbb{R}} \cap [1, \infty)$, and let ν be the Lebesgue measure restricted to $[1, \infty)$. Define, for $(x, y) \in X \times Y$,

$$f(x, y) := e^{-xy} - 2e^{-2xy}.$$

Show that $f \notin L_1(\mu \times \nu)$.

7.3.13. Exercise: Let X be a topological space and let $\mathcal{B}_X$ be the σ-algebra of Borel subsets of X. A function $f : X \longrightarrow \mathbb{R}$ is said to be **Borel measurable** if $f^{-1}(E) \in \mathcal{B}_X \ \forall \, E \in \mathcal{B}_{\mathbb{R}}$. Prove the following:

(i) f is Borel measurable iff $f^{-1}(U) \in \mathcal{B}_X$ for every open set $U \subseteq \mathbb{R}$. (Hint: Use the 'σ-algebra technique'.)

(ii) Let $f : X \longrightarrow \mathbb{R}$ be continuous. Show that f is Borel measurable.

(iii) Let $\{f_n\}_{n \geq 1}$ be a sequence of Borel measurable functions on X such that $f(x) := \lim_{n \to \infty} f_n(x)$ exists $\ \forall \, x \in X$. Show that f also is Borel measurable.

(iv) Consider $\mathbb{R}^2$ with the product topology and let f, g be Borel measurable functions on $\mathbb{R}$. Show that the function ϕ on $\mathbb{R}^2$ defined by

$$\phi(x, y) := f(x)g(y), \quad x \in X, y \in Y,$$

is Borel measurable.

7.3.14. Exercise: Let $f : \mathbb{R}^2 \longrightarrow \mathbb{R}$ be Borel measurable. Show that for $x \in X$ fixed, $y \longmapsto f(x, y)$ is a Borel measurable function on $\mathbb{R}$. Is the function $x \longmapsto f(x, y)$, for $y \in Y$ fixed, also Borel measurable?

*7.3.15. Example: Assume the continuum hypothesis and let $<$ be the well-order on $[0, 1]$ such that $\forall x \in [0, 1], \{y \in [0, 1] \,|\, y < x\}$ is at most a countable set (see appendix C). Let

$$E := \{(x, y) \in [0, 1] \times [0, 1] \,|\, x < y\}.$$

Then $\forall$ y fixed and $\forall$ $x \in [0,1], \chi_E(x,y) = 1$ if $x < y$ and 0 otherwise. Hence $\chi_E(x,y)$ is the indicator function of a countable set for $y \in [0,1]$ fixed. Thus it is a Borel measurable function. Similarly, for $x \in [0,1]$ fixed, $y \longmapsto \chi_E(x,y)$ is Borel measurable, for it is the indicator function of $[0,1] \setminus C$, a countable set. However, χ_E is not Borel measurable on $[0,1] \times [0,1]$. To see this, note that $\mathcal{B}_{[0,1] \times [0,1]} = \mathcal{B}_{[0,1]} \otimes \mathcal{B}_{[0,1]}$. Thus if χ_E were Borel measurable, then by theorem 7.3.1 we should have

$$\int_{[0,1] \times [0,1]} \chi_E(x,y) d(\lambda \times \lambda)(x,y)$$

$$= \int_{[0,1]} \left(\int_{[0,1]} \chi_E(x,y) d\lambda(x) \right) d\lambda(y)$$

$$= \int_{[0,1]} \left(\int_{[0,1]} \chi_E(x,y) d\lambda(y) \right) d\lambda(x). \quad (7.13)$$

However, it is easy to see that for $x,y \in [0,1]$,

$$\int_{[0,1]} \chi_E(x,y) d\lambda(y) = 1 \text{ and } \int_{[0,1]} \chi_E(x,y) d\lambda(x) = 0.$$

This contradicts (7.13). Hence χ_E is not Borel measurable.

7.3.16. Exercise: Let $f : \mathbb{R}^2 \longrightarrow \mathbb{R}$ be such that for $x \in X$ fixed, $y \longmapsto f(x,y)$ is Borel measurable and for $y \in Y$ fixed, $x \longmapsto f(x,y)$ is continuous.

(i) For every $n \geq 1$ and $x,y \in \mathbb{R}$, define

$$f_n(x,y) := (i - nx)f((i-1)/n, y) + (nx - i + 1)f(i/n, y),$$

whenever $x \in [(i-1)/n, i/n), i \in \mathbb{Z}$. Show that each $f_n : \mathbb{R}^2 \longrightarrow \mathbb{R}$ is continuous and hence is Borel measurable.

(ii) Show that $f_n(x,y) \to f(x,y)$ as $n \to \infty$ for every $(x,y) \in \mathbb{R}^2$, and hence f is Borel measurable.

7.3.17. Exercise: Let $(X, \mathcal{A})$ and $(Y, \mathcal{B})$ be measurable spaces and let $f : X \times Y \longrightarrow \mathbb{R}$ be a nonnegative $\mathcal{A} \otimes \mathcal{B}$-measurable function. Let μ be a σ-finite measure on $(Y, \mathcal{B})$. For any $E \in \mathcal{B}$ and $x \in X$, let

$$\eta(x, E) := \int_E f(x,y) d\mu(y).$$

Show that $\eta(x, E)$ has the following properties:

(i) For every fixed $E \in \mathcal{B}, \longmapsto \eta(x, E)$ is an $\mathcal{A}$-measurable function.

(ii) For every fixed $x \in X, E \longmapsto \eta(x, E)$ is a measure on $(Y, \mathcal{B})$.

A function $\eta : X \times \mathcal{B} \longrightarrow [0, \infty)$ having properties (i) and (ii) above is called a **transition measure**. If η is a transition measure with $\eta(x, Y) = 1 \ \forall \, x \in X$, then η is called a **transition probability**. Transition probabilities play an important role in the theory of probability. Fubini's theorems can be extended to transition measures. For details see Parthasarathy [28].

7.4. Lebesgue measure on $\mathbb{R}^2$ and its properties

We now specialize the construction of $(X \times Y, \mathcal{A} \otimes \mathcal{B}, \mu \times \nu)$ to the particular case when $X = Y = \mathbb{R}$, $\mathcal{A} = \mathcal{B} = \mathcal{L}_{\mathbb{R}}$ and $\mu = \nu = \lambda$, the Lebesgue measure. We have already seen that $\mathcal{B}_{\mathbb{R}} \otimes \mathcal{B}_{\mathbb{R}} = \mathcal{B}_{\mathbb{R}^2}$ and that $(\mathbb{R}^2, \mathcal{L}_{\mathbb{R}} \otimes \mathcal{L}_{\mathbb{R}}, \lambda \times \lambda)$ is not complete. The completion of this measure space, denoted by $(\mathbb{R}^2, \mathcal{L}_{\mathbb{R}^2}, \lambda_{\mathbb{R}^2})$, is called the **Lebesgue measure space**. Elements of $\mathcal{L}_{\mathbb{R}^2}$ are called the **Lebesgue measurable subsets** of $\mathbb{R}^2$, and $\lambda_{\mathbb{R}^2}$ is called the **Lebesgue measure** on $\mathbb{R}^2$. The following proposition ensures that $\lambda_{\mathbb{R}^2}$ is the unique extension of the natural concept of area in $\mathbb{R}^2$.

7.4.1. Proposition: *Let $\tilde{\mathcal{I}}$ denote the collection of left-open, right-closed intervals in $\mathbb{R}$, and let $\tilde{\mathcal{I}}^2 := \{I \times J \,|\, I, J \in \tilde{\mathcal{I}}\}$. Then the following hold:*

(i) *$\tilde{\mathcal{I}}^2$ is a semi-algebra of subsets of $\mathbb{R}^2$, and $\mathcal{S}(\tilde{\mathcal{I}}^2) = \mathcal{B}_{\mathbb{R}^2}$.*

(ii) *$\lambda_{\mathbb{R}^2}(I \times J) = \lambda(I)\lambda(J), \ \forall \, I, J \in \tilde{\mathcal{I}}.$*

(iii) *The measure space $(\mathbb{R}^2, \mathcal{L}_{\mathbb{R}^2}, \lambda_{\mathbb{R}^2})$ is the completion of the measure spaces $(\mathbb{R}^2, \mathcal{L}_{\mathbb{R}} \otimes \mathcal{L}_{\mathbb{R}}, \lambda \times \lambda)$ and $(\mathbb{R}^2, \mathcal{B}_{\mathbb{R}^2}, \lambda_{\mathbb{R}^2})$.*

Proof: Statement (ii) is obvious. To prove (i), we note that $\tilde{\mathcal{I}}^2 = \tilde{\mathcal{I}} \times \tilde{\mathcal{I}}$ and, by exercise 7.1.4 (ii), $\mathcal{B}_{\mathbb{R}} \otimes \mathcal{B}_{\mathbb{R}} = \mathcal{S}(\tilde{\mathcal{I}}) \otimes \mathcal{S}(\tilde{\mathcal{I}}) = \mathcal{S}(\tilde{\mathcal{I}} \times \tilde{\mathcal{I}}) = \mathcal{S}(\tilde{\mathcal{I}}^2)$. Since $\mathcal{B}_{\mathbb{R}} \otimes \mathcal{B}_{\mathbb{R}} = \mathcal{B}_{\mathbb{R}^2}$, this completes the proof. To prove (iii), we note that $\mathcal{L}_{\mathbb{R}^2}$ is the class of $\overset{*}{\lambda}_{\mathbb{R}^2}$-measurable subsets of $\mathbb{R}^2$, where $\lambda_{\mathbb{R}^2} = \lambda \times \lambda$ is the measure on the semi-algebra $\tilde{\mathcal{I}}^2$ given by $\lambda_{\mathbb{R}^2}(I \times J) = \lambda(I)\lambda(J)$. Thus $(\mathbb{R}^2, \mathcal{L}_{\mathbb{R}^2}, \lambda_{\mathbb{R}^2})$ is the completion of the measure space $(\mathbb{R}^2, \mathcal{B}_{\mathbb{R}^2}, \lambda_{\mathbb{R}^2})$. Also $\lambda_{\mathbb{R}^2} = \lambda \times \lambda$ on the σ-algebra $\mathcal{L}_{\mathbb{R}} \otimes \mathcal{L}_{\mathbb{R}}$. Hence $(\mathbb{R}^2, \mathcal{L}_{\mathbb{R}^2}, \lambda_{\mathbb{R}^2})$ is also the completion of $(\mathbb{R}^2, \mathcal{L}_{\mathbb{R}} \otimes \mathcal{L}_{\mathbb{R}}, \lambda \times \lambda)$. ∎

7.4.2. Exercise (Regularity of $\lambda_{\mathbb{R}^2}$): Prove the following:

(i) $\lambda_{\mathbb{R}^2}(U) > 0$ for every nonempty open subset U of $\mathbb{R}^2$.

(ii) A set $E \in \mathcal{L}_{\mathbb{R}^2}$ iff $\ \forall \, \epsilon > 0$, there exists an open set U such that $E \subseteq U$ and $\lambda(U \setminus E) < \epsilon$.
(Hint: Proceed as in theorem 4.2.2.)

(iii) $\lambda_{\mathbb{R}^2}(K) < +\infty$ for every compact subset K of $\mathbb{R}$.

(iv) $\lambda_{\mathbb{R}^2}(U) = \sup\{\lambda_{\mathbb{R}^2}(K) \,|\, K \text{ compact}, \ K \subseteq U\}$.

(Hint: Given U open, there exists a sequence of compact sets K_n such that $K_n \uparrow U$.)

(v) If $E \in \mathcal{B}_{\mathbb{R}^2}$ is such that $\lambda_{\mathbb{R}^2}(E) < +\infty$, then

$$\lambda_{\mathbb{R}^2}(E) = \sup\{\lambda_{\mathbb{R}^2}(k) \mid K \subseteq E, K \text{ compact}\}.$$

We describe next some properties of the Lebesgue measure $\lambda_{\mathbb{R}^2}$. For $E \subseteq \mathbb{R}^2$ and $\boldsymbol{x} \in \mathbb{R}^2$, let $E + \boldsymbol{x} := \{\boldsymbol{y} + \boldsymbol{x} \mid \boldsymbol{y} \in E\}$.

7.4.3. Theorem: *The Lebesgue measure $\lambda_{\mathbb{R}^2}$ has the following properties:*

(i) *Let $E \in \mathcal{B}_{\mathbb{R}^2}$ and $\boldsymbol{x} \in \mathbb{R}^2$. Then $E + \boldsymbol{x} \in \mathcal{B}_{\mathbb{R}^2}$ and*

$$\lambda_{\mathbb{R}^2}(E) = \lambda_{\mathbb{R}^2}(E + \boldsymbol{x}).$$

(This property of $\lambda_{\mathbb{R}^2}$ is called **translation invariance.**)

(ii) *For every nonnegative Borel measurable function f on $\mathbb{R}^2$ and $\boldsymbol{y} \in \mathbb{R}^2$,*

$$\int f(\boldsymbol{x} + \boldsymbol{y})\, d\lambda_{\mathbb{R}^2}(\boldsymbol{x}) = \int f(\boldsymbol{x})\, d\lambda_{\mathbb{R}^2}(\boldsymbol{x}) = \int f(-\boldsymbol{x})\, d\lambda_{\mathbb{R}^2}(\boldsymbol{x}).$$

(iii) *Let μ be any σ-finite measure on $\mathcal{B}_{\mathbb{R}^2}$ such that $\mu(E + \boldsymbol{x}) = \mu(E)$ $\forall\, E \in \mathcal{B}_{\mathbb{R}^2}, \boldsymbol{x} \in \mathbb{R}^2$. Suppose*

$$0 < \mu(E_0) = C\lambda_{\mathbb{R}^2}(E_0) < +\infty,$$

for some $E_0 \in \mathcal{B}$ and for some $C \geq 0$. Then

$$\mu(E) = C\lambda_{\mathbb{R}^2}(E), \ \ \forall\, E \in \mathcal{B}_{\mathbb{R}}.$$

Proof: (i). The proof is once again an application of the 'σ-algebra monotone class technique'. So, we only sketch the proof. Let

$$\mathcal{A} := \{E \in \mathcal{B}_{\mathbb{R}^2} \mid E + \boldsymbol{x} \in \mathcal{B}_{\mathbb{R}^2}\}.$$

One shows that $\mathcal{A}$ is a σ-algebra of subsets of $\mathbb{R}^2$ and $\mathcal{A}$ includes all open sets, proving $\mathcal{A} = \mathcal{B}_{\mathbb{R}^2}$. Next, let

$$\mathcal{M} := \{E \in \mathcal{B}_{\mathbb{R}^2} \mid \lambda(E + \boldsymbol{x}) = \lambda(E)\}.$$

One shows that $\mathcal{M}$ is a monotone class including $\mathcal{R} = \{(A \times B) \mid A, B \in \mathcal{B}_{\mathbb{R}}\}$ and $\mathcal{M}$ is closed under finite disjoint unions. Thus $\mathcal{M}$ includes $\mathcal{F}(\mathcal{R})$, the algebra generated by $\mathcal{R}$, and hence includes the monotone class generated by $\mathcal{F}(\mathcal{R})$, i.e., the σ-algebra generated by $\mathcal{F}(\mathcal{R})$ (see theorem 3.10.7). Since $\mathcal{M}(\mathcal{F}(\mathcal{R})) = \mathcal{B}_{\mathbb{R}^2}$, the proof of (i) is complete.

(ii) The proof is an application of the 'simple function technique' and is left as an exercise.

(iii) We first note that (i) and (ii) above hold when $\lambda_{\mathbb{R}^2}$ is replaced by any translation invariant measure μ on $\mathcal{B}_{\mathbb{R}^2}$. One can give a proof on lines as in the case of the Lebesgue measure on $\mathbb{R}$, see section 4.4. We give another proof which is an application of Fubini's theorem. Showing that $\mu(E) = C\lambda_{\mathbb{R}^2}(E) \ \forall \ E \in \mathcal{B}_{\mathbb{R}^2}$ is equivalent to proving that

$$\lambda_{\mathbb{R}^2}(E_0)\mu(E) = \mu(E_0)\lambda_{\mathbb{R}^2}(E), \ \forall \ E \in \mathcal{B}_{\mathbb{R}^2}.$$

Since $\lambda_{\mathbb{R}^2}$ is translation invariant, using (ii) we have $\forall \ E \in \mathcal{B}_{\mathbb{R}^2}$

$$\begin{aligned}
\lambda_{\mathbb{R}^2}(E_0)\mu(E) &= \lambda_{\mathbb{R}^2}(E_0) \int \chi_E(\boldsymbol{y})d\mu(\boldsymbol{y}) \\
&= \int \lambda_{\mathbb{R}^2}(E_0 - \boldsymbol{y})\chi_E(\boldsymbol{y})d\mu(\boldsymbol{y}) \\
&= \int \left(\int \chi_{E_0}(\boldsymbol{x} + \boldsymbol{y})d\lambda_{\mathbb{R}^2}(\boldsymbol{x}) \right) \chi_E(\boldsymbol{y})d\mu(\boldsymbol{y}).
\end{aligned}$$

Using Fubini's theorem (7.3.1),

$$\lambda_{\mathbb{R}^2}(E_0)\mu(E) = \int \left(\int \chi_E(\boldsymbol{y})\chi_{E_0}(\boldsymbol{x} + \boldsymbol{y})d\mu(\boldsymbol{y}) \right) d\lambda_{\mathbb{R}^2}(\boldsymbol{x}).$$

Now using translation invariance of μ and theorem 7.3.1 again, we have

$$\begin{aligned}
\lambda_{\mathbb{R}^2}(E_0)\mu(E) &= \int \left(\int \chi_E(\boldsymbol{y} - \boldsymbol{x})\chi_{E_0}(\boldsymbol{y})d\mu(\boldsymbol{y}) \right) d\lambda_{\mathbb{R}^2}(\boldsymbol{x}) \\
&= \int \left(\int \chi_E(\boldsymbol{y} - \boldsymbol{x})d\lambda_{\mathbb{R}^2}(\boldsymbol{x}) \right) \chi_{E_0}(\boldsymbol{y})d\mu(\boldsymbol{y}) \\
&= \mu(E_0)\lambda_{\mathbb{R}^2}(E). \ \blacksquare
\end{aligned}$$

•**7.4.4. Exercise:** Show that for $f \in L_1(\mathbb{R}^2, \mathcal{L}_{\mathbb{R}^2}, \lambda_{\mathbb{R}^2})$, $\boldsymbol{x} \in \mathbb{R}^2$, the function $\boldsymbol{y} \longmapsto f(\boldsymbol{x} + \boldsymbol{y})$ is integrable and

$$\int f(\boldsymbol{x} + \boldsymbol{y})d\lambda_{\mathbb{R}^2}(\boldsymbol{x}) = \int f(\boldsymbol{x})d\lambda_{\mathbb{R}^2}(\boldsymbol{x}).$$

(Hint: Use exercise 5.3.27 and theorem 7.4.3.)

•**7.4.5. Exercise:** Let $E \in \mathcal{L}_{\mathbb{R}^2}$ and $\boldsymbol{x} = (x, y) \in \mathbb{R}^2$. Let

$$\boldsymbol{x}E := \{(xt, yr) \mid (t, r) \in E\}.$$

Prove the following:

(i) $\boldsymbol{x}E \in \mathcal{L}_{\mathbb{R}^2}$ for every $\boldsymbol{x} \in \mathbb{R}, E \in \mathcal{L}_{\mathbb{R}^2}$, and $\lambda_{\mathbb{R}^2}(\boldsymbol{x}E) = |xy|\lambda_{\mathbb{R}^2}(E)$.

(ii) For every nonnegative Borel measurable function $f : \mathbb{R}^2 \longrightarrow \mathbb{R}$,

$$\int f(\boldsymbol{x}\boldsymbol{t})d\lambda_{\mathbb{R}^2}(\boldsymbol{t}) = |xy| \int f(\boldsymbol{t})d\lambda_{\mathbb{R}^2}(\boldsymbol{t}),$$

where for $\boldsymbol{x} = (x, y)$ and $\boldsymbol{t} = (s, r), \boldsymbol{x}\boldsymbol{t} := (xs, yr)$.

(iii) Let $\lambda_{\mathbb{R}^2}\{\boldsymbol{x} \in \mathbb{R}^2 \mid |\boldsymbol{x}| \le 1\} =: \pi$. Then

$$\lambda_{\mathbb{R}^2}\{\boldsymbol{x} \in \mathbb{R}^2 \mid |\boldsymbol{x}| < 1\} = \pi \text{ and } \lambda_{\mathbb{R}^2}\{\boldsymbol{x} \in \mathbb{R}^2 \mid |\boldsymbol{x}| < r\} = \pi r^2.$$

(iv) Let E be a vector subspace of $\mathbb{R}^2$. Then $\lambda_{\mathbb{R}^2}(E) = 0$ if E has dimension less than 2.

The claim of exercise 7.4.5(i) can be reinterpreted as follows. Let $T : \mathbb{R}^2 \longrightarrow \mathbb{R}^2$ be the linear transformation whose matrix is given by $\begin{bmatrix} x & 0 \\ 0 & y \end{bmatrix}$. Then for $\boldsymbol{x} = (x, y)$ we have $\boldsymbol{x}E = T(E)$ and

$$\lambda_{\mathbb{R}^2}(T(E)) = |xy| \, \lambda_{\mathbb{R}^2}(E).$$

In case $x = 0$ or $y = 0$, then T is a singular linear transformation and we have $\lambda_{\mathbb{R}^2}(T(E)) = 0 \; \forall \, E \in \mathcal{B}_{\mathbb{R}^2}$. If neither $x = 0$, nor $y = 0$, i.e., $|xy| = |\det(T)| \neq 0$, i.e., T is a nonsingular linear transformation, then

$$\lambda_{\mathbb{R}^2}(T(E)) = |\det T| \lambda_{\mathbb{R}^2}(E),$$

where $\det T$ denote the determinant of the matrix of T with respect to the standard basis of $\mathbb{R}^2$. The question arises: given a linear transformation $T : \mathbb{R}^2 \longrightarrow \mathbb{R}^2$, can we say that $\lambda_{\mathbb{R}^2}(T(E)) = |\det T| \lambda_{\mathbb{R}^2}(E)$? The answer is given by the following theorem.

7.4.6. Theorem: *Let $T : \mathbb{R}^2 \longrightarrow \mathbb{R}^2$ be a linear transformation and $E \in \mathcal{L}_{\mathbb{R}^2}$. Then $T(E) \in \mathcal{L}_{\mathbb{R}^2}$ and*

$$\lambda_{\mathbb{R}^2}(T(E)) = |\det T| \, \lambda_{\mathbb{R}^2}(E).$$

Proof: If T is singular, then $T(\mathbb{R}^2)$ is a subspace of $\mathbb{R}^2$ and has dimension less than 2. Thus using exercise 7.4.5(iv), $\lambda_{\mathbb{R}^2}(T(\mathbb{R}^2)) = 0$ and hence $\lambda_{\mathbb{R}^2}^*(T(E)) = 0 \; \forall \, E \in \mathcal{L}_{\mathbb{R}^2}$. Hence $T(E) \in \mathcal{L}_{\mathbb{R}^2}$ and

$$\lambda_{\mathbb{R}^2}(T(E)) = 0 = |\det T| \lambda_{\mathbb{R}^2}(E).$$

Now suppose that T is nonsingular. Then T is bijective and both T and T^{-1} are continuous. Suppose $E \in \mathcal{B}_{\mathbb{R}^2}$. Then, clearly, $T(E) \in \mathcal{B}_{\mathbb{R}^2}$. Define

$$\mu_T(E) := \lambda_{\mathbb{R}^2}(T(E)), \quad E \in \mathcal{B}_{\mathbb{R}^2}.$$

It is easy to check that μ_T is a σ-finite measure on $\mathcal{B}_{\mathbb{R}^2}$ and

$$\mu_T(E + \boldsymbol{x}) = \mu_T(E) \; \forall \; \boldsymbol{x} \in \mathbb{R}^2, E \in \mathcal{B}_{\mathbb{R}^2}.$$

Further, if we take $U := (0, 1) \times (0, 1)$, then U is a nonempty bounded open set, and so is $T(U)$. Thus $0 < \mu_T(U) < +\infty$, and by theorem 7.4.3, there exists a constant $C(T) > 0$ such that

$$\mu_T(E) = C(T) \, \lambda_{\mathbb{R}^2}(E) \; \forall \, E \in \mathcal{B}_{\mathbb{R}^2}.$$

Hence $\forall \; E \in \mathcal{B}_{\mathbb{R}^2}$,

$$\lambda_{\mathbb{R}^2}(T(E)) = C(T) \, \lambda_{\mathbb{R}^2}(E).$$

Note that this holds for every nonsingular linear transformation T, and we have to show that $C(T) = |\det T|$. The map $T \longmapsto C(T), T$ nonsingular, has the following properties:

(i) $C(D) = |\det D|$ for every diagonal transformation D.
We have already seen this in exercise 7.4.5.

(ii) $C(O) = 1$, if O is any orthogonal transformation.
This is because an orthogonal transformation in $\mathbb{R}^2$ leaves the set $E := \{\boldsymbol{x} \in \mathbb{R}^2 | \, |\boldsymbol{x}| \le 1\}$ invariant.

(iii) $C(T_1 T_2) = C(T_1)C(T_2) \ \forall \ T_1, T_2$ nonsingular.
This is easy to verify using the definition of $C(T)$.

Now, let T be any nonsingular linear transformation. By the singular value decomposition (see appendix E) for linear transformations, there exist orthogonal transformations P and Q such that $T = PDQ$, where D is some diagonal transformation. Thus

$$C(T) = C(P)C(D)C(Q) = C(D) = |\det D|.$$

But,

$$|\det(T)| = |\det(PDQ)| = |\det D|,$$

since P and Q are orthogonal and thus $|\det P| = |\det Q| = 1$. Hence

$$\lambda_{\mathbb{R}^2}(T(E)) = C(T)\lambda_{\mathbb{R}^2}(E) = |\det T|\lambda_{\mathbb{R}^2}(E).$$

This proves the theorem for sets $E \in \mathcal{B}_{\mathbb{R}^2}$. It is easy to extend it to sets $E \in \mathcal{L}_{\mathbb{R}^2}$ (see the next exercise). ∎

7.4.7. Exercise: Let $T : \mathbb{R}^2 \to \mathbb{R}$ be a linear map.

(i) If $N \subseteq \mathbb{R}^2$ is such that $\lambda^*_{\mathbb{R}^2}(N) = 0$, show that $\lambda^*_{\mathbb{R}^2}(T(N)) = 0$.

(ii) Use (i) above and proposition 7.4.1(ii) to complete the proof of theorem 7.4.6 for sets $E \in \mathcal{L}_{\mathbb{R}^2}$.

7.4.8. Exercise: Consider the vectors $(a_1, b_1), (a_2, b_2) \in \mathbb{R}^2$ and let

$$P := \{(\alpha_1 a_1 + \alpha_2 a_2, \alpha_1 b_1 + \alpha_2 b_2) \in \mathbb{R}^2 \, | \, \alpha_1, \alpha_2 \in \mathbb{R}, 0 \le \alpha_i \le 1\},$$

called the **parallelogram** determined by these vectors. Show that

$$\lambda_{\mathbb{R}^2}(P) = |a_1 b_2 - a_2 b_1|.$$

7.4.9. Exercise: Let $E \in \mathcal{L}_{\mathbb{R}^2}$ with $0 < \lambda(E) < \infty$. Show that there exists a unique point $(c_1, c_2) \in \mathbb{R}^2$ such that

$$\int x \chi_E(x + c_1, y + c_2) d\lambda_{\mathbb{R}^2}(x, y) = 0$$

and

$$\int y\chi_E(x+c_1,y+c_2)d\lambda_{\mathbb{R}^2}(x,y) = 0.$$

In fact,

$$c_1 = \frac{1}{\lambda(E)}\int x\chi_E(x,y)d\lambda_{\mathbb{R}^2}(x,y)$$

and

$$c_2 = \frac{1}{\lambda(E)}\int y\chi_E(x,y)d\lambda_{\mathbb{R}^2}(x,y).$$

($\boldsymbol{c} = (c_1,c_2)$ is called the **centroid of** E.)

7.4.10. Theorem (Integration of 'radial' functions): *Let* $f : [0,\infty) \longrightarrow$ *$(0,\infty)$ be a nonnegative measurable function. Then*

$$\int_{\mathbb{R}^2} f(|\boldsymbol{x}|)d\lambda_{\mathbb{R}^2}(\boldsymbol{x}) = 2\pi \int_0^\infty f(r)rd\lambda(r).$$

Proof: The proof is once again an application of the 'simple function technique'. We give the proof in steps

Step 1: The theorem holds for $f = \chi_{(a,b)}$, $0 \leq a < b < +\infty$.

First note that, by exercise 7.4.5, for $f = \chi_{(a,b)}$

$$\begin{aligned}
\int_{\mathbb{R}^2} \chi_{(a,b)}(|\boldsymbol{x}|)\,d\lambda_{\mathbb{R}^2}(\boldsymbol{x}) &= \lambda_{\mathbb{R}^2}\left\{(x,y) \in \mathbb{R}^2 \mid a^2 < x^2 + y^2 < b^2\right\} \\
&= \pi(b^2 - a^2).
\end{aligned}$$

Also, by the monotone convergence theorem and theorem 5.5.1,

$$\begin{aligned}
2\pi \int_0^\infty \chi_{(a,b)}(x)xd\lambda(x) &= \lim_{n\to\infty} 2\pi \int_0^n \chi_{(a,b)}(x)xd\lambda(x) \\
&= 2\pi \int_a^b xdx \\
&= \pi(b^2 - a^2).
\end{aligned}$$

Step 2: Let $\{E_n\}_{n\geq 1}$ be a sequence of sets from $[0,\infty) \cap \mathcal{L}_{\mathbb{R}}$ such that either the E_n's are pairwise disjoint, or the E_n's are increasing. If the theorem holds for each χ_{E_n}, then the theorem holds for χ_E also, where $E = \bigcup_{n=1}^\infty E_n$.

For this, let $F_n := \bigcup_{k=1}^n E_k$ and $\phi_n = \chi_{F_n}$, $n = 1, 2, \ldots$. Then $\{\phi_n\}_{n\geq 1}$ is an increasing sequence of nonnegative measurable functions, and by the monotone convergence theorem we have

$$\int_{\mathbb{R}^2} \chi_E(|\boldsymbol{x}|)\,d\lambda_{\mathbb{R}}(\boldsymbol{x}) = \lim_{n\to\infty} \int_{\mathbb{R}^2} \phi_n(|\boldsymbol{x}|)\,d\lambda_{\mathbb{R}^2}(\boldsymbol{x}). \tag{7.14}$$

In case the E_n's are pairwise disjoint, using the monotone convergence theorem, the right hand side of (7.14) is given by

$$
\begin{aligned}
\lim_{n\to\infty} \int_{\mathbb{R}^2} \phi_n(|\boldsymbol{x}|) &= \lim_{n\to\infty} \int_{\mathbb{R}^2} \left(\sum_{k=1}^{n} \chi_{E_k}(|\boldsymbol{x}|)\, d\lambda_{\mathbb{R}^2}(\boldsymbol{x}) \right) \\
&= \lim_{n\to\infty} \sum_{k=1}^{n} \int_{\mathbb{R}^2} \chi_{E_k}(|\boldsymbol{x}|)\, d\lambda_{\mathbb{R}^2}(\boldsymbol{x}) \\
&= 2\pi \lim_{n\to\infty} \sum_{k=1}^{n} \int_0^\infty \chi_{E_k}(r)\, r\, d\lambda(r) \\
&= 2\pi \lim_{n\to\infty} \int_0^\infty \left(\sum_{k=1}^{n} \chi_{E_k}(r) \right) r\, d\lambda(r) \\
&= 2\pi \lim_{n\to\infty} \int_0^\infty \phi_n(r)\, r\, d\lambda(r) \\
&= 2\pi \int_0^\infty \chi_E(r)\, r\, d\lambda(r).
\end{aligned}
$$

Hence

$$
\int_{\mathbb{R}^2} \chi_E(|\boldsymbol{x}|) = 2\pi \int_0^\infty \chi_E(r)\, r\, d\lambda(r).
$$

When $\{E_n\}_{n\geq 1}$ is an increasing sequence, each $F_n = E_n$, and once again, using the monotone convergence theorem, the right hand side of (7.14) is given by

$$
\begin{aligned}
\lim_{n\to\infty} \int_{\mathbb{R}^2} \phi_n(|\boldsymbol{x}|)\, d\lambda_{\mathbb{R}^2}(\boldsymbol{x}) &= \lim_{n\to\infty} \int \chi_{E_n}(|\boldsymbol{x}|)\, d\lambda_{\mathbb{R}^2}(\boldsymbol{x}) \\
&= 2\pi \lim_{n\to\infty} \int_0^\infty \chi_{E_n}(r)\, r\, d\lambda(r) \\
&= 2\pi \int_0^\infty \chi_E(r)\, r\, d\lambda(r).
\end{aligned}
$$

Thus the required claim holds for $f = \chi_E$.

Step 3: The theorem holds for $f = \chi_U$, U being any open subset of $[0,\infty)$.

To see this we note that U is a countable union of pairwise disjoint open intervals. The required claim now follows from step 1 and step 2.

Step 4: The theorem holds for $f = \chi_N$, where $N \subset [0,\infty)$ and $\lambda(N) = 0$.

To prove this, first note that $N = \bigcup_{n=1}^\infty (N \cap [0,n))$, and in view of step 2, it is enough to prove the claim for each $\chi_{N\cap[0,n)}$. Since $\lambda(N \cap [0,n)) = 0$, using theorem 4.2.2 we can choose a decreasing sequence $\{U_k\}_{k\geq 1}$ of open sets such that $N \cap (0,n) \subseteq \bigcap_{k=1}^\infty U_k$ and $\lim_{n\to\infty} \lambda(U_k) = 0$. Without loss of generality, we may also assume that $U_k \subset (0, n) \; \forall \; k$. Then $\; \forall \; k$, by step 3, we have

$$\int \chi_{N \cap (0,n)}(|\boldsymbol{x}|) \, d\lambda_{\mathbb{R}^2}(\boldsymbol{x}) \;\; \leq \;\; \int \chi_{U_k}(|\boldsymbol{x}|) \, d\lambda_{\mathbb{R}^2}(\boldsymbol{x})$$

$$= \;\; 2\pi \int_0^\infty \chi_{U_k}(r) r \, d\lambda(r)$$

$$\leq \;\; 2\pi n \lambda(U_k).$$

Since this holds $\; \forall \; k$, letting $k \to \infty$, we have

$$\int \chi_{N \cap (0,n)}(|\boldsymbol{x}|) \, d\lambda_{\mathbb{R}^2}(\boldsymbol{x}) = 0.$$

Clearly,

$$2\pi \int_0^\infty \chi_{N \cap (0,n)}(r) r \, d\lambda(r) = 0.$$

Hence

$$\int_0^\infty \chi_{N \cap (0,n)}(|\boldsymbol{x}|) \, d\lambda_{\mathbb{R}^2}(\boldsymbol{x}) \;=\; 2\pi \int_0^\infty \chi_{N \cap (0,n)}(r) r \, d\lambda(r) \;=\; 0.$$

Since $\lambda(N \cap [0, n)) = \lambda(N \cap (0, n))$, the required claim follows.

Step 5: The theorem holds when $f = \chi_E, E \in \mathcal{L}_{\mathbb{R}}$ and $E \subseteq [0, \infty)$.

For this, note that we can write $E = \bigcup_{n=1}^\infty E \cap [0, n)$. In view of step 2, it is enough to prove the claim for $E_n := E \cap [0, n) \; \forall \; n$. Fix n and choose a decreasing sequence of open sets $\{U_k\}_{k \geq 1}$ of $[0, \infty)$, using theorem 4.2.2, such that

$$U_k \supseteq E_n \; \forall \; k \;\; \text{with} \;\; \lambda(U_k) < +\infty \;\; \text{and} \;\; \lim_{k \to \infty} \lambda(U_k) = \lambda(E).$$

Put $F := \bigcap_{k=1}^\infty U_k$ and $N := F \setminus E_n$. Then $\lambda(N) = 0$ and $F = E_n \cup N$. By the dominated convergence theorem and step 3, we have

$$\int \chi_F(|\boldsymbol{x}|) \, d\lambda_{\mathbb{R}^2}(\boldsymbol{x}) \;=\; \lim_{k \to \infty} \int \chi_{U_k}(|\boldsymbol{x}|) d\lambda_{\mathbb{R}^2}(\boldsymbol{x})$$

$$= \;\; \lim_{k \to \infty} 2\pi \int \chi_{U_k}(x)(x) x \, d\lambda(x)$$

$$= \;\; 2\pi \int_0^\infty \chi_F(x) x \, d\lambda(x).$$

Since $E_n \cap N = \emptyset$ and the theorem holds for χ_N by step 4, it follows that the theorem holds for every χ_{E_n} and hence for χ_E.

Step 6: The theorem holds for any nonnegative measurable function.

This is an application of the 'simple function technique'. First we note that the required claim is linear in f, i.e., if it holds for functions f_1, f_2 and α, β are reals, then it also holds for $\alpha f_1 + \beta f_2$. This together with step 5 tells us that the theorem holds for nonnegative simple measurable functions. Since every nonnegative measurable function is a limit of an increasing sequence of nonnegative simple measurable functions, an application of the monotone convergence theorem will give us the required claim. ∎

7.4.11. Exercise: Let $f : [0, \infty) \longrightarrow \mathbb{R}$ be a measurable function. Show that, if either of the two integrals in theorem 7.4.10 exists, then so does the other and the equality holds.

7.4.12. Exercise: Let $f : (a, b) \times (c, d) \longrightarrow \mathbb{R}$ be such that

  (i) f is continuous;

 (ii) $\dfrac{\partial f}{\partial x}$ exists and is continuous;

(iii) for some $t \in (a, b), \dfrac{d}{dy} f(t, y)$ exists $\forall\ y$;

(iv) $\dfrac{\partial}{\partial y} \left(\dfrac{\partial f}{\partial x} \right)$ exists and is continuous.

Show that $\dfrac{\partial f}{\partial y}$ and $\dfrac{\partial}{\partial x} \left(\dfrac{\partial f}{\partial y} \right)$ exist. Moreover,

$$\frac{\partial}{\partial x} \left(\frac{\partial f}{\partial y} \right) = \frac{\partial}{\partial y} \left(\frac{\partial f}{\partial x} \right).$$

(Hint: Use Fubini's theorem and the fundamental theorem of calculus to show that $\forall\ \xi \in (a, b), \eta \in (c, d)$ and $s < y$

$$f(\xi, \eta) - f(t, \eta) - f(\xi, s) + f(t, s) = \int_s^\eta \int_t^\xi \frac{\partial}{\partial y} \left(\frac{\partial t}{\partial x} \right) dx\, dy,$$

and note that the inner integral on the right is a continuous function of ξ.)

7.5. Product of finitely many measure spaces

The ideas developed in sections 7.2, 7.3 and 7.4 can be easily extended to define the product of a finite number of measure spaces.

For $n \geq 2$, let $(X_i, \mathcal{A}_i, \mu_i), i = 1, 2, \ldots, n$, be σ−finite measure spaces. Suppose we have defined the product measure space $(X_1 \times \cdots \times X_{n-1}, \mathcal{A}_1 \otimes \cdots \otimes \mathcal{A}_{n-1}, \mu_1 \times \cdots \times \mu_{n-1})$, which we write as

$$\left(\prod_{i=1}^{n-1} X_i, \bigotimes_{i=1}^{n-1} \mathcal{A}_i, \prod_{i=1}^{n-1} \mu_i \right).$$

Using the ideas of section 7.2, we can define the product measure space

$$\left(\left(\prod_{i=1}^{n-1} X_i\right) \times X_n, \left(\bigotimes_{i=1}^{n-1} \mathcal{A}_i\right) \otimes \mathcal{A}_n, \left(\prod_{i=1}^{n-1} \mu_i\right) \times \mu_n\right).$$

The sets $\left(\prod_{i=1}^{n-1} X_i\right) \times X_n$ and $\prod_{i=1}^{n} X_i := X_1 \times \cdots \times X_{n-1} \times X_n$ can be identified via the bijection

$$((x_1, \ldots, x_{n-1}), x_n) \longmapsto (x_1, \ldots x_n), \quad x_i \in X_i, \ 1 \leq i \leq n.$$

Let $\mathcal{R}_n := \{A_1 \times A_2 \times \cdots \times A_n \mid A_i \in \mathcal{A}_i\}$. It is easy to verify that $\mathcal{R}_n$ is a semi-algebra of subsets of $\prod_{i=1}^{n} X_i$. Let $\bigotimes_{i=1}^{n} \mathcal{A}_i$ denote the σ-algebra of subsets of $\prod_{i=1}^{n} X_i$ generated by $\mathcal{R}_n$. It is easy to check that

$$\left(\bigotimes_{i=1}^{n-1} \mathcal{A}_i\right) \otimes \mathcal{A}_n = \bigotimes_{i=1}^{n} \mathcal{A}_i,$$

keeping in mind the identification $\left(\prod_{i=1}^{n-1} X_i\right) \times X_n = \prod_{i=1}^{n} X_i$.

Next, it is easy to see that the measure $\left(\prod_{i=1}^{n-1} \mu_i\right) \times \mu_n$ on $\bigotimes_{i=1}^{n} \mathcal{A}_i$ has the property that $\forall A_i \in \mathcal{A}_i, \ i = 1, 2, \ldots, n,$

$$\left[\left(\prod_{i=1}^{n-1} \mu_i\right) \times \mu_n\right](A_1 \times \cdots \times A_n) = \prod_{i=1}^{n} \mu_i(A_i).$$

Moreover, that this is the only measure with this property follows from the uniqueness theorem (3.10.8). We denote the measure $\left(\prod_{i=1}^{n-1} \mu_i\right) \times \mu_n$ by $\prod_{i=1}^{n} \mu_i$ and call it the **product measure.** The measure space

$$\left(\prod_{i=1}^{n} X_i, \bigotimes_{i=1}^{n} \mathcal{A}_i, \prod_{i=1}^{n} \mu_i\right)$$

is called the **product of the measure spaces** $(X_i, \mathcal{A}_i, \mu_i), \ i = 1, 2, \ldots n,$ and is usually denoted by $\prod_{i=1}^{n}(X_i, \mathcal{A}_i, \mu_i)$.

7.5.1. Exercise: Let $(X_i, \mathcal{A}_i, \mu_i), i = 1, 2, \ldots n,$ be σ-finite measure spaces and let $1 \leq m < n$. Show that the product measure spaces

$$\left(\left(\prod_{i=1}^{m} X_i\right) \times \left(\prod_{i=m+1}^{n} X_i\right), \left(\bigotimes_{i=1}^{m} \mathcal{A}_i\right) \times \left(\bigotimes_{i=m+1}^{n} \mathcal{A}_i\right), \left(\prod_{i=1}^{m} \mu_i\right) \times \left(\prod_{i=m+1}^{n} \mu_i\right)\right)$$

and $(\prod_{i=1}^{n} X_i, \bigotimes_{i=1}^{n} \mathcal{A}_i, \prod_{i=1}^{n} \mu_i)$ are same if the underlying sets are identified in the natural way.

In the special case when each $X_i = \mathbb{R}, \mathcal{A}_i = \mathcal{L}$ and $\mu_i = \lambda$, the Lebesgue measure, the completion of the product measure space as obtained above is denoted by $(\mathbb{R}^n, \mathcal{L}_{\mathbb{R}^n}, \lambda_{\mathbb{R}^n})$. The σ-algebra $\mathcal{L}_{\mathbb{R}^n}$ is called the σ-algebra of **Lebesgue measurable sets** of $\mathbb{R}^n$, and $\lambda_{\mathbb{R}^n}$ is called the **Lebesgue measure** on $\mathbb{R}^n$. It is not difficult to show that $\mathcal{L}_{\mathbb{R}^n}$ includes $\mathcal{B}_{\mathbb{R}^n}$, the σ-algebra of Borel subsets of $\mathbb{R}^n$.

•**7.5.2. Exercise:** Let $E \subseteq \mathbb{R}^n$ and let $p \in \mathbb{N}$. Show that $\overset{*}{\lambda}_{\mathbb{R}^n}(E) = 0$ iff $\forall\ \epsilon > 0$ there exists a sequence $\{B_k\}_{k \geq 1}$ of open balls in $\mathbb{R}^n$ such that each has radius less than p, and

$$E \subseteq \bigcup_{k=1}^{\infty} B_k \text{ and } \sum_{k=1}^{\infty} \overset{*}{\lambda}_{\mathbb{R}^n}(B_k) < \epsilon.$$

(Hint: Cover $\mathbb{R}^n$ by countably many disjoint 'cubes' of side sufficiently small.)

•**7.5.3. Exercise:** Extend exercise 7.4.2, theorem 7.4.3, exercise 7.4.4 and theorems 7.4.6, 7.4.10 to $(\mathbb{R}^n, \mathcal{L}_{\mathbb{R}^n}, \lambda_{\mathbb{R}^n})$. (See also exercise 9.3.17.)

We can also extend Fubini's theorems (7.3.1 and 7.3.3) to finite product spaces. We merely state these theorems, and ask the reader to supply their proofs.

7.5.4. Theorem (Fubini): *Let $f : \prod_{i=1}^{n} X_i \longrightarrow \mathbb{R}$ be a nonnegative function. If f is $\bigotimes_{i=1}^{n} \mathcal{A}_i$-measurable and $i_1, i_2, \ldots i_n$ is any permutation of $1, 2, \ldots, n$, then*

$$\int \left(\cdots \left(\int \left(\int f(x_1, \ldots x_n) d\mu_{i_1}(x_{i_1}) \right) d\mu_{i_2}(x_{i_2}) \right) \cdots \right) d\mu_{i_n}(x_{i_n})$$

is well-defined (i.e., all the integrands are measurable with respect to the products of relevant σ-algebras) and is equal to

$$\int_X f(x_1, \ldots, x_n) d \left(\prod_{i=1}^{n} \mu_i \right) (x_1, \ldots x_n),$$

where $X = \prod_{i=1}^{n} X_i$.

7.5.5. Theorem (Fubini): *Let $f \in L_1 \left(\prod_{i=1}^{n} (X_i, \mathcal{A}_i, \mu_i) \right)$. Then for every permutation $i_1, \ldots, i_n$ of $1, 2, \ldots, n$, the integral*

$$\int_{X_{i_n}} \left(\cdots \left(\int_{X_{i_2}} \left(\int_{X_{i_1}} f(x_{i_1}, \ldots, x_{i_n}) d\mu_{i_1}(x_{i_1}) \right) d\mu_{i_2}(x_{i_2}) \right) \cdots \right) d\mu_{i_n}(x_n)$$

exists (i.e., the integrands are integrable functions on relevant product spaces) and is equal to

$$\int_X f(x_1, \dots, x_n)\, d\left(\prod_{i=1}^n \mu_i\right)(x_1, \dots, x_n).$$

7.5.6. Exercise: Let $f \in L_1(\mathbb{R}^{n+m}, \mathcal{L}_{\mathbb{R}^{n+m}}, \lambda_{\mathbb{R}^{n+m}})$. Prove the following:

(i) For a.e. $(\lambda_{\mathbb{R}^n})\, a \in \mathbb{R}^n$, the function $y \longmapsto f(a, y)$ is defined for a.e. $(\lambda_{\mathbb{R}^m})\, y \in \mathbb{R}^m$ and is integrable.

(ii) For a.e. $(\lambda_{\mathbb{R}^m})\, b \in \mathbb{R}^m$, the function $x \longmapsto f(x, b)$ is defined for a.e. $(\lambda_{\mathbb{R}^n})\, x \in \mathbb{R}^n$ and is integrable.

(iii) The functions

$$y \longmapsto \int_{\mathbb{R}^m} f(x, y)\, d\lambda_{\mathbb{R}^n}(x) \quad \text{and} \quad x \longmapsto \int_{\mathbb{R}^n} f(x, y)\, d\lambda_{\mathbb{R}^m}(y)$$

are defined a.e. x $(\lambda_{\mathbb{R}^n})$ and a.e. y $(\lambda_{\mathbb{R}^m})$, respectively, and are integrable.

(iv)

$$\int_{\mathbb{R}^n} \int_{\mathbb{R}^m} f(x, y)\, d\lambda_{\mathbb{R}^m}(y)\, d\lambda_{\mathbb{R}^n}(x) = \int_{\mathbb{R}^{n+m}} f(x, y)\, d(\lambda_{\mathbb{R}^n} \times \lambda_{\mathbb{R}^m})(x, y)$$

$$= \int_{\mathbb{R}^m} \int_{\mathbb{R}^n} f(x, y)\, d\lambda_{\mathbb{R}^n}(x)\, d\lambda_{\mathbb{R}^m}(y).$$

7.5.7. Exercise: For $x \in \mathbb{R}^n$ and $r > 0$, let

$$B(x, r) := \{y \in \mathbb{R}^n \mid |x - y| < r\}.$$

Using theorem 7.4.6 (for general n), show that

$$\lambda_{\mathbb{R}^n}(B(x, r)) = r^n \lambda_{\mathbb{R}^n}(B(x, 1)).$$

7.5.8. Product spaces and probability theory:

We remarked in note 3.1.10 that a probability space $(X, \mathcal{S}, \mu)$ gives a mathematical model for the analysis of a statistical experiment. Consider two statistical experiments $(X, \mathcal{A}, \mu)$ and $(Y, \mathcal{B}, \nu)$ such that the outcome of one has no effect on the outcome of the other. Then a model that represents them jointly is given by the produced spaces $(X \times Y, \mathcal{A} \otimes \mathcal{B}, \mu \times \nu)$. In general, given a finite number of statistical experiments $(X_i, \mathcal{S}_i, \mu_i)$, $i = 1, 2, \dots, n$, a model that gives a joint representation of these n experiments is the product probability space, $(\prod_{i=1}^n X_i, \bigotimes_{i=1}^n \mathcal{S}_i, \prod_{i=1}^n \mu_i)$. In many practical situations one is interested in analyzing a sequence of statistical experiments $\{(X_i, \mathcal{S}_i, \mu_i)\}_{i \geq 1}$. For example, consider the experiment of tossing a coin (the most basic statistical experiment), which has two possible outcomes: heads and tails denoted by 0 and 1. Suppose the same coin is tossed n times. Thus each outcome is an n-tuple having 0 and 1 as entries, and there are 2^n such n-tuples. Thus the sample space of this experiment (or a joint representation of n experiments, each being tossing a coin) is $X = \prod_{i=1}^{n} X_i$, $X_i := \{0, 1\} \ \forall \ i$. The σ-algebra $\mathcal{S}$ is $\mathcal{P}(X)$, all subsets of X, and $\forall \ x \in X$, $p(\{x\}) = 1/2^n$, assuming that the coin is 'unbiased', i.e., there is equal probability of a head or a tail appearing in each toss. Now suppose one is interested in analyzing the following question: what happens to the number of heads appearing in n tosses as n becomes larger and larger? Of course, the intuitive answer to this question is: it is probable that the number of heads equals the number of tails. To analyze this question mathematically, we should let $n \to \infty$. Thus the sample space for the joint representation of this experiment will be X, the set of all sequences $\{x_n\}_{n \geq 1}$ where each $x_n = 0$ or 1. We should construct a suitable σ-algebra $\mathcal{S}$ of subsets of X and define a suitable probability measure μ on $\mathcal{S}$ and try to analyze.

$$\mu \left\{ \mathbf{x} = \{x_n\}_{n \geq 1} \in X \ \middle| \ \lim_{n \to \infty} \frac{1}{n} \left(\sum_{k=1}^{n} x_k \right) = \frac{1}{2} \right\}.$$

For a detailed discussion of the product of an infinite number of probability spaces and their application to probability theory and statistics, see Billingsley [5] and Parthasarathy [28].

Chapter 8

Modes of convergence and L_p-spaces

Throughout this chapter we shall work with a fixed σ-finite measure space $(X, \mathcal{S}, \mu)$, which is assumed to be complete. As explained in chapter 5, the reason to assume that $(X, \mathcal{S}, \mu)$ is complete is to have the property that if f and g are functions on X such that f is $\mathcal{S}$-measurable and $\mu^*\{x \in X | f(x) \neq g(x)\} = 0$, then g is also $\mathcal{S}$-measurable (see exercise 5.3.27 and proposition 5.3.28). In situations when $(X, \mathcal{S}, \mu)$ is not complete, one can always consider its completion and work with it.

The main aim of this chapter is to analyze the convergence of sequences of measurable functions. Given a sequence $\{f_n\}_{n \geq 1}$ of measurable functions on $(X, \mathcal{S}, \mu)$, we have already come across concepts like pointwise convergence of $\{f_n\}_{n \geq 1}$ to a measurable function f, i.e., when $\{f_n(x)\}$ converges to $f(x) \; \forall \; x \in X$. When a sequence does not converge pointwise, one would like to find other methods of analyzing the behavior of the sequence $\{f_n\}_{n \geq 1}$ for large n. Analysis of these methods, and the relations between them, is the main aim of this chapter. But before we do that, we extend the notion of measurability and integration to complex-valued functions.

8.1. Integration of complex-valued functions

Let $(X, \mathcal{S}, \mu)$ be a measure space and let $\mathbb{C}$ denote the field of **complex numbers.** For a function $f : X \longrightarrow \mathbb{C}$, consider the functions $\mathrm{Re}\,(f)$ and $\mathrm{Im}\,(f)$ defined by: $\forall \; x \in X$,

$$\mathrm{Re}\,(f)(x) := \text{ Real part of } f(x)$$

and

$$\mathrm{Im}\,(f)(x) := \text{Imaginary part of } f(x).$$

The functions $\mathrm{Re}\,(f)$ and $\mathrm{Im}\,(f)$ are called, respectively, the **real part** and the **imaginary part** of the function f. Note that $\mathrm{Re}\,(f)$ and $\mathrm{Im}\,(f)$ are real-valued functions on X.

8.1.1. Definition: A complex-valued function $f : X \longrightarrow \mathbb{C}$ is said to be **measurable** if both $\mathrm{Re}\,(f)$ and $\mathrm{Im}\,(f)$ are measurable functions. We say f is **μ-integrable** if both $\mathrm{Re}\,(f)$ and $\mathrm{Im}\,(f)$ are integrable. In that case we define the **integral** of f, denoted by $\int f d\mu$, to be

$$\int f d\mu := \int \mathrm{Re}\,(f) d\mu + i \int \mathrm{Im}\,(f) d\mu.$$

We denote the set of all complex-valued μ-integrable functions on X by $L_1(X, \mathcal{S}, \mu)$ itself. Whenever we restrict ourselves to only real-valued μ-integrable functions on X, we shall specify it by $L_1^r(X, \mathcal{S}, \mu)$. Our next theorem tells us that $L_1(X, \mathcal{S}, \mu)$ is as nice a space as $L_1^r(X, \mathcal{S}, \mu)$ is.

8.1.2. Theorem:

(i) *Let $f, g \in L_1(X, \mathcal{S}, \mu)$ and $\alpha, \beta \in \mathbb{C}$. Then $\alpha f + \beta g \in L_1(X, \mathcal{S}, \mu)$ and*

$$\int (\alpha f + \beta g) d\mu = \alpha \int f d\mu + \beta \int g d\mu.$$

(ii) *Let $f : X \longrightarrow \mathbb{C}$ be a measurable function. Then $f \in L_1(X, \mathcal{S}, \mu)$ iff $|f| \in L_1^r(X, \mathcal{S}, \mu)$. Further, in either case,*

$$\left| \int f d\mu \right| \leq \int |f| d\mu.$$

(iii) *Let $f \in L_1(X, \mathcal{S}, \mu)$ and $E \in \mathcal{S}$. Then $\chi_E f \in L_1(X, \mathcal{S}, \mu)$. We write*

$$\int_E f d\mu := \int \chi_E f d\mu.$$

If $E_1, E_2 \in \mathcal{S}$ and $E_1 \cap E_2 = \emptyset$, then

$$\int_{E_1 \cup E_2} f d\mu = \int_{E_1} f d\mu + \int_{E_2} f d\mu.$$

(iv) *Let $f \in L_1(X, \mathcal{S}, \mu)$, and let $\{E_n\}_{n \geq 1}$ be a sequence of pairwise disjoint sets from $\mathcal{S}$. Then the series $\sum_{n=1}^{\infty} (\int_{E_n} f d\mu)$ is absolutely convergent. Also, $(\chi_E f) \in L_1(X, \mathcal{S}, \mu)$, where $E := \bigcup_{n=1}^{\infty} E_n$, and*

$$\int_E f d\mu = \sum_{n=1}^{\infty} \int_{E_n} f d\mu.$$

Proof: (i) is straightforward and is left as an exercise. To prove (ii), let $f \in L_1(X, \mathcal{S}, \mu)$. Then $\mathrm{Re}\,(f)$, $\mathrm{Im}\,(f) \in L_1^r(X, \mathcal{S}, \mu)$. Since

$$|f| \leq \sqrt{2}\,(\,|\mathrm{Re}\,(f)| + |\mathrm{Im}\,(f)|\,),$$

clearly, $|f| \in L_1^r(X, \mathcal{S}, \mu)$. Conversely, let f be a complex-valued measurable function. Then $\mathrm{Re}\,(f)$ and $\mathrm{Im}\,(f)$ are measurable functions. If $|f| \in L_1^r(X, \mathcal{S}, \mu)$, then

$$|\mathrm{Re}\,(f)| \leq |f| \ \text{ and } \ |\mathrm{Im}\,(f)| \leq |f|.$$

Thus by proposition 5.4.3, we have $\mathrm{Re}\,(f) \in L_1^r(X, \mathcal{S}, \mu)$ and $\mathrm{Im}\,(f) \in L_1^r(X, \mathcal{S}, \mu)$. Finally, to prove that

$$\left| \int f d\mu \right| \leq \int |f| d\mu,$$

let $\alpha := |\int f d\mu|$. Then $0 \leq \alpha < \infty$, and there is a $0 \leq \theta < 2\pi$ such that

$$\alpha = \exp(-i\theta) \left(\int f d\mu \right).$$

Let $\exp(-i\theta)f := f_1 + if_2$, where f_1, f_2 are real-valued. Clearly, $f_1, f_2 \in L_1^r(X, \mathcal{S}, \mu)$ and

$$\alpha = \int \exp(-i\theta) f d\mu = \int f_1 d\mu + i \int f_2 d\mu.$$

Since α is real, we have $\int f_2 d\mu = 0$ and $\alpha = \int f_1 d\mu$. Thus

$$\alpha = \int f_1 d\mu = \left| \int f_1 d\mu \right| \leq \int |f_1| d\mu \leq \int |f| d\mu.$$

To prove (iii), we note that for every $E \in \mathcal{S}$, $|\chi_E f| \leq |f|$ and hence $|\chi_E f| \in L_1^r(X, \mathcal{S}, \mu)$. Thus by (ii), $\chi_E f \in L_1(X, \mathcal{S}, \mu)$. It is easy to see that

$$\int_{E_1 \cup E_2} f \, d\mu = \int_{E_1} f d\mu + \int_{E_2} f d\mu$$

whenever $E_1, E_2 \in \mathcal{S}$ and $E_1 \cap E_2 = \emptyset$. Finally, let $\{E_n\}_{n \geq 1}$ be a sequence of pairwise disjoint sets in $\mathcal{S}$. Consider the series $\sum_{n=1}^{\infty}(\int_{E_n} f d\mu)$. Then $\forall\, m$, if $A_m := \bigcup_{n=1}^m E_n$ and $E := \bigcup_{n=1}^{\infty} E_n$, then

$$\sum_{n=1}^m \left| \int_{E_n} f d\mu \right| \leq \sum_{n=1}^m \int_{E_n} |f| d\mu = \int_{A_m} |f| d\mu \leq \int_E |f| d\mu.$$

Thus $\{\sum_{n=1}^m |\int_{E_n} f d\mu|\}_{m \geq 1}$ is a monotonically increasing sequence and, being bounded above, is convergent. In fact $\forall\, m$,

$$\left| \sum_{n=1}^m \int_{E_n} f d\mu - \int_E f d\mu \right| = \left| \int_{A_m} f d\mu - \int_E f d\mu \right|$$

$$\leq \int |\chi_E - \chi_{A_m}| |f| d\mu.$$

By the dominated convergence theorem, the right hand side of the last inequality converges to zero as $n \longrightarrow \infty$. Hence (iii) holds. ∎

8.1.3. Exercise: Let $f \in L_1(X, \mathcal{S}, \mu)$ be such that

$$\left| \int f \, d\mu \right| = \int |f| \, d\mu.$$

What can you conclude about f?

That the integral of complex-valued functions behaves as nicely with respect to limiting operations as the integral of real-valued functions is the content of the next theorem.

8.1.4. Theorem (Complex form of Lebesgue's dominated convergence): *Let* $\{f_n\}_{n \geq 1}$ *be a sequence in* $L_1(X, \mathcal{S}, \mu)$. *Let* $f(x) := \lim\limits_{n \to \infty} f_n(x)$ *exist for a.e.* $x \in X$ *and let there exist a function* $g \in L_1^r(X, \mathcal{S}, \mu)$ *such that* $\forall\, n,\ |f_n(x)| \leq g(x)$ *for a.e.* $x(\mu)$. *Then* $f \in L_1(X, \mathcal{S}, \mu)$ *and*

$$\lim_{n \to \infty} \int f_n \, d\mu = \int f \, d\mu.$$

Proof: Let $f(x) := \lim\limits_{n \to \infty} f_n(x)$, whenever it exists. Since $f_n \in L_1(X, \mathcal{B}, \mu)$, $\forall\, n$, $\operatorname{Re}(f_n)$ and $\operatorname{Im}(f_n)$ are measurable functions. Further,

$$(\operatorname{Re} f)(x) = \lim_{n \to \infty} \operatorname{Re}(f_n(x)) \quad \text{for a.e. } x(\mu)$$

and

$$(\operatorname{Im} f)(x) = \lim_{n \to \infty} \operatorname{Im}(f_n(x)) \quad \text{for a.e. } x(\mu).$$

Thus $\operatorname{Re}(f)$ and $\operatorname{Im}(f)$ are both measurable by proposition 5.3.14. Note that $|f|$ is a real-valued measurable function and $|f(x)| \leq g(x)$ for a.e. x. Thus $|f| \in L_1^r(X, \mathcal{S}, \mu)$, and hence $f \in L_1(X, \mathcal{S}, \mu)$. Furthermore, for all n, $|f(x) - f_n(x)|$ is a real-valued measurable function with $\lim\limits_{n \to \infty} |f(x) - f_n(x)| = 0$ for a.e. x and

$$|f(x) - f_n(x)| \leq 2g(x) \quad \text{for a.e. } x(\mu).$$

Hence by Lebesgue's dominated convergence theorem (5.4.9), we have

$$\lim_{n \to \infty} \left| \int f_n \, d\mu - \int f \, d\mu \right| \leq \lim_{n \to \infty} \int |f_n - f| \, d\mu = 0. \quad \blacksquare$$

•8.1.5. Exercise:

(i) Let $f : X \to \mathbb{C}$. Show that f is measurable iff $f^{-1}(E) \in \mathcal{S}$ for every Borel set $E \subseteq X$.

(ii) Extend the claim of exercise 5.3.27 to complex-valued measurable functions.

8.1.6. Exercise: Let $\{f_n\}_{n\geq 1}$ be a sequence of $\mathcal{S}$-measurable complex-valued functions on $(X, \mathcal{S}, \mu)$. Show that the following statements are equivalent:

(i) $(\sum_{n=1}^{\infty} |f_n|) \in L_1^r(X, \mathcal{S}, \mu)$.

(ii) $\sum_{n=1}^{\infty} \int |f_n| d\mu < +\infty$.

Further, if either of the above is true, then $(\sum_{n=1}^{\infty} f_n) \in L_1(X, \mathcal{S}, \mu)$ and

$$\int \left(\sum_{n=1}^{\infty} f_n \right) d\mu = \sum_{n=1}^{\infty} \int f_n \, d\mu.$$

8.1.7. Exercise: State and prove the Riesz-Fischer theorem (theorem 5.6.1) for complex-valued integrable functions.

8.1.8. Exercise: Let $f \in L_1(X, \mathcal{S}, \mu)$ and

$$\int_E f d\mu = 0 \ \text{ for every } E \in \mathcal{S}.$$

Show that $f(x) = 0$ for a.e. $x(\mu)$ (see proposition 5.4.6).

8.1.9. Theorem: *Let $f \in L_1(X, \mathcal{S}, \mu)$, where $\mu(X) < \infty$. Let S be a closed subset of $\mathbb{C}$ such that $\forall E \in \mathcal{S}$ with $\mu(E) > 0$,*

$$\left(\frac{1}{\mu(E)} \int_E f \, d\mu \right) \in S.$$

Then $f(x) \in S$ for a.e. $x \in X$.

Proof: We have to show that $\mu\{x \in X \mid f(x) \notin S\} = 0$. Since $S^c := \mathbb{C} \setminus S$ is an open set, there exist countably many open balls $\{B_n\}_{n\geq 1}$ in $\mathbb{C}$ such that $S^c = \bigcup_{n=1}^{\infty} B_n$. Thus

$$\{x \in X \mid f(x) \notin S\} = \left\{ x \in X \,\middle|\, f(x) \in \bigcup_{n=1}^{\infty} B_n \right\} = \bigcup_{n=1}^{\infty} f^{-1}(B_n).$$

Since $f^{-1}(B_n) \in \mathcal{S} \ \forall \ n$, see exercise 8.1.5, to prove the required claim it is enough to show that $\mu(f^{-1}(B_n)) = 0 \ \forall \ n$. Fix an integer n and let B_n have center z_0 and radius r_0. Let $E_n := f^{-1}(B_n)$ and suppose, if possible,

$\mu(E_n) > 0$. Then

$$\left| \frac{1}{\mu(E_n)} \int_{E_n} f d\mu - z_0 \right| = \left| \frac{1}{\mu(E_n)} \int_{E_n} (f(x) - z_0)d\mu(x) \right|$$

$$\leq \frac{1}{\mu(E_n)} \int_{E_n} |f(x) - z_0|d\mu(x)$$

$$\leq r_0,$$

i.e.,

$$\left(\frac{1}{\mu(E_n)} \int_{E_n} f \, d\mu \right) \in B_n \subseteq S^c.$$

which contradicts the hypothesis. Hence $\mu(E_n) = 0$. ∎

8.2. Convergence: Pointwise, almost everywhere, uniform and almost uniform

All the functions considered in this section are defined on a fixed σ-finite, complete measure space $(X, \mathcal{S}, \mu)$ and are complex-valued, unless stated otherwise.

8.2.1. Definition: Let $\{f_n\}_{n\geq 1}$ be a sequence of measurable functions and let f be a measurable function on X.

(i) We say $\{f_n\}_{n\geq 1}$ converges **pointwise** to f if $\{f_n(x)\}_{n\geq 1}$ converges to $f(x)$ for every $x \in X$, i.e., given $x \in X$ and $\epsilon > 0$, $\exists\, n_0 := n_0(x, \epsilon)$ such that

$$|f_n(x) - f(x)| < \epsilon, \,\forall\, n \geq n_0.$$

(ii) We say $\{f_n\}_{n\geq 1}$ is convergent to f **almost everywhere** if

$$N := \{x \in X \mid \{f_n(x)\}_{n\geq 1} \text{ does not converge to } f(x)\} \in \mathcal{S}$$

and $\mu(N) = 0$.

(iii) We say $\{f_n\}_{n\geq 1}$ converges **uniformly** to f if given $\epsilon > 0$, $\exists\, n_0 := n_0(\epsilon)$ such that

$$|f_n(x) - f(x)| < \epsilon \,\forall\, n \geq n_0 \text{ and } \forall\, x \in X.$$

We write these as $f_n \xrightarrow{p} f$, $f_n \xrightarrow{a.e.} f$ (or $f_n \longrightarrow f$ a.e.) and $f_n \xrightarrow{u} f$, respectively.

8.2.2. Exercise: Show that $f_n \xrightarrow{u} f \Rightarrow f_n \xrightarrow{p} f \Rightarrow f_n \xrightarrow{a.e.} f$. Construct examples to show that the reverse implications need not be true.

We shall show that even though uniform convergence is not implied by pointwise convergence, the situation is not that bad.

8.2.3. Proposition: *Let $\{f_n\}_{n\geq1}$ be a sequence of measurable functions such that $f_n \xrightarrow{\text{a.e.}} f, f$ a measurable function. Let $E \in \mathcal{S}$ be such that $\mu(E) < +\infty$ and let $\epsilon, \delta > 0$ be arbitrary. Then there exist a set $E_\epsilon \in \mathcal{S}$ and a positive integer n_0, depending upon ϵ and δ, such that the following hold:*

(i) *$E_\epsilon \subseteq E$ and $\mu(E \setminus E_\epsilon) < \epsilon$.*

(ii) *$|f_n(x) - f(x)| < \delta \ \forall \ n \geq n_0$ and $\forall \ x \in E_\epsilon$.*

Proof: Let $N^c := \{x \in X | \lim_{n\to\infty} f_n(x) = f(x)\}$. Then by the given hypothesis, $\mu(N) = 0$. Further, for all fixed $\delta > 0$,

$$N^c \subseteq \bigcup_{m=1}^{\infty} \{x \in X \mid |f_n(x) - f(x)| < \delta \ \forall \, n \geq m\}.$$

Let

$$E_m(\delta) := \{x \in X \mid |f_n(x) - f(x)| < \delta \ \forall \ n \geq m\}.$$

Then $\{E_m(\delta)\}_{m\geq1}$ is an increasing sequence of sets in $\mathcal{S}$ and

$$N^c \subseteq \bigcup_{m=1}^{\infty} E_m(\delta).$$

Thus $\{E \cap E_m^c(\delta)\}_{m\geq1}$ is a decreasing sequence of sets in $\mathcal{S}$ and

$$\bigcap_{m=1}^{\infty} (E \cap E_m^c(\delta)) \subseteq E \cap N.$$

Since $\mu(E) < +\infty$, we have $\lim_{n\to\infty} \mu(E \cap E_m^c(\delta)) = 0$. Thus given $\epsilon > 0$, $\exists \ n_0$ such that $\mu(E \cap E_{n_0}^c(\delta)) < \epsilon$. Put $E_\epsilon := E_{n_0}(\delta) \cap E$. Then

$$E_\epsilon \subseteq E \ \text{ with } \ \mu(E \setminus E_\epsilon) < \epsilon.$$

Further, $\forall \, x \in E_\epsilon$, by definition,

$$|f_n(x) - f(x)| < \delta, \ \forall \, n \geq n_0. \ \blacksquare$$

8.2.4. Theorem (Egoroff): *Let $f_n, n \geq 1$, and f be measurable functions such that $f_n \xrightarrow{\text{a.e.}} f$. Let $E \in \mathcal{S}$ with $\mu(E) < +\infty$. Then, given $\epsilon > 0$, there is a set $E_\epsilon \in \mathcal{S}$ such that*

(i) *$E_\epsilon \subseteq E$ and $\mu(E \cap E_\epsilon^c) < \epsilon$.*

(ii) *$f_n \xrightarrow{u} f$ on E_ϵ.*

Proof: Let $\epsilon > 0$ be fixed. Using proposition 8.2.3 for every $\delta = 1/m$, we choose $E_m \in \mathcal{S}$ and a positive integer n_m such that

$$E_m \subseteq E \ \text{ with } \ \mu(E \cap E_m^c) < \epsilon/2^m$$

and
$$|f_n(x) - f(x)| < 1/m \; \forall \, x \in E_m \; \text{ and } \; \forall \, n \geq n_m.$$
Let $E_\epsilon := \bigcap_{m=1}^{\infty} E_m$. Then $E_\epsilon \subseteq E$ and

$$\mu(E \cap E_\epsilon^c) \leq \sum_{m=1}^{\infty} \mu(E \cap E_m^c) < \sum_{m=1}^{\infty} \epsilon/2^m = \epsilon.$$

Also $\forall \, m$,
$$|f_n(x) - f(x)| < 1/m \; \forall \, x \in E_\epsilon \; \text{ and } \; \forall \, n \geq n_m.$$
Hence $f_n \xrightarrow{u} f$ on E_ϵ. ∎

8.2.5. Definition: Let $f, f_n, n \geq 1$, be measurable functions and $E \in \mathcal{S}$. We say $\{f_n\}_{n\geq 1}$ converges **almost uniformly** to f on E if $\forall \, \epsilon > 0$, $\exists \, E_\epsilon \in \mathcal{S}$ such that

(i) $E_\epsilon \subseteq E$ with $\mu(E \cap E_\epsilon^c) < \epsilon$.

(ii) f_n converges uniformly to f on $E \cap E_\epsilon$.

We write this as $f_n \xrightarrow{\text{a.u.}} f$ or $f_n \longrightarrow f$ a.u.

In view of the above definition, Egoroff's theorem can be restated as: *if $f_n \to f$ a.e. on a set E and $\mu(E) < +\infty$, then $f_n \longrightarrow f$ almost uniformly on E.* As a particular case, if $\mu(X) < +\infty$, we have the following proposition.

8.2.6. Proposition: *If $\mu(X) < +\infty$ and $f_n \longrightarrow f$ a.e. on X, then $f_n \longrightarrow f$ almost uniformly on X.*

The converse of this proposition is also true.

8.2.7. Proposition: *If $\mu(X) < +\infty$ and $f_n \longrightarrow f$ almost uniformly on X, then $f_n \to f$ a.e.*

Proof: By the given hypothesis, for every integer $n \geq 1$ we can choose a set $F_n \in \mathcal{S}$ such that

$$\mu(F_n) < 1/n \; \text{ and } \; \{f_n\}_{n\geq 1} \text{ converges uniformly to } f \text{ on } F_n^c.$$
Let $F := \bigcap_{n=1}^{\infty} F_n$. Then

$$\mu(F) < \mu(F_n) < 1/n, \; \forall \, n.$$

Hence $\mu(F) = 0$ and, for $x \in F^c, f_n(x) \to f(x)$ as $n \to \infty$. Hence $f_n \to f$ a.e. ∎

8.2.8. Exercise: Let $f_n = \chi_{(n,\infty)}, n = 1, 2, \ldots$. Then $\{f_n\}_{n\geq 1}$ is a sequence of Lebesgue measurable functions on $\mathbb{R}$. Show that $\{f_n\}_{n\geq 1}$ is convergent pointwise but not almost uniformly with respect to the Lebesgue measure λ on $\mathbb{R}$.

•8.2.9. Exercise: Let $f_n, n \geq 1$, and f be measurable functions. For $\epsilon > 0$ and $m = 1, 2, \ldots$, let

$$A_m^\epsilon := \{x \in X \mid |f_m(x) - f(x)| \geq \epsilon\}.$$

Prove the following:

(i) $f_n \xrightarrow{\text{a.u.}} f$ iff

$$\text{for every } \epsilon > 0, \quad \lim_{n \to \infty} \mu \left(\bigcup_{m=n}^{\infty} A_m^\epsilon \right) = 0.$$

(ii) $f_n \xrightarrow{p} f$ iff

$$\text{for every } \epsilon > 0, \quad \left\{ \bigcup_{m=n}^{\infty} A_m^\epsilon \right\}_{n \geq 1} \quad \text{decreases to } \emptyset.$$

(iii) $f_n \xrightarrow{\text{a.e.}} f$ iff

$$\text{for every } \epsilon > 0, \quad \mu \left(\bigcap_{n=1}^{\infty} \bigcup_{m=n}^{\infty} A_m^\epsilon \right) = 0.$$

(iv) If $\mu(X) < +\infty$, then $f_n \xrightarrow{\text{a.e.}} f$ iff

$$\text{for every } \epsilon > 0, \quad \lim_{n \to \infty} \mu \left\{ x \in X \mid \sup_{m \geq n} |f_m(x) - f(x)| \geq \epsilon \right\} = 0.$$

As an application of Egoroff's theorem, we show that on the Lebesgue measure space $(\mathbb{R}, \mathcal{L}, \lambda)$, every measurable function is almost continuous. We need the following class of special simple functions, as considered in definition 2.1.1.

8.2.10. Definition: Let $I \subseteq \mathbb{R}$ be an interval and let $\Phi : I \longrightarrow \mathbb{R}$ be defined by

$$\Phi(x) := \sum_{i=1}^{n} a_i \chi_{I_i}(x),$$

where $\{I_1, I_2, \ldots, I_n\}$ are pairwise disjoint bounded intervals with $I = \bigcup_{i=1}^{n} I_i$ and $a_1, \ldots, a_n$ are real numbers. Such a function Φ is called a **step function** on I.

8.2.11. Exercise: Let S_0 denote the class of step functions on an interval I. Let $\Phi, \Psi \in S_0$ and let $\alpha \in \mathbb{R}$. Show that $\Phi + \Psi, \alpha\Phi, \max\{\Phi, \Psi\} \in S_0$. Do the functions $|\Phi|, \Phi^+, \Phi^-, \min\{\Phi, \Psi\}$ belong to S_0?

•**8.2.12. Exercise:** Let Φ be a step function on an interval I, and let $\epsilon > 0$ be given. Show that there exists a continuous function g on I such that

$$\lambda(\{x \in \mathbb{R} \mid \Phi(x) \neq g(x)\}) < \epsilon.$$

8.2.13. Proposition: *Let $f : [a,b] \longrightarrow \mathbb{R}^*$ be any measurable function such that $f(x)$ is finite for a.e. $x(\lambda)$, and let $\epsilon > 0$ be arbitrary. Then there exist a step function Φ and a continuous function g on $[a,b]$ such that*

$$\lambda(\{x \in [a,b] \mid |f(x) - \Phi(x)| \geq \epsilon\}) < \epsilon$$

and

$$\lambda(\{x \in [a,b] \mid |f(x) - g(x)| \geq \epsilon\}) < \epsilon.$$

Proof: We may assume without loss of generality that f is real-valued.

Step 1: Let $f = \alpha \chi_A$, where $\alpha \in \mathbb{R}$, $A \in \mathcal{L}$ and $A \subseteq [a,b]$. Then by theorem 4.2.1, we can choose pairwise disjoint open intervals $I_1, I_2, \ldots, I_n$ such that

$$\lambda\left(\left(\bigcup_{i=1}^{n} I_i\right) \triangle A\right) < \epsilon.$$

Let

$$\bigcup_{i=n+1}^{m} I_i := \mathbb{R} \setminus \left(\bigcup_{i=1}^{n} I_i\right),$$

where $I_{n+1}, \ldots, I_m$ are disjoint intervals. Put

$$\Phi := \alpha \sum_{i=1}^{n} \chi_{I_i} + \sum_{i=n+1}^{m} a_i \chi_{I_i},$$

where each $a_i = 0$ for $i = n+1, \ldots, m$. Consider the restriction of Φ to $[a,b]$. Then Φ is a step function on $[a,b]$. Further,

$$\{x \in [a,b] \mid |f(x) - \Phi(x)| \geq \epsilon\} = \emptyset, \quad \text{if } \epsilon > 1,$$

and for $0 < \epsilon \leq 1$,

$$\{x \in [a,b] \mid |f(x) - \Phi(x)| \geq \epsilon\} \subseteq \left[\left(\bigcup_{i=1}^{n} I_i\right) \triangle A\right].$$

Hence

$$\lambda(\{x \in [a,b] \mid |f(x) - \Phi(x)| \geq \epsilon\}) < \epsilon.$$

Using exercise 8.2.12 and Φ, we can also find a continuous function g on $I = [a,b]$ such that

$$\lambda(\{x \in [a,b] \mid |f(x) - g(x)| \geq \epsilon\}) < \epsilon.$$

Step 2: Let f be any simple measurable function on $[a, b]$. Let f have the representation,

$$f := \sum_{i=1}^{n} a_i \chi_{A_i},$$

where $a_1, a_2, \ldots, a_n$ are real numbers and $A_1, A_2, \ldots, A_n$ are pairwise disjoint sets in $\mathcal{L}$ with $\bigcup_{i=1}^{n} A_i = [a, b]$. For each $i = 1, 2, \ldots, n$, let Φ_i, g_i be the step function and the continuous function, respectively, on $[a, b]$ such that

$$\lambda(\{x \in [a, b] \mid |a_i \chi_{A_i}(x) - \Phi_i(x)| \geq \epsilon/n\}) < \epsilon/n$$

and

$$\lambda(\{x \in [a, b] \mid |a_i \chi_{A_i}(x) - g(x)| \geq \epsilon/n\}) < \epsilon/n.$$

Put

$$\Phi := \sum_{i=1}^{n} \Phi_i \ \text{ and } \ g := \sum_{i=1}^{n} g_i.$$

It is easy to show that Φ and g have the required properties.

Step 3: Let f be a bounded measurable function. Then by exercise 5.3.7, there exists a simple function s on $[a, b]$ such that

$$|f(x) - s(x)| < \epsilon/2 \ \forall \ x \in [a, b].$$

Let Φ be the step function and g be the continuous function, as given by step 2, such that

$$\lambda(\{x \in [a, b] \mid |s(x) - \Phi(x)| \geq \epsilon/2\}) < \epsilon/2$$

and

$$\lambda(\{x \in [a, b] \mid |s(x) - g(x)| \geq \epsilon/2\}) < \epsilon/2.$$

Then

$$\{x \in [a, b] \mid |f(x) - \Phi(x)| \geq \epsilon\} \subseteq \{x \in [a, b] \mid |s(x) - \Phi(x)| \geq \epsilon/2\}$$

and

$$\{x \in [a, b] \mid |f(x) - g(x)| \geq \epsilon\} \subseteq \{x \in [a, b] \mid |s(x) - g(x)| \geq \epsilon/2\}.$$

Hence, Φ and g have the required properties.

Step 4: Let f be an arbitrary measurable function. For $n = 1, 2, \ldots$, let

$$E_n := \{x \in [a, b] \mid |f(x)| \geq n\},$$

Then E_n is a decreasing sequence of measurable sets and $\bigcap_{n=1}^{\infty} E_n = \emptyset$. Thus $\lim_{n \to \infty} \lambda(E_n) = 0$, and we can choose n_0 such that $\lambda(E_{n_0}) < \epsilon/2$. Let

$$\tilde{f}(x) := \begin{cases} f(x) & \text{if } x \notin E_{n_0}, \\ n_0 & \text{if } x \in E_{n_0}. \end{cases}$$

By step 3 applied to $\tilde{f}$, we get a step function Φ and a continuous function g on $[a, b]$ such that

$$\lambda(\{x \in [a, b] \mid |\tilde{f}(x) - \Phi(x)| \geq \epsilon/2\}) < \epsilon/2$$

and

$$\lambda(\{x \in [a, b] \mid |\tilde{f}(x) - g(x)| \geq \epsilon/2\}) < \epsilon/2.$$

Let

$$A := \{x \in [a, b] \mid |f(x) - \Phi(x)| \geq \epsilon/2\}$$

and

$$\tilde{A} := \{x \in [a, b] \mid |\tilde{f}(x) - \Phi(x)| \geq \epsilon/2\}.$$

Then $\lambda(\tilde{A}) < \epsilon/2$. Since

$$\begin{aligned}
\{x \in [a, b] \mid |f(x) - \Phi(x)| \geq \epsilon\} \quad &\subseteq \quad A \\
&\subseteq \quad E_{n_0} \cup (E_{n_0}^c \cap A) = E_{n_0} \cup (E_{n_0}^c \cap \tilde{A}),
\end{aligned}$$

we have

$$\lambda(\{x \in [a, b] \mid |f(x) - \Phi(x)| \geq \epsilon\}) < \lambda(E_{n_0}) + \lambda(\tilde{A}) < \epsilon.$$

Similarly, it can be shown that $\lambda(\{x \in [a, b] \mid |f(x) - g(x)| \geq \epsilon\}) < \epsilon$. This completes the proof. ∎

8.2.14. Theorem (Luzin): *Let $f : \mathbb{R} \longrightarrow \mathbb{R}$ be a measurable function. Then, given $\epsilon > 0$, there exists a continuous function $g : \mathbb{R} \longrightarrow \mathbb{R}$ such that $\lambda(\{x \in \mathbb{R} \mid f(x) \neq g(x)\}) < \epsilon$.*

Proof: Let us first consider the case when $f : [a, b] \longrightarrow \mathbb{R}$. Let $\epsilon > 0$ be given. By proposition 8.2.13, we can find a continuous function g_n on $[a, b]$ such that

$$\lambda(\{x \in [a, b] \mid |f(x) - g_n(x)| \geq \epsilon/3.2^n\}) \leq \epsilon/3.2^n.$$

Let

$$E_n := \{x \in [a, b] \mid |f(x) - g_n(x)| \geq \epsilon/3.2^n\} \text{ and } E := \bigcup_{n=1}^{\infty} E_n.$$

Then $\lambda(E) < \epsilon/3$, and for $x \notin E$,

$$|f(x) - g_n(x)| < \epsilon/3.2^n \,\forall\, n.$$

Thus $g_n(x) \to f(x)$, $\forall\, x \in E^c \cap [a, b]$. Now by Egoroff's theorem (8.2.4), we can choose $F \subseteq E^c \cap [a, b]$ such that

$$\lambda(F) < \epsilon/3, \quad \text{and} \quad g_n(x) \to f(x) \text{ uniformly on } E^c \cap F^c \cap [a, b].$$

Using theorem 4.2.2, we choose a closed set $C \subseteq E^c \cap F^c \cap [a, b]$ such that

$$\lambda((E^c \cap F^c \cap [a, b] \setminus C)) < \epsilon/3.$$

Then $g_n \longrightarrow f$ uniformly on the closed set C, and

$$\lambda([a,b] \setminus C) \leq \lambda(E) + \lambda(F) + \lambda((E^c \cap F^c \cap [a,b] \setminus C) < \epsilon.$$

Thus f is continuous on the closed set C. Since $[a,b] \setminus C$ is open, it is a disjoint union of countably many intervals. We define $g(x) := f(x)$ if $x \in C$ and linearly on the intervals in $[a,b] \setminus C$ so that g is continuous on $[a,b]$. Clearly,

$$\lambda\{x \in [a,b] \mid |f(x) \neq g(x)\} \leq \lambda([a,b] \setminus C) < \epsilon.$$

This proves the theorem in the special case.

When $f : \mathbb{R} \longrightarrow \mathbb{R}$, we write $\mathbb{R} = \bigcup_{n=-\infty}^{+\infty}[n,n+1)$ and choose, for every n, a closed set $C_n \subset (n,n+1)$ such that f is continuous on C_n and, by the earlier case,

$$\lambda([n,n+1] \setminus C_n) < \epsilon/(2^n + 1).$$

Put $C := \bigcup_{n=-\infty}^{\infty} C_n$. Then it is easy to see that C is a closed subset of $\mathbb{R}$ with $\lambda(\mathbb{R} \setminus C) < \epsilon$, and f is continuous on C. Once again we define $g : \mathbb{R} \longrightarrow \mathbb{R}$ such that $g(x) := f(x) \ \forall \ x \in C$ and $g(x)$ is defined linearly on $\mathbb{R} \setminus C$. Then g satisfies the required properties. ∎

8.3. Convergence in measure

Quite often, one comes across sequences of measurable functions on a measure space $(X, \mathcal{S}, \mu)$ which do not converge pointwise or a.e. One would like to know: do they converge in some other way? Here is one way of analyzing such sequences which is very useful in the theory of probability (see note 8.3.15).

8.3.1. Definition: Let $f, f_n, n \geq 1$, be measurable functions. We say the sequence $\{f_n\}_{n \geq 1}$ **converges in measure** to f if $\forall \ \epsilon > 0$,

$$\lim_{n \to \infty} \mu(\{x \in X \mid |f_n(x) - f(x)| \geq \epsilon\}) = 0.$$

We write this as $f_n \xrightarrow{m} f$.

8.3.2. Examples:

(i) Let $f_n, n \geq 1$, be measurable functions on the Lebesgue measure space $(\mathbb{R}, \mathcal{L}, \lambda)$, defined by $f_n := \chi_{[n,n+1]}$. Then $\lim_{n \to \infty} f_n(x) = f(x) = 0 \ \forall \ x \in \mathbb{R}$. But

$$\lambda(\{x \in \mathbb{R} \mid |f_n(x)| \geq 1\}) = \lambda([n,n+1]) = 1 \ \forall \ n,$$

and hence $\{f_n\}_{n \geq 1}$ does not converge to f in measure. Thus pointwise convergence or convergence a.e. does not imply convergence in measure.

(ii) Consider the measure space $([0,1], \mathcal{L}_{[0,1]}, \lambda)$, where $\mathcal{L}_{[0,1]} := \mathcal{L} \cap [0,1]$ and λ is the Lebesgue measure restricted to $\mathcal{L}_{[0,1]}$. For every $n \in \mathbb{N}$, choose the unique integer $m \in \mathbb{N}$ such that $2^m \leq n < 2^{m+1}$, and let $0 \leq k < 2^m$ be such that $n = 2^m + k$. The correspondence $n \longmapsto (m, k)$ is one-one, and $m \to \infty$ as $n \to \infty$. For $n \geq 1$, let

$$f_n := \chi_{I_m^k} \quad \text{whenever} \quad n = k + 2^m, \quad \text{where} \quad I_m^k := [k/2^m, (k+1)/2^m].$$

Then $\{f_n\}_{n \geq 1}$ is a sequence of measurable functions on $([0, 1], \mathcal{L}_{[0,1]}, \lambda)$. Further, $\forall \ x \in [0, 1]$ and given any $n \in \mathbb{N}$, let $x \in I_m^k$, for some m and k such that $n = 2^m + k$ and $0 \leq k < 2^m$. Then $x \in \left[\ell_0/2^{m+1}, (\ell_0 + 1)/2^{m+1}\right]$ for some $2^k \leq \ell_0 < 2^{m+1} - 1$. Let $n' := \ell_0 + 2^{m+1}$. Then

$$n' = \ell_0 + 2^{m+1} > 2^{m+1} = 2^m + 2^m > k + 2^m = n$$

and $f_{n'}(x) = 1$. Thus $\forall \ x \in [0, 1]$ and $\forall \ n \geq 1$, $\exists \ n' > n$ such that $f_{n'}(x) = 1$, i.e., $\{f_n\}_{n \geq 1}$ does not converge pointwise to $f \equiv 0$. On the other hand, given any $\epsilon > 0$,

$$\{x \in [0, 1] \mid |f_n(x)| \geq \epsilon\} = \begin{cases} \emptyset & \text{if } \epsilon > 1, \\ I_m^k & \text{if } \epsilon \leq 1 \text{ and } n = 2^m + k. \end{cases}$$

Thus

$$\lambda(\{x \in [0, 1] \mid |f_n(x)| \geq \epsilon\}) \ \leq \ 1/2^m, \ \text{if } 2^m \leq n < 2^{m+1}.$$

Hence

$$\lim_{n \to \infty} \lambda(\{x \in [0, 1] \mid |f_n(x)| \geq \epsilon\}) = 0,$$

i.e., $\{f_n\}_{n \geq 1}$ converges to f in measure.

The above examples show that convergence in measure neither implies nor is implied by convergence pointwise (or a.e.). However, when $\mu(X) < +\infty$, convergence a.e. implies convergence in measure, as shown in the next proposition.

8.3.3. Proposition: *Let $\mu(X) < +\infty$, and let $\{f_n\}_{n \geq 1}$ converge a.e. to f. Then $\{f_n\}_{n \geq 1}$ converges in measure to f.*

Proof: Recall that $\{f_n\}_{n \geq 1}$ converges in measure to f iff $\forall \ \epsilon > 0$,

$$\lim_{n \to \infty} \mu(\{x \in X \mid |f_n(x) - f(x)| \geq \epsilon\}) = 0.$$

Let

$$A_n(\epsilon) := \{x \in X \mid |f_n(x) - f(x)| \geq \epsilon\}.$$

Then

$$A_n(\epsilon) \subseteq \bigcup_{m \geq n}^{\infty} A_m(\epsilon).$$

Thus, $\lim_{n\to\infty} \mu(A_n(\epsilon)) = 0$ will be true if $\lim_{n\to\infty} \mu\left(\bigcup_{m\geq n}^{\infty} A_m(\epsilon)\right) = 0$. But, $\{\bigcup_{m\geq n}^{\infty} A_m(\epsilon)\}_{n\geq 1}$ is a decreasing sequence of sets in $\mathcal{S}$ and it decreases to $\bigcap_{n=1}^{\infty} \bigcup_{m=n}^{\infty} A_m(\epsilon)$. Since $\mu(X) < +\infty$, we have

$$\lim_{n\to\infty} \mu\left(\bigcup_{m=n}^{\infty} A_m(\epsilon)\right) = \mu\left(\bigcap_{n=1}^{\infty} \bigcup_{m=n}^{\infty} A_m(\epsilon)\right).$$

Since $f_n \longrightarrow f$ a.e. and

$$\bigcap_{n=1}^{\infty} \bigcup_{m=n}^{\infty} A_m(\epsilon) \subseteq \{x \in X \mid f_n(x) \text{ does not converge to } f(x)\},$$

we have

$$\mu\left(\bigcap_{n=1}^{\infty} \bigcup_{m=n}^{\infty} A_m(\epsilon)\right) = 0.$$

Hence $\lim_{n\to\infty} \mu(A_n(\epsilon)) = 0$, i.e., $\{f_n\}_{n\geq 1}$ converges to f in measure. ∎

•**8.3.4. Exercise:** Let $\{f_n\}_{n\geq 0}$ and $\{g_n\}_{n\geq 0}$ be sequences of measurable functions on $(X, \mathcal{S}, \mu)$ such that $\{f_n\}_{n\geq 1}$ converges to f_0 and $\{g_n\}_{n\geq 1}$ converges to g_0 in measure. Prove the following statements:

(i) $\{|f_n|\}_{n\geq 1}$ converges to $|f_0|$ in measure.

(ii) $\{f_n \pm g_n\}_{n\geq 1}$ converges to $f_0 \pm g_0$ in measure.

(iii) If $f_n(x) = g_n(x)$ for a.e. x, then $f_0(x) = g_0(x)$ for a.e. x, i.e., for convergence in measure, limit is unique a.e.

8.3.5. Exercise: Let $(X, \mathcal{S}, \mu)$ be a finite measure space. Let $\{f_n\}_{n\geq 0}$ be a sequence of measurable functions such that $\forall \ \epsilon > 0$

$$\sum_{n=1}^{\infty} \mu(\{x \in X \mid |f_n(x) - f_0(x)| \geq \epsilon\}) < +\infty.$$

Show that $\{f_n\}_{n\geq 1}$ converges to f_0 a.e.

(Hint: the given condition implies that $\{f_n\}_{n\geq 1}$ converges to f_0 in measure.)

In example 8.3.2 we showed that convergence in measure need not imply convergence a.e. However, the following 'partial' implication holds.

8.3.6. Theorem (Riesz): *Let $\{f_n\}_{n\geq 1}$ be a sequence of measurable functions converging in measure to a measurable function f. Then there exists a subsequence $\{f_{n_k}\}_{k\geq 1}$ of $\{f_n\}_{n\geq 1}$ such that $\{f_{n_k}\}_{k\geq 1}$ converges to f almost everywhere.*

Proof: To construct the subsequence $\{f_{n_k}\}_{n \geq 1}$ which converges a.e. to f, in view of exercise 8.2.9, we should construct $\{f_{n_k}\}_{k \geq 1}$ such that

$$\mu\left(\bigcap_{j=1}^{\infty} \bigcup_{k=j}^{\infty} \{x \in X \mid |f_{n_k}(x) - f(x)| \geq 1/k\}\right) = 0. \tag{8.1}$$

For, if

$$x \notin A := \bigcap_{j=1}^{\infty} \bigcup_{k=j}^{\infty} \{x \in X \mid |f_{n_k}(x) - f(x)| \geq 1/k\},$$

then $x \in \bigcap_{k=j_0}^{\infty} \{x \in X \mid |f_{n_k}(x) - f(x)| < 1/k\}$ for some j_0. Thus for every $k \geq j_0$, $|f_{n_k}(x) - f(x)| < 1/k$, i.e., $f_{n_k}(x) \longrightarrow f(x)$. So, to complete the proof we should construct a subsequence $\{f_{n_k}\}_{k \geq 1}$ such that (8.1) holds. Let

$$A_j := \bigcup_{k=j}^{\infty} \{x \in X \mid |f_{n_k}(x) - f(x)| \geq 1/k\}. \tag{8.2}$$

Since $A \subseteq A_j$, we have $\mu(A) \leq \mu(A_j)$. If we could construct $\{f_{n_k}\}_{k \geq 1}$ such that $\mu(A_j) \longrightarrow 0$ as $j \longrightarrow \infty$, we will be through. For example, if we could choose the subsequence $\{f_{n_k}\}_{n \geq 1}$ such that

$$\mu(\{x \in X \mid |f_{n_k}(x) - f(x)| \geq 1/k\}) < 1/2^{k+1},$$

then

$$\mu(A_j) \leq \sum_{k=j}^{\infty} \mu(\{x \in X \mid |f_{n_k}(x) - f(x)| \geq 1/k\}) \leq \sum_{k=j}^{\infty} 1/2^{k+1} = 1/2^j,$$

and we will be through. So we have only to choose $\{f_{n_k}\}_{k \geq 1}$ such that (8.2) holds. For this we proceed as follows: since $\{f_n\}_{n \geq 1}$ converges to f in measure, given $\epsilon = 1$, we can choose n_1 such that

$$\mu(\{x \in X \mid |f_{n_1}(x) - f(x)| \geq 1\}) < 1/2.$$

Suppose $n_1 < n_2 < \ldots < n_{k-1}$ have been selected. Choose $n_k > n_{k-1}$ such that

$$\mu(\{x \in X \mid |f_{n_k}(x) - f(x)| \geq 1/k\}) < 1/2^{k+1},$$

using the fact that the sequence $\{f_n\}_{n \geq 1}$ converges to f in measure. The required subsequence $\{f_{n_k}\}_{k \geq 1}$ exists by induction, and this completes the proof. ∎

8.3.7. Note: As an application of the above theorem, we show that the condition "$f_n \longrightarrow f$ a.e." in Fatou's lemma, the monotone convergence theorem and Lebesgue's dominated convergence theorem can be replaced by $f_n \longrightarrow f$ in measure. For example, suppose $f_n \longrightarrow f$ in measure and $\exists \, g \in L_1(\mu)$ such that $|f_n| \le g \; \forall \; n$. Then

$$\int f_n d\mu \longrightarrow \int f d\mu.$$

To see this, let us choose any subsequence $\{f_{n_k}\}_{k\ge1}$ of $\{f_n\}_{n\ge1}$. Then $f_{n_k} \longrightarrow f$ in measure. By theorem 8.3.6, we can choose further a subsequence $\{f_{n_{k_j}}\}_{j\ge1}$ of $\{f_{n_k}\}_{k\ge1}$ such that $f_{n_{k_j}} \longrightarrow f$ a.e. But then by Lebesgue's dominated convergence theorem (5.4.9), $\int f_{n_{k_j}} d\mu \longrightarrow \int f d\mu$. Thus any subsequence $\{\int f_{n_k} d\mu\}_{k\ge1}$ of $\{\int f_n d\mu\}_{n\ge1}$ has a subsequence converging to $\int f d\mu$. Hence

$$\int f d\mu = \lim_{n\to\infty} \int f_n d\mu.$$

8.3.8. Exercise: Let $\{f_n\}_{n\ge1}$ converge in measure to f. Let $|f_n| \le g \; \forall \; n$ and for some $g \in L_1(\mu)$. Show that

$$\int |f_n - f| d\mu \longrightarrow 0.$$

(Hint: Use exercise 8.3.4 and the note above.)

8.3.9. Exercise: Let $\{f_n\}_{n\ge1}$ be a sequence of measurable functions on $(X, \mathcal{S}, \mu)$. Show that $\{f_n\}_{n\ge1}$ converges in measure to a measurable function f iff every subsequence of $\{f_n\}_{n\ge1}$ has a further subsequence which converges a.e. to f.

•**8.3.10. Exercise:** Let $\{f_n\}_{n\ge1}$ be a sequence of measurable functions. We say $\{f_n\}_{n\ge1}$ is **Cauchy in measure** if for every $\epsilon > 0$ there exists a positive integer n_0 such that $\forall \, m, n \ge n_0$,

$$\mu(\{x \in X \mid |f_n(x) - f_m(x)| \ge \epsilon\}) < \epsilon.$$

Prove the following:

(a) If $\{f_n\}_{n\ge1}$ is convergent in measure, then $\{f_n\}_{n\ge1}$ is Cauchy in measure.

(b)   (i) If $\{f_n\}_{n\ge1}$ is Cauchy in measure, then there exist positive integers $n_1 < n_2 < \ldots$ such that $\forall \, k$,

$$\mu(\{x \in X \mid |f_{n_k}(x) - f_{n_{k+1}}(x)| > 1/2^k\}) < 1/2^k.$$

     (ii) The subsequence $\{f_{n_k}(x)\}_{k\ge1}$ is Cauchy for a.e. x, and hence there exists a measurable function f such that $f_{n_k}(x) \to f(x)$ for a.e. $x(\mu)$.

     (iii) The subsequence $\{f_{n_k}\}_{k\ge1}$, and hence the sequence $\{f_n\}_{n\ge1}$ itself, converges in measure to f.

8.3.11. Exercise: Let $\{f_n\}_{n\geq1}$ be a sequence of measurable functions such that $\{f_n\}_{n\geq1}$ converges a.u. to a measurable function f. Show that $\{f_n\}_{n\geq1}$ converges to f in measure.

8.3.12. Exercise: Let $\{f_n\}_{n\geq1}$ be a sequence of measurable functions such that $\{f_n\}_{n\geq1}$ converges a.e. to a function f. Let $\exists\ g \in L_1(\mu)$ such that $|f_n| \leq g\ \forall\ n$. Show that $\{f_n\}_{n\geq1}$ converges to f a.u. and hence in measure. (Hint: $\{x \in X \mid f_n(x) - f(x)| \geq \epsilon\} \subseteq \{x : g(x) \geq \epsilon/2\}$, and the latter is a set of finite measure.)

* 8.3.13. Exercise: Let $(X, \mathcal{S}, \mu)$ be a finite measure space and let $\mathcal{M}(X)$ denote the set of all measurable functions on X. Identify functions in $\mathcal{M}(X)$ if they agree a.e. (μ). For $f, g \in \mathcal{M}(X)$, define

$$d(f,g) := \int \frac{|f(x) - g(x)|}{1 + |f(x) - g(x)|}\ d\mu(x).$$

Show that d is a metric on $\mathcal{M}(X)$. Further, for a sequence $\{f_n\}_{n\geq1}$ in $\mathcal{M}(X)$ and $f \in \mathcal{M}(X), d(f_n, f) \to 0$ as $n \to \infty$ iff $\{f_n\}_{n\geq1}$ converges to f in measure. In view of exercise 8.3.10, $(\mathcal{M}(X), d)$ is a complete pseudo-metric space.

(Hint: $\dfrac{|a + b|}{1 + |a + b|} \leq \dfrac{|a|}{1 + |a|} + \dfrac{|b|}{1 + |b|}$, and for $0 < \epsilon < 1$, if $|a| > \epsilon$ then $\dfrac{|a|}{1 + |a|} > \dfrac{\epsilon}{2}$).

*8.3.14. Exercise: Let $(\mathcal{M}(X), d)$ be as in exercise 8.3.13. For every $n = 1, 2, \dots$, define

$$V_n := \{f \in \mathcal{M}(X) \mid \mu\{x \in X \mid |f(x)| \geq 1/n\} < 1/n\}.$$

Prove the following:

(a) The family $\{V_n\}_{n\geq1}$ has the following properties:
  (i) If $f \in V_n$ and $|\lambda| \leq 1$, then $\lambda f \in V_n$.
  (ii) For every n, m there exists k such that $V_k \subseteq V_n \cap V_m$.
  (iii) If $\mu(\{x \in X \mid f(x) \neq 0\}) > 0$, then $\exists\ n$ such that $f \notin V_n$.
  (iv) For every $f \in \mathcal{M}(X)$ and $\forall\ n$, $\exists\ \lambda \in \mathbb{R}$ such that $\lambda f \in V_n$.
  (v) For every n, $\exists\ m$ such that $V_m + V_m \subset V_n$, where

$$V_n + V_m := \{f + g \mid f, g \in V_m\}.$$

(b) For every $f \in \mathcal{M}(X)$, let

$$V_f := \{f + V_n \mid n = 1, 2, \dots\}.$$

Then $\{V_f \mid f \in \mathcal{M}(X)\}$ defines a local neighborhood base for a Hausdorff topology on $\mathcal{M}(X)$.

(c) A sequence $\{f_n\}_{n \geq 1}$ converge to f in this topology iff $f_n \to f$ in measure.

(d) Clearly $\mathcal{M}(X)$ is a linear space over $\mathbb{R}$ with addition and scalar multiplication defined by

$$\begin{aligned}
\mathcal{M}(X) \times \mathcal{M}(X) &\longrightarrow \mathcal{M}(X), \\
(f, g) &\longmapsto f + g, \\
\mathbb{R} \times \mathcal{M}(X) &\longrightarrow \mathcal{M}(X), \\
(\lambda, f) &\longmapsto \lambda f.
\end{aligned}$$

Let $\mathcal{M}(X) \times \mathcal{M}(X)$ be given the product topology. Show that the maps defined above are continuous. One says that $\mathcal{M}(X)$ is a **'topological vector space'** under the addition and scalar multiplication defined above.

8.3.15. Note: When $(X, \mathcal{S}, \mu)$ is a probability space, convergence in measure is called **convergence in probability**. Recall (see note 3.11.10) that a probability space $(X, \mathcal{S}, \mu)$ gives a mathematical model for 'statistical experiments'. An observation about the outcomes of the experiment is a function f on the sample space X. To be able to make probability statements about f, it has to be a measurable function. Measurable functions on the sample space X are called **random variables** in probability theory. Thus a sequence of observations $\{f_n\}_{n \geq 1}$ in an experiment may not converge to an observation f at every possible outcome $x \in X$. One would like to know the probability that the observation f_n is away from f by an error ϵ, i.e., analyze $\mu\{x \mid |f_n(x) - f(x)| \geq \epsilon\}$. So it is natural to ask: does $\mu\{x \mid |f_n(x) - f(x)| \geq \epsilon\} \to 0$ as $n \to \infty$, i.e., does $f_n \to f$ in probability?

8.4. L_p-spaces

In section 5.6, we analyzed $L_1[a, b]$, the space of Lebesgue integrable functions on $[a, b]$. We saw that $L_1[a, b]$ is a vector space over $\mathbb{R}$, and that for $f \in L_1[a, b]$, we can define the notion of absolute value of f, i.e., $\|f\|_1$. Further, this notion of absolute value can be used to define the L_1-metric on $L_1[a, b]$ so that $L_1[a, b]$ becomes a complete metric space. In this section we look at examples of a family of spaces of this type, called L_p-spaces. Throughout this section, we fix a measure space $(X, \mathcal{S}, \mu)$ which is σ-finite and complete.

8.4.1. Definition: Let $0 < p < \infty$. Let $L_p(\mu) := L_p(X, \mathcal{S}, \mu)$ denote the space of all complex-valued $\mathcal{S}$-measurable functions on X such that

$$\int |f|^p d\mu < +\infty.$$

The space $L_p(\mu)$ is called the space of pth**-power integrable functions.**

8.4.2. Proposition: *The space $L_p(X, \mathcal{S}, \mu)$ is a vector space over $\mathbb{C}$.*

Proof: Let $\alpha \in \mathbb{C}$ and $f \in L_p(X, \mathcal{S}, \mu)$. Then clearly $\alpha f \in L_p(X, \mathcal{S}, \mu)$, as αf is $\mathcal{S}$-measurable, and

$$\int |\alpha f|^p d\mu = |\alpha|^p \int |f|^p d\mu < O + \infty.$$

Also for $f, g \in L_p(X, \mathcal{B}, \mu)$, it is easy to see that $f + g$ is $\mathcal{S}$-measurable. Further, since

$$|f + g|^p \leq (|f| + |g|)^p \leq 2^p \max\{|f|^p, |g|^p\} \leq 2^p(|f|^p + |g|^p),$$

we have

$$\int |f + g|^p d\mu \leq 2^p \left(\int |f|^p d\mu + \int |g|^p d\mu \right) < +\infty.$$

Hence $f + g \in L_p(X, \mathcal{S}, \mu)$. ∎

8.4.3. Definition: Let $f \in L_p(X, \mathcal{B}, \mu)$. Define $\|f\|_p$, called the pth**-norm** of f, as follows:

$$\|f\|_p := \left(\int |f|^p d\mu \right)^{1/p}.$$

Since $\|f\|_p = \|g\|_p$ if $f(x) = g(x)$ for a.e. $x(\mu)$, we treat such f and g as the same element of $L_p(X, \mathcal{B}, \mu)$. To show that $\|f\|_p$ has the properties of a metric (as was the case for $p = 1$ in section 5.6), we need some inequalities.

8.4.4. Lemma: *For nonnegative real numbers a, b and $0 < t < 1$, the following inequalities hold:*

(i) $a^t b^{1-t} \leq ta + (1 - t)b.$

(ii) $(\frac{a + b}{2})^{1/t} \leq \frac{1}{2}(a^{1/t} + b^{1/t}).$

Proof: Let $0 < t < 1$ be fixed and consider the function

$$f(x) := (1 - t) + tx - x^t, x > 0.$$

To prove (i) we have to show that $f(a/b) \geq 0 = f(1)$. It is easy to see that $f(x)$ has a minimum at $x = 1$ and hence $\forall x > 0$,

$$0 = f(1) \leq f(x) = (1 - t) + tx - x^t.$$

In particular, if $x = a/b$, we have

$$(1 - t) + t(a/b) - (a/b)^t \geq 0,$$

i.e.,

$$(a/b)^t \ \leq \ t(a/b) + (1-t),$$

i.e.,

$$a^t b^{1-t} \ \leq \ at + (1-t)b.$$

This proves (i). To prove (ii), we consider the function $g(x) = x^{1/t}$, $x > 0$. It is easy to show that g is a convex function. Thus $\forall \ a, b > 0$,

$$((a+b)/2)^{1/t} \ \leq \ 1/2(a^{1/t} + b^{1/t}). \quad \blacksquare$$

●**8.4.5. Exercise:** Let $0 < t < \infty$ and $0 < p < 1$. Show that

  (i) $(1+t)^p < 1 + t^p$.

  (ii) $(1+t)^{1/p} > 1 + t^{1/p}$.

8.4.6. Theorem (Hölder's inequality): *Let $p > 1$ and $q > 1$ be such that $1/p + 1/q = 1$. Let $f \in L_p(\mu)$ and $g \in L_q(\mu)$. Then $fg \in L_1(\mu)$ and*

$$\int |fg| d\mu \ \leq \ \left(\int |f|^p d\mu \right)^{1/p} \left(\int |g|^q d\mu \right)^{1/q}.$$

Proof: Let

$$A := \left(\int |f|^p d\mu \right)^{1/p} \quad \text{and} \quad B := \left(\int |g|^q d\mu \right)^{1/q}.$$

If $A = 0$, then clearly $f(x) = 0$ for a.e. $x(\mu)$, and hence the required claim holds trivially (with the equality sign). Similarly, if $B = 0$, the required claim holds. So, suppose $A \neq 0$ and $B \neq 0$. Then by lemma 8.4.4, for all fixed x with

$$a = \left(\frac{|f(x)|}{A} \right)^p, \ b = \left(\frac{|g(x)|}{B} \right)^q \quad \text{and} \quad t = 1/p,$$

we have

$$\frac{|f(x)g(x)|}{AB} \ \leq \ \frac{|f(x)|^p}{pA^p} + \frac{|g(x)|^q}{qB^q}.$$

Thus $fg \in L_1(\mu)$ and

$$\int |f(x)g(x)| d\mu \ \leq \ (1/p + 1/q)AB \ = \ AB. \quad \blacksquare$$

8.4.7. Corollary: *Let $p, q > 1$ be real numbers with $1/p + 1/q = 1$. Let $\{a_n\}_{n \geq 1}$ and $\{b_n\}_{n \geq 1}$ be sequences of complex numbers such that*

$$\sum_{n=1}^{\infty} |a_n|^p < \infty \quad \text{and} \quad \sum_{n=1}^{\infty} |b_n|^q < \infty.$$

Then $\sum_{n=1}^{\infty} |a_n b_n| < +\infty$ *and*

$$\left(\sum_{n=1}^{\infty} |a_n b_n| \right) \leq \left(\sum_{n=1}^{\infty} |a_n|^p \right)^{1/p} \left(\sum_{n=1}^{\infty} |b_n|^q \right)^{1/q}.$$

In particular, if $a_n = b_n = 0 \ \forall \ n \geq k$, *then*

$$\sum_{n=1}^{k} |a_n b_n| \leq \left(\sum_{n=1}^{k} |a_n|^p \right)^{1/p} \left(\sum_{n=1}^{k} |b_n|^q \right)^{1/q}.$$

Proof: Consider the special case of $(X, \mathcal{S}, \mu)$ with $X = \mathbb{N}, \mathcal{S} = \mathcal{P}(\mathbb{N})$ and $\mu(\{z\}) = 1 \ \forall \ z \in \mathbb{N}$, and apply theorem 8.4.6. ∎

8.4.8. Note: In the special case when $p = q = 2$, Hölder's inequality is known as the **Cauchy-Schwarz inequality**.

8.4.9. Theorem (Minkowski's inequality): *Let* $1 \leq p < \infty$ *and* $f, g \in L_p(\mu)$. *Then* $f + g \in L_p(\mu)$ *and*

$$\|f + g\|_p \leq \|f\|_p + \|g\|_p.$$

Proof: When $p = 1$, the inequality is obvious. So, suppose $1 < p < \infty$. We have already seen in proposition 8.4.2 that $f + g \in L_p(\mu)$. Since $p = (p-1)q$, it follows that $|f + g|^{p-1} \in L_q(\mu)$. By Hölder's inequality, both $|f||f + g|^{p-1}$ and $|g||f + g|^{p-1}$ belong to $L_1(\mu)$ with

$$\int |f||f + g|^{p-1} d\mu \leq \|f\|_p \left(\int |f + g|^{q(p-1)} \right)^{1/q} = \|f\|_p \|f + g\|_p^{p/q}$$

and

$$\int |g||f + g|^{p-1} d\mu \leq \|g\|_p \left(\int |f + g|^{q(p-1)} \right)^{1/q} = \|g\|_p \|f + g\|_p^{p/q}.$$

Thus

$$\begin{aligned}
\|f + g\|_p^p &= \int |f + g|^p d\mu \\
&= \int |f + g||f + g|^{p-1} d\mu \\
&\leq \int (|f| + |g|)(|f + g|^{p-1}) d\mu \\
&\leq \int |f||f + g|^{p-1} d\mu + \int |g||f + g|^{p-1} d\mu \\
&\leq (\|f\|_p + \|g\|_p)\|f + g\|_p^{p/q}.
\end{aligned}$$

Hence

$$\|f+g\|_p^{p-p/q} \le \|f\|_p + \|g\|_p,$$

i.e.,

$$\|f+g\|_p \le \|f\|_p + \|g\|_p. \qquad \blacksquare$$

8.4.10. Theorem (Riesz-Fischer): *The space* $L_p(X,\mathcal{S},\mu)$, *for* $1 \le p < \infty$, *is a complete metric space with the metric defined by*

$$d_p(f,g) := \|f-g\|_p \ \forall \ f,g \in L_p(X,\mathcal{S},\mu).$$

Of course, here we identify $f,g \in L_p(X,\mathcal{S},\mu)$ if $f(x) = g(x)$ for a.e. $x(\mu)$.

Proof: That $d_p(f,g)$ is a metric on $L_p(X,\mathcal{S},\mu)$ follows from our identification and the Minkowski's inequality. The proof of the completeness of $L_p(X,\mathcal{S},\mu)$ can be based on the ideas of the proof of theorem 5.6.1. We outline the steps below and ask the reader to verify them. Let $\{f_n\}_{n\ge 1}$ be a Cauchy sequence in $L_p(X,\mathcal{S},\mu)$.

(i) Choose $n_1 < n_2 < \cdots < n_k < \cdots$ such that $\ \forall \ k$,

$$\|f_{n_{k+1}} - f_{n_k}\|_p < 2^{-k}.$$

(ii) Let $g_k := |f_{n_1}| + \sum_{j=1}^{k} |f_{n_{j+1}} - f_{n_j}|$, $k \ge 1$. Then

$$\| |g_k|^p \|_1 < \left(\|f_{n_1}\|_p + \sum_{k=1}^{\infty} \|f_{n_{k+1}} - f_{n_k}\|_p \right)^p < +\infty,$$

and hence $g_k \in L_p(X,\mathcal{S},\mu) \ \forall \ k \ge 1$.

(iii) Let $g(x) := \lim_{k\to\infty} g_k(x), x \in X$. Using monotone convergence theorem and (i), deduce that $g \in L_p(X,\mathcal{S},\mu)$, i.e.,

$$\int \left(|f_{n_1}| + \sum_{j=1}^{\infty} |f_{n_{j+1}} - f_{n_j}| \right)^p d\mu < \infty.$$

(iv) From (iii), using exercise 5.4.2(ii), deduce that

$$f(x) := f_{n_1}(x) - \sum_{j=1}^{\infty} (f_{n_{j+1}}(x) - f_{n_j}(x))$$

exists for a.e. $x(\mu)$, i.e., $f_{n_k}(x) \longrightarrow f(x)$ for a.e. $x(\mu)$.

(v) Deduce that $f \in L_p(X, \mathcal{S}, \mu)$ by showing that $|f_{n_{k+1}}|^p \le (g_k)^p$ $\forall$ k, applying Lebesgue's dominated convergence theorem and using (ii) above. Finally, using the inequality $|f_{n_{k+1}} - f|^p \le g^p$, deduce that $\|f_{n_k} - f\|_p \longrightarrow 0$ as $k \to \infty$.

(For an alternative proof, see also exercise 8.4.15.) ∎

8.4.11. Note: In theorem 8.4.10, we showed that $L_p(\mu), 1 \le p < \infty$, is a complete metric space under the metric

$$d_p(f, g) := \|f - g\|_p := \left(\int |f - g|^p d\mu \right)^{1/p}.$$

It is natural to ask the same question for $0 < p < 1$. If $0 < p < 1$, define for $f, g \in L_p(\mu)$

$$d_p(f, g) := \int |f - g|^p d\mu.$$

Using the inequality (see exercise 8.4.5)

$$1 + t^p \ge (1 + t)^p \quad \forall \ t \ge 0,$$

it is easy to see that d_p is a metric on $L_p(\mu)$. Also, proceeding as in theorem 8.4.10, we can show that $L_p(\mu)$ is a complete metric space for $0 < p < 1$. In the case $1 \le p < \infty, f \longmapsto \|f\|_p$ is a real-valued map on $L_p(\mu)$ with the properties: $\forall$ $f, g \in L_p(\mu)$ and $\alpha \in \mathbb{C}$

(i) $\|f\|_p \ge 0$, and $\|f\|_p = 0$ iff $f = 0$.

(ii) $\|\alpha f\|_p = |\alpha| \|f\|_p$.

(iii) $\|f + g\|_p \le \|f\|_p + \|g\|_p$, called the **triangle inequality.**

Such a function can be defined on any vector space, and is called a **norm.** A vector space with a norm is called a **normed linear space.** Thus for $1 \le p < \infty$, the L_p-spaces are examples of normed linear spaces which are also complete under the metric $\|f - g\|_p$, the metric induced by the norm. Such normed linear spaces are called **Banach spaces.** However, when $0 < p < 1, f \longmapsto \|f\|_p$ is no longer a norm, as it fails to satisfy the triangle inequality. To see this, consider a measure space $(X, \mathcal{S}, \mu)$ such that $\exists$ $A, B \in \mathcal{S}$ with $A \cap B = \emptyset$ and $0 < \mu(A) < \infty, 0 < \mu(B) < \infty$. Let α, β be positive real numbers. Then

$$\|\alpha \chi_A\|_p = \left(\int |\alpha|^p \chi_A(x) d\mu(x) \right)^{1/p} = \alpha (\mu(A))^{1/p}.$$

Similarly, $\|\beta\chi_B\|_p = \beta(\mu(B))^{1/p}$. Further,

$$\|\alpha\chi_A + \beta\chi_B\|_p = \left[\int (\alpha\chi_A + \beta\chi_B)^p \, d\mu\right]^{1/p}$$

$$= \left[\int (\alpha^p\chi_A + \beta^p\chi_B) \, d\mu\right]^{1/p}$$

$$= (\alpha^p\mu(A) + \beta^p\mu(B))^{1/p}.$$

Now, using exercise 8.4.5(ii) with $t = (\beta/\alpha)^p(\mu(B)/\mu(A))$, we have

$$\left(1 + \left(\frac{\beta}{\alpha}\right)^p \frac{\mu(B)}{\mu(A)}\right)^{1/p} > 1 + \left(\frac{\beta}{\alpha}\right)\left(\frac{\mu(B)}{\mu(A)}\right)^{1/p},$$

i.e.,

$$(\alpha^{1/p}\mu(A) + \beta^{1/p}\mu(B))^{1/p} > \alpha(\mu(A))^{1/p} + \beta(\mu(B))^{1/p},$$

i.e.,

$$\|\alpha\chi_A + \beta\chi_B\|_p > \|\alpha\chi_A\|_p + \|\beta\chi_B\|_p.$$

This is the reason that L_p-spaces for $0 < p < 1$ are not very interesting to study.

8.4.12. Exercise:

(i) Let $0 < p < 1$ and $-\infty < q < 0$ be such that $1/p + 1/q = 1$. Let f, g be positive functions such that $f \in L_p(\mu)$ and $g \in L_q(\mu)$. Show that

$$\|f\|_p\|g\|_q < \int fg\,d\mu.$$

(Hint: Apply Hölder's inequality to $(fg)^p \in L_{1/p}$ and $g^{-p} \in L_{-p/q}$.)

(ii) If $\mu(X) < \infty$ and $1 \le p \le q < \infty$, show that $L_q(\mu) \subseteq L_p(\mu)$.
(Hint: Apply Hölder's inequality to $|f|^p \in L_{q/p}(\mu)$ and $1 \in L_{(q-p)/q}(\mu)$.)

8.4.13. Definition: Let $\{f_n\}_{n\geq 1}$ be a sequence of functions in $L_p(\mu)$, $1 \le p < \infty$, and let $f \in L_p(\mu)$. We say $\{f_n\}_{n\geq 1}$ **converges in L_p** (or in the pth mean) to f if $\|f_n - f\|_p \to 0$ as $n \to \infty$.

The next theorem describes the relation between convergence in the pth mean and other modes of convergence.

8.4.14. Theorem:

(i) *If $\{f_n\}_{n\geq 1}$ is a sequence in L_p and it converges in L_p to $f \in L_p$, then*

$$\|f_n\|_p \to \|f\|_p.$$

(ii) *In general, convergence in the pth mean does not imply any one of uniform convergence, or almost uniform convergence, or convergence a.e.*

(iii) *Convergence in the pth mean always implies convergence in measure.*

(iv) *In general, none of uniform convergence, or almost uniform convergence, or convergence in measure, or convergence a.e. imply convergence in the pth mean.*

(v) *If the underlying measure space is finite, then uniform convergence implies convergence in the pth mean, but none of almost uniform convergence or convergence a.e. need imply convergence in the pth mean. Also, convergence in the pth mean need not imply almost uniform convergence or convergence a.e.*

Proof: The proof of (i) follows from the inequality

$$\left| \, \|f_n\|_p - \|f\|_p \, \right| \leq \|f_n - f\|_p.$$

(ii) Consider the measure space $([0,1], \mathcal{L}_{[0,1]}, \lambda)$ and the sequence $\{f_n\}_{n\geq 1}$ as in example 8.3.2 (ii), i.e.,

$$f_n := \chi_{I_m^k}, \ I_m^k := [k/2^m, (k+1)/2^m], \text{ with } n = k + 2^m.$$

Since each f_n is the indicator function of a subinterval of $[0,1]$, $f_n \in L_p(\lambda)$. It is easy to see that for $1 \leq p < \infty$,

$$\left(\int |f_n|^p d\mu \right)^{1/p} = (1/2^m)^{1/p}.$$

Thus $\{f_n\}_{n\geq 1}$ converges to $f \equiv 0$ in the pth mean. However, we have already seen that $\{f_n\}_{n\geq 1}$ does not converge to f at any point of $[0,1]$. Clearly, convergence in the pth mean cannot imply uniform or almost uniform convergence, because on finite measure spaces both imply convergence a.e. Also, convergence in the pth mean does not imply convergence a.e., as shown above.

(iii) Let $\{f_n\}_{n\geq 1}$ and $f \in L_p(X, \mathcal{S}, \mu)$, and let $\{f_n\}_{n\geq 1}$ converge to f in L_p. Let $\epsilon > 0$ be arbitrary and

$$E := \{x \in X \mid |f_n(x) - f(x)| \geq \epsilon\}.$$

Then

$$\int |f_n(x) - f(x)|^p d\mu(x) = \int_E |f_n(x) - f(x)|^p d\mu(x)$$
$$+ \int_{E^c} |f_n(x) - f(x)|^p d\mu(x)$$
$$\geq \epsilon^p \mu(E) + \int_{E^c} |f_n(x) - f(x)|^p d\mu$$
$$\geq \epsilon^p \mu(E).$$

Thus $\mu(E) \leq \|f_n - f\|_p^p / \epsilon^p$. This implies that $\{f_n\}_{n \geq 1}$ converges to f in measure.

(iv) Consider the Lebesgue measure space $(\mathbb{R}, \mathcal{L}, \lambda)$ and let

$$f_n(x) := n^{-1/p} \chi_{[0,n]}(x), \; x \in \mathbb{R}.$$

Then $\{f_n\}_{n \geq 1}$ converges to $f \equiv 0$ uniformly. However,

$$\int |f_n|^p d\lambda = 1 \; \forall \; n.$$

Hence $\{f_n\}_{n \geq 1}$ does not converge to f in the pth mean.

Next consider the measure space $([0,1], \mathcal{L}_{[0,1]}, \lambda)$ and let

$$g_n(x) := n^{1/p} \chi_{[0,1/n]}(x), \; x \in [0,1].$$

Then it is easy to see that $\{g_n\}_{n \geq 1}$ converges almost uniformly, in measure and pointwise to $f \equiv 0$. However,

$$\int_{[0,1]} |g_n|^p d\lambda = 1 \; \forall \; n,$$

and hence $\{g_n\}_{n \geq 1}$ does not converge to f in the pth mean.

(v) Let $(X, \mathcal{S}, \mu)$ be a measure space such that $\mu(X) < \infty$, and let $\{f_n\}_{n \geq 1}$ be a sequence of functions in $L_p(X, \mathcal{S}, \mu)$ converging uniformly to a measurable function f on X. Then given $\epsilon > 0$, we can find n_0 such that

$$|f_n(x) - f(x)| < \epsilon \; \forall \; n \geq n_0 \text{ and } \forall \; x \in X.$$

Since

$$|f|^p = (|f_n - f| + |f_n|)^p$$
$$\leq (2 \max\{|f_n - f|, |f_n|\})^p$$
$$\leq 2^p \max\{|f_n - f|^p, |f_n|^p\}$$
$$\leq 2^p (|f_n - f|^p + |f_n|^p),$$

we have

$$\int |f|^p d\mu \;\leq\; 2^p \int |f_{n_0} - f|^p d\mu + 2^p \int |f_{n_0}|^p d\mu$$

$$\leq\; 2^p \epsilon^p \mu(X) + 2^p \|f_n\|_p^p \;<\; +\infty.$$

Hence $f \in L_p(X, \mathcal{S}, \mu)$ and, for $n \geq n_0$,

$$\|f_n - f\|_p = \left(\int |f_n - f|^p d\mu \right)^{1/p} \leq \epsilon (\mu(X))^{1/p}.$$

Thus $\{f_n\}_{n \geq 1}$ converges to f in the pth mean. That none of almost uniform convergence or convergence in measure or convergence a.e. need imply convergence in the pth mean follows from the second example in (iv) above. Also, even if $\mu(X) < +\infty$, convergence in the pth mean does not imply convergence a.e. (as given by the example in (ii)). Thus convergence in the pth mean cannot imply either uniform convergence or almost uniform convergence. ■

•**8.4.15. Exercise:** Prove that $L_p(X, \mathcal{S}, \mu)$ is complete under the metric d_p as follows: Let $\{f_n\}_{n \geq 1}$ be a sequence in $L_p(X, \mathcal{S}, \mu)$ which is Cauchy with respect to the metric d_p. Show that

(i) $\{f_n\}_{n \geq 1}$ is also Cauchy in measure.

(ii) $\sup_n \int |f_n|^p d\mu < +\infty.$

(iii) Using exercise 8.3.10 (b), find a subsequence $\{f_{n_k}\}_{k \geq 1}$ of $\{f_n\}_{n \geq 1}$ which is convergent a.e. to, say, f. Use (ii) to deduce that $f \in L_p(X, \mathcal{S}, \mu)$. Show that $\{f_{n_k}\}_{n \geq 1}$, and hence $\{f_n\}_{n \geq 1}$ itself, converges to f in $L_p(X, \mathcal{S}, \mu)$.

•**8.4.16. Exercise:** Let $f \in L_p(X, \mathcal{S}, \mu)$, where $1 \leq p < \infty$. Show that $\forall\, \epsilon > 0$,

$$\mu(\{x \in X \mid |f(x)| \geq 0\}) \;\leq\; \|f\|_p / \epsilon^p.$$

This is called **Chebyshev's inequality** for L_p-functions (see also exercise 5.4.5.).

8.5. *Necessary and sufficient conditions for convergence in L_p

As we saw above, in general convergence in measure or convergence a.e. need not imply convergence in the pth mean. One would like to find sufficient conditions for convergence in the pth mean. Let $f, f_n \in L_p(X, \mathcal{B}, \mu), n \geq 1$. Let $\{f_n\}_{n \geq 1}$ converge to f in $L_p(X, \mathcal{S}, \mu)$. Since

$$\big|\, \|f_n\|_p - \|f\|_p \,\big| \;\leq\; \|f_n - f\|_p,$$

it follows that $\{\|f_n\|_p\}_{n\geq 1}$ converges to $\|f\|_p$. Conversely, suppose $f, f_n \in L_p(X, \mathcal{S}, \mu), n \geq 1$, are such that $f_n \to f$ a.e. and $\|f_n\|_p \to \|f\|_p$. Can we claim that $\{f_n\}_{n\geq 1}$ converges to f in L_p? The answer is in the affirmative and is given by our next theorem.

8.5.1.   Theorem: *Let $1 \leq p < \infty$ and $f, f_n \in L_p(X, \mathcal{S}, \mu), n \geq 1$. Let $f_n \to f$ a.e. and $\|f_n\|_p \to \|f\|_p$. Then $\|f_n - f\|_p \to 0$ as $n \to \infty$.*

Proof: We first note that by lemma 8.4.4 (ii),

$$|f_n - f|^p \leq 2^{p-1}(|f_n|^p + |f|^p).$$

Since $|f_n - f|^p \to 0$ a.e. and $g_n := 2^{p-1}(|f_n|^p + |f|^p) \to 2^p|f|^p$ with $\int |f|^p d\mu < +\infty$, it follows from exercise 5.4.13 that

$$\lim_{n\to\infty} \int |f_n - f|^p d\mu = 0. \quad \blacksquare$$

In order to state some more necessary and sufficient conditions, we introduce the following definition.

8.5.2.   Definition: Let $\mathcal{G}$ be a collection of integrable functions. We say that $\mathcal{G}$ is **equicontinuous** at $\emptyset$ if for any $\epsilon > 0$ and for any decreasing sequence $\{E_n\}_{n\geq 1}$ of measurable sets with $\bigcap_{n=1}^{\infty} E_n = \emptyset$, $\exists\ n_0$ such that

$$\int_{E_n} |g| d\mu < \epsilon \quad \forall\ g \in \mathcal{G}\ \text{ and }\ \forall\ n > n_0.$$

8.5.3. Examples:

(i) Let $\mathcal{G} = \{g_1, g_2, \ldots, g_k\}$ be any finite collection of integrable functions. Then $\forall\ j, 1 \leq j \leq k$,

$$\lim_{n\to\infty} \int_{E_n} |g_j| d\mu = 0$$

whenever $\{E_n\}_{n\geq 1}$ is a decreasing sequence of measurable sets such that $\bigcap_{n=1}^{\infty} E_n = \emptyset$ (see proposition 5.2.6 and theorem 3.6.3). Thus $\forall\ j, \exists\ n_j$ such that

$$\int_{E_n} |g_j| d\mu < \epsilon, \ n \geq n_j.$$

If $n_0 := \max\{n_1, \ldots, n_k\}$, then

$$\int_{E_n} |g_j| d\mu < \epsilon \ \forall\ n \geq n_0 \text{ and } 1 \leq j \leq k.$$

Thus $\mathcal{G}$ is equicontinuous.

(ii) Consider the Lebesgue measure space $(\mathbb{R}, \mathcal{L}, \lambda)$ and let

$$g_n := \chi_{[n,n+1]}, n = 1, 2, \ldots .$$

Consider the sequence $\{E_k\}_{k \geq 1}$, where $E_k = [k, \infty)$. Then $\{E_k\}_{k \geq 1}$ is a decreasing sequence and $\bigcap_{k=1}^{\infty} E_k = \emptyset$. But

$$\int_{E_k} |g_n| d\lambda = 1 \text{ for } n \geq k.$$

Thus $\mathcal{G} = \{g_1, g_2, \ldots\}$ is not equicontinuous.

8.5.4. Definition: Let $\mathcal{G}$ be a collection of integrable functions. We say $\mathcal{G}$ is **uniformly absolutely continuous** if, given any $\epsilon > 0$, $\exists \, \delta > 0$ such that for $E \in \mathcal{S}$

$$\mu(E) < \delta \text{ implies } \int_E |g| d\mu < \epsilon \; \forall \; g \in \mathcal{G}.$$

8.5.5. Example: The collections $\mathcal{G}$ of examples 8.5.3(i) and (ii) both are uniformly absolutely continuous. Example 8.5.3(ii) shows that every collection $\mathcal{G}$ which is uniformly absolutely continuous need not be equicontinuous. However, the converse is always true, as shown in the next proposition.

8.5.6. Proposition: *If a collection $\mathcal{G}$ of integrable functions is equicontinuous, then $\mathcal{G}$ is also uniformly absolutely continuous.*

Proof: Suppose $\mathcal{G}$ is not uniformly absolutely continuous. Then $\forall \, n$, $\exists \, \epsilon > 0$, a set $E_n \in \mathcal{S}$ and a function $f_n \in \mathcal{G}$ such that

$$\mu(E_n) < 1/2^n \text{ but } \int_{E_n} |f_n| d\mu \geq \epsilon.$$

Let $F_n := \bigcup_{k=n}^{\infty} E_k, \quad n = 1, 2, \ldots .$ Then $\{F_n\}_{n \geq 1}$ is a decreasing sequence of measurable sets. Let $F := \bigcap_{n=1}^{\infty} F_n$. Then

$$\mu(F) \leq \mu(F_n) \leq \sum_{k=n}^{\infty} \mu(E_k) < \sum_{k=n}^{\infty} 1/2^n = 1/2^{n-1}.$$

Thus $\mu(F) = 0$ and

$$\int_{F_n \setminus F} |g_n| d\mu = \int_{F_n} |g_n| d\mu \geq \int_{E_n} |g_n| d\mu \geq \epsilon.$$

But, $\{F_n \setminus F\}_{n \geq 1}$ is a decreasing sequence of sets and $\bigcap_{n=1}^{\infty}(F_n \setminus F) = \emptyset$. This contradicts the equicontinuity of $\mathcal{G}$. $\blacksquare$

•**8.5.7. Exercise:** Let $(X, \mathcal{S}, \mu)$ be a measure space and $\mu(X) < \infty$. Let $\mathcal{G}$ be a collection of measurable functions. Show that $\mathcal{G}$ is uniformly absolutely continuous iff $\mathcal{G}$ is equicontinuous.

8.5.8. Theorem: *Let $\{f_n\}_{n\geq 1}$ be a sequence of functions in $L_p(X, \mathcal{S}, \mu)$, $1 \leq p < \infty$. Then $\{f_n\}_{n\geq 1}$ converges to $f \in L_p$ iff $\{f_n\}_{n\geq 1}$ converges to f in measure and $\mathcal{G} := \{|f_n|^p \mid n = 1, 2, \ldots\}$ is equicontinuous at $\emptyset$.*

Proof: Suppose that $\{f_n\}_{n\geq 1}$ converges to f in L_p. We know, by theorem 8.4.14, that $\{f_n\}_{n\geq 1}$ converges in measure to f. To check the equicontinuity of $\mathcal{G} := \{|f_n|^p \mid n = 1, 2, \ldots\}$, let $\epsilon > 0$ be given. Since $\{f_n\}_{n\geq 1}$ is convergent in L_p, it is also Cauchy in L_p, and thus $\exists\, n_0$ such that

$$\int |f_n - f_m|^p d\mu \;<\; \epsilon/2^{p+1}, \quad \forall\; n \text{ and } m \geq n_0.$$

Let $\{E_k\}_{k\geq 1}$ be any decreasing sequence in $\mathcal{S}$ with $\bigcap_{k=1}^{\infty} E_k = \emptyset$. Using proposition 5.2.6 and theorem 3.6.3, $\forall\, n$ we can choose a positive integer k_n such that

$$\int_{E_k} |f_n|^p d\mu \;<\; \epsilon/2^{p+1} \quad \forall\; k \geq k_n.$$

If $k_0 := \max\{k_1, k_2, \ldots, k_{n_0}\}$, then $\forall\; n \leq n_0$ and $k > k_0$, we have

$$\int_{E_k} |f_n|^p d\mu \;<\; \epsilon/2^{p+1}.$$

Also, since

$$|f_n|^p \;\leq\; 2^p (|f_{n_0}|^p + |f_{n_0} - f_n|^p),$$

we have, for $n \geq n_0$ and $k \geq k_0$,

$$\begin{aligned}
\int_{E_k} |f_n|^p d\mu \;&\leq\; 2^p \Big(\int_{E_k} |f_{n_0}|^p d\mu + \int_{E_k} |f_{n_0} - f_n|^p d\mu \Big) \\
&<\; 2^p \left(\epsilon/2^{p+1} + \epsilon/2^{p+1} \right) \;=\; \epsilon.
\end{aligned}$$

Hence $\mathcal{G} = \{|f_n|^p \mid n = 1, 2, \ldots\}$ is equicontinuous.

Conversely, let $\{f_n\}_{n\geq 1}$ converge in measure to a measurable function f, and let $\mathcal{G} := \{|f_n|^p \mid n = 1, 2, \ldots\}$ be equicontinuous. We have to show that $\{f_n\}_{n\geq 1}$ converges in L_p. In view of theorem 8.4.10, it is enough to show that $\{f_n\}_{n\geq 1}$ is Cauchy in L_p. Let $\epsilon > 0$ be given. We consider two cases.

Case (i): Let $\mu(X) < +\infty$. Since $\mathcal{G}$ is also uniformly absolutely continuous (proposition 8.5.6), we can find $\delta > 0$ such that $\forall\; n \geq 1$ and $\forall\; E \in \mathcal{S}$ with $\mu(E) < \delta$,

$$\int_E |f_n|^p d\mu \;<\; \epsilon/2^{p+2}. \tag{8.3}$$

Let

$$E_{n,k} := \left\{ x \in X \mid |f_n(x) - f_k(x)| \geq \left(\frac{\epsilon\, \mu(X)}{2} \right)^{1/p} \right\}.$$

Then

$$\int_{E_{n,k}^c} |f_n - f_k|^p d\mu \; \leq \; \frac{\epsilon\, \mu(E_{n,k}^c)}{2\,\mu(X)} \; \leq \; \epsilon/2\,. \tag{8.4}$$

Also, since $\{f_n\}_{n\geq 1}$ is convergent in measure, it is Cauchy in measure and hence we can choose a positive integer n_0 such that $\;\forall\; n$ and $k \geq n_0$,

$$\mu(E_{n,k}) < \delta.$$

Then it follows from (8.3) that $\;\forall\, n \geq 1$ and $k \geq n_0$,

$$\int_{E_{n,k}} |f_n|^p d\mu \; < \; \epsilon/2^{p+2}.$$

Hence $\;\forall\; n \geq 1$ and $k \geq n_0$,

$$\int_{E_{n,k}} |f_n - f_k|^p d\mu \; \leq \; 2^p \int_{E_{n,k}^c} |f_n|^p d\mu + 2^p \int_{E_{n,k}} |f_n|^p d\mu$$

$$\leq \; 2^p \left(\epsilon/2^{p+2} + \epsilon/2^{p+2} \right) = \epsilon/2\,. \tag{8.5}$$

From (8.4) and (8.5) it follows that $\{f_n\}_{n\geq 1}$ is Cauchy in L_p. This completes the proof for case (i).

Case (ii): Let $\mu(X) = +\infty$. Since μ is σ-finite, we can write $X = \bigcup_{n=1}^{\infty} X_n$ such that $\;\forall\, n \geq 1,\ \mu(X_n) < +\infty$. Let

$$E_j := \bigcup_{n=j}^{\infty} X_n, \, j = 1, 2, \ldots .$$

Then $\{E_j\}_{j\geq 1}$ is a decreasing sequence of sets with $\bigcap_{j=1}^{\infty} E_j = \emptyset$. From the equicontinuity of $\mathcal{G}$ at $\emptyset$, we have an integer j_0 such that $\;\forall\, n$,

$$\int_{E_{j_0}} |g_n|^p d\mu \; < \; \epsilon/2^{p+2}.$$

Thus

$$\int_{E_{j_0}} |g_n - g_k|^p d\mu \; \leq \; 2^p \int_{E_{j_0}} |g_n|^p d\mu + 2^p \int_{E_{j_0}} |g_k|^p d\mu \; < \; \epsilon. \tag{8.6}$$

Since

$$\mu(E_{j_0}^c) \; \leq \; \sum_{n=1}^{j_0 - 1} \mu(X_j) \; < \; +\infty,$$

by case (i),

$$\int_{E_{j_0}^c} |g_n - g_k|^p d\mu \; < \; \epsilon \text{ for all sufficiently large } n, k. \tag{8.7}$$

Hence, combining (8.6) and (8.7), we see that $\{g_n\}_{n\geq 1}$ is Cauchy in L_p and hence is convergent. $\blacksquare$

8.5.9. Corollary (An extension of the dominated convergence theorem): *Let* $\{g_n\}_{n\geq 1}$ *be a sequence of measurable functions on* $(X, \mathcal{S}, \mu)$ *such that* $g_n \to g$ *in measure, where* g *also is a measurable function. Let* $h \in L_p(\mu)$ *be such that* $|g_n| \leq h$ *a.e.* (μ) *for all* n. *Then* $\{g_n\}_{n\geq 1}$ *converges to* g *in* L_p.

Proof: In view of theorem 8.5.8, we only have to show that $\mathcal{G} = \{|g_n|^p \mid n = 1, 2, \dots\}$ is equicontinuous at $\emptyset$. Let $\{E_n\}_{n\geq 1}$ be any decreasing sequence of measurable sets with $\bigcap_{n=1}^{\infty} E_n = \emptyset$. Then by theorem 3.6.3 and proposition 5.2.6,

$$\lim_{n\to\infty} \int_{E_n} |h| d\mu = 0.$$

Thus, given $\epsilon > 0$, $\exists\ n_0$ such that

$$\int_{E_n} |h| d\mu < \epsilon, \ \forall\ n \geq n_0.$$

Hence $\forall\ n \geq n_0$ and $\forall\ m$,

$$\int_{E_n} |g_m| d\mu \leq \int_{E_n} |h| d\mu < \epsilon,$$

proving equicontinuity of $\{|g_n|^p \mid n = 1, 2, \dots\}$ at $\emptyset$. ∎

In the case $\mu(X) < +\infty$, another useful criterion for convergence in L_p is described in terms of 'uniform integrability' of functions, which we define next.

8.5.10. Definition: A collection $\mathcal{G}$ of measurable functions on $(X, \mathcal{S}, \mu)$ is said to be **uniformly integrable** if

$$\lim_{t\to\infty} \left(\sup_{f \in \mathcal{G}} \int_{\{x \mid |f(x)| \geq t\}} |f(x)| d\mu(x) \right) = 0.$$

8.5.11. Examples:

(i) Let $\{f_n\}_{n\geq 1}$ be any sequence of measurable functions such that $\forall\ n$ $|f_n| \leq g$ a.e., g an integrable function. Then $\{f_n\}_{n\geq 1}$ is uniformly integrable. To see this, first note that since g is integrable,

$$\lim_{t\to\infty} \int_{\{x \mid g(x) \geq t\}} g(x) d\mu(x) = 0.$$

Thus, given $\epsilon > 0$, we can choose $t := t(\epsilon)$ such that

$$\int_{\{x \mid g(x) \geq t\}} g(x) d\mu(x) < \epsilon.$$

Since by the given hypothesis

$$\{x \mid |f_n(x)| \geq t\} \subseteq \{x \mid g(x) \geq |f_n(x)| \geq t\} \cup N,$$

where $\mu(N) = 0$, we have

$$\int_{\{x \mid |f_n(x)| \geq t\}} |f_n(x)| d\mu(x) \leq \int_{\{x \mid g(x) \geq t\}} g(x) d\mu(x) < \epsilon.$$

(ii) Let $\{f_k\}_{k \geq 1}$ be any sequence of integrable functions such that $\{f_k \mid k \geq 1\}$ is a finite set, say $\{f_1, f_2, \dots, f_n\}$. Then $\{f_k\}_{k \geq 1}$ is uniformly integrable, since

$$|f_k| \leq g := \sum_{j=1}^{n} |f_j|, \ \forall \ k.$$

(iii) If $\{f_n\}_{n \geq 1}$ and $\{g_n\}_{n \geq 1}$ are uniformly integrable, then $\{f_n + g_n\}_{n \geq 1}$ is also uniformly integrable. For this, let $h_n := \max\{|f_n|, |g_n|\}$. Then we have $|f_n + g_n| \leq 2h_n$, and hence

$$\{x \mid |f_n(x) + g_n(x)| \geq 2t\} \subseteq \{x \mid h_n(x) > t\}.$$

Thus

$$\int_{\{x \mid |f_n(x)+g_n(x)| \geq 2t\}} |f_n(x) + g_n(x)| \, d\mu(x)$$

$$\leq 2 \int_{\{x \mid h_n(x) > t\}} h_n(x) d\mu(x)$$

$$\leq 2 \int_{\{x \mid h_n(x) > t\} \cap \{x \mid h_n(x) = |f_n(x)|\}} h_n(x) d\mu(x)$$

$$+ 2 \int_{\{x \mid h_n(x) > t\} \cap \{x \mid h_n(x) = |g_n(x)|\}} h_n(x) d\mu(x)$$

$$\leq 2 \int_{\{x \mid |f_n(x)| > t\}} |f_n(x)| \, d\mu(x)$$

$$+ 2 \int_{\{x \mid |g_n(x)| > t\}} |g_n(x)| \, d\mu(x).$$

From the above inequality it follows that $\{f_n + g_n\}_{n \geq 1}$ is uniformly integrable.

8.5.12. Exercise:

(i) Let $\mu(X) < +\infty$ and let $\mathcal{G}$ be uniformly integrable. Show that $\mathcal{G} \subseteq L_1(\mu)$.

(ii) Consider the measure space $([0,1], \mathcal{L}_{[0,1]}, \lambda)$ and let $f_n := (n/\log n)\chi_{[0,1/n]}$, $n = 1, 2, \dots$. Show that $\{f_n\}_{n \geq 1}$ is uniformly integrable and $\int f_n d\lambda \to 0$, although $\{f_n\}_{n \geq 1}$ is not dominated by any integrable function.

When $\mu(X) < \infty$, an equivalent description of uniform integrability is given by the following theorem.

8.5.13. Theorem: *Let* $\mathcal{G}$ *be a family of measurable functions on* $(X, \mathcal{S}, \mu)$ *where* $\mu(X) < \infty$. *Then the following are equivalent:*

(i) $\mathcal{G}$ *is uniformly integrable.*

(ii) $\sup_{g \in \mathcal{G}} \left(\int |g| d\mu \right) < +\infty$, *and* $\mathcal{G}$ *is uniformly absolutely continuous.*

Proof: Suppose (i) holds. Then, given $\epsilon = 1$, we can choose t large enough so that

$$\sup_{g \in \mathcal{G}} \left(\int_{\{x \,|\, |g(x)| \geq t\}} |g(x)| d\mu(x) \right) < 1.$$

Thus $\forall \; g \in \mathcal{G}$,

$$\int |g(x)| \, d\mu(x) = \int_{\{x \,|\, |g(x)| \geq t\}} |g(x)| \, d\mu(x) + \int_{\{x \,|\, |g(x)| < t\}} |g(x)| \, d\mu(x)$$

$$\leq \; 1 + t\mu(X).$$

Hence g is integrable and

$$\sup_{g \in \mathcal{G}} \left(\int |g(x)| d\mu(x) \right) < +\infty.$$

Next, let $\epsilon > 0$ be given. Since $\mathcal{G}$ is uniformly integrable, we can choose t sufficiently large so that $\forall \; g \in \mathcal{G}$,

$$\int_{\{x \,|\, |g(x)| \geq t\}} |g(x)| \, d\mu(x) < \epsilon/2.$$

Then $\forall \; E \in \mathcal{S}$,

$$\int_E |g(x)| \, d\mu = \int_{\{x \,|\, |g(x)| \geq t\} \cap E} |g(x)| \, d\mu(x) + \int_{\{x \,|\, |g(x)| < t\} \cap E} |g(x)| \, d\mu(x)$$

$$< \; \epsilon/2 + t\mu(E).$$

Hence if we choose $\delta(\epsilon) = \epsilon/2t$, then $\forall \; E \in \mathcal{S}$

$$\mu(E) < \delta(\epsilon) \text{ implies } \int_E |g| d\mu < \epsilon \; \forall \; g \in \mathcal{G}.$$

This proves that (i) $\Rightarrow$ (ii).

Conversely, suppose (ii) holds. Let

$$K := \sup_{g \in \mathcal{G}} \int |g| \, d\mu.$$

Then $\forall\ t > 0$ and $g \in \mathcal{G}$,

$$\int |g|\,d\mu = \int_{\{x\mid |g(x)|\geq t\}} |g(x)|\,d\mu(x) + \int_{\{x\mid |g(x)|<t\}} |g(x)|\,d\mu(x)$$

$$\geq \int_{\{x\mid |g(x)|\geq t\}} |g(x)|\,d\mu(x)$$

$$\geq t\mu(\{x\mid |g(x)| \geq t\}).$$

Thus

$$\mu(\{x\mid |g(x)| \geq t\}) \;\leq\; \frac{1}{t}\int |g|d\mu \;\leq\; K/t.$$

Let $\epsilon > 0$ be given. If we choose $\delta > 0$ as given by the uniform absolute continuity of $\mathcal{G}$, then for $t > K/\delta$ we will have

$$\mu(\{x\mid |g(x)| \geq t\}) \;<\; K/t \;<\; \delta.$$

Thus for all $t > K/\delta$,

$$\int_{\{x\mid |g(x)|\geq t\}} |g(x)|d\mu(x) \;<\; \epsilon.$$

This proves that (ii) $\Rightarrow$ (i). ∎

8.5.14. Theorem: *Let $\{g_n\}_{n\geq 1}$ be a sequence of measurable functions on $(X, \mathcal{S}, \mu)$ with $\mu(X) < +\infty$. Let g be a measurable function on $(X, \mathcal{S}, \mu)$. Then the following statements are equivalent.*

(i) *$\{|g_n|^p\}_{n\geq 1}$ is uniformly integrable and $g_n \to g$ in measure.*

(ii) *$\{|g_n|^p\mid n = 1, 2, \ldots\}$ is equicontinuous and $g_n \to g$ in measure.*

(iii) *$\{|g_n|^p\mid n = 1, 2, \ldots\}$ is uniformly absolutely continuous and $g_n \to g$ in measure.*

(iv) *$g_n \to g$ in L_p.*

Proof: In view of exercise 8.5.7 and theorem 8.5.8, we have (ii) $\Leftrightarrow$ (iii) $\Leftrightarrow$ (iv). To complete the proof we show that (i) $\Leftrightarrow$ (iv).

Suppose $\{g_n\}_{n\geq 1}$ is uniformly integrable. Then it follows from theorem 8.5.13 that $\{g_n\}_{n\geq 1}$ is uniformly absolutely continuous and hence equicontinuous at $\emptyset$, by exercise 8.5.7. Thus (i) $\Rightarrow$ (ii) $\Leftrightarrow$ (iv). Conversely, let (iv) hold. Then (iii) holds. Also, $\{g_n\}_{n\geq 1}$ being Cauchy in L_p, given $\epsilon > 0$ we can choose n_0 such that

$$\int |g_{n_0} - g_n|^p d\mu < \epsilon, \;\; \forall\ n \geq n_0.$$

Thus $\forall\ n \geq n_0$,

$$\int |g_n|^p d\mu \quad \leq \quad 2^p \int |g_n - g_{n_0}|^p d\mu + 2^p \int |g_{n_0}|^p d\mu$$

$$\leq \quad 2^p \epsilon + 2^p \int |g_{n_0}| d\mu.$$

Hence

$$\sup_n \int |g_n|^p d\mu \quad \leq \quad \max\left\{ 2^p \epsilon + 2^p \int |g_{n_0}| d\mu, \int |g_1|^p d\mu, \ldots, \int |g_{n_0-1}|^p d\mu \right\}$$

$$< \quad +\infty.$$

It follows from theorem 8.5.13 that $\{|g_n|^p \mid n = 1, 2, \ldots\}$ is uniformly integrable. ∎

8.6. Dense subspaces of L_p

In section 5.7 we showed that $L_1(\mathbb{R})$ has nice dense subspaces. In this section, we first construct dense subspaces of $L_p(X, \mathcal{S}, \mu)$ when $(X, \mathcal{S}, \mu)$ is an abstract measure space, and later specialize to $(\mathbb{R}^n, \mathcal{L}_{\mathbb{R}^n}, \lambda_n)$, the Lebesgue measure space, λ_n denoting the Lebesgue measure on $\mathbb{R}^n$. As before, let $(X, \mathcal{S}, \mu)$, a σ-finite, complete measure space, be fixed. We shall call a function $s \in L_p(X, \mathcal{S}, \mu)$ **simple** if both $\mathrm{Re}\,(s)$ and $\mathrm{Im}\,(s)$ are simple functions.

8.6.1. Theorem: *Let* $f \in L_p(X, \mathcal{S}, \mu), 1 \leq p < \infty$, *and* $\epsilon > 0$. *Then there exists a simple function* $s \in L_p(X, \mathcal{S}, \mu)$ *such that* $\|f - s\|_p < \epsilon$ *and* $|s| \leq |f|$.

Proof: First suppose that $f \geq 0$ and $f \in L_p$. Then by proposition 5.3.2 there is an increasing sequence $\{s_n\}_{n \geq 1}$ of nonnegative simple functions such that $\{s_n(x)\}_{n \geq 1}$ is increasing and $s_n(x) \to f(x)$ for a.e. $x(\mu)$. Thus

$$0 < |f - s_n|^p < f^p \quad \text{a.e. } (\mu).$$

Hence $s_n \in L_p(\mu)\ \forall\ n$ and, by Lebesgue's dominated convergence theorem,

$$\lim_{n \to \infty} \int |f - s_n|^p d\mu = 0.$$

Thus, given $\epsilon > 0$, we can choose n_0 such that

$$|s_{n_0}| \leq |f| \quad \text{and} \quad \|s_{n_0} - f\|_p^p < \epsilon.$$

For $f \in L_p(\mu)$ arbitrary, we can write

$$f = (\mathrm{Re}\,f)^+ - (\mathrm{Re}\,f)^- + i((\mathrm{Im}\,f)^+ - (\mathrm{Im}\,f)^-),$$

where each of $(\mathrm{Re}\,f)^+, (\mathrm{Re}\,f)^-, (\mathrm{Im}\,f)^+$ and $(\mathrm{Im}\,f)^-$ is a nonnegative function in $L_p(\mu)$. Thus, given $\epsilon > 0$, we can choose simple functions $s_i, 1 \leq i \leq 4$ such that

$$|s_1| \leq |(\mathrm{Re}\,f)^+|, \ |s_2| \leq |(\mathrm{Re}\,f)^-|, \ |s_3| \leq |(\mathrm{Im}\,f)^+|, \ |s_4| \leq |(\mathrm{Im}\,f)^-|$$

with
$$\|s_1 - (\operatorname{Re} f)^+\|_p < \epsilon/4, \ \|s_2 - (\operatorname{Re} f)^-\|_p < \epsilon/4,$$
and
$$\|s_3 - (\operatorname{Im} f)^+\|_p < \epsilon/4, \ \|s_4 - (\operatorname{Im} f)^-\|_p < \epsilon/4.$$
Put
$$s := s_1 - s_2 + i(s_3 - s_4).$$
Then s is a simple function and $s \in L_p(\mu)$. Further, $\|f - s\|_p \leq \epsilon$. Also,
$$|s|^2 = (s_1 - s_2)^2 + (s_3 - s_4)^2 \leq \sum_{i=1}^{4} s_i^2 \leq |f|^2,$$
as $(\operatorname{Re} f)^+ (\operatorname{Re} f)^- = 0$ and $(\operatorname{Im} f)^+ (\operatorname{Im} f)^- = 0$. ∎

8.6.2. Theorem: *Let $1 \leq p < \infty$, and let $C_c(\mathbb{R}^n)$ denote the space of continuous (complex-valued) functions on $\mathbb{R}^n$ with compact support. Then $C_c(\mathbb{R}^n)$ is dense in $L_p(\mathbb{R}^n, \mathcal{L}_{\mathbb{R}^n}, \lambda_n)$.*

Proof: Let $g \in C_c(\mathbb{R}^n)$ and let $K := \operatorname{supp}(g)$, the closure of the set $\{x \in \mathbb{R}^n \mid g(x) \neq 0\}$. Then K is compact and
$$|g|^p \leq \left(\sup_{x \in K} |g(x)|^p \right) \chi_K.$$
Since $\lambda_n(K) < +\infty$, it follows that $|g|^p$ is integrable, and hence $g \in L_p := L_p$ $(\mathbb{R}^n, \mathcal{L}_{\mathbb{R}^n}, \lambda_n)$. Thus $C_c(\mathbb{R}^n) \subseteq L_p$. To show that $C_c(\mathbb{R}^n)$ is dense, let $\epsilon > 0$ be arbitrary and let $f \in L_p$. We have to find a function $g \in C_c(\mathbb{R}^n)$ such that $\|f - g\|_p < \epsilon$. For this, we may assume without loss of generality that f is real-valued and $f \geq 0$. Further, by theorem 8.6.1, we can find a simple nonnegative function s such that $\|f - s\|_p < \epsilon$. Since s is a finite linear combination of indicator functions of sets with finite Lebesgue measure (as $s \in L_p$), we have only to prove the theorem in the case when $f = \chi_A, A \in \mathcal{L}_{\mathbb{R}^n}$ and $\lambda_n(A) < +\infty$. Since λ_n is regular, by exercise 7.5.3, we can find a compact set K and an open set U in $\mathbb{R}^n$ such that
$$K \subseteq A \subseteq U \ \text{ and } \ \lambda_n(U \setminus K) < (\epsilon/2)^p.$$
Next, using Urysohn's lemma (see appendix D), we can find a continuous function $g : \mathbb{R}^n \longrightarrow [0,1]$ with $\operatorname{supp}(g) \subseteq U$, such that $g(x) = 1 \ \forall \ x \in K$ and $g(x) = 0 \ \forall \ x \notin U$. Clearly, $g \in L_p$ and
$$|g - \chi_A| \leq \chi_U - \chi_K.$$
Hence
$$\int |g - \chi_A|^p d\lambda_n \leq \int |\chi_U - \chi_K|^p d\lambda_n \leq 2^p \lambda_n(U \setminus K) < \epsilon^p.$$
Thus $\|g - \chi_A\|_p < \epsilon$. This completes the proof. ∎

8.6.3. Corollary: *Let* $1 \le p < \infty$. *For* $f \in L_p(\mathbb{R}^n)$ *and* $h \in \mathbb{R}^n$, *let*

$$f_h(x) := f(x+h), \quad x \in \mathbb{R}^n.$$

Then $f_h \in L_p(\mathbb{R}^n)$ *and* $\lim_{h \to 0} \|f_h - f\|_p = 0.$

Proof: Let $\epsilon > 0$ be given, and let $f \in L_p(\mathbb{R}^n)$. By theorem 8.6.2, $\exists\, g \in C_c(\mathbb{R}^n)$ such that

$$\|f - g\|_p < \epsilon/3. \tag{8.8}$$

Since g is continuous and has compact support, say K, g is uniformly continuous. Thus $\exists\, \delta > 0$ such that

$$|g(x) - g(y)| < \epsilon/3(2\lambda_n(K))^{1/p}, \text{ whenever } |x - y| < \delta.$$

Thus $\forall\, h \in \mathbb{R}^n$ with $|h| < \delta$, we have

$$\begin{aligned}
\|g - g_h\|_p &= \left(\int |g(x) - g(h+x)|^p d\lambda_n(x) \right)^{1/p} \\
&= \left(\int_{K \cup (K-h)} |g(x) - g(x+h)|^p d\lambda_n(x) \right)^{1/p} \\
&< \epsilon/3. \tag{8.9}
\end{aligned}$$

Hence $\forall\, h \in \mathbb{R}^n$ with $|h| < \delta$, we have

$$\|f - f_h\|_p \le \|f - g\|_p + \|g_h - g\|_p + \|g_h - f_h\|_p. \tag{8.10}$$

Since $\|g_h - f_h\|_p = \|g - f\|_p$, from (8.8), (8.9) and (8.10) we have

$$\|f - f_h\|_p < \epsilon \text{ whenever } 0 < |h| < \delta.$$

Hence, $\lim_{h \to 0} \|f_n - f\| = 0.$ ∎

8.7. Convolution and regularization of functions

In this section all a.e. statements are with respect to the Lebesgue measure on $\mathbb{R}^n$. Also, we denote $L_1(\mathbb{R}^n, \mathcal{L}_{\mathbb{R}^n}, \lambda_n)$ by $L_1(\mathbb{R}^n), n \ge 1$.

8.7.1. Example: Let $f \in L_1(\mathbb{R})$ and let a be a positive real number. Define

$$(T_a f)(x) := \frac{1}{2a} \int_{x-a}^{x+a} f(t) d\lambda(t), \quad x \in \mathbb{R}.$$

The function $T_a f$ is called the **symmetric moving average** (or **smoothing**) of f. It is easy to see that $(T_a f)(x)$ is well-defined. Let

$$F(x) := \int_{-\infty}^{x} f(t) d\lambda(t), \quad x \in \mathbb{R}.$$

Then
$$(T_af)(x) = \frac{F(x+a) - F(x-a)}{2a}, \quad x \in \mathbb{R}.$$

Since F is absolutely continuous (see theorem 6.1.1), it is easy to check that T_af is also absolutely continuous. Also,

$$
\begin{aligned}
(T_af)(x) &= \frac{1}{2a} \int_{x-a}^{x+a} f(t) d\lambda(t) \\
&= \frac{1}{2a} \int_{\mathbb{R}} \chi_{[x-a,x+a]}(t) f(t) d\lambda(t) \\
&= \frac{1}{2a} \int_{\mathbb{R}} \chi_{[-a,+a]}(t-x) f(t) d\lambda(t) \\
&= \frac{1}{2a} \int_{\mathbb{R}} \chi_{[-a,+a]}(t) f(t+x) d\lambda(t).
\end{aligned}
$$

The last equality holds because of exercise 5.6.6. Thus

$$(T_af)(x) = \frac{1}{2a} \int_{\mathbb{R}} f(t+x) \chi_{[-a,+a]}(t) d\lambda(t).$$

Hence
$$\int_{\mathbb{R}} |(T_af)(x)| d\lambda(x) \le \int_{\mathbb{R}} |f(t+x)| d\lambda(t) = \|f\|_1.$$

Thus $T_af \in L_1(\mathbb{R})$ and

$$
\begin{aligned}
|(T_af)(x) - f(x)| &= \frac{1}{2a} \Big| \int_{\mathbb{R}} f(t+x) \chi_{[-a,+a]}(t) d\lambda(t) \\
&\quad - \int_{\mathbb{R}} f(x) \chi_{[-a,+a]}(t) d\lambda(t) \Big| \\
&\le \frac{1}{2a} \int_{\mathbb{R}} |f(t+a) - f(x)| \chi_{[-a,+a]}(t) d\lambda(t).
\end{aligned}
$$

Hence
$$\|T_af - f\|_1 \le \frac{1}{2a} \int_{\mathbb{R}} \left(\int_{\mathbb{R}} |f(t+x) - f(x)| \chi_{[-a,+a]}(t) d\lambda(t) \right) d\lambda(x).$$

Using Fubini's theorem, we have

$$
\begin{aligned}
\|T_af - f\|_1 &\le \frac{1}{2a} \int_{\mathbb{R}} \chi_{[-a,+a]}(t) \left(\int_{\mathbb{R}} |f(t+x) - f(x)| d\lambda(x) \right) d\lambda(t) \\
&= \frac{1}{2a} \int_{\mathbb{R}} \chi_{[-a,+a]}(t) \, h(t) \, d\lambda(t),
\end{aligned}
$$

where
$$h(t) := \int_{\mathbb{R}} |f(t+x) - f(x)| d\lambda(x).$$

By corollary 8.6.3, $h(t) \to 0$ as $t \to 0$. Thus, given $\epsilon > 0$, we can choose $a > 0$ sufficiently small so that

$$h(t) \leq \epsilon, \; \forall \, t \in [-a, +a].$$

Hence for this choice of a, we have

$$\|T_a f - f\|_1 \leq \frac{1}{2a} \int_{\mathbb{R}} \chi_{[-a,+a]}(t) \, h(t) \, d\lambda(t) < \epsilon.$$

Thus, given $\epsilon > 0$, we have found an $a > 0$ such that $T_a f$ is continuous (in fact absolutely continuous) and is close to f in the L_1-metric. Note that $(T_a f)(x)$ is nothing but the average of f over an interval centered at x of length $2a$. Even though f may not be continuous, its averaging is continuous. This example is a particular case of a general procedure, which we describe next.

8.7.2. Definition: Let $f, \, g : \mathbb{R}^n \longrightarrow \mathbb{C}$ be measurable functions. Whenever, for $x \in \mathbb{R}^n$,

$$\int |f(x - y)| \, |g(y)| d\lambda_n(y) < +\infty,$$

we define

$$(f * g)(x) := \int f(x - y)g(y)d\lambda_n(y).$$

The function $f * g$ is called the **convolution** of f with g.

8.7.3. Example: Consider $T_a f$, for $f \in L_1(\mathbb{R})$ and $a > 0$, as defined in example 8.7.1. Then for $x \in \mathbb{R}$,

$$
\begin{aligned}
(T_a f)(x) &= \frac{1}{2a} \int \chi_{[x-a,x+a]}(t) \, f(t) \, d\lambda(t) \\
&= \frac{1}{2a} \int \chi_{[-a,+a]}(t - x) \, f(t) \, d\lambda(t) \\
&= \frac{1}{2a} \int \chi_{[-a,+a]}(x - t) \, f(t) \, d\lambda(t) \\
&= \left[\left(\frac{1}{2a} \chi_{[-a,+a]} \right) * f \right](x).
\end{aligned}
$$

8.7.4. Theorem: *Let f, g be measurable functions on $\mathbb{R}^n$. Then the following hold:*

  (i) *If $(f * g)(x)$ exists, then so does $(g * f)(x)$, and*

$$(f * g)(x) = (g * f)(x).$$

  (ii) *If $f \in L_1(\mathbb{R}^n)$ and g is bounded a.e., then $(f * g)(x)$ exists $\forall \, x \in \mathbb{R}^n$ and is a bounded, uniformly continuous function.*

  (iii) *If f, g are in $C_c(\mathbb{R}^n)$, then so is $(f * g)$.*

(iv) *Let p, q be real numbers such that $1 < p, q < \infty$ and $1/q + 1/p = 1$. If $f \in L_p(\mathbb{R}^n)$ and $g \in L_q(\mathbb{R}^n)$, then $(f * g)(x)$ exists $\forall\ x \in \mathbb{R}^n$. Moreover, $f * g$ is a continuous function and it* **vanishes at infinity,** *i.e.,*

$$\lim_{|x| \to \infty} |(f * g)(x)| = 0.$$

(v) *If $f, g \in L_1(\mathbb{R}^n)$, then $(f * g)(x)$ exists for a.e. x, and $f * g \in L_1(\mathbb{R}^n)$ with*

$$\|f * g\|_1 \le \|f\|_1 \|g\|_1.$$

Proof: (i) Let $(f * g)(x)$ exist, i.e.,

$$\int |f(x - y)|\, |g(y)| d\lambda_n(y) < +\infty.$$

Since

$$(f * g)(x) = \int f(x - y) g(y) d\lambda_n(y),$$

making a change of the variables, y to $y + x$ followed by y to $-y$, and using exercise 7.5.3, we have

$$(f * g)(x) = \int f(x) g(x - y) d\lambda_n(y) = (g * f)(x).$$

(ii) Since g is bounded a.e., there exist a set N and a real number $M \ge 0$ such that $\mu(N) = 0$ and $|g(x)| \le M\ \forall\ x \in N^c$. Then $\forall\ x \in \mathbb{R}^n$,

$$
\begin{aligned}
\int |f(x - y)|\, |g(y)| d\lambda_n(y) &= \int_{N^c} |f(x - y)|\, |g(y)| d\lambda_n(y) \\
&\le M \int |f(x - y)| d\lambda_n(y) \\
&= M\|f\|_1 < +\infty.
\end{aligned}
$$

Hence $(f * g)(x)$ exists and $|(f * g)(x)| \le M\|f\|_1,\ \forall\ x \in \mathbb{R}^n$. Thus it is a bounded function. For $x, z \in \mathbb{R}$,

$$
\begin{aligned}
|(f * g)(x) - (f * g)(z)| &\le \int_{N^c} |f(x - y) - f(z - y)|\, |g(y)|\, d\lambda_n(y) \\
&\le M \int |f(x - y) - f(z - y)|\, d\lambda_n(y) \\
&= M\|f_{x-z} - f\|_1.
\end{aligned}
$$

Further, given $\epsilon > 0$, if we choose $\delta > 0$ by corollary 8.6.3 such that

$$|x - z| < \delta \text{ implies } \|f_{x-z} - f\| < \epsilon/M,$$

then

$$|(f * g)(x) - (f * g)(z)| < \epsilon \text{ whenever } |x - z| < \epsilon.$$

This proves (ii).

(iii) Let $f, g \in C_c(\mathbb{R}^n)$. Let

$$K_1 := \operatorname{supp}(f) \quad \text{and} \quad K_2 := \operatorname{supp}(g).$$

Then $f(x-y) = 0 \ \forall \ (x-y) \notin K_1$ and $g(y) = 0 \ \forall \ y \notin K_2$. Thus $f(x-y)g(y) = 0$ whenever either $y \notin K_2$ or $x \notin K_1 + y$. Hence

$$(f * g)(x) = 0 \ \text{if} \ x \notin (K_1 + K_2), \ \text{i.e.,} \ \operatorname{supp}(f + g) \subseteq (K_1 + K_2).$$

That $f * g$ is continuous follows from (ii), since f, g are bounded and $f, g \in L_1(\mathbb{R}^n)$.

(iv) Let $1 < p, q < \infty$ with $1/p + 1/q = 1$. Let $f \in L_p(\mathbb{R}^n)$ and $g \in L_q(\mathbb{R}^n)$. Using Hölder's inequality, we have for every x,

$$\int |f(x - y)| \, |g(y)| d\lambda_n(y) \ \leq \ \|f_y\|_p \|g\|_q = \|f\|_p \|g\|_q \ < \ +\infty.$$

Hence $(f * g)(x)$ exists for every $x \in \mathbb{R}^n$, and

$$|(f * g)(x)| \ \leq \ \|f\|_p \|g\|_q.$$

Thus $f * g$ is a bounded function. To show that $f * g$ is continuous and vanishes at ∞, we first show that $f * g$ is a uniform limit of a sequence from $C_c(\mathbb{R}^n)$. For this, since $f \in L_p(\mathbb{R}^n)$ and $g \in L_q(\mathbb{R}^n)$, by theorem 8.6.2 we can choose sequences $\{f_k\}_{k \geq 1}$ and $\{g_k\}_{k \geq 1}$ in $C_c(\mathbb{R}^n)$ such that

$$\|f_k - f\|_p \longrightarrow 0 \quad \text{and} \quad \|g_k - g\|_q \longrightarrow 0.$$

By (iii), $f_k * g_k \in C_c(\mathbb{R}^n) \ \forall \ k$, and by Hölder's inequality we have $\forall \ x \in \mathbb{R}^n$,

$$\begin{aligned}
|(f_k * g_k)(x) - (f * g)(x)| & \\
\leq \ |(f_k * g_k)(x) - (f_k * g)(x)| &+ |(f_k * g)(x) - (f * g)(x)| \\
\leq \ \int |f_k(x - y)| \, |(g_k - g)(y)| d\lambda_n(y) & \\
+ \int |(f_k - f)(x - y)| & \, |g(y)| d\lambda_n(y) \\
\leq \ \|f_k\|_p \|g_k - g\|_q &+ \|f_k - f\|_p \|g\|_q.
\end{aligned}$$

From this it follows that $\{(f_k * g_k)\}_{n \geq 1}$ converges uniformly to $f * g$. Thus $f * g$ is continuous. Further, let $\epsilon > 0$ be given. Choose k such that $\forall \ x \in \mathbb{R}^n$

$$\sup_{x \in \mathbb{R}^n} |(f_k * g_k)(x) - (f * g)(x)| \ < \ \epsilon.$$

Let $M > 0$ be such that $(f_k * g_k)(x) = 0 \ \forall \ x \in \mathbb{R}^n$ with $|x| > M$. Then for such x,

$$\begin{aligned}
|(f * g)(x)| &\leq \ |(f_k * g_k)(x) - (f * g)(x)| + |(f_k * g)(x)| \\
&= \ |(f_k * g_k)(x) - (f * g)(x)| \\
&\leq \ \sup_{x \in \mathbb{R}^n} |(f_k * g_k)(x) - (f * g)(x)| \ \leq \ \epsilon.
\end{aligned}$$

Hence $\lim\limits_{|x|\to\infty} |(f * g)(x)| = 0$, i.e., $f * g$ vanishes at ∞.

(v) Let $f, g \in L_1(\mathbb{R}^n)$. Consider the function

$$(f, g)(x, y) := f(x)g(y), \quad (x, y) \in (\mathbb{R}^n \times \mathbb{R}^n).$$

Clearly $(f, g) \in L_2(\mathbb{R}^{2n})$. Thus using Fubini's theorem we get

$$
\begin{aligned}
\|f\|_1 \|g\|_1 &= \left(\int |f(x)| d\lambda_n(x) \right) \left(\int |g(y)| d\lambda_n(y) \right) \\
&= \int \left(\int |f(x-y)| \, |g(y)| d\lambda_n(x) \right) d\lambda_n(y) \\
&= \iint |f(x-y)| \, |g(y)| d\lambda_{2n}(x, y) \\
&< \infty.
\end{aligned}
$$

Hence it follows from exercise 5.4.2 (ii) that

$$\int |f(x-y)| \, |g(y)| d\lambda_n(y) < +\infty \text{ for a.e. } x.$$

Thus $(f * g)(x)$ exists for a.e. x, and

$$\int |(f * g)(x)| d\lambda_n(x) \leq \iint |f(x-y)| \, |g(y)| d\lambda_n(x) d\lambda_n(y) = \|f\|_1 \|g\|_1.$$

Thus $f * g \in L_1(\mathbb{R}^n)$ with $\|f * g\|_1 \leq \|f\|_1 \|g\|_1$. ∎

8.7.5. Exercise: Let $f, g, h \in L_1(\mathbb{R}^n)$. Show that

(i) $f * (g \pm h) = f * g \pm f * h$.

(ii) $f * (g * h) = (f * g) * h$.

8.7.6. Definition: Let f be a measurable function on $\mathbb{R}^n$. We say f is **locally integrable** if f is integrable on every compact subset of $\mathbb{R}^n$.

Let $L_1^{loc}(\mathbb{R}^n)$ denote the space of all locally integrable functions on $\mathbb{R}^n$.

•**8.7.7. Exercise:** Prove the following:

(i) $f \in L_1^{loc}(\mathbb{R}^n)$ iff $\forall \, x \in \mathbb{R}^n \, \exists$ a neighborhood V_x of x such that f is integrable on V_x.

(ii) If $f \in L_p(\mathbb{R}^n)$, then f vanishes at ∞.

(iii) If f is a bounded measurable function on $\mathbb{R}^n$ then $f \in L_1^{loc}(\mathbb{R}^n)$.

8.7.8. Definition: Let U be an open subset of $\mathbb{R}^n$ and let $f : U \longrightarrow \mathbb{R}$. We say that f is a C^∞**-function** on U if f has continuous partial derivatives of all orders at every point of U. We denote the set of all such functions by

$C^\infty(U)$. Let $C_c^\infty(U)$ denote the set of those functions from $C^\infty(U)$ which have compact support.

8.7.9. Example: We have already seen in corollary 5.7.2 that $f : \mathbb{R} \longrightarrow \mathbb{R}$, defined by

$$f(x) := \begin{cases} \exp(1/(x^2 - 1)) & \text{if } |x| < 1, \\ 0 & \text{if } |x| \geq 1, \end{cases}$$

is a C^∞-function on $\mathbb{R}$. In fact, $f \in C_c^\infty(\mathbb{R})$ with $\text{supp}(f) = [-1, +1]$. Consider the function $\phi : \mathbb{R}^n \longrightarrow \mathbb{R}$ defined by

$$\phi(x) := f(|x|), \quad x \in \mathbb{R}^n,$$

where $|x|^2 = (x_1^2 + \cdots + x_n^2)$ for $x = (x_1, \ldots, x_n) \in \mathbb{R}^n$. Clearly, $0 \leq \phi(x) \leq 1$ and $\text{supp}(\phi) = \{x \in \mathbb{R}^n | \, |x| \leq 1\} := \overline{B(0,1)}$. It is easy to check that ϕ is a C^∞-function on $\mathbb{R}^n$.

8.7.10. Theorem: *Let $\phi \in C_c^\infty(\mathbb{R}^n)$ be a nonnegative function such that*

$$\phi(x) = 0 \; \forall \; x \in \mathbb{R}^n \text{ with } |x| > 1, \text{ and } \int \phi(x)d\lambda_n(x) = 1.$$

Let $\epsilon > 0$ be arbitrary and

$$\phi_\epsilon(x) := \epsilon^{-n}\phi(x/\epsilon), \quad x \in \mathbb{R}^n.$$

Then the following are true:

(i) *ϕ_ϵ is a nonnegative C_c^∞-function on $\mathbb{R}^n$ with*

$$\text{supp}(\phi_\epsilon) \subseteq \overline{B(0,\epsilon)} := \{x \in \mathbb{R}^n | \, |x| \leq \epsilon\} \text{ and } \|\phi_\epsilon\|_1 = 1.$$

(ii) *Let $f \in L_1^{loc}(\mathbb{R}^n)$ and $f_\epsilon := \phi_\epsilon * f$. Then $f_\epsilon \in C^\infty(\mathbb{R}^n)$. If f is uniformly continuous, then $f_\epsilon \longrightarrow f$ uniformly as $\epsilon \to 0$.*

(iii) *Let $f \in L_p(\mathbb{R}^n)$ and $f_\epsilon := \phi_\epsilon * f$. Then $f_\epsilon \in L_p(\mathbb{R}^n) \cap C^\infty(\mathbb{R}^n)$ and $f_\epsilon \longrightarrow f$ in L_p.*

The functions f_ϵ are called **regularizations** of f.

Proof: (i) Since ϕ is nonnegative and $\phi \in C_c^\infty(\mathbb{R})$ with $\text{supp}(\phi) \subseteq \overline{B(0,1)}$, clearly ϕ_ϵ is also a nonnegative C_c^∞-function on $\mathbb{R}^n$ with $\text{supp}(\phi_\epsilon) \subseteq \overline{B(0,\epsilon)}$. That $\|\phi_\epsilon\| = 1$ follows from the fact that $\|\phi\|_1 = 1$ and exercise 7.5.3.

(ii) Let $f \in L_1^{loc}(\mathbb{R}^n)$ and $f_\epsilon := \phi_\epsilon * f$. Clearly, f_ϵ is well-defined and

$$\begin{aligned} f_\epsilon(x) - f_\epsilon(y) &= (\phi_\epsilon * f)(x) - (\phi_\epsilon * f)(y) \\ &= \int \phi_\epsilon(x - z)f(z)d\lambda_n(z) - \int \phi_\epsilon(y - z)f(z)d\lambda_n(z) \\ &= \int \left(\phi_\epsilon(x - z) - \phi_\epsilon(y - z) \right) f(z) \, d\lambda_n(z). \end{aligned} \tag{8.11}$$

Since ϕ_ϵ is uniformly continuous with

$$\phi_\epsilon(x-z) - \phi_\epsilon(y-z) = 0 \ \text{ if } \ z \notin \overline{B(x,\epsilon)} \cup \overline{B(y,\epsilon)}$$

and f is integrable on compact sets, it follows from (8.11) that f_ϵ is uniformly continuous. Further, using (8.11) and the dominated convergence theorem, it is easy to show that f_ϵ is a C^∞-function on $\mathbb{R}^n$. In fact, $\forall\, k$

$$\frac{\partial^k f_\epsilon}{\partial x_j^k} = \left(\frac{\partial^k \phi_\epsilon}{\partial x_j^k} \right) * f.$$

Finally, to see that $f_\epsilon \longrightarrow f$ uniformly whenever f is uniformly continuous, we note that

$$
\begin{aligned}
f_\epsilon(x) &= \int \phi_\epsilon(x-y) f(y) d\lambda_n(y) \\
&= \frac{1}{\epsilon^n} \int \left(\frac{\phi(x-y)}{\epsilon} \right) f(y) d\lambda_n(y) \\
&= \int \phi(z) f(x - \epsilon z) d\lambda_n(z).
\end{aligned}
$$

Thus

$$
\begin{aligned}
|f_\epsilon(x) - f(x)| &= |\int f(x - \epsilon z)\phi(z) d\lambda_n(z) - \int f(x)\phi(z) d\lambda_n(z)| \\
&\leq \int |f(x - \epsilon z) - f(x)| \, \phi(z) \, d\lambda_n(z).
\end{aligned}
$$

Since f is uniformly continuous, given $\eta > 0$ we can choose ϵ_0 such that $\forall\, \epsilon < \epsilon_0, |z| \leq 1$ and $\forall\, x \in \mathbb{R}^n$,

$$|f(x - \epsilon z) - f(x)| < \eta.$$

Thus $\forall\, \epsilon < \epsilon_0$ and $\forall\, x$,

$$|f_\epsilon(x) - f(x)| < \eta \int \phi(z) d\lambda_n(z) = \eta.$$

Hence $f_\epsilon \to f$ uniformly.

(iii) Let $f \in L_p(\mathbb{R}^n)$. Then, by exercise 8.7.7 and (ii), $f_\epsilon := \phi_\epsilon * f$ is well defined, and $f_\epsilon \in C^\infty(\mathbb{R}^n)$. To show that $f_\epsilon \in L_p(\mathbb{R}^n)$, we note that

$$
\begin{aligned}
f_\epsilon(x) &= \int f(x - \epsilon z)\phi(z) d\lambda_n(z) \\
&= \int f(x - \epsilon z) d\mu(z),
\end{aligned}
$$

where

$$\mu(E) := \int_E \phi(z) d\lambda_n(z), \ \forall\, E \in \mathcal{L}_{\mathbb{R}^n}.$$

It follows from proposition 5.2.6 that μ is a measure on $\mathcal{L}_{\mathbb{R}^n}$ and $\mu(\mathbb{R}^n) = 1$. Now, using Hölder's inequality, we have

$$f_\epsilon(x) \leq \left(\int |f(x - \epsilon z)|^p d\mu(z) \right)^{1/p} \left(\int 1 d\mu \right)^{1/q},$$

where $q > 1$ is such that $1/p + 1/q = 1$. Since $\mu(\mathbb{R}^n) = 1$, we have

$$
\begin{aligned}
\int |f_\epsilon(x)|^p d\lambda_n(x) &\leq \int \left(\int |f(x - \epsilon z)|^p d\mu(z) \right) d\lambda_n(x) \\
&= \int \left(\int |f(x - \epsilon z)|^p d\lambda_n(x) \right) d\mu(z) \\
&= \int \|f\|_p^p d\mu(z) \\
&= \|f\|_p^p.
\end{aligned}
\tag{8.12}
$$

Hence $f_\epsilon \in L_p(\mathbb{R}^n)$. To show that $f_\epsilon \to f$ in L_p, let $\eta > 0$ be given. Using theorem 8.6.2, choose $g \in C_c(\mathbb{R}^n)$ such that $\|f - g\|_p \leq \eta/3$. Then

$$\|f_\epsilon - f\|_p \leq \|f_\epsilon - g_\epsilon\|_p + \|g_\epsilon - g\|_p + \|g - f\|_p.
\tag{8.13}$$

Also, using (8.12), we have

$$\|g_\epsilon - f_\epsilon\|_p = \|(g - f)_\epsilon\|_p \leq \|g - f\|_p.$$

Further, since g is uniformly continuous, (i) implies that $g_\epsilon \to g$ uniformly. Since $\mathrm{supp}(g_\epsilon) \subseteq \mathrm{supp}(g) \cup \overline{B(0, \epsilon)}$, it follows that $g_\epsilon \to g$ in L_p also. Hence

$$\|g_\epsilon - g\|_p < \eta/3 \quad \text{for all sufficiently small } \epsilon.$$

From this and (8.13), it follows that for all sufficiently small $\epsilon > 0$ we have $\|f_\epsilon - f\|_p < \eta$, i.e., $f_n \to f$ in L_p. ∎

8.7.11. Corollary: *The space $C_c^\infty(\mathbb{R}^n)$ is dense in $L_p(\mathbb{R}^n)$.*

Proof: Let $f \in L_p(\mathbb{R}^n)$ and let $\epsilon > 0$ be given. Then using Lebesgue's dominated convergence theorem, we can choose a positive integer k such that

$$\|f - \chi_{B(0,k)} f\|_p < \epsilon/2.
\tag{8.14}$$

Since $\chi_{B(0,k)} f \in L_p(\mathbb{R}^n)$ and has compact support, we can choose $\epsilon > 0$ such that $(\chi_{B(0,k)} f)_\epsilon \in C_c^\infty(\mathbb{R}^n)$ and

$$\|(\chi_{B(0,k)} f)_\epsilon - \chi_{B(0,k)} f\|_p < \epsilon/2.
\tag{8.15}$$

Hence for $g := (\chi_{B(0,k)} f)_\epsilon \in C_c^\infty(\mathbb{R}^n)$, it follows from (8.14) and (8.15) that $\|f - g\|_p < \epsilon$. ∎

In view of theorem 8.7.10, it is natural to ask the question: For $x \in \mathbb{R}^n$ and f a locally integrable function, when does $f_\epsilon(x) = (f * \phi_\epsilon)(x) \longrightarrow f(x)$? Since $\int \phi_\epsilon(y) d\lambda_n(y) = 1$, we have

$$
\begin{aligned}
| f_\epsilon(x) - f(x) | &= | (\phi_\epsilon * f)(x) - f(x) | \\
&= \left| \int \phi_\epsilon(x - y) f(y) d\lambda_n(y) - f(x) \right| \\
&= \left| \int \phi_\epsilon(x - y)(f(y) - f(x)) d\lambda_n(y) \right| \\
&\leq (1/\epsilon^n) \int \phi\left(\frac{x - y}{\epsilon}\right) | f(y) - f(x) | \, d\lambda_n(y) \\
&\leq (1/\epsilon^n) \left(\sup_{y \in \overline{B(x,1)}} |\phi(y)| \right) \int_{\overline{B(x,\epsilon)}} |f(y) - f(x)| \, d\lambda_n(y).
\end{aligned}
$$

In case $n = 1$, the above inequality is

$$
|f_\epsilon(x) - f(x)| \leq (1/\epsilon) \left(\sup_{y \in \overline{B(x,1)}} |\phi(y)| \right) \int_{x-\epsilon}^{x+\epsilon} |f(y) - f(x)| \, d\lambda(y).
$$

Thus if $x \in \mathbb{R}$ is such that $\lim_{\epsilon \to 0} (1/\epsilon) \int_{x-\epsilon}^{x+\epsilon} |f(y) - f(x)| d\lambda(y) = 0$, we will have $f_\epsilon(x) \longrightarrow f(x)$. Such points are the Lebesgue points of f. Since almost every point of $\mathbb{R}$ is a Lebesgue point for $f \in L_1(\mathbb{R})$ (see theorem 6.3.2), we have the following:

8.7.12. Corollary: *If $f \in L_1(\mathbb{R})$, then*

$$
f_\epsilon(x) := (\phi_\epsilon * f)(x) \longrightarrow f(x) \text{ for a.e. } x(\lambda).
$$

8.7.13. Note: Corollary 8.7.12 is also true for $f \in L_1(\mathbb{R}^n)$. See note 9.2.12.

8.7.14. Note: Let X be a Banach space over $\mathbb{R}$ (or $\mathbb{C}$) under the norm $\|\cdot\|$. One calls X a **Banach algebra** if there exists a binary operation, referred to as multiplication, from $X \times X$ to X, denoted by $(x, y) \longmapsto xy$, such that for $x, y, z \in X$ and $\alpha \in \mathbb{R}$ (or $\mathbb{C}$), the following hold:

(i) $x(yz) = (xy)z$.

(ii) $x(y + z) = xy + xz; (y + z)x = yx + zx$.

(iii) $\alpha(xy) = (\alpha x)y = x(\alpha y)$.

(iv) $\|xy\| \leq \|x\| \, \|y\|$.

A Banach algebra X is said to be **commutative** if the multiplication on X is commutative, i.e., $xy = yx \; \forall \; x, y \in X$. We say X is a **Banach algebra with identity** if it is a Banach algebra and there exists some element $e \in X$ such that $ex = xe = x, \; \forall \; x \in X$. If we consider the Banach space $L_1(\mathbb{R}^n)$ over $\mathbb{C}$ with convolution of functions as multiplication, then it follows from theorem 8.7.4 and exercise 8.7.5 that $L_1(\mathbb{R}^n)$ is a commutative Banach algebra. It is easy to show that $L_1(\mathbb{R}^n)$ *is a Banach algebra without identity*, i.e., there does not exist any $g \in L_1(\mathbb{R}^n)$ such that $g * f = f$ for every $f \in L_1(\mathbb{R}^n)$. For example if $n = 1$, suppose that for some $g \in L_1(\mathbb{R})$ we have $g * f = f$, $\forall\, f \in L_1(\mathbb{R})$. Choose any real number $\delta > 0$ such that

$$\int_{-2\delta}^{+2\delta} |g(x)| d\lambda(x) < 1,$$

which is possible by proposition 5.4.6(iii). Let $f = \chi_{[-\delta,\delta]}$. Then $f \in L_1(\mathbb{R})$ and $\forall\, x \in \mathbb{R}$,

$$f(x) = (g * f)(x) = \int_{x-\delta}^{x+\delta} g(t) d\lambda(t).$$

In particular, for $x \in [-\delta, +\delta]$, $1 = f(x) = (g * f)(x)$. Thus

$$1 = \left| \int_{x-\delta}^{x+\delta} g(t) d\lambda(t) \right| \le \int_{x-\delta}^{x+\delta} |g(t)| d\lambda(t) \le \int_{-2\delta}^{2\delta} |g(t)| d\lambda(t) < 1,$$

which is a contradiction. Hence $L_1(\mathbb{R})$ is a commutative Banach algebra without identity. A family of functions $\{f_\epsilon\}_{\epsilon > 0}$ in $L_1(\mathbb{R}^n)$ is called an **approximate identity** if it has the following properties:

(i) Each f_ϵ is nonnegative.

(ii) For each $\epsilon > 0$, $\|f_\epsilon\| = 1$.

(iii) For every neighborhood V of $0 \in \mathbb{R}^n$, $\lim_{\epsilon \to 0} \int_V f_\epsilon(x) d\lambda_n(x) = 0$.

An obvious example of an approximate identity for $L_1(\mathbb{R}^n)$ is given by the following. Let

$$f_\epsilon := \left(\frac{1}{\lambda(B(0, \epsilon))} \right) \chi_{B(0,\epsilon)}, \quad \epsilon > 0.$$

Example 8.7.9 and the functions $\phi_\epsilon, \epsilon > 0$, as defined in theorem 8.7.10 tell us that $L_1(\mathbb{R}^n)$ has an approximate identity from $C_c^\infty(\mathbb{R}^n)$. Approximate identities are useful because of their properties as given in theorem 8.7.10 and corollary 8.7.12.

8.8. $L_\infty(X, \mathcal{S}, \mu)$: The space of essentially bounded functions

8.8.1. Definition: A measurable function $f : X \longrightarrow \mathbb{R}^*$ or $\mathbb{C}$ is said to be **essentially bounded** if there exists some real number M such that $\mu(\{x \in X \,|\, |f(x)| > M\}) = 0$.

We denote by $L_\infty(X, \mathcal{S}, \mu)$ the set of all essentially bounded functions. For $f \in L_\infty(X, \mathcal{S}, \mu)$ define

$$\|f\|_\infty := \inf \{M \,|\, \mu\{x \in X \,|\, |f(x)| > M\} = 0\}.$$

We call $\|f\|_\infty$ the **essential supremum** of f.

8.8.2. Theorem: *Let $f, g \in L_\infty(X, \mathcal{S}, \mu)$ and let α, β be scalars. Then the following hold:*

(i) *$\alpha f \in L_\infty(X, \mathcal{S}, \mu)$ and*

$$\|\alpha f\|_\infty = |\alpha| \, \|f\|_\infty.$$

(ii) *$(f + g) \in L_\infty(X, \mathcal{B}, \mu)$ and*

$$\|f + g\|_\infty \leq \|f\|_\infty + \|g\|_\infty.$$

(iii) *$\|f\|_\infty = 0$ iff $f(x) = 0$ a.e. $x(\mu)$.*

(iv) *There exists a set $E \in \mathcal{S}$ such that $\mu(E) = 0$ and*

$$\|f\|_\infty = \sup_{x \in X \setminus E} |f(x)|.$$

Thus $\mu(\{x \in X \mid |f(x)| > \|f\|_\infty\}) = 0$.

(v) *$\|f\|_\infty = \sup\{N \mid \mu(\{x \in X \mid |f(x)| > N\}) > 0\}$.*

Proof: (i) Since $\forall \, M \in \mathbb{R}$ and α a scalar,

$$\{x \in X \mid |f(x)| > M\} = \{x \in X \mid |(\alpha f)(x)| > M|\alpha|\},$$

it is easy to see that $(\alpha f) \in L_\infty(X, \mathcal{B}, \mu)$ for every $f \in L_\infty(X, \mathcal{B}, \mu)$ and

$$\|\alpha f\|_\infty = |\alpha| \, \|f\|_\infty.$$

(ii) Let $f, g \in L_\infty(X, \mathcal{B}, \mu)$ and let $\epsilon > 0$ be arbitrary. We can choose $M_1, M_2 \in \mathbb{R}$ such that

$$\mu(\{x \in X \mid |f(x)| > M_1\}) = 0 \quad \text{with} \quad \|f\|_\infty > M_1 - \epsilon/2$$

and

$$\mu(\{x \in X \mid |g(x)| > M_2\}) = 0 \quad \text{with} \quad \|g\|_\infty > M_2 - \epsilon/2.$$

Let

$$E_1 := \{x \in X \mid |f(x)| > M_1\} \quad \text{and} \quad E_2 := \{x \in X \mid |g(x)| > M_2\}.$$

Then $\mu(E_1 \cup E_2) = 0$ and, for $x \notin E_1 \cup E_2$,

$$|f(x) + g(x)| \leq |f(x)| + |g(x)| \leq M_1 + M_2.$$

Thus

$$\{x \in X \mid |f(x) + g(x)| > (M_1 + M_2)\} \subseteq E_1 \cup E_2,$$

and hence

$$\mu(\{x \in X \mid |f(x) + g(x)| > (M_1 + M_2)\}) = 0.$$

Further,

$$\|f + g\|_\infty \leq M_1 + M_2 \leq \|f\|_\infty + \|g\|_\infty + \epsilon.$$

Since $\epsilon > 0$ is arbitrary, we have

$$\|f + g\|_\infty \leq \|f\|_\infty + \|g\|_\infty.$$

This proves (ii). The proof of (iii) is easy. To prove (iv), let

$$E := \{x \in X \mid |f(x)| > \|f\|_\infty\}.$$

Then

$$E = \bigcup_{n=1}^\infty \{x \in X \mid |f(x)| > (\|f\|_\infty + 1/n)\}.$$

By definition of $\|f\|_\infty$, for every $n \geq 1$ we can find an $M_n > 0$ such that

$$\|f\|_\infty \leq M_n < \|f\|_\infty + 1/n \quad \text{and} \quad \mu(\{x \in X \mid |f(x)| > M_n\}) = 0.$$

Thus for every $n \geq 1$,

$$\mu(\{x \in X \mid |f(x)| > \|f\|_\infty + 1/n\}) = 0$$

and hence $\mu(E) = 0$. Define

$$f^*(x) := \begin{cases} f(x) & \text{if } x \notin E, \\ 0 & \text{if } x \in E. \end{cases}$$

Since $f^*(x) = f(x)$ for a.e. $x(\mu)$, we have

$$\|f\|_\infty = \|f^*\|_\infty = \sup_{x \in X} |f^*(x)| = \sup_{x \in X \setminus E} |f(x)|.$$

This proves (iv).

To prove (v), note that if N is such that $\mu(\{x \in X \mid |f(x)| > N\}) > 0$, then $N \leq \|f\|_\infty$. For if not, then we will have by (iv), for a.e. x,

$$|f(x)| \leq \|f\|_\infty \leq N,$$

which is not true. Hence

$$\alpha := \sup\{N \mid \mu\{x \in X \mid |f(x)| > N\} > 0\} \leq \|f\|_\infty.$$

On the other hand, clearly

$$\mu(\{x \in X \mid |f(x)| > \|f\|_\infty\}) = \mu(X) > 0.$$

Thus $\alpha \geq \|f\|_\infty$ also. This proves (v). ∎

8.8.3. Corollary: *For $f, g \in L_\infty(X, \mathcal{S}, \mu)$, let*

$$d_\infty(f, g) := \|f - g\|_\infty.$$

Then for $f, g, h \in L_\infty(X, \mathcal{S}, \mu)$, the following hold:

(i) *$d_\infty(f, g) \geq 0$, and $= 0$ iff $f(x) = g(x)$ for a.e. $x(\mu)$.*

(ii) *$d_\infty(f, g) \leq d_\infty(f, h) + d_\infty(h, g)$.*

(iii) *If $\{f_n\}_{n \geq 1}$ is a sequence in $L_\infty(X, \mathcal{S}, \mu)$, then $d_\infty(f_n, f) \to 0$ as $n \to \infty$ iff $f_n \to f$ uniformly a.e.*

(iv) *If $\{f_n\}_{n\geq 1}$ is a Cauchy sequence in $L_\infty(X,\mathcal{S},\mu)$, i.e., $d_\infty(f_n,f_m) \to 0$ as $n,m \to \infty$, then $\exists\, h \in L_\infty(X,\mathcal{S},\mu)$ such that $d_\infty(f_n,h) \to 0$ as $n \to \infty$.*

Proof: (i) and (ii) are easy. To prove (iii), let $d_\infty(f_n,f) \to 0$ as $n \to \infty$. Then by theorem 8.8.2(iv), there exists $E_n \in \mathcal{S}$ such that $\mu(E_n) = 0$ and

$$\|f_n - f\|_\infty = \sup_{x \in X \setminus E_n} |f_n(x) - f(x)|.$$

Let $E = \bigcup_{n=1}^\infty E_n$. Then $\mu(E) = 0$ and $\forall\, x \notin E$,

$$|f_n(x) - f(x)| \leq \sup_{x \in X \setminus E_n} |f_n(x) - f(x)| = \|f_n - f\|_\infty.$$

Hence $f_n \to f$ uniformly on $X \setminus E$.

Conversely, if $f_n \to f$ uniformly a.e., let $A \in \mathcal{S}$ be the set such that $\mu(A) = 0$ and $f_n \to f$ uniformly on A^c. Then, given $\epsilon > 0$, $\exists\, n_0$ such that $\forall\, x \notin A$ and $n \geq n_0$, $|f_n(x) - f(x)| \leq \epsilon$. Thus $\forall\, n \geq n_0$,

$$\{x \in X \mid |f_n(x) - f(x)| > \epsilon\} \subseteq X \setminus A.$$

Hence $\mu(\{x \in X \mid |f_n(y) - f(x)| > \epsilon\}) = 0$. Thus $\|f_n - f\|_\infty < \epsilon\ \forall\, n \geq n_0$, i.e., $d_\infty(f_n,f) \to 0$.

(iv) Let $d_\infty(f_n,f_m) \to 0$ as $n,m \to \infty$. By theorem 8.8.2(iv), $\exists\, E_n$, $E_{n,m} \in \mathcal{S}$ such that $\mu(E_n) = 0$ and $\mu(E_{n,m}) = 0$ with

$$\|f_n - f_m\|_\infty = \sup_{x \in X \setminus E_{n,m}} |f_n(x) - f_m(x)|$$

and

$$\|f_n\|_\infty = \sup_{x \in X \setminus E_n} |f_n(x)|.$$

Put

$$E := \left(\bigcup_{n=1}^\infty E_n\right) \cup \left(\bigcup_{k,m=1}^\infty E_{k,m}\right).$$

Then $\mu(E) = 0$, and $\{f_n\}_{n\geq 1}$ is uniformly Cauchy on $X \setminus E$. Thus there is a measurable function h such that $f_n \to h$ uniformly on $X \setminus E$. We first show that h is bounded on $X \setminus E$. Note that $\forall\, x \in X \setminus E$,

$$|h(x)| \leq |f_n(x) - h(x)| + |f_n(x)|.$$

Thus

$$\sup_{X \setminus E} |h(x)| \leq \sup_{X \setminus E} |f_n(x) - h(x)| + \|f_n\|_\infty.$$

Since $f_n \to h$ uniformly on E and $d_\infty(f_n, f_m) \to 0$, it is easy to see that both terms on the right hand side of the above equality are bounded for all n sufficiently large. Finally, if we define $h(x) = 0$ on E, then $h \in L_\infty$. Since

$$\|f_n - h\|_\infty \leq \sup_{x \in X \setminus E} |f_n(x) - h(x)|,$$

it follows that $d_\infty(f_n, h) \to 0$. ∎

8.8.4. Remarks:

(i) For $f, g \in L_\infty(X, \mathcal{S}, \mu)$, let us write

$$f \sim g \text{ if } f(x) = g(x) \text{ for a.e. } x(\mu).$$

Then '$\sim$' is an equivalence relation. We denote the set of equivalence classes by $L_\infty(X, \mathcal{B}, \mu)$ itself. For any element $f \in L_\infty(X, \mathcal{S}, \mu)$, which is in fact an equivalence class, we can define $\|f\|_\infty$ by choosing any element in the equivalence class f. Then $\|f\|_\infty$ is well-defined, and $L_\infty(X, \mathcal{S}, \mu)$ is a Banach space under this norm.

(ii) We showed in theorem 8.5.1 that for $f_n, f \in L_p(X, \mathcal{S}, \mu)$, where $1 \leq p < \infty$ and $n = 1, 2, \ldots$, then $d_p(f_n, f) \to 0$ whenever $f_n \to f$ a.e. and $\|f_n\|_p \to \|f\|_p$. The corresponding result is false in $L_\infty(X, \mathcal{S}, \mu)$. For example, consider $L_\infty([0,1], \mathcal{L}_{[0,1]}, \lambda), f_n := \chi_{(1/n, 1)}, n = 1, 2, \ldots$. Then $f_n \to f \equiv 1$ and $\|f_n\|_\infty = 1 = \|f\|_\infty$. However, $\{f_n\}_{n \geq 1}$ cannot converge to f, for $\|f_n - f\|_\infty = 1 \ \forall \ n$.

(iii) In theorem 8.6.2, we showed that $C_c(\mathbb{R}^n)$ is dense in $L_p(\mathbb{R}^n)$ for $1 \leq p < \infty$. This is not true for $L_\infty(\mathbb{R}^n)$. The reason for this is simple. Note that for $f \in C_c(\mathbb{R}^n), \|f\|_\infty = \sup_{x \in \mathbb{R}^n} |f(x)|$. Thus if $C_c(\mathbb{R}^n)$ were dense in $L_\infty(\mathbb{R}^n)$, then every function in $L_\infty(\mathbb{R}^n)$ would become continuous, which is obviously not true. The closure of $C_c(\mathbb{R}^n)$ in the $L_\infty(\mathbb{R}^n)$ topology is $C_0(\mathbb{R}^n)$, the space of continuous functions vanishing at infinity. (See theorem 8.7.4(iv) for the definition of a function vanishing at infinity.)

8.8.5. Exercise: Let $f \in L_\infty(X, \mathcal{S}, \mu)$, where $(X, \mathcal{S}, \mu)$ is a finite measure space. Prove the following statements:

(i) For $1 \leq p < \infty, f \in L_p(X, \mathcal{S}, \mu)$ and $\|f\|_p \leq \|f\|_\infty (\mu(X))^{1/p}$.

(ii) If $N > 0$ is such that $\mu(\{x \in X | |f(x)| > N\}) > 0$, show that

$$N(\mu(X))^{1/p} \leq \|f\|_p.$$

(iii) Let $\{p_n\}_{n \geq 1}$ be any monotonically increasing sequence of real numbers such that $p_n \geq 1 \ \forall \ n$ and $\{p_n\}_{n \geq 1}$ is not bounded above. Using (i), (ii) above and theorem 8.8.2(v), show that

$$\|f\|_\infty = \lim_{n \to \infty} \|f\|_{p_n}.$$

8.9. $L_2(X, \mathcal{S}, \mu)$: The space of square integrable functions

The reason for analyzing the space $L_2(X, \mathcal{S}, \mu)$ in detail is the following. We have already seen in sections 8.4 and 8.8 that for $1 \leq p \leq \infty$, the spaces $L_p(X, \mathcal{S}, \mu)$ are linear spaces and have a notion of distance (norm) under which they are complete. Let us recall, for $f \in L_2(X, \mathcal{S}, \mu)$, that

$$\|f\|_2 := \left(\int |f(x)|^2 d\mu(x) \right)^{1/2}.$$

If we treat $f \in L_2(X, \mathcal{S}, \mu)$ as a 'vector' with uncountable components, $f(x)$ being the xth component, $x \in X$, then $\|f\|_2$ can be viewed as a generalization of the Euclidean magnitude of a vector in $\mathbb{R}^n$ with summation being replaced by integration. We recall that on $\mathbb{R}^n$, we have the notion of dot product of vectors, which is related to the magnitude of vectors and helps us to define the notion of angles on $\mathbb{R}^n$. That such a dot product can also be defined on $L_2(X, \mathcal{S}, \mu)$ and enables one to do geometry on $L_2(X, \mathcal{S}, \mu)$, is the reason we discuss this space in detail.

8.9.1. Definition: For $f, g \in L_2(X, \mathcal{S}, \mu)$, we define

$$\langle f, g \rangle := \int f(x)\, \overline{g}(x)\, d\mu(x),$$

whenever it exists, where $\overline{g}$ denote the complex conjugate function: $\overline{g}(x) := \overline{g(x)}\ \forall\, x \in X$.

8.9.2. Proposition (Cauchy-Schwarz inequality): *For every* $f, g \in L_2(X, \mathcal{S}, \mu)$, $\langle f, g \rangle$ *is a well-defined scalar and*

$$|\langle f, g \rangle| \leq \|f\|_2 \|g\|_2.$$

The scalar $\langle f, g \rangle$ is called the **inner product** of f and g.

Proof: It follows from Hölder's inequality (8.4.6) with $p = q = 2$. ∎

8.9.3. Proposition: *For* $f, g, h \in L_2(X, \mathcal{S}, \mu)$ *and* $\alpha, \beta \in \mathbb{C}$, *the following hold:*

    (i) $\langle f, f \rangle \geq 0$, *and equality holds iff* $f = 0$.

    (ii) $\langle f, g \rangle = \overline{\langle g, f \rangle}$.

    (iii) $\langle \alpha f + \beta g, h \rangle = \alpha \langle f, h \rangle + \beta \langle g, h \rangle$.

    (iv) $\langle f, \alpha g + \beta h \rangle = \overline{\alpha} \langle f, g \rangle + \overline{\beta} \langle f, h \rangle$.

    (v) $\|f\|_2 = \langle f, f \rangle^{1/2}$.

Proof: All the statements are easy to check and are left as exercises. ■

8.9.4. Note: In the Cauchy-Schwarz inequality, the equality holds iff $f = \langle f, g \rangle g$, i.e., f and g are linearly dependent.

•**8.9.5. Exercise:** Let $\{f_n\}_{n \geq 1}, \{g_n\}_{n \geq 1}$ be sequences in $L_2(X, \mathcal{S}, \mu)$ such that $\lim_{n \to \infty} \|f_n \to f\|_2 = 0$, $\lim_{n \to \infty} \|g_n \to g\|_2 = 0$ for $f, g \in L_2(X, \mathcal{S}, \mu)$. Show that
$$\langle f_n, h \rangle \to \langle f, h \rangle, \langle h, g_n \rangle \to \langle h, g \rangle, \langle f_n, g_n \rangle \to \langle f, g \rangle$$
for every $h \in L_2(X, \mathcal{S}, \mu)$. In other words, the inner product map $\langle \cdot, \cdot \rangle :$ $L_2 \times L_2 \longrightarrow \mathbb{C}$ is continuous in each variable and jointly.

8.9.6. Note: Given an arbitrary vector space H over the field $\mathbb{R}$ (or $\mathbb{C}$), if there is a map $\langle \cdot, \cdot \rangle : H \times H \longrightarrow \mathbb{R}$ (or $\mathbb{C}$) having the properties (i) to (iv) as given in proposition 8.9.3, then it is called an **inner product space**. On every inner product space H, it is easy to show that $\|u\| := \langle u, u \rangle^{1/2}, u \in H$, is indeed a norm on H, called the **norm induced** by the inner product. Further, the Cauchy-Schwarz inequality holds:
$$|\langle u, v \rangle| \leq \|u\| \, \|v\|, \; \forall u, v \in H.$$
This can be proved as follows: For $u \in H$, let $\|u\| = (\langle u, u \rangle)^{1/2}$. If either $u = 0$ or $v = 0$, then clearly $|\langle u, v \rangle| = 0 = \|u\| \, \|v\|$. So, let $u, v \in H$ be such that $u \neq 0$ and $v \neq 0$. Then $\|u\| > 0$ and $\|v\| > 0$. Let $u' = u/\|u\|$ and $v' = v/\|v\|$. Then $\langle u', u' \rangle = 1 = \langle v', v' \rangle$ and
$$\begin{aligned} 0 &\leq \langle u' - \langle u', v' \rangle v', \, u' - \langle u', v' \rangle v' \rangle \\ &= \langle u', u' \rangle + |\langle u', v' \rangle|^2 \langle v', v' \rangle - 2|\langle u', v' \rangle|^2 \\ &= 1 - |\langle u', v' \rangle|^2. \end{aligned}$$
Hence
$$|\langle u', v' \rangle| \leq 1 = \|u'\| \|v'\|,$$
i.e.,
$$|\langle u, v \rangle| \leq \|u\| \|v\|.$$
If H is also complete under the norm induced by the inner product, then H is called a **Hilbert space**. Thus $L_2(X, \mathcal{S}, \mu)$ is an example of a Hilbert space. We shall not go into the general theory of Hilbert spaces. We discuss some results for $L_2(X, \mathcal{S}, \mu)$ which are in fact true, without any change in the arguments, for general Hilbert spaces also.

•**8.9.7. Exercise (Parallelogram identity):** Let $f, g \in L_2(X, \mathcal{S}, \mu)$. Then
$$\|f + g\|_2^2 + \|f - g\|_2^2 = 2\|f\|_2^2 + 2\|g\|_2^2.$$

8.9.8. Definition: Let $f, g \in L_2(X, \mathcal{S}, \mu)$. We say that f and g are **orthogonal**, and write $f \perp g$, if $\langle f, g \rangle = 0$. For a subset S of $L_2(X, \mathcal{B}, \mu)$, we write $f \perp S$ if $\langle f, h \rangle = 0 \ \forall \ h \in S$.

•8.9.9. Exercise:

(i) Let $f \in L_2(X, \mathcal{S}, \mu)$ be such that $f \perp g \ \forall \ g \in L_2(X, \mathcal{S}, \mu)$. What can you conclude about f?

(ii) **Pythagoras identity**: Let $f, g \in L_2(X, \mathcal{S}, \mu)$ and $f \perp g$. Show that

$$\|f + g\|_2^2 = \|f\|_2^2 + \|g\|_2^2.$$

8.9.10. Exercise (Bessel's inequality): Let $f_1, f_2, \ldots, f_n$ be elements of $L_2(X, \mathcal{S}, \mu)$ such that $\|f_i\|_2 = 1 \ \forall \ i$ and $f_i \perp f_j$ for $i \neq j$. Show that

$$\sum_{j=1}^{n} |\langle f, f_j \rangle|^2 \leq \|f\|_2^2.$$

(Hint: Consider $\langle z, z \rangle$, where $z = f - \sum_{j=1}^{n} \langle f, f_j \rangle f_j$.)

8.9.11. Definition: Let S be a nonempty subset of $L_2(X, \mathcal{S}, \mu)$.

(i) We say S is a **subspace** of $L_2(X, \mathcal{S}, \mu)$ if $\ \forall \ \alpha, \beta \in \mathbb{C}$ and $f, g \in L_2(X, \mathcal{B}, \mu)$, we have $\alpha f + \beta g \in S$.

(ii) We say S is a **closed subspace** if it is closed under the $\| \cdot \|_2$ metric, i.e., for every sequence $\{f_n\}_{n \geq 1}$ in S with $\lim_{n \to \infty} \|f_n - f\|_2 = 0$ for some $f \in L_2(X, \mathcal{S}, \mu)$, we have $f \in S$.

•8.9.12. Example: Let $(X, \mathcal{S}, \mu)$ be a (complete) measure space. Let $\mathcal{S}_0$ be a σ-algebra of subsets of X such that $\mathcal{S}_0 \subseteq \mathcal{S}$ and such that $(X, \mathcal{S}_0, \mu)$ is also complete. Let

$$M := \{f \in L_2(X, \mathcal{S}, \mu) \mid f \text{ is } \mathcal{S}_0\text{-measurable}\}.$$

Clearly M is a subspace of $L_2(X, \mathcal{S}, \mu)$. In fact, M is a closed subspace of $L_2(X, \mathcal{S}, \mu)$. To see this, let $\{f_n\}_{n \geq 1}$ be a sequence in M such that $f_n \to f$ in $L_2(X, \mathcal{S}, \mu)$. Then it follows from theorems 8.3.6 and 8.4.14(ii) that there exists a subsequence $\{f_{n_k}\}_{k \geq 1}$ of $\{f_n\}_{n \geq 1}$ such that $f_{n_k} \to f$ a.e. (μ). Since each f_{n_k} is $\mathcal{S}_0$-measurable, it follows that f is also $\mathcal{S}_0$-measurable, i.e., $f \in M$. Hence M is a closed subspace.

8.9.13. Proposition: *Let S be any nonempty subset of $L_2(X, \mathcal{S}, \mu)$ and let*

$$S^\perp := \{g \in L_2(X, \mathcal{S}, \mu) \mid \langle f, g \rangle = 0 \ \forall \ f \in S\}.$$

Then $S^{\perp}$ is a closed subspace of $L_2(X, \mathcal{S}, \mu)$.

The set $S^{\perp}$ is called the **orthogonal complement** of S.

Proof: It is easy to see that $S^{\perp}$ is a subspace of $L_2(X, \mathcal{S}, \mu)$. That $S^{\perp}$ is also closed, follows from exercise 8.9.5. $\blacksquare$

We next prove a result which seems geometrically obvious.

8.9.14. Theorem: *Let $f \in L_2(X, \mathcal{S}, \mu)$, and let S be a closed subspace of $L_2(X, \mathcal{S}, \mu)$. Let*

$$\alpha := \inf \{ \|f - g\|_2 \mid g \in S \}.$$

Then there exists a unique function $f_0 \in S$ such that $\alpha = \|f - f_0\|_2$. Further, if $f \notin S$ then $0 \neq (f - f_0) \perp S$.

Proof: We first prove the uniqueness of f_0. Suppose f_0 and $f_1 \in S$ are such that

$$\|f - f_0\|_2 = \|f - f_1\|_2 = \inf \{ \|f - g\|_2 \mid g \in S \} := \alpha.$$

Since $f_0, f_1 \in S$ and S is a subspace, we have $(f_0 + f_1)/2 \in S$ and thus

$$\alpha \leq \|(f_0 + f_1)/2 - f\|_2 = \|f_0 + f_1 - 2f\|_2 / 2.$$

Also, by the parallelogram identity (exercise 8.9.7),

$$
\begin{aligned}
\|f_1 - f_0\|_2^2 &= \|(f_1 - f) - (f_0 - f)\|_2^2 \\
&= 2\|f_1 - f\|_2^2 + 2\|f - f_0\|_2^2 - \|f_1 + f_0 - 2f\|_2^2 \\
&\leq 2\alpha^2 + 2\alpha^2 - 4\alpha^2 = 0.
\end{aligned}
$$

Hence $\|f_1 - f_0\|_2^2 = 0$, i.e., $f_1 = f_0$ a.e. This proves the uniqueness. To prove the existence, by the definition of α, $\exists \, g_n \in S$ such that

$$\lim_{n \to \infty} \|g_n - f\|_2 = \alpha.$$

Since $(g_n + g_m)/2 \in S \; \forall \, n, m$, we have $\|g_n + g_m\|_2 / 2 \geq \alpha$, and the parallelogram identity gives us

$$
\begin{aligned}
\|g_n - g_m\|_2^2 &= 2\|g_n - f\|_2^2 + 2\|g_m - f\|_2^2 - \|g_n + g_m - 2f\|_2^2 \\
&\leq 2\|g_n - f\|_2^2 + 2\|g_m - f\|_2^2 - 4\alpha^2.
\end{aligned}
$$

Hence $\lim_{n,m \to \infty} \|g_n - g_m\|_2 = 0$. This shows that $\{g_n\}_{n \geq 1}$ is a Cauchy sequence in $L_2(\mu)$. By the completeness of $L_2(\mu)$, there exists $f_0 \in L_2(\mu)$ such that

$$\lim_{n \to \infty} \|g_n - f_0\| = 0.$$

Since S is closed, clearly $f_0 \in S$. Further,

$$\big| \|f_0 - f\|_2 - \|g_n - f\| \big| \leq \|g_n - f_0\|_2.$$

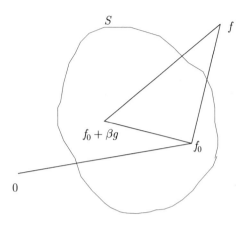

Figure 26

Thus

$$\|f_0 - f\|_2 = \lim_{n \to \infty} \|g_n - f\| = \alpha.$$

Next, suppose $f \notin S$. Then $h := f_0 - f \neq 0$. For every fixed $g \in S$, consider the function

$$\phi(\beta) := \|h + \beta g\|_2^2, \quad \beta \in \mathbb{C}.$$

Clearly, $f_0 + \beta g \in S$, and hence

$$\phi(\beta) = \|h + \beta g\|_2^2 = \|(f_0 + \beta g) - f\|_2^2 \geq \alpha^2,$$

i.e., $\phi(\beta) - \alpha^2 \geq 0$. Since $\alpha^2 = \|h\|^2$, we have

$$
\begin{aligned}
0 \leq \phi(\beta) - \alpha^2 &= \|h + \beta g\|_2^2 - \|h\|^2 \\
&= \overline{\beta}\langle h, g \rangle + \beta\langle g, h \rangle + |\beta|^2\langle g, g \rangle.
\end{aligned}
$$

In particular, if we choose $\beta = t\langle h, g \rangle, t \in \mathbb{R}$, then

$$0 \leq 2t|\langle h, g \rangle|^2 + t^2|\langle h, g \rangle|^2\|g\|_2^2 \ \forall \ t \in \mathbb{R}.$$

The right hand side is a quadratic in t and it has a minimum at $t = 0$. Hence the coefficient of the linear term must be zero, i.e., $\langle h, g \rangle = 0$. Thus $h \perp S$. This proves the theorem completely. ∎

8.9.15. Corollary: *Let S be a proper closed subspace of $L_2(X, \mathcal{B}, \mu)$. Then $S^\perp \neq \{0\}$.*

Next we give two applications of theorem 8.9.14. Our first application says that if S is any closed subspace of $L_2(X, \mathcal{S}, \mu)$, then $L_2(X, \mathcal{S}, \mu) = S + S^\perp := \{f + g | f \in S, g \in S^\perp\}$ with $S \cap S^\perp = \{0\}$.

8.9.16. Theorem: *Let S_1, S_2 be subsets of $L_2(X, \mathcal{S}, \mu)$. Then the following hold:*

(i) *$S_1^\perp$ is a closed subspace of $L_2(X, \mathcal{S}, \mu)$ and $S_1 \cap S_1^\perp \subseteq \{0\}$. If S_1 is also a subspace, then $S_1 \cap S_1^\perp = \{0\}$.*

(ii) *$S_1^\perp \subseteq S_2^\perp$ if $S_2 \subseteq S_1$.*

(iii) *$S_1 \subseteq (S_1^\perp)^\perp$, with equality iff S_1 is a closed subspace of $L_2(X, \mathcal{S}, \mu)$.*

(iv) *If S_1 and S_2 are closed subspaces and $f \perp g \ \forall \ f \in S_1$ and $\forall \ g \in S_2$, then $S_1 + S_2 := \{f + g \mid f \in S_1, g \in S_2\}$ is also a closed subspace.*

(v) *If S_1 is a closed subspace, then $S_1 \cap S_1^\perp = \{0\}$ and $L_2(X, \mathcal{S}, \mu) = S_1 + S_1^\perp$. Thus every $f \in L_2(X, \mathcal{S}, \mu)$ can be uniquely expressed as $f = g + h$, where $g \in S_1$ and $h \in S_1^\perp$.*
    *(This is also expressed as $L_2(X, \mathcal{S}, \mu) = S_1 \oplus S_1^\perp$, and is called the **projection theorem**.)*

Proof: (i) and (ii) are easy to check.

To see (iii), clearly $S_1 \subseteq (S_1^\perp)^\perp$. Suppose S_1 is a closed subspace and $f \in (S_1^\perp)^\perp$. By theorem 8.9.14, $\exists \ f_0 \in S_1$ such that $(f - f_0) \in S^\perp$. Also, $f_0 \in S_1 \subseteq (S_1^\perp)^\perp$ and $f \in (S_1^\perp)^\perp$ imply $(f - f_0) \in (S_1^\perp)^\perp$. Thus $(f - f_0) \in S_1^\perp \cap (S_1^\perp)^\perp = \{0\}$. Hence $f = f_0 \in S_1$. This proves (iii).

To prove (iv), it is easy to see that $S_1 + S_2$ is a subspace of $L_2(X, \mathcal{B}, \mu)$. To show that it is also closed, let $\{f_n\}_{n \geq 1}$ be a sequence in $S_1 + S_2$ such that $\|f_n - f\|_2 \to 0$ as $n \to \infty$ for some $f \in L_2(X, \mathcal{S}, \mu)$. Let $f_n = g_n + h_n$, where $g_n \in S_1$ and $h_n \in S_2 \ \forall \ n$. Since $\langle h_n, g_n \rangle = 0 \ \forall \ n$, by Pythagoras' identity (8.9.9(ii)) we have

$$\|g_n - g_m\|_2^2 + \|h_n - h_m\|_2^2 = \|(g_n + h_n) - (g_m + h_m)\|_2^2.$$

Hence both $\{g_n\}_{n \geq 1}$ and $\{h_n\}_{n \geq 1}$ are Cauchy sequences in $L_2(X, \mathcal{S}, \mu)$. Let $g, h \in L_2(X, \mathcal{S}, \mu)$ be such that

$$\lim_{n \to \infty} \|g_n - g\|_2 = 0 = \lim_{n \to \infty} \|h_n - h\|_2.$$

But then $g \in S_1$ and $h \in S_2$, as both S_1 and S_2 are closed. Also,

$$\|f_n - (g + h)\|_2 \leq \|g_n - g\|_2 + \|h_n - h\|_2.$$

Hence $\lim_{n \to \infty} \|f_n - (g + h)\|_2 = 0$. Thus $f = g + h$. This proves that $S_1 + S_2$ is a closed subspace of $L_2(X, \mathcal{B}, \mu)$.

Finally, to prove (v), let S_1 be a closed subspace. That $S_1 \cap S_1^\perp = \{0\}$ follows from (i). Also, $S_1 + S_1^\perp$ is a closed subspace of $L_2(X, \mathcal{B}, \mu)$. Since

$$S_1 \subseteq (S_1 + S_1^\perp) \text{ and } S_1^\perp \subseteq (S_1 + S_1^\perp),$$

we have

$$(S_1 + S_1^\perp)^\perp \subseteq S_1^\perp \text{ and } (S_1 + S_1^\perp)^\perp \subseteq (S_1^\perp)^\perp = S_1.$$

Thus

$$\{0\} \subseteq (S_1 + S_1^\perp)^\perp \subseteq S_1 \cap S_1^\perp \subseteq \{0\}.$$

Hence $(S_1 + S_1^\perp)^\perp = \{0\}$, and by corollary 8.9.15,

$$S_1 \oplus S_1^\perp = L_2(X, \mathcal{S}, \mu). \blacksquare$$

As our second application of theorem 8.9.14, we characterize all bounded linear functions on L_2, as defined next.

8.9.17. Definition: A map $T : L_2(X, \mathcal{S}, \mu) \longrightarrow \mathbb{C}$ is called a **bounded linear functional** if it has the following properties:

(i) For every $f, g \in L_2(X, \mathcal{S}, \mu)$ and $\alpha, \beta \in \mathbb{C}$,

$$T(\alpha f + \beta g) = \alpha T(f) + \beta T(g).$$

(ii) There exists a real number M such that

$$|T(f)| \leq M\|f\|_2, \ \forall \ f \in L_2(X, \mathcal{S}, \mu).$$

8.9.18. Proposition: *Let* $T : L_2(X, \mathcal{S}, \mu) \longrightarrow \mathbb{C}$ *be such that* $\forall \ f, g \in L_2(X, \mathcal{S}, \mu)$ *and* $\alpha, \beta \in \mathbb{C}$

$$T(\alpha f + \beta g) = \alpha T(f) + \beta T(g).$$

Then the following are equivalent:

(i) *T is bounded, i.e.,* $\exists \ M \in \mathbb{R}$ *such that*

$$|T(f)| \leq M\|f\|_2, \ \forall \ f \in L_2(X, \mathcal{S}, \mu).$$

(ii) *T is continuous.*

(iii) *T is continuous at* $0 \in L_2(X, \mathcal{S}, \mu)$.

Proof: Suppose (i) holds and $f \in L_2(X, \mathcal{S}, \mu)$. Let $\{f_n\}_{n \geq 1}$ be any sequence in $L_2(X, \mathcal{S}, \mu)$ such that $\|f_n - f\|_2 \to 0$ as $n \to \infty$. Then

$$|T(f_n) - T(f)| = |T(f_n - f)| \leq M\|f_n - f\|_2.$$

Thus $\{T(f_n)\}_{n \geq 1}$ converges to $T(f)$, showing that T is continuous (in fact uniformly continuous), i.e., (ii) holds.

Clearly, (ii) $\Rightarrow$ (iii). Finally, let (iii) hold. Then given $\epsilon > 0$, $\exists$ $\delta > 0$ such that $|T(f)| < \epsilon$ $\forall$ $f \in L_2(X, \mathcal{S}, \mu)$ with $\|f\|_2 \leq \delta$. If $g \in L_2(X, \mathcal{B}, \mu)$ is arbitrary and $\|g\|_2 \neq 0$, then

$$\left\| \frac{\delta g}{\|g\|_2} \right\|_2 = \delta.$$

Thus

$$\left| T\left(\frac{\delta g}{\|g\|_2} \right) \right| < \epsilon, \text{ i.e., } |T(g)| < \frac{\epsilon \|g\|_2}{\delta}.$$

Hence (i) holds with $M = \epsilon / \delta$. $\blacksquare$

8.9.19. Example: Let $g \in L_2(X, \mathcal{S}, \mu)$ be fixed. Define the map

$$T_g : L_2(X, \mathcal{B}, \mu) \longrightarrow \mathbb{C}$$

as follows:

$$T_g(f) = \langle f, g \rangle = \int f \bar{g} \, d\mu \ \forall \ f \in L_2(X, \mathcal{S}, \mu).$$

It is easy to see that T_g is linear, i.e.,

$$T_g(\alpha f_1 + \beta f_2) = \alpha T_g(f_1) + \beta T_g(f_2)$$

$\forall \ \alpha, \beta \in \mathbb{C}$ and $f_1, f_2 \in L_2(X, \mathcal{S}, \mu)$. Also, by the Cauchy-Schwarz inequality,

$$|T_g(f)| = |\langle f, g \rangle| \leq \|g\|_2 \|f\|_2.$$

Hence T_g is a bounded linear functional on $L_2(X, \mathcal{S}, \mu)$. We note that $g \in (\mathrm{Ker}(T_g))^{\perp}$, where

$$\mathrm{Ker}(T_g) := \{ f \in L_2(X, \mathcal{B}, \mu) \, | \, T_g(f) = 0 \}.$$

$\mathrm{Ker}(T_g)$ is called the **kernel** of T_g. Our next theorem tell us that every bounded linear functional on $L_2(X, \mathcal{S}, \mu)$ is of this type.

8.9.20. Theorem (Riesz representation): *Let $T : L_2(X, \mathcal{B}, \mu) \longrightarrow \mathbb{C}$ be a bounded linear functional. Then there is a unique $g_0 \in L_2(X, \mathcal{S}, \mu)$ such that*

$$T(f) = \langle f, g_0 \rangle \ \forall \ f \in L_2(X, \mathcal{S}, \mu).$$

Proof: We note that in case there does exist a $g_0 \in L_2(X, \mathcal{S}, \mu)$ such that $T(f) = \langle f, g_0 \rangle \ \forall \ f$, then clearly $g_0 \in (\mathrm{Ker}(T))^{\perp}$, where

$$\mathrm{Ker}(T) := \{ f \in L_2(X, \mathcal{B}, \mu) \, | \, T(f) = 0 \}.$$

So to find g_0, first note that $\mathrm{Ker}(T)$ is a subspace of $L_2(X, \mathcal{S}, \mu)$, because T is linear. Further, since T is continuous, $\mathrm{Ker}(T)$ is in fact a closed subspace of $L_2(X, \mathcal{B}, \mu)$. Now, there are two possibilities. First, $\mathrm{Ker}(T) = L_2(X, \mathcal{S}, \mu)$, i.e., $T(f) = 0 \ \forall \ f \in L_2(X, \mathcal{S}, \mu)$, in which case $T(f) = \langle f, 0 \rangle$, $\forall \ f \in$

$L_2(X, \mathcal{S}, \mu)$. On the other hand, if $T(f) \neq 0$ for some $f \in L_2(X, \mathcal{S}, \mu)$, then $\mathrm{Ker}(T)$ is a proper closed subspace of $L_2(X, \mathcal{S}, \mu)$. Hence $(\mathrm{Ker}(T))^\perp \neq \{0\}$ by corollary 8.9.15. Let $0 \neq g \in (\mathrm{Ker}(T))^\perp$. This g may not be the required g_0, for the required g_0 has to have the property that

$$T(g_0) = \langle g_0, g_0 \rangle.$$

Let $\alpha := T(g)$. Then $\alpha \neq 0$, for otherwise we will have $g \in \mathrm{Ker}(T) \cap (\mathrm{Ker}(T))^\perp = \{0\}$. i.e., $g = 0$.

$$T\left(\frac{\langle g, g \rangle}{\alpha} g\right) = \langle g, g \rangle.$$

Let $g_0 := (\alpha/\langle g, g \rangle)g$. Then $\forall\, \beta \in \mathbb{C}$,

$$T(\beta g) = \beta T(g) = \alpha\beta.$$

Also,

$$\langle \beta g, g_0 \rangle = \beta \langle g, g_0 \rangle = \beta \langle g, \frac{\alpha}{\langle g, g \rangle} g \rangle = \alpha\beta.$$

Hence

$$T(\beta g) = \langle \beta g, g_0 \rangle, \ \forall\, \beta \in \mathbb{C}. \tag{8.16}$$

Also,

$$T(f) = 0 = \langle f, g_0 \rangle, \ \text{if} \ f \in \mathrm{Ker}(T). \tag{8.17}$$

For a general $f \in L_2(X, \mathcal{S}, \mu)$ with $f \notin \mathrm{Ker}(T)$, note that $(f - \beta g) \in \mathrm{Ker}(T)$ iff

$$0 = T(f - \beta g) = T(f) - \beta T(g),$$

i.e.,

$$\beta = \frac{T(g)}{T(f)}.$$

Thus if $f \notin \mathrm{Ker}(T)$, then

$$\left(f - \frac{T(g)}{T(f)} g\right) \in \mathrm{Ker}(T)$$

and hence, by (8.16) and (8.17),

$$\begin{aligned}
T(f) &= T\left(f - \frac{T(g)}{T(f)} g\right) + T\left(\frac{T(g)}{T(f)}(g)\right) \\
&= \left\langle f - \frac{T(g)}{T(f)} g, g_0 \right\rangle + \left\langle \frac{T(g)}{T(f)} g, g_0 \right\rangle \\
&= \langle f, g_0 \rangle.
\end{aligned}$$

The uniqueness of g_0 follows from the fact that if $\langle f, g_0 \rangle = \langle f, g_1 \rangle \ \forall\, f \in L_2(X, \mathcal{S}, \mu)$, then $\langle f, g_0 - g_1 \rangle = 0 \ \forall\, f \in L_2(X, \mathcal{S}, \mu)$. In particular, if we take $f = g_0 - g_1$, then $\|g_0 - g_1\|_2^2 = 0$ and hence $g_0 = g_1$. ∎

8.9.21. Note: In theorem 8.9.16, we showed that, given a closed subspace M of $L_2(X, \mathcal{S}, \mu)$, every element $f \in L_2(X, \mathcal{S}, \mu)$ can be written uniquely as $f = g + h$, where $g \in M$ and $h \in M^{\perp}$. Let us denote g by $P_M(f)$, called the **projection** of f onto M. Geometrically, $P_M(f)$ is the unique best approximator of f in M. The properties of the map $P_M : L_2(X, \mathcal{S}, \mu) \to L_2(X, \mathcal{S}, \mu)$ are given in the next theorem.

8.9.22. Theorem: $P_M : L_2(X, \mathcal{S}, \mu) \to L_2(X, \mathcal{S}, \mu)$, as defined in note 8.9.21 above, has the following properties: $\forall\, f, g \in L_2(X, \mathcal{S}, \mu)$

(i) P_M is linear and $P_M(f) = f$ whenever $f \in M$.

(ii) $f - P_M(f) \in M^{\perp}$.

(iii) $\langle P_M(f), g \rangle = \langle f, P_M(g) \rangle = \langle P_M(f), P_M(g) \rangle$.

(iv) $P_M(P_M(f)) = f$.

(v) $\|f\|_2^2 = \|P_M(f)\|_2^2 + \|f - P_M(f)\|_2^2$.

(vi) P_M is continuous.

Proof: The statements (i) and (ii) follow from the definition of P_M. For $f, g \in L_2(X, \mathcal{S}, \mu)$, using (ii) we have

$$\langle P_M(f), g \rangle = \langle P_M(f), P_M(g) \rangle + \langle P_M(f), g - P_M(g) \rangle$$
$$= \langle P_M(f), P_M(g) \rangle.$$

Similarly,

$$\langle P_M(f), P_M(g) \rangle = \langle f, P_M(g) \rangle = \langle P_M(f), P_M(g) \rangle.$$

Hence (iii) holds. Statement (iv) follows from (i), as $P_M(f) \in M$. Finally, $\forall\, f \in L_2(X, \mathcal{S}, \mu)$, since $P_M(f) \perp (f - P_M(f))$, it follows from exercise 8.9.9 that

$$\|f\|_2^2 = \|P_M(f)\|_2^2 + \|f - P_M(f)\|_2^2.$$

This proves (v). Also it follows from (v) that for $f, g \in L_2(X, \mathcal{S}, \mu)$,

$$\|P_M(f) - P_M(g)\|_2^2 \leq \|f - g\|_2^2,$$

which implies that P_M is continuous (in fact uniformly continuous). ∎

We close this section with an application of theorem 8.9.22. This finds applications in probability theory and statistics.

8.9.23. Theorem (Existence of conditional expectation): *Let* $(X, \mathcal{S}, \mu)$ *be a probability space and let* $\mathcal{S}_0$ *be a* σ-*algebra of subsets of* X *with* $\mathcal{S}_0 \subseteq \mathcal{S}$. *Then for every* $f \in L_2(X, \mathcal{S}, \mu)$ *there exists a function* $\hat{f} \in L_2(X, \mathcal{S}_0, \mu)$ *such that* $\forall\, E \in \mathcal{S}_0$,

$$\int_E f\, d\mu = \int_E \hat{f}\, d\mu.$$

The function $\hat{f}$ is called the **conditional expectation** of g given the sub-σ-algebra $\mathcal{S}_0$.

Proof: Let

$$M_0 := \{f \in L_2(X, \mathcal{S}, \mu) \mid f \text{ is } \mathcal{S}_0\text{-measurable}\}.$$

It follows from example 8.9.12 that M_0 is a closed subspace of $L_2(X, \mathcal{S}, \mu)$. Let $E \in \mathcal{S}_0$. Since $\mu(X) = 1$, $\chi_E \in L_2(X, \mathcal{S}_0, \mu)$. Thus using theorem 8.9.22, we have

$$
\begin{aligned}
\int f d\mu &= \langle f, \chi_E \rangle \\
&= \langle f, P_M(\chi_E) \rangle \\
&= \langle P_M f, \chi_E \rangle \\
&= \int_E P_M(f) d\mu.
\end{aligned}
$$

Thus $\hat{f} := P_M(f)$ is the required function. ∎

8.9.24. Note: In probability theory and statistics, the above theorem (and its generalization as proved in theorem 9.1.18) has great significance. As mentioned in note 3.11.10, a probability space $(X, \mathcal{S}, \mu)$ gives a mathematical model for analyzing a statistical experiment. An observation on X, the space of all 'outcomes' in the experiment, is called a **random variable** in probability theory. Mathematically, it is a measurable function on the measurable space $(X, \mathcal{S})$. Let us consider the problem of 'predicting' a random variable f given the knowledge of another random variable, say ϕ. We note that all the information about the random variable ϕ is contained in $\mathcal{S}_0$, the collection of events defined by $\mathcal{S}_0 := \{\phi^{-1}(E) | E \in \mathcal{B}_{\mathbb{R}}\}$. Clearly $\mathcal{S}_0 \subseteq \mathcal{S}$ and is a σ-algebra of subsets of X. Thus the problem is to predict f given the σ-algebra $\mathcal{S}_0$. In case we assume f is square integrable, i.e., $f \in L_2(X, \mathcal{S}, \mu)$, we want to find $\hat{f} \in L_2(X, \mathcal{S}, \mu)$ such that

$$\|f - \hat{f}\| \leq \|f - g\| \ \forall \ g \in L_2(X, \mathcal{S}_0, \mu).$$

The function $\hat{f}$ is called a **conditional expectation** of f given $\mathcal{S}_0$, and theorem 8.9.23 tells us that such a function exists. A generalization of this is proved in theorem 9.1.18.

8.10. L_2-convergence of Fourier series

As we pointed out in the historical notes (section 1.3), the problem of investigating the convergence of Fourier series motivated mathematicians to look for an extension of the integral concept. It is natural to ask the question: did the extended integral, i.e., the Lebesgue integral, achieve success in this direction? One can say without any doubt that one of the pioneering applications of the Lebesgue integral lies in the study of Fourier series. We shall not go into the general theory of Fourier series, but only prove an important result (the Riesz-Fischer theorem) which has applications in many branches of mathematics, physics and electrical engineering. For the general theory of Fourier series, one can consult Bhatia [4], Carslaw [7], Körner [22], Titchmarch [40] and Zygmund [42].

8.10.1. Definition: For $f \in L_1^r[-\pi, \pi]$, let

$$a_n := \frac{1}{\pi} \int_{-\pi}^{\pi} f(x) \cos nx \, d\lambda(x), \quad n = 0, 1, 2, \ldots,$$

and

$$b_n := \frac{1}{\pi} \int_{-\pi}^{\pi} f(x) \sin nx \, d\lambda(x), \quad n = 1, 2, \ldots.$$

The scalars a_n, b_n are called the **Fourier coefficients** of f, and the series

$$\frac{a_0}{2} + \sum_{n=1}^{\infty} (a_n \cos nx + b_n \sin nx)$$

is called the **Fourier series** of f. Let

$$s_n(x) := \frac{a_0}{2} + \sum_{k=1}^{n} (a_k \cos kx + b_n \sin kx), \quad x \in [-\pi, \pi].$$

The function $s_n(x)$ is called the nth-**partial sum** of the Fourier series of f at x. The main problem analyzed in the theory of Fourier series is the following: when does $\{s_n(x)\}_{n \geq 1}$ converge to $f(x), x \in [-\pi, \pi]$? This is known as the pointwise convergence problem of Fourier series. For $f \in L_1[-\pi, \pi]$ and $x \in [-\pi, \pi]$, if $\lim_{n \to \infty} s_n(x) = f(x)$, we say that f has pointwise representation by its Fourier series at x. The answer to the pointwise convergence problem is not easy, and, given the nature and scope of this text, we shall not go into it. For details one can consult any one of the texts listed above. We state below an important relation between functions and their Fourier coefficients, for a proof of which the reader can check any one of the texts cited above or Hewitt and Stromberg [18].

8.10.2. Theorem (Uniqueness of the Fourier series): *If $f \in L_1^r[-\pi, \pi]$ is such that all its Fourier coefficients are zero, then $f(x) = 0$ for a.e. x, i.e., a function is uniquely determined by its Fourier coefficients.*

Though the pointwise representation of a function $f \in L_1^r[-\pi, \pi]$ by its Fourier series is undeniably of great intrinsic interest, it has its limitations.

First of all, not every function $f \in L_1^r[-\pi, \pi]$ can have a pointwise representation one has to put extra conditions on f to get a pointwise representation.
Secondly, $f \in L_1^r[-\pi, \pi]$ need be defined only a.e. Thus pointwise representation makes sense only a.e. Finally, from the point of view of many applications, pointwise representations have very little utility. Such consideration
motivated mathematicians to look for some other methods of analyzing the
convergence problem. We consider below one such method, namely the convergence of Fourier series in the L_2-metric. For other methods we refer to
the texts cited earlier.

Let $f \in L_2^r[-\pi, \pi]$. Using the Cauchy-Schwarz inequality, it follows that
$f \in L_1^r[-\pi, \pi]$ also. Let a_n, b_n be its Fourier coefficients and let $s_n(x)$ be the
n^{th}-partial sum of the Fourier-series of f. In the terminology of section 8.9,
if we write

$$\phi_k(x) := \cos kx \quad \text{and} \quad \psi_k(x) := \sin kx,$$

then

$$a_k = \langle f, \phi_k \rangle / \pi \quad \text{and} \quad b_k = \langle f, \psi_k \rangle / \pi.$$

8.10.3. Lemma: *For nonnegative integers n and m, the following relations
hold:*

$$\begin{aligned}
\langle \psi_n, \phi_m \rangle &= 0; \\
\langle \psi_n, \psi_m \rangle &= 0 \text{ if } n \neq m \text{ and } = \pi \text{ if } n = m; \\
\langle \phi_n, \phi_m \rangle &= 0 \text{ if } n \neq m \text{ and } = \pi \text{ if } n = m.
\end{aligned}$$

Proof: Exercise. ∎

8.10.4. Theorem (Bessel's inequality): *For $f \in L_2^r[-\pi, \pi]$,*

$$\frac{|a_0|^2}{2} + \sum_{n=1}^{\infty} (|a_n|^2 + |b_n|^2) \leq \frac{1}{\pi} \|f\|_2^2.$$

Proof: Using lemma 8.10.3, it is easy to check that $\forall \, k$,

$$0 \leq \frac{1}{\pi} \|f - s_k\|_2^2 = \frac{1}{\pi} \|f\|_2^2 - \left\{ \frac{|a_0|^2}{2} + \sum_{n=1}^{k} (|a_n|^2 + |b_n|^2) \right\}.$$

Hence

$$\frac{|a_0|^2}{2} + \sum_{n=1}^{\infty} (|a_n|^2 + |b_n|^2) \leq \frac{1}{\pi} \|f\|_2^2. \quad \blacksquare$$

The above theorem has a converse, as given in the next theorem.

8.10.5. Theorem (Riesz-Fischer): *Let* $\{a_n\}_{n\geq 0}$ *and* $\{b_n\}_{n\geq 1}$ *be sequences of real numbers such that*

$$\frac{|a_0|^2}{2} + \sum_{n=1}^{\infty}(|a_n|^2 + |b_n|^2) < +\infty.$$

Then there exists a unique function $f \in L_2^r[-\pi, \pi]$ *such that* a_n, b_n *are its Fourier coefficients.*

Proof: Let us define for $x \in [-\pi, \pi]$

$$g_n(x) := \frac{a_0}{2} + \sum_{k=1}^{n}(a_k \cos kx + b_k \sin kx).$$

Clearly, each $g_n \in L_2^r[-\pi, \pi]$, and using lemma 8.10.3 it is easy to verify that for $n > m$,

$$\frac{1}{\pi}\|g_n - g_m\|_2^2 = \sum_{k=m+1}^{n}(|a_n|^2 + |b_2|^2).$$

Hence $\{g_n\}_{n\geq 1}$ is a Cauchy sequence in $L_2^r[-\pi, \pi]$, and, by the completeness of $L_2^r[-\pi, \pi]$, $\exists f \in L_2^r[-\pi, \pi]$ such that $\|g_n - f\|_2 \longrightarrow 0$. To complete the proof, we show that f has a_n, b_n as Fourier coefficients. First note that for $n > k$,

$$\langle g_n, \phi_k \rangle/\pi = a_k.$$

Also, using exercise 8.9.5, we have

$$\lim_{n\to\infty} \langle g_n, \phi_k \rangle/\pi = \langle f, \phi_k \rangle/\pi.$$

Hence $\langle f, \phi_k \rangle/\pi = a_k$. Similarly, $\langle f, \psi_k \rangle/\pi = b_k$. This proves that f has Fourier coefficients a_n, b_n. Since $f \in L_2^r[-\pi, \pi]$ implies that $f \in L_1^r[-\pi, \pi]$ (see exercise 8.4.12(ii)), the uniqueness of f follows from theorem 8.10.2. ∎

8.10.6. Corollary: *Let* $f \in L_2^r[-\pi, \pi]$. *Then the Fourier series of* f *converges to* f *in the* L_2*-norm, i.e.,* $\|s_n - f\|_2 \longrightarrow 0$ *as* $n \longrightarrow \infty$. *Further,*

$$\frac{1}{\pi}\|f\|_2^2 = \frac{|a_0|^2}{2} + \sum_{n=1}^{\infty}(|a_n|^2 + |b_n|^2).$$

This is called **Parseval's identity**.

Proof: First note that by Bessel's inequality (8.10.4), we have

$$\frac{|a_0|^2}{2} + \sum_{n=1}^{\infty}(|a_n|^2 + |b_n|^2) \leq \frac{1}{\pi}\|f\|_2^2 < +\infty.$$

Thus it follows from theorem 8.10.5 that there is a unique function $g \in L_2^r[-\pi, \pi]$ such that g has Fourier coefficients a_n, b_n and $\|g_n - g\|_2 \longrightarrow 0$ as $n \longrightarrow \infty$, where

$$g_n(x) := a_0/2 + \sum_{k=1}^{n}(a_k \cos kx + b_k \sin kx).$$

By the uniqueness theorem (8.10.2), it follows that $f = g$ and $g_n = s_n$, the nth partial sum of the Fourier series of f. Thus $\|s_n - f\|_2 \longrightarrow 0$ as $n \longrightarrow \infty$. Since

$$| \, \|s_n\|_2 - \|f\|_2 | \leq \|s_n - f\|_2,$$

we get $\|s_n\|_2 \longrightarrow \|f\|_2$ as $n \to \infty$. Since

$$\frac{1}{\pi}\|s_n\|_2^2 = \frac{|a_0|^2}{2} + \sum_{k=1}^{n}(|a_k|^2 + |b_k|^2),$$

it follows that

$$\frac{|a_0|^2}{2} + \sum_{k=1}^{\infty}(|a_k|^2 + |b_k|^2) = \frac{1}{\pi}\|f\|_2^2. \quad \blacksquare$$

8.10.7 Note: A careful observation of the above arguments will tell the reader that Fourier coefficients can be defined for Riemann integrable functions also (as was done historically first), and Bessel's inequality remains valid. However, Riesz-Fischer critically uses the fact that $L_2^r[-\pi, \pi]$ is complete under the L_2-metric, which is not true for Riemann integrable functions.

8.10.8. Corollary (Euler's identity): $\sum_{\ell=1}^{\infty} \frac{1}{(2\ell+1)^2} = \pi^2/8.$

Proof: Consider the function

$$f(x) := \begin{cases} 0 & \text{if } -\pi \leq x < 0, \\ 1 & \text{if } 0 \leq x \leq \pi, \end{cases}$$

and apply Parseval's identity (8.10.6). $\blacksquare$

Chapter 9

The Radon-Nikodym theorem and its applications

9.1. Absolutely continuous measures and the Radon-Nikodym theorem

One of the methods of constructing a new measure from a given measure is the following. Let $(X, \mathcal{S}, \mu)$ be a given measure space and let f be a nonnegative real-valued measurable function on X. For $E \in \mathcal{S}$, define

$$\nu(E) := \int_E f d\mu.$$

It was shown in proposition 5.2.6 that ν is a measure on $(X, \mathcal{S})$. In fact, the measure ν is related to μ by the property that $\nu(E) = 0$ whenever $\mu(E) = 0$ for $E \in \mathcal{S}$. Thus, if ν is obtained from μ via integration, then every μ-null set is also a ν-null set. This motivates the next definition.

9.1.1. Definition: Let μ and ν be two measures on $(X, \mathcal{S})$. We say ν is **absolutely continuous** with respect to μ if $\nu(E) = 0$ whenever $\mu(E) = 0, E \in \mathcal{S}$. We write this as $\nu \ll \mu$.

9.1.2. Examples:

(i) Let $(X, \mathcal{S}, \mu)$ be a measure space and f be a nonnegative measurable function on $(X, \mathcal{S})$. As indicated above, $\nu \ll \mu$, where

$$\nu(E) := \int_E f d\mu, \ E \in \mathcal{S}.$$

(ii) Let μ denote the **counting measure** on the Lebesgue measurable space $(\mathbb{R}, \mathcal{L}_{\mathbb{R}})$, i.e., for $E \in \mathcal{L}_{\mathbb{R}}, \mu(E) :=$ number of elements in E, if E is a finite set, and $\mu(E) := +\infty$ otherwise. Then $\lambda \ll \mu$, where λ is the Lebesgue measure on $(\mathbb{R}, \mathcal{L}_{\mathbb{R}})$.

(iii) Let $X = \mathbb{N}$ and $\mathcal{S} = \mathcal{P}(\mathbb{N})$. Define $\mu(\emptyset) = \nu(\emptyset) = 0$ and $\forall \; E \in \mathcal{S}$, $E \neq \emptyset$, let

$$\mu(E) := \sum_{n \in E} 2^n \quad \text{and} \quad \nu(E) := \sum_{n \in E} 1/2^n.$$

It is easy to verify that $\mu(E) = 0$ iff $\nu(E) = 0$. Hence $\mu \ll \nu$ and $\nu \ll \mu$.

An equivalent way of describing absolute continuity is given in the next theorem.

9.1.3. Theorem: *Let μ, ν be measures on $(X, \mathcal{S})$. Then the following hold:*

(i) *If ν is finite and $\nu \ll \mu$, then for every $\epsilon > 0$, $\exists \; \delta > 0$ such that $\nu(E) < \epsilon$ whenever $\mu(E) < \delta$, $E \in \mathcal{S}$.*

(ii) *If for every $\epsilon > 0$, $\exists \; \delta > 0$ such that $\nu(E) < \epsilon$ whenever $\mu(E) < \delta$, $E \in \mathcal{S}$, then $\nu \ll \mu$.*

Proof: (i) Suppose the claim is false. Then $\exists \; \epsilon > 0$ and sets $E_n \in \mathcal{S}$ such that

$$\mu(E_n) < 2^{-n} \quad \text{but} \quad \nu(E_n) \geq \epsilon, \; n = 1, 2, \ldots .$$

Let

$$A_n := \bigcup_{k=n}^{\infty} E_k \quad \text{and} \quad A := \bigcap_{n=1}^{\infty} A_n.$$

Then $\forall \; n$,

$$\mu(A) \; \leq \; \mu(A_n) \; \leq \; \sum_{k=n}^{\infty} \mu(E_n) \; < \; 1/2^{n+1}.$$

Hence $\mu(A) = 0$. Since $\{A_n\}_{n \geq 1}$ is a decreasing sequence and ν is a finite measure, by theorem 3.6.3

$$\nu(A) = \lim_{n \to \infty} \nu(A_n) \geq \epsilon.$$

This is a contradiction, as $\nu \ll \mu$. This proves (i).

(ii) Let $\mu(E) = 0$. Then $\mu(E) < \delta \; \forall \; \delta > 0$. Thus by the hypothesis it follows that $\nu(E) < \epsilon$, $\forall \; \epsilon > 0$. Hence $\nu(E) = 0$, i.e., $\nu \ll \mu$. ∎

9.1.4. Exercise: Show that the conclusion of theorem 9.1.3(i) fails if ν is not finite.

(Hint: Consider the measures μ and ν as constructed in example 9.1.2(iii).)

Recall that in section 3.5 we showed that every measure μ on $(\mathbb{R}, \mathcal{B}_{\mathbb{R}})$, which is finite on finite intervals is given by a monotonically increasing right continuous function F, and conversely every such F gives rise to a measure μ_F on $(\mathbb{R}, \mathcal{B}_{\mathbb{R}})$. It is natural to ask the question: when is $\mu_F \ll \lambda$ (here λ as usual is the Lebesgue measure on $\mathbb{R}$)? The answer is given in the next theorem.

9.1.5. Theorem: *Let $F : \mathbb{R} \longrightarrow \mathbb{R}$ be a monotonically increasing right continuous function and μ_F be the measure induced by F on $(\mathbb{R}, \mathcal{B}_{\mathbb{R}})$. Then $\mu_F \ll \lambda$ if and only if F is absolutely continuous on every bounded interval.*

Proof: Let μ_F be absolutely continuous and let $[a, b]$ be any bounded interval. We want to show that F is absolutely continuous on $[a, b]$. We consider the restriction of μ_F on $[a, b]$ and let $\epsilon > 0$ be given. Since μ_F is finite on $[a, b]$, by theorem 9.1.3 (i) we can choose a $\delta > 0$ such that

$$\mu_F(A) < \epsilon \text{ whenever } \lambda(A) < \delta, \ A \subseteq [a, b].$$

In particular, if A is a union of a finite number of pairwise disjoint intervals $[a_i, b_i], i = 1, 2, \ldots n$, then

$$\sum_{i=1}^{n}(b_i - a_i) = \lambda(A) < \delta \text{ implies } \mu_F(A) = \sum_{i=1}^{n}(F(b_i) - F(a_i)) < \epsilon,$$

showing that F is absolutely continuous.

Conversely, suppose F is absolutely continuous on every bounded interval. Let $E \in \mathcal{B}_{\mathbb{R}}$ be such that $\lambda(E) = 0$. We have to show that $\mu_F(E) = 0$. It is enough to show that $\mu_F(E \cap [a, b]) = 0 \ \forall \ a, b \in \mathbb{R}$. Fix $a, b \in \mathbb{R}$ with $a < b$. Since F is absolutely continuous on $[a, b]$, given $\epsilon > 0$, we can choose $\delta > 0$ such that whenever the $[a_i, b_i], 1 \leq i \leq n$, are pairwise disjoint subintervals of $[a, b]$, then

$$\sum_{i=1}^{n}(b_i - a_i) < \delta \text{ implies } \sum_{i=1}^{n}|F(b_i) - F(a_i)| < \epsilon.$$

By theorem 4.2.2, we can find an open set U such that $E \subset U$ and $\lambda(U) < \delta/2$. Since U is an open set, it is union of a sequence of pairwise disjoint intervals. Without loss of generality we can assume that we have a sequence $\{(a_n, b_n]\}_{n \geq 1}$ of left-open, right-closed intervals such that

$$E \cap [a, b] \subseteq \bigcup_{n=1}^{\infty}(a_n, b_n] \subset [a, b] \cap U$$

and

$$\sum_{n=1}^{\infty}\lambda(a_n, b_n] \leq \lambda(U) \leq \delta/2.$$

Then

$$\sum_{n=1}^{k} \lambda(a_n, b_n) \; < \; \delta/2 \; < \; \delta,$$

and hence

$$\sum_{n=1}^{k} [F(b_n) - F(a_n)] < \epsilon, \;\; \forall\, k.$$

Thus

$$\sum_{n=1}^{\infty} [F(b_n) - F(a_n)] < \epsilon.$$

Now

$$\mu_F(E \cap [a,b]) \; \leq \; \sum_{n=1}^{\infty} \mu_F\,(a_n, b_n\,] \; = \; \sum_{n=1}^{\infty} [F(b_n) - F(a_n)] \; < \; \epsilon.$$

Since this holds $\forall\, \epsilon > 0$, we have $\mu_F(E \cap [a,b]) = 0$. Hence $\mu_F \ll \lambda$. ∎

9.1.6. Remark: Let μ_F be the Lebesgue-Stieltjes measure induced by an absolutely continuous distribution function F. Let $(\mathbb{R}, \bar{\mathcal{B}}_F, \bar{\mu}_F)$ denote the completion of the measure space $(\mathbb{R}, \mathcal{B}_\mathbb{R}, \mu_F)$. Clearly, $\bar{\mathcal{B}}_F \supseteq \mathcal{B}_\mathbb{R}$. Let $E \in \mathcal{L}_\mathbb{R}$ and $\lambda(E) = 0$. Then $E \subseteq A$ for some $A \in \mathcal{B}_\mathbb{R}$ with $\lambda(A) = 0$. But then $\mu_F(A) = 0$, as $\mu_F \ll \lambda$. Hence $\mu_F^*(A) = 0$, i.e., $A \in \bar{\mathcal{B}}_F$. Now it follows from theorem 4.2.2 and theorem 3.11.8 that $\mathcal{L}_\mathbb{R} \subseteq \bar{\mathcal{B}}_F$.

9.1.7. Exercise: Let μ_1, μ_2, μ_3 be measures on $(X, \mathcal{S})$. Prove the following:

  (i) $\mu_1 \ll (\mu_1 + \mu_2)$.

  (ii) If $\mu_1 \ll \mu_2$ and $\mu_2 \ll \mu_3$, then $\mu_1 \ll \mu_3$.

  (iii) If $\mu_1 \ll \mu_3$ and $\mu_2 \ll \mu_3$, then $(\mu_1 + \mu_2) \ll \mu_3$.

9.1.8. Exercise: For $E \in \mathcal{L}_\mathbb{R}$, the class of Lebesgue measurable subsets of $\mathbb{R}$, let

$$\mu(E) := \sum_{n=1}^{\infty} \frac{1}{2^n} \left(\frac{\lambda(E \cap [-n, n])}{2n} \right).$$

Show that μ is a probability measure on $(\mathbb{R}, \mathcal{L}_\mathbb{R})$, i.e., μ is a measure and $\mu(\mathbb{R}) = 1$. Let $\mu_x(E) := \mu(E + x), E \in \mathcal{L}_\mathbb{R}, x \in \mathbb{R}$. Show that

$$\mu_x \ll \mu \ll \mu_y, \;\; \forall\, x, y \in \mathbb{R}.$$

    As pointed in the beginning of the section, given a measure μ and a nonnegative measurable function f, the measure $\nu(E) := \int_E f d\mu, E \in \mathcal{S}$, is absolutely continuous with respect to μ. The questions arise: can one describe all the measures μ which are absolutely continuous with respect to μ? Do absolutely continuous measures always arise only via integration? The answers to these questions are given by the Radon-Nikodym theorem. The proof we give below of this theorem uses the results of section 8.9. An alternative proof, which requires the concept of signed measures and the Hahn decomposition (theorem 10.1.8), will be described in theorem 10.2.2. We first prove a theorem, due to John von Neumann, from which the Radon-Nikodym theorem can be deduced.

9.1.9. Theorem (von Neumann): *Let ν and μ be two σ-finite measures on a measurable space $(X, \mathcal{S})$. Then there exist mutually disjoint sets $X_i \in \mathcal{S}, 1 \leq i \leq 3$, such that the following hold:*

(i) $X = \bigcup_{i=1}^{3} X_i$.

(ii) $\nu(X_3) = \mu(X_1) = 0$.

(iii) *There exists a nonnegative measurable function g on X such that $g(x) > 0 \ \forall \ x \in X_2$, and $\ \forall \ E \in \mathcal{S}$ with $E \subseteq X_2$ we have*

$$\nu(E) = \int_E g d\mu.$$

Proof: Case (i): Let μ, ν both be finite. Then $\mu + \nu$ is a finite measure and

$$L_2(\mu + \nu) \subseteq L_1(\mu + \nu) \subseteq L_1(\nu).$$

To see this, note that the constant function $h \equiv 1$ belongs to $L_2(\mu + \nu)$ and by the Cauchy-Schwarz inequality, for $f \in L_2(\mu + \nu)$, we have

$$\int |f| d(\mu + \nu) \ \leq \ ((\mu + \nu)(X))^{1/2} \left(\int |f|^2 d(\mu + \nu) \right)^{1/2}.$$

Thus $f \in L_1(\mu + \nu)$. For $f \in L_1(\mu + \nu)$, it is obvious that

$$\int |f| d\nu \ \leq \ \int |f| d(\mu + \nu),$$

i.e., $f \in L_1(\nu)$. Let $T : L_2(\mu + \nu) \longrightarrow \mathbb{R}$ be defined by

$$T(f) = \int f d\nu, \quad f \in L_2(\mu + \nu).$$

Then it follows from the above discussion that T is a well-defined map. Clearly T is linear and

$$|T(f)| \ \leq \ (\nu(X))^{1/2} \|f\|_2, \quad f \in L_2(\mu + \nu).$$

Thus T is a bounded linear functional on $L_2(\mu + \nu)$. By the Riesz representation theorem (8.9.20), there exists a function $f_0 \in L_2(\mu + \nu)$ such that $\forall \ f \in L_2(\mu + \nu)$,

$$T(f) = \int f \overline{f_0} \, d(\mu + \nu),$$

i.e.,

$$\int f d\nu = \int f \overline{f_0} \, d(\mu + \nu).$$

Putting $f = \chi_E, E \in \mathcal{S}$, we have

$$\nu(E) = \int_E \overline{f_0} \, d(\mu + \nu).$$

Since this holds $\forall E \in \mathcal{S}$ and $f_0 \in L_1(\mu + \nu)$, it follows from theorem 8.1.9 that $\overline{f_0}(x)$ is real-valued for a.e. x and $f_0(x) \geq 0$ for a.e. $(\mu + \nu), x \in X$. Further, $\forall E \in \mathcal{S}$,

$$(\mu + \nu)(E) \geq \nu(E) = \int_E f_0 \, d(\mu + \nu),$$

i.e.,

$$\int_E (1 - f_0) \, d(\mu + \nu) \geq 0.$$

Once again this implies, by theorem 8.1.9, that $0 \leq f_0(x) \leq 1$ for a.e. $(\mu + \nu)x \in X$. Let

$$\begin{aligned}
N &:= \{x \in X \mid f_0(x) > 1\} \cup \{x \in X \mid f_0(x) < 0\}, \\
X_1' &:= \{x \in X \mid f_0(x) = 1\}, \ X_1 := X_1' \cup N, \\
X_2 &:= \{x \in X \mid 0 < f_0(x) < 1\}, \\
X_3 &:= \{x \in X \mid f_0(x) = 0\}.
\end{aligned}$$

Note that $(\mu + \nu)(N) = 0$. Further, the $X_i \in \mathcal{S}, 1 \leq i \leq 3$, and are pairwise disjoint with $\cup_{i=1}^3 X_i = X$. Also,

$$\nu(X_3) = \int_{X_3} f_0 d(\mu + \nu) = 0$$

and

$$\mu(X_1') = (\mu + \nu)(X_1') - \nu(X_1') = \int_{X_1'} (1 - f_0) d(\mu + \nu) = 0.$$

Since $\mu(N) = 0$, we get $\mu(X_1) = 0$. Finally, $\forall E \in \mathcal{S}, E \subset X_2$,

$$\nu(E) = \int_E f_0 d(\mu + \nu).$$

Thus

$$\nu(E) - \int_E f_0 d\nu = \int_E f_0 d\mu,$$

i.e.,

$$\int_E (1 - f_0) d\nu = \int_E f_0 d\mu.$$

Since this holds $\forall E \subset X_2$, it follows that

$$\int_{X_2} s(1 - f_0) d\nu = \int_{X_2} s f_0 d\mu,$$

for every nonnegative simple measurable function s. An application of the monotone convergence theorem gives

$$\int_{X_2} f(1 - f_0)d\nu = \int_{X_2} f f_0 d\mu,$$

for every nonnegative measurable function f. In particular, for $E \subseteq X_2, E \in \mathcal{S}$, let

$$f(x) := \begin{cases} \dfrac{\chi_E(x)}{1 - f_0(x)} & \text{if } x \notin X_1, \\[2ex] 0 & \text{otherwise.} \end{cases}$$

Then $\forall E \in \mathcal{S}$ with $E \subseteq X_2$,

$$\nu(E) = \int_E \frac{f_0(x)}{1 - f_0(x)}d\mu.$$

Define

$$g(x) := \begin{cases} \dfrac{f_0(x)}{1 - f_0(x)} & \text{for } x \in X_2, \\[2ex] 0 & \text{otherwise.} \end{cases}$$

Then g is a nonnegative measurable function and, $\forall E \in \mathcal{S}$ with $E \subseteq X_2$,

$$\nu(E) = \int_E g d\mu.$$

Case (ii): We now consider the case when μ, ν are both σ-finite. We can write $X = \bigcup_{i=1}^{\infty} Y_i$, where the sets $Y_i \in \mathcal{S}$ are pairwise disjoint, $\nu(Y_i) < \infty$ and with $\mu(Y_i) < \infty \ \forall \ i \geq 1$. By case (i), for every $i \geq 1$, we can find mutually disjoint sets $X_i^1, X_i^2, X_i^3 \in \mathcal{S}$ such that $Y_i = X_i^1 \cup X_i^2 \cup X_i^3$ with $\mu(X_i^1) = \nu(X_i^3) = 0$. Further, for every $i \geq 1$ there exists a measurable function g_i such that $g_i(x) > 0$ for a.e. $(\mu)x \in X_i^2, g_i(x) = 0$ for a.e. $(\mu)x \in X_i^1 \cup X_i^3$, and $\forall \ E \in \mathcal{S}$,

$$\nu(E \cap X_i^2) = \int_{E \cap X_i^2} g_i d\mu.$$

We put

$$X_1 := \bigcup_{i=1}^{\infty} X_i^1, \ X_2 := \bigcup_{i=1}^{\infty} X_i^2, \ X_3 := \bigcup_{i=1}^{\infty} X_i^3$$

and define

$$g(x) := \begin{cases} g_i(x) & \text{if } x \in X_i^2 \text{ for some } i, \\ 0 & \text{otherwise.} \end{cases}$$

Then X_1, X_2, X_3 and g satisfy the required properties. ∎

9.1.10. Theorem (Lebesgue decomposition): *Let* μ, ν *be two σ-finite measures on a measurable space* $(X, \mathcal{S})$. *Then there exist σ-finite measures* ν_a *and* ν_s *with the following properties:*

(i) $\nu = \nu_a + \nu_s$.

(ii) *There exists a nonnegative measurable function f such that*

$$\nu_a(E) = \int_E f d\mu \ \text{ for every } E \in \mathcal{S}.$$

(iii) *There exists a set $A \in \mathcal{S}$ such that* $\mu(A^c) = \nu_s(A) = 0$.

Furthermore, such a decomposition is unique.

Proof: By theorem 9.1.9, we have disjoint sets X_1, X_2 and X_3 in $\mathcal{S}$ such that $X = X_1 \cup X_2 \cup X_3$, and $\nu(X_3) = \mu(X_1) = 0$. Further,

$$\nu(E \cap X_2) = \int_{E \cap X_2} g d\mu, \ \forall \, E \in \mathcal{S},$$

for some nonnegative measurable function g on X with the properties $g(x) > 0$ on X_2 and $g(x) = 0$ on X_2^c. Let $A := X_2 \cup X_3$. Define $\forall \ E \in \mathcal{S}$,

$$\nu_a(E) := \nu(A \cap E) \ \text{ and } \ \nu_s(E) := \nu(E \cap X_1).$$

Then $\nu = \nu_a + \nu_s$ and $\nu_s(A) = \mu(A^c) = 0$. Finally, $\forall \ E \in \mathcal{S}$,

$$\nu_a(E) = \nu(E \cap (X_3 \cup X_2)) = \nu(E \cap X_2) = \int_{E \cap X_2} g d\mu.$$

Define

$$f(x) := \begin{cases} g(x) & \text{if } x \in X_2, \\ 0 & \text{if } x \in X_1 \cup X_3. \end{cases}$$

Then f is a nonnegative measurable function on X and

$$\nu_a(E) = \int_E f d\mu \ \forall \ E \in \mathcal{S}.$$

This proves the existence part of the theorem. To prove the uniqueness, suppose there also exist measures $\nu_a^{'}$ and $\nu_s^{'}$, a set $A^{'} \in \mathcal{S}$ and a nonnegative measurable function $f^{'}$ such that

$$\begin{aligned} \nu &= \nu_a^{'} + \nu_s^{'}, \\ \mu((A^{'})^c) &= \nu_s^{'}(A^{'}) = 0, \\ \nu_a^{'}(E) &= \int_E f^{'} d\mu, \ \forall \ E \in \mathcal{S}. \end{aligned}$$

Then

$$\mu((A^{'} \cap A)^c) = 0 = \nu_s(A^{'} \cap A) = \nu_s^{'}(A^{'} \cap A).$$

Further,

$$\nu_a((A^{'} \cap A)^c) = 0 = \nu_a^{'}((A^{'} \cap A)^c). \tag{9.1}$$

Since
$$\nu_a(E) + \nu_s(E) = \nu_a'(E) + \nu_s'(E),$$
we have, $\forall\ E \in \mathcal{S}$ with $\nu(E) < +\infty$,
$$\nu_a(E) - \nu_a'(E) = \nu_s'(E) - \nu_s(E).$$
Since
$$\nu_a(E \cap (A' \cap A)^c) - \nu_a'(E \cap (A' \cap A)^c) = 0,$$
the above implies that
$$\nu_a(E \cap (A' \cap A)) - \nu_a'(E \cap (A' \cap A))$$
$$= \nu_s(E \cap (A' \cap A)) - \nu_s'(E \cap (A' \cap A)) = 0.$$
Thus, $\forall E \in \mathcal{S}$ with $\nu(E) < +\infty$,
$$\nu_a(E \cap (A' \cap A)) = \nu_a'(E \cap (A' \cap A)). \tag{9.2}$$
From (9.1) and (9.2) we have $\nu_a(E) = \nu_a'(E)$, $\forall\ E \in \mathcal{S}$ with $\nu(E) < +\infty$. Now, using the σ-finiteness of ν, it is easy to show that $\nu_a = \nu_a'$. Similarly, $\nu_s = \nu_s'$. $\blacksquare$

9.1.11. Definition: Let μ, ν be measures on $(X, \mathcal{S})$. We say μ is **singular** with respect to ν if for some $E \in \mathcal{S}, \mu(E) = \nu(E^c) = 0$. In that case we write $\mu \perp \nu$.

9.1.12. Remark: The measure ν_s of theorem 9.1.10 is such that $\nu_s \perp \nu_a$ and $\nu_s \perp \mu$.

9.1.13. Exercise: Let μ_1, μ_2 and ν be measures on $(X, \mathcal{S})$ and let α, β be nonnegative real numbers. Prove the following:

   (i) $\mu_1 \perp \mu_2$ iff $\mu_2 \perp \mu_1$.
   (ii) $(\alpha\mu_1 + \beta\mu_2) \perp \nu$ if $\mu_i \perp \nu, i = 1, 2$.
   (iii) $\nu = 0$ if $\nu \ll \mu_1$ and $\nu \perp \mu_1$.

9.1.14. Exercise: Let μ be the counting measure on $\mathcal{L}_{\mathbb{R}}$ (see example 9.1.2(ii)). Show that μ does not have a Lebesgue decomposition with respect to λ, the Lebesgue measure. Why does this not contradict the claim of theorem 9.1.10?

9.1.15. Theorem (Radon-Nikodym): *Let μ, ν be σ-finite measures on a measurable space $(X, \mathcal{S})$ such that $\nu \ll \mu$. Then there exists a nonnegative measurable function f such that*
$$\nu(E) = \int_E f d\mu, \ \forall\ E \in \mathcal{S}.$$

Further, if g is any other measurable function such that the above holds, then $f(x) = g(x)$ for a.e. $x(\mu)$.

Proof: Since $\nu \ll \mu$, in the Lebesgue decomposition theorem $\nu_a = \nu$ and $\nu_s = 0$. Further, there is a nonnegative measurable function f such that

$$\nu(E) = \int_E f d\mu, \ E \in \mathcal{S}.$$

To prove the uniqueness of f, let there exist another nonnegative measurable function g such that

$$\nu(E) = \int_E g_1 d\mu, \ \forall \, E \in \mathcal{S}.$$

Suppose there exists a set $E \in \mathcal{S}$ such that $\mu(E) > 0$ and $f(x) > g(x) \ \forall$ $x \in E$. Since μ, ν are σ-finite, we can choose $A \in \mathcal{S}$ such that $\mu(A) < \infty, \nu(A) < +\infty$ and $\mu(E \cap A) > 0$. Then

$$0 < \int_{A \cap E} (f(x) - g(x)) \, d\mu(x) \ = \ \nu(A \cap E) - \nu(A \cap E) \ = \ 0,$$

a contradiction. Thus $f(x) \le g(x)$ for a.e. $x(\mu)$. Similarly, $f(x) \ge g(x)$ for a.e. $x(\mu)$. ∎

9.1.16. Definition: Let μ, ν be σ-finite measures on $(X, \mathcal{S})$ such that $\nu \ll \mu$. The unique measurable function f (as given by theorem 9.1.15) such that, $\forall \ E \in \mathcal{S}$,

$$\nu(E) = \int_E f d\mu$$

is called the **Radon-Nikodym derivative** of ν with respect to μ and is denoted by $\dfrac{d\nu}{d\mu}(x)$.

9.1.17. Example: Let $F : \mathbb{R} \longrightarrow \mathbb{R}$ be a monotonically increasing absolutely continuous function, and μ_F the Lebesgue-Stieltjes measure induced by F on $(\mathbb{R}, \mathcal{B}_\mathbb{R})$. Then $\mu_F \ll \lambda$ (by theorem 9.1.5) and

$$\frac{d\mu_F}{d\lambda}(x) = F'(x), \text{ for a.e. } x(\lambda).$$

To see this, we note that by the fundamental theorem of calculus (6.3.6), for $a < b$,

$$\int_a^b F'(x) d\lambda(x) \ = \ F(b) - F(a)$$
$$= \ \mu_F(a, b]$$
$$= \ \int_a^b \frac{d\mu}{d\lambda}(x) d\lambda(x).$$

From this, using exercise 5.3.4 (iii), it follows that

$$\int_E F'(x)d\lambda(x) = \int_E \frac{d\mu}{d\lambda}(x)d\lambda(x), \ \forall \ E \in \mathcal{L}_{\mathbb{R}}.$$

Hence, using exercise 5.3.4 (ii) and the uniqueness of the Radon-Nikodym derivative, we have

$$F'(x) = \frac{d\mu_F}{d\lambda}(x) \text{ for a.e. } x(\lambda).$$

As an application of the Radon-Nikodym theorem, we have the following:

9.1.18 Theorem (Existence of conditional expectation): *Let* $(X, \mathcal{S}, \mu)$ *be a probability space and* $f \in L_1(X, \mathcal{S}, \mu)$*. Let* $\mathcal{S}_0$ *be a* σ*-algebra of subsets of* X *such that* $\mathcal{S}_0 \subseteq \mathcal{S}$*. Then there exists a function* $\hat{f} : X \to \mathbb{R}$ *such that*

(i) *$\hat{f}$ is $\mathcal{S}_0$-measurable and μ-integrable.*

(ii) *For every $E \in \mathcal{S}_0$,*

$$\int_E \hat{f} d\mu = \int_E f d\mu.$$

Proof: Consider f^+, the positive part of f. Then $f^+ \in L_1(X, \mathcal{S}, \mu)$. Let, $\forall \ E \in \mathcal{S}_0$,

$$\nu(E) := \int_E f d\mu.$$

Then ν is a finite measure on $(X, \mathcal{S}_0)$. Clearly ν is absolutely continuous with respect to μ. Thus, by the Radon-Nikodym theorem, there exists a nonnegative $\mathcal{S}_0$-measurable and μ-integrable function $g_1 : X \to \mathbb{R}$ such that $\forall \ E \in \mathcal{S}_0$,

$$\int_E f^+ d\mu = \nu(E) = \int_E g_1 \, d\mu. \tag{9.3}$$

Similar considerations applied to f^-, the negative part of f, give a nonnegative $\mathcal{S}_0$-measurable and μ-integrable function $g_2 : X \to \mathbb{R}$ such that $\forall \ E \in \mathcal{S}_0$,

$$\int_E f^- d\mu = \int_E g_2 \, d\mu. \tag{9.4}$$

It follows from (9.3) and (9.4) that $f := g_1 - g_2$ is the required function. ∎

9.1.19. Exercise: Let μ, ν be σ-finite measures on $(X, \mathcal{S})$ such that $\nu \ll \mu$. Show that for every nonnegative measurable function f on X,

$$\int f d\nu = \int f \frac{d\nu}{d\mu} d\mu \ .$$

Further, if $f \in L_1(\nu)$, then $f \dfrac{d\nu}{d\mu} \in L_1(\mu)$, and the above equality holds. (Hint: Use the simple function technique.)

9.1.20. Exercise: Let μ be the counting measure on the Lebesgue measurable space $(\mathbb{R}, \mathcal{L}_{\mathbb{R}})$ (see example 9.1.2(ii)). Show that $\lambda \ll \mu$ but there exists no measurable function f such that $\forall\ E \in \mathcal{L}_{\mathbb{R}}$,

$$\lambda(E) = \int_E g\,d\mu.$$

This shows that the condition of μ being σ-finite is necessary for the Radon-Nikodym theorem to hold.

9.1.21. Exercise: Let μ_1, μ_2 and ν be σ-finite measures on $(X, \mathcal{S})$. Prove the following:

(i) If $\mu_i \ll \nu, i = 1, 2$, then $(\mu_1 + \mu_2) \ll \nu$ and

$$\frac{d(\mu_1 + \mu_2)}{d\nu}(x) = \frac{d\mu_1}{d\nu}(x) + \frac{d\mu_2}{d\nu}(x)\ \text{ for a.e. } x(\nu).$$

(ii) If $\mu_1 \ll \mu_2$ and $\mu_2 \ll \mu_1$, then

$$\left(\frac{d\mu_1}{d\mu_2}(x)\right)\left(\frac{d\mu_2}{d\mu_1}(x)\right) = 1\ \text{ for a.e. } x(\mu_1)\ \text{ and a.e. } x(\mu_2).$$

9.1.22. Exercise: Let F be the Lebesgue singular function (see example 6.2.4(iv)). Show that $\mu_F \perp \lambda$.

9.1.23. Note: In 9.1.15 we derived the Radon-Nikodym theorem from theorem 9.1.9, which used the structure of linear functionals on L_2-spaces. A more direct proof is given in theorem 10.2.2, where we prove it also for 'signed measures'. The Radon-Nikodym theorem can be proved for more general measure spaces, called decomposable measure spaces, see for example Hewitt and Stromberg [18].

9.2. Computation of the Radon-Nikodym derivative

The Radon-Nikodym theorem is an existence theorem. In general, it is not possible to find the Radon-Nikodym derivative $\dfrac{d\mu}{d\nu}$ when $\mu \ll \nu$. In this section, we look at the problem of identifying the Radon-Nikodym derivative $\dfrac{d\mu}{d\lambda}$ for measures μ on $(\mathbb{R}^n, \mathcal{B}_{\mathbb{R}^n})$ such that $\mu \ll \lambda$, the Lebesgue measure on $\mathbb{R}^n$. The motivation for such a computation comes from the following proposition. (In this section all the a.e. statements are with respect to the Lebesgue measure λ on $\mathbb{R}^n$.)

9.2.1. Proposition: *Let μ be a finite measure on $(\mathbb{R}, \mathcal{B}_{\mathbb{R}})$ and $F(x) :=$ $\mu(-\infty, x], x \in \mathbb{R}$. Then the following are true:*

(i) *$F(x)$ is differentiable for a.e. x, and at these points*

$$F'(x) = \lim_{r \to 0} \frac{\mu(x-r, x+r)}{\lambda(x-r, x+r)} \ .$$

(ii) *If $\mu \ll \lambda$, then for a.e. $x(\lambda)$,*

$$\frac{d\mu}{d\lambda}(x) = F'(x) = \lim_{r \to 0} \frac{\mu(x-r, x+r)}{\lambda(x-r, x+r)} \ .$$

Proof: Clearly, F is monotonically increasing and hence $F'(x)$ exists for a.e. x, by theorem 6.2.1. Next, observe that F is a right continuous function and $\mu = \mu_F$, the Lebesgue-Stieltjes measure induced by F. Now, it will follow from theorem 9.1.5 and example 9.1.17 that $\dfrac{d\mu}{d\lambda}(x) = F'(x)$ for a.e. x if $\mu \ll \lambda$. Thus to complete the proof of both (i) and (ii), we only have to show that for a.e. x,

$$F'(x) = \lim_{r \to 0} \frac{\mu(x-r, x+r)}{\lambda(x-r, x+r)} \ .$$

Let $x_0 \in \mathbb{R}$ be fixed such that $F'(x_0)$ exists and let $\epsilon > 0$ be given. Choose $\delta > 0$ such that

$$\left| \frac{F(x) - F(x_0)}{x - x_0} - F'(x_0) \right| < \epsilon \text{ whenever } 0 < |x - x_0| < \delta.$$

Let $r > 0$ be such that $2r < \delta$. Then

$$\left| \frac{F(x_0 + r) - F(x_0 - r)}{2r} - F'(x_0) \right|$$

$$\leq \left| \frac{F(x_0 + r) - F(x_0) - rF'(x_0)}{2r} \right|$$

$$+ \left| \frac{F(x_0) - F(x_0 - r) - rF'(x_0)}{2r} \right|$$

$$\leq \frac{1}{2} \left| \frac{F(x_0 + r) - F(x_0)}{r} - F'(x_0) \right|$$

$$+ \frac{1}{2} \left| \frac{F(x_0) - F(x_0 - r)}{r} - F'(x_0) \right|$$

$$< \epsilon/2 + \epsilon/2 = \epsilon.$$

Hence $\forall \ 0 < r < \delta/2$,

$$\left| \frac{\mu(x_0 - r, x_0 + r)}{\lambda(x_0 - r, x_0 + r)} - F'(x_0) \right| < \epsilon.$$

This proves the required claim. ∎

The above theorem motivates the following definition. For $x \in \mathbb{R}^n$ and $r > 0$, let $B(x,r) := \{y \in \mathbb{R}^n \mid |x - y| < r\}$.

9.2.2. Definition: Let μ be a finite measure on $(\mathbb{R}^n, \mathcal{B}_{\mathbb{R}^n})$. We say μ is **differentiable** at $x \in \mathbb{R}^n$ if

$$(D\mu)(x) := \lim_{r \to 0} \frac{\mu(B(x,r))}{\lambda(B(x,r))}$$

exists, and in that case $(D\mu)(x)$ is called the **derivative** of μ at x.

9.2.3. Examples:

(i) Let μ_F be any Lebesgue-Stieltjes measure on $\mathbb{R}$ such that $(\mu_F)(\mathbb{R}) < +\infty$. Then, as shown in proposition 9.2.1, $(D\mu_F)(x)$ exists, if $F'(x)$ exists, and the two are equal.

(ii) Let μ be defined on $\mathcal{B}_{\mathbb{R}}$ by

$$\mu(E) := \lambda(E \cap [-1, +1]), \ E \in \mathcal{B}_{\mathbb{R}}.$$

It is easy to see that μ is differentiable at every $x \in \mathbb{R}$. Further, $(D\mu)(x) = 1$ if $|x| < 1$, and $(D\mu)(x) = 0$ if $|x| \geq 1$.

The aim of this section is to prove the following theorem.

9.2.4. Theorem: *Let μ be a finite measure on $(\mathbb{R}^n, \mathcal{B}_{\mathbb{R}^n})$. Then the following are true:*

(i) *If $A \in \mathcal{B}_{\mathbb{R}^n}$ and $\mu(A) = 0$, then $(D\mu)(x) = 0$ for a.e. $(\lambda)x \in A$.*

(ii) *If $\mu \ll \lambda$, then $(D\mu)(x) = \dfrac{d\mu}{d\lambda}(x)$ for a.e. $x(\lambda)$.*

(iii) *$(D\mu)(x)$ exists for a.e. $x(\lambda)$.*

The proof of the theorem needs several elementary results, which we prove first. Recall that λ is a regular measure on $(\mathbb{R}^n, \mathcal{B}_{\mathbb{R}^n})$. The next lemma implies that every finite measure on $(\mathbb{R}^n, \mathcal{B}_{\mathbb{R}^n})$ is regular.

9.2.5. Lemma: *Let (X, d) be a complete separable metric space and let μ be a finite measure on $\mathcal{B}_X$, the σ-algebra of Borel subsets of X. Then μ is **regular**, i.e., $\forall \ E \in \mathcal{B}_X$,*

$$\begin{aligned} \mu(E) &= \inf\{\mu(U) \mid U \ open, U \supseteq E\} \\ &= \sup\{\mu(C) \mid C \ closed, C \subseteq E\} \\ &= \sup\{\mu(K) \mid K \ compact, K \subseteq E\}. \end{aligned}$$

(In other words, every measure is regular on a complete separable metric space. See also note 4.2.9.)

Proof: We first show that $\forall\ E \in \mathcal{B}_X$,

$$\begin{aligned} \mu(E) &= \inf\{\mu(U) \mid U \text{ open}, U \supseteq E\} \\ &= \sup\{\mu(C) \mid C \text{ closed}, C \subseteq E\}. \end{aligned} \tag{9.5}$$

The proof is an application of the 'σ-algebra technique'. First note that proving (9.5) is equivalent to showing that for any $\epsilon > 0$, there are an open set U_ϵ and a closed set C_ϵ such that

$$C_\epsilon \subseteq E \subseteq U_\epsilon \text{ and } \mu(U_\epsilon \setminus C_\epsilon) < \epsilon.$$

Let $\mathcal{S}$ be the collection of all sets $E \in \mathcal{B}_X$ for which this holds. We shall show that $\mathcal{S}$ is a σ-algebra and $\mathcal{S}$ includes all closed sets, proving that $\mathcal{S} = \mathcal{B}_X$. Clearly, $E \in \mathcal{S}$ implies $E^c \in \mathcal{S}$. Let $\{E_n\}_{n \geq 1}$ be a sequence of sets from $\mathcal{S}$ and let $\epsilon > 0$ be given. Then $\forall\ n$, we can choose an open set U_n and a closed set C_n such that

$$C_n \subseteq E_n \subseteq U_n \text{ and } \mu(U_n \setminus C_n) < \epsilon/2^{n+1} .$$

Let

$$U := \bigcup_{n=1}^{\infty} U_n \text{ and } F_n := \bigcup_{k=1}^{n} C_k, n \geq 1.$$

Then U is open, F_n is closed for all $n \geq 1$, and $\{U \setminus F_n\}_{n \geq 1}$ decreases to $U \setminus \bigcup_{n=1}^{\infty} C_n$. Since μ is finite, we have

$$\begin{aligned} \lim_{n \to \infty} \mu(U \setminus F_n) &= \mu\left(U \setminus \bigcup_{n=1}^{\infty} C_n\right) \\ &= \mu\left(\bigcup_{n=1}^{\infty} U_n \setminus \bigcup_{n=1}^{\infty} C_n\right) \\ &\leq \mu\left(\bigcup_{n=1}^{\infty} (U_n \setminus C_n)\right) \\ &\leq \sum_{n=1}^{\infty} \mu(U_n \setminus C_n) < \epsilon. \end{aligned}$$

Hence $\exists\ n$ such that $\mu(U \setminus F_n) < \epsilon$. Since $F_n \subseteq \bigcup_{n=1}^{\infty} E_n \subseteq U$, this proves that $\bigcup_{n=1}^{\infty} E_n \in \mathcal{S}$. Next, let C be any closed subset of X. Let

$$U_n := \{x \in X \mid d(x, y) < 1/n\ \forall\ y \in C\}.$$

Note that it is an open set for every n, and $C = \bigcap_{n=1}^{\infty} U_n$. Since μ is finite, $\mu(C) = \lim_{n \to \infty} \mu(U_n)$. Hence, given $\epsilon > 0$, we can choose n such that $\mu(U_n) - \mu(C) < \epsilon$. Clearly, $C \subseteq U_n$ and $\mu(U_n - C) < \epsilon$, i.e., $C \in \mathcal{S}$. In particular, $\emptyset \in \mathcal{S}$. This proves that $\mathcal{S}$ is a σ-algebra and includes all closed sets. Thus $\mathcal{S} = \mathcal{B}_X$. This proves (9.5). Note that till now we have not used the fact that X is a complete separable metric space.

Finally, we show that $\forall\ E \in \mathcal{B}_X$,

$$\mu(E) = \sup\{\mu(K) \mid K \text{ compact, } K \subseteq E\}.$$

Let $\epsilon > 0$ be given. Choose a closed set $C \subseteq E$ such that $\mu(E \setminus C) < \epsilon$. Let D be any countable dense subset of X. Then

$$X = \bigcup_{x \in D} \bigcup_{n=1}^{\infty} B(x, 1/n), \text{ where } B(x, 1/n) := \{y \in X \mid d(x,y) < 1/n\}.$$

Let

$$\overline{B(x, 1/n)} := \{y \in X \mid d(x,y) \leq 1/n\}.$$

Then for every n, we can choose $x_{n_j} \in D, j = 1, 2, \dots$, such that

$$C = \bigcup_{j=1}^{\infty} (\overline{B(x_{n_j}, 1/n)} \cap C).$$

Since μ is finite, for every $n \geq 1$ we can choose k_n such that

$$\mu\left(C \setminus \bigcup_{j=1}^{k_n} \overline{B(x_{n_j}, 1/n)}\right) < \epsilon/2^{n+1}.$$

Let

$$K := \bigcap_{n=1}^{\infty} \bigcup_{j=1}^{k_n} \left(\overline{B(x_{n_j}, 1/n)} \cap C\right).$$

Then K is a closed and totally bounded set. Since X is complete, K is a compact set and

$$\mu(E \setminus K) \leq \mu(E \setminus C) + \mu(C \setminus K) < \epsilon/2 + \epsilon/2 = \epsilon.$$

This completes the proof. ∎

An obvious corollary of the above lemma is the following.

9.2.6. Corollary: *Let μ be any finite measure on $(\mathbb{R}^n, \mathcal{B}_{\mathbb{R}^n})$. Then $\forall\ E \in \mathcal{B}_{\mathbb{R}^n}$,*

$$
\begin{aligned}
\mu(E) &= \sup\{\mu(U) \mid U \text{ open, } U \supseteq E\} \\
&= \inf\{\mu(C) \mid C \text{ closed, } C \subseteq E\} \\
&= \sup\{\mu(K) \mid K \text{ compact, } K \subseteq E\},
\end{aligned}
$$

i.e., every finite measure on $(\mathbb{R}^n, \mathcal{B}_{\mathbb{R}^n})$ is regular.

9.2.7. Lemma: *Given open balls $B_1, B_2, \ldots, B_k$ in $\mathbb{R}^n$, there exist among them pairwise disjoint balls $B_{n_1}, \ldots, B_{n_m}$ such that*

$$\lambda \left(\bigcup_{i=1}^{k} B_i \right) \leq 3^n \sum_{j=1}^{m} \lambda(B_{n_j}).$$

Proof: Let B_j have radius $r_j, 1 \leq j \leq k$. We may assume that $r_1 \geq r_2 \geq \cdots \geq r_k$. Choose $n_1 = 1$. Choose n_2 to be the smallest integer, if there is any, such that B_{n_2} is disjoint from B_{n_1}. Let n_3 be the smallest integer, if there is any, such that B_{n_3} is disjoint from B_{n_1} and B_{n_2}. We continue this process till the finite set $\{B_1, \ldots, B_k\}$ is exhausted. This will give us pairwise disjoint balls $B_{n_1}, \ldots, B_{n_m}$, if any, from the given balls. Note that each $B_i, 1 \leq i \leq k$, must intersect some B_{n_j} for $n_j \geq i, 1 \leq j \leq m$. Also note that if any two open balls $B(x, r)$ and $B(x', r')$ intersect and $z \in B(x, r) \cap B(x', r')$ with $r' < r$, then $\forall \ z' \in B(x', r')$,

$$d(x, z') \ \leq \ d(x, z) + d(z, x') + d(x', z') \ < \ r + r' + r' < 3r.$$

Thus $B(x', r') \subseteq B(x, 3r)$. Next, let $z \in B_i$ for some i, and let n_j be such that $B_i \cap B_{n_j} \neq \emptyset$. Then $r_i \leq r_{n_j}$, and we have $B_i \subseteq A_{n_j}$, where A_{n_j} is an open ball with the same center as B_{n_j} but with radius three times that of B_{n_j}. Thus

$$\bigcup_{i=1}^{k} B_i \subseteq \bigcup_{j=1}^{m} A_{n_j},$$

and using exercise 7.5.7, we have

$$\lambda \left(\bigcup_{i=1}^{k} B_i \right) \leq \lambda \left(\bigcup_{j=1}^{m} A_{n_j} \right) \leq \sum_{j=1}^{m} \lambda(A_{n_j}) \ = \ 3^n \sum_{j=1}^{m} \lambda(B_{n_j}). \ \blacksquare$$

9.2.8. Definition: Let μ be a finite measure on $\mathcal{B}_{\mathbb{R}^n}$. For $x \in \mathbb{R}$, let

$$(\overline{D}\mu)(x) := \limsup_{\delta \downarrow 0} \left\{ \frac{\mu(B(x, r))}{\lambda(B(x, r))} \mid 0 < r \leq \delta \right\}$$

and

$$(\underline{D}\mu)(x) := \liminf_{\delta \downarrow 0} \left\{ \frac{\mu(B(x, r))}{\lambda(B(x, r))} \mid 0 < r \leq \delta \right\}.$$

We call $(\overline{D}\mu)(x)$ and $(\underline{D}\mu)(x)$ the **upper** and **lower derivative** of μ at x, respectively.

9.2.9. Lemma: *The functions $\overline{D}\mu$ and $\underline{D}\mu$ are Borel measurable functions on $\mathbb{R}$, and μ is differentiable at x iff $(\overline{D}\mu)(x) = (\underline{D}\mu)(x) < +\infty$.*

Proof: That μ is differentiable at x iff $(\overline{D}\mu)(x) = (\underline{D}\mu)(x) < +\infty$ is easy to check. To show the Borel measurability of $(\overline{D}\mu)(x)$, it is enough to show that for any fixed δ, the function

$$\phi_\delta(x) := \sup\left\{\frac{\mu(B(x,r))}{\lambda(B(x,r))} \mid 0 < r \leq \delta\right\}, \quad x \in \mathbb{R}^n,$$

is measurable. Let $\alpha \in \mathbb{R}$ and let $E := \{x \in \mathbb{R}^n \mid \phi_\delta(x) > \alpha\}$. We shall show that E is in fact an open set. For this, let $x \in E$. Then there exists $0 < r \leq \delta$ such that

$$\frac{\mu(B(x,r))}{\lambda(B(x,r))} > \alpha.$$

Let $\eta > 0$ be arbitrary and let $|x - y| < \eta$. Then $B(x,r) \subseteq B(y,r+\eta)$. Thus

$$\begin{aligned}\mu(B(y,r+\eta)) &\geq \mu(B(x,r))\\ &= \frac{\mu(B(x,r))}{\lambda(B(x,r))}\lambda(B(x,r))\\ &= \frac{\mu(B(x,r))}{\lambda(B(x,r))}\lambda(B(y,r)).\end{aligned}$$

Hence for every $y \in B(x,r)$ with $|x-y| < \eta$, using exercise 7.5.7, we have

$$\begin{aligned}\frac{\mu(B(y,r+\eta))}{\lambda(B(y,r+\eta))} &\geq \left(\frac{\mu(B(x,r))}{\lambda(B(x,r))}\right)\left(\frac{\lambda(B(y,r))}{\lambda(B(y,r+\eta))}\right)\\ &= \left(\frac{r}{r+\eta}\right)^n\left(\frac{\mu(B(x,r))}{\lambda(B(x,r))}\right).\end{aligned}$$

Since $\forall\ \eta > 0$, $(r/(r+\eta))^n < 1$ and it converges to 1 as $\eta \to 0$, we can choose η_0 such that

$$\left(\frac{r}{r+\eta_0}\right)^n\left(\frac{\mu(B(x,r))}{\lambda(B(x,r))}\right) > \alpha.$$

For this choice of η_0 we have $B(x,\eta_0) \subseteq E$. Hence E is an open set. Similar arguments will prove that $(\underline{D}\mu)(x)$ is also Borel measurable. ∎

9.2.10. Lemma: *Let $\alpha \in \mathbb{R}, \alpha > 0$ and $A \in \mathcal{B}_{\mathbb{R}^n}$. Then*

(i) $\lambda(\{x \in A \mid (\overline{D}\mu)(x) > \alpha\}) \leq 3^n\mu(A)/\alpha$.

(ii) $\lambda(\{x \in A \mid (\overline{D}\mu)(x) > 0\}) = 0$ *whenever* $\mu(A) = 0$.

Proof: Let $E := \{x \in A \mid (\overline{D}\mu)(x) > \alpha\}$. By lemma 9.2.9, $E \in \mathcal{B}_{\mathbb{R}^n}$. Let K be any compact set and V be any open set such that $K \subseteq E \subseteq V$. We shall show that

$$\mu(K) < 3^n\mu(V)/\alpha.$$

Let K and V as above be fixed. For $x \in K$, since $x \in E$, $\exists$ $r_x > 0$ such that $B(x, r_x) \subset V$ and

$$\frac{\mu(B(x, r_x))}{\lambda(B(x, r_x))} > \alpha. \tag{9.6}$$

The family $\{B(x, r_x)\}_{x \in K}$ forms an open cover of K, and hence there exist points $x_1, \dots, x_m \in K$ such that

$$K \subseteq \bigcup_{i=1}^{m} B(x_i, r_{x_i}). \tag{9.7}$$

By lemma 9.2.7, we get a pairwise disjoint subcollection, say $B_1, B_2, \dots, B_k$, of $\{B(x_i, r_{x_i}) \mid 1 \leq i \leq m\}$, such that

$$\lambda\left(\bigcup_{i=1}^{m} B(x_i, r_{x_i})\right) \leq 3^n \sum_{j=1}^{k} \lambda(B_j). \tag{9.8}$$

From (9.6), (9.7) and (9.8) we have

$$\lambda(K) \leq 3^n \sum_{j=1}^{k} \lambda(B_j) < \frac{3^n}{\alpha} \sum_{j=1}^{n} \mu(B_j) \leq \frac{3^n \mu(V)}{\alpha}.$$

Now it follows from the regularity of λ (exercise 7.5.3) and the regularity of μ (corollary 9.2.6) that

$$\lambda(E) \leq 3^n \mu(A)/\alpha.$$

This proves (i).

To prove (ii), note that

$$\{x \in A \mid (\overline{D}\mu)(x) > 0\} = \bigcup_{k=1}^{\infty} \{x \in A \mid (\overline{D}\mu)(x) \geq 1/k\},$$

and by (i), $\lambda(\{x \in A \mid (\overline{D}\mu)(x) \geq 1/k\}) = 0$ $\forall k$ if $\mu(A) = 0$. ∎

9.2.11. Lemma: *Let $f \in L_1(\mathbb{R}^n)$ with $f(x) \geq 0$. Define*

$$\mu(E) := \int_E f(x) d\lambda(x), \quad E \in \mathcal{B}_{\mathbb{R}^n}.$$

Then μ is a finite measure on $\mathcal{B}_{\mathbb{R}^n}$, and $(D\mu)(x)$ exists for a.e. $x(\lambda)$, and $(D\mu)(x) = f(x)$ for a.e. $x(\lambda)$.

Proof: Clearly, μ is a finite measure on $\mathcal{B}_{\mathbb{R}^n}$, and $\forall$ $x \in \mathbb{R}^n$,

$$0 \leq (\underline{D}\mu)(x) \leq (\overline{D}\mu)(x).$$

Thus to prove the required claim, it is enough to show that

$$\lambda(\{x \in \mathbb{R}^n \mid (\underline{D}\mu(x) < f(x) < (\overline{D})\mu(x)\}) = 0.$$

We first show that $\lambda(\{x \in \mathbb{R}^n \mid (\overline{D}\mu)(x) > f(x)\}) = 0$. Since

$$\{x \in \mathbb{R}^n \mid (\overline{D}\mu)(x) > f(x)\} = \bigcup_{r \in \mathbb{Q}} \{x \in \mathbb{R}^n \mid (\overline{D}\mu)(x) > r > f(x)\},$$

to prove the required claim it is enough to show that $\forall \ r \in \mathbb{Q}$,

$$\lambda(\{x \in \mathbb{R}^n \mid (\overline{D}\mu)(x) > r > f(x)\}) = 0. \tag{9.9}$$

For $r \in \mathbb{Q}$ fixed, let

$$E_r := \{x \in \mathbb{R}^n \mid (\overline{D}\mu)(x) > r > f(x)\} \ \text{ and } \ A_r := \{x \in \mathbb{R}^n \mid f(x) \geq r\}.$$

Then A_r is a Lebesgue measurable set with $\lambda(A_r) < +\infty$ and $E_r \subseteq A_r^c$. To prove (9.9), it is enough to show that $(\overline{D}\mu)(x) \leq r$ for a.e. $(\lambda)x \in A_r^c$. Let $x_0 \in \mathbb{R}^n$ be fixed, and B any open ball with center x_0. Then

$$\begin{aligned}
\mu(B) &= r\lambda(B) + (\mu(B) - r\lambda(B)) \\
&= r\lambda(B) + \int_B (f(x) - r) \, d\lambda(x) \\
&\leq r\lambda(B) + \int_{B \cap A_r} (f(x) - r) \, d\lambda(x).
\end{aligned}$$

Let

$$\nu(E) := \int_{A_r \cap E} (f(x) - r) d\lambda(x), \quad E \in \mathcal{B}_{\mathbb{R}^n}. \tag{9.10}$$

Since $\lambda(A_r) \leq \|f\|_1/r < +\infty$, ν is a finite measure on $\mathcal{B}_{\mathbb{R}^n}$ and

$$\mu(B) \leq r\lambda(B) + \nu(B).$$

Thus

$$\frac{\mu(B)}{\lambda(B)} \leq r + \frac{\nu(B)}{\lambda(B)}.$$

Since this holds for every open ball with center x_0, we have

$$(\overline{D}\mu)(x_0) \leq r + (\overline{D}\nu)(x_0).$$

Thus $(\overline{D}\mu)(x) \leq r$, whenever $(\overline{D}\nu)(x) = 0$. In view of lemma 9.2.10, we would be through if we could say $\nu(A_r^c) = 0$. If A_r were a Borel set, this would follow from (9.6). Since A_r need not be a Borel set (even though A_r is Lebesgue measurable), we cannot deduce that. However, we can find a Borel set F with $A_r \subseteq F$ and $\lambda(F) = \lambda(A_r)$ (see exercise 7.5.3). Then $\nu(F^c) = 0$, and hence we have $(\overline{D}\nu)(x) = 0$ for a.e. $x \in F^c$. Since $\lambda(F \setminus A_\epsilon) = 0$, we have $(\overline{D}\nu)(x) = 0$ for a.e. $x \in A_r^c$. This proves that $(\overline{D}\mu)(x) \leq r$ for a.e. $x \in A_r^c$. Thus (9.9) holds, and we get

$$\lambda(\{x \in \mathbb{R}^n \mid \overline{D}\mu(x) > f(x)\}) = 0.$$

A similar argument will prove that

$$\lambda(\{x \in \mathbb{R}^n \mid \underline{D}\mu(x) < f(x) = 0\}). \quad \blacksquare$$

9.2.12. Note: Let $f \in L_1(\mathbb{R}^n)$. Applying lemma 9.2.11 to f^+ and f^-, we get, for a.e. $x \in \mathbb{R}^n$,

$$f(x) = \lim_{r \to 0} \left(\frac{1}{\lambda(B(x,r))} \int_{B(x,r)} f(y) d\lambda(y) \right). \qquad (9.11)$$

A particular case of this (for $n = 1$) is theorem 6.3.2. The points where (9.11) holds are called the **Lebesgue points** of f.

Proof of theorem 9.2.4: (i) Let $A \in \mathcal{B}_{\mathbb{R}^n}$ be such that $\mu(A) = 0$. Since $0 \le (\underline{D}\mu)(x) \le (\overline{D}\mu)(x) \;\forall\, x \in \mathbb{R}^n$, to prove the required claim it is enough to show that $\lambda(\{x \in A \mid (\overline{D}\mu)(x) > 0\}) = 0$, and this follows by lemma 9.2.10.

(ii) Let $f := \dfrac{d\mu}{d\lambda}$. Since μ is finite, $f \in L_1(\mu)$ and

$$\mu(E) = \int_E f(x) d\lambda(x), \; E \in \mathcal{B}_{\mathbb{R}^n}.$$

Thus, by lemma 9.2.11, $(D\mu)(x)$ exists for a.e. $x \in \mathbb{R}^n$ and is equal to $f(x)$.

(iii) That $(D\mu)(x)$ exists for a.e. x follows from the Lebesgue decomposition of μ (theorem 9.1.10) along with (i) and (ii). ∎

9.2.13. Exercise: Let $F : [a,b] \longrightarrow \mathbb{R}$ be a monotonically increasing function. Show that F is differentiable a.e. (theorem 6.2.1), as follows:

(i) Let

$$\tilde{F}(x) := \begin{cases} F(x+) & \text{if } x \in [a,b), \\ F(b) & \text{if } x = b. \end{cases}$$

Show that $\tilde{F}$ is monotonically increasing and is right continuous on $[a,b]$. Further, $F'(x)$ exists whenever $\tilde{F}'(x)$ does.

(ii) Let $\mu_{\tilde{F}}$ be the Lebesgue-Steiltjes measure induced on $[a,b]$ by $\tilde{F}$. Apply theorem 9.2.4 and proposition 9.2.1 to deduce that $(D\mu_{\tilde{F}})(x)$ exists for a.e. x, and $\tilde{F}'(x) = (D\mu_{\tilde{F}})(x)$.

We shall see an application of theorem 9.2.4 in the next section.

9.3. Change of variable formulas

A change of variable formula is one which enables us to shift the integration from one space to another (in a hope that it will be easier to calculate it on that space). We have already seen examples of such formulas earlier, e.g., theorem 6.3.12, corollary 6.3.13 and theorem 6.3.16. In the abstract setting, the situation can be described as follows: let $(X, \mathcal{B})$ and $(Y, \mathcal{S})$ be measurable spaces and let $T : X \longrightarrow Y$ be a transformation. Let $f : Y \longrightarrow \mathbb{R}$ (or $\mathbb{C}$) be

$\mathcal{S}$-measurable on Y. Consider the composite function $(f \circ T) : X \longrightarrow \mathbb{R}$ (or $\mathbb{C}$). If T has the property that $T^{-1}(E) \in \mathcal{B} \ \forall \ E \in \mathcal{S}$ (in that case T is said to be **measurable**), then it is easy to check that $f \circ T$ is $\mathcal{B}$-measurable on X. Next, suppose μ is a measure on $(X, \mathcal{B})$. Define

$$\nu(E) := \mu(T^{-1}(E)) \ \forall \ E \in \mathcal{S}.$$

Then ν is a measure on $(Y, \mathcal{S})$. We denote it by μT^{-1}, and call it the **measure induced by** T on $(Y, \mathcal{S})$. The following can be called the **abstract change of variable formula.**

9.3.1. Theorem: *Let $T : (X, \mathcal{B}) \longrightarrow (Y, \mathcal{S})$ be a measurable function and let μ be a measure on $(X, \mathcal{B})$. Then for any $\mathcal{S}$-measurable map f on Y,*

$$\int_Y f(y)d(\mu T^{-1})(y) = \int_X (f \circ T)(x)d\mu(x),$$

in the sense that if the integral on either side exists, then so does the integral on the other side, and the two are equal.

Proof: The proof is an application of the 'simple function technique' and is left as an exercise. ∎

9.3.2. Corollary: *Let $(X, \mathcal{B}), (Y, \mathcal{S})$ and T be as in theorem 9.3.1. Let μ be a σ-finite measure on $(X, \mathcal{B})$ and ν be a σ-finite measure on $(Y, \mathcal{S})$ such that $\nu(T(E)) = 0$ whenever $\mu(E) = 0$. Then there exists a nonnegative measurable function ϕ on $(Y, \mathcal{S})$ such that $\ \forall \ f \in L_1(Y, \mathcal{S}, \nu), (f \circ T) \in L_1(X, \mathcal{B}, \mu)$ and $\ \forall \ E \in \mathcal{S}$*

$$\int_E f(y)d\nu(y) = \int_{T^{-1}(E)} (f \circ T)(x)(\phi \circ T)(x)d\mu(x).$$

Proof: Let $E \in \mathcal{B}$ and $(\mu T^{-1})(E) = 0$. Then, by the given hypothesis,

$$\nu(E) = \nu(T(T^{-1}(E))) = 0.$$

Hence $\nu \ll \mu T^{-1}$. Since μ is σ-finite, the measure μT^{-1} is also σ-finite, and by the Radon-Nikodym theorem (9.1.15), there exists a nonnegative $\mathcal{S}$-measurable function ϕ such that $\ \forall \ f \in L_1(Y, \mathcal{S}, \nu), \ f\phi \in L_1(Y, \mathcal{S}, \mu T^{-1})$ and

$$\int_Y f(y)d\nu(y) = \int_Y f(y)\phi(y)d(\mu T^{-1})(y). \tag{9.12}$$

By theorem 9.3.1,

$$\int_Y f(y)\phi(y)d(\mu T^{-1})(y) = \int_X (f \circ T)(x)(\phi \circ T)(x)d\mu(x). \tag{9.13}$$

Combining (9.12) and (9.13) and replacing f by $f\chi_E$ for $E \in \mathcal{S}$, we get the required equality. ∎

9.3.3. Remark: Let us look at a particular case of the above corollary. Let $T : [a, b] \longrightarrow [c, d]$ be monotonically increasing, onto and absolutely continuous. Then $\lambda(T(E)) = 0$ whenever $\lambda(E) = 0$ (see proposition 6.1.9). Thus by corollary 9.3.2 we have $\forall\ f \in L_1[c, d]$,

$$\int_c^d f(y)d\lambda(y) = \int_a^b (f \circ T)(x)(\phi \circ T)(x)d\lambda(x) \tag{9.14}$$

where

$$\phi(x) := \frac{d\lambda}{d\lambda T^{-1}}(x) \quad \text{for a.e. } x(\lambda).$$

Let us compute $\phi(x)$. From (9.14), for $f \equiv 1$, we have

$$T(b) - T(a) = d - c = \int_a^b \phi(T(y))d\lambda(y). \tag{9.15}$$

Also $\forall\ x \in [a, b]$, $[a, x] \subseteq T^{-1}(T([a, x]))$. Thus, taking

$$f = \chi_{T[a,x]} = \chi_{[T(a),T(x)]}$$

in (9.14), we have

$$
\begin{aligned}
T(x) - T(a) &= \int_c^d \chi_{[T(a),T(x)]}(y)\, d\lambda(y) \\
&= \int_c^d \chi_{[T(a,x)]}(y)\, d\lambda(y) \\
&= \int_a^b \chi_{T[a,x]}(T(z))(\phi \circ T)(z)\, d\lambda(z) \\
&\geq \int_a^x (\phi \circ T)(z)\, d\lambda(z).
\end{aligned}
\tag{9.16}
$$

Similarly, $\forall\ x \in [a, b]$,

$$T(b) - T(x) \geq \int_x^b (\phi \circ T)(z)d\lambda(z). \tag{9.17}$$

From (9.15), (9.16) and (9.17) we have

$$T(b) - T(x) = \int_x^b (\phi \circ T)(z)d\lambda(z), \quad \forall\ x \in [a, b].$$

Now by the fundamental theorem of calculus,

$$T'(x) = (\phi \circ T)(x) \quad \text{for a.e. } x(\lambda).$$

Thus by corollary 9.3.2 we get the relation

$$\int_c^d f(y)d\lambda(y) = \int_a^b (f \circ T)(x)T'(x)\,d\lambda(x),$$

which was also proved in corollary 6.3.13.

To extend this result to $\mathbb{R}^n$, we have to look for transformations $T :$ $\mathbb{R}^n \longrightarrow \mathbb{R}^n$ which will ensure that $\lambda(T(E)) = 0$ whenever $\lambda(E) = 0$, λ here being the Lebesgue measure on $\mathbb{R}^n$, and hope to identify $\dfrac{d\lambda}{d\lambda T^{-1}}$. One such situation is described by the next theorem. For a linear transformation T on $\mathbb{R}^n$, let $\det T$ denote the **determinant** of $[T]$, where $[T]$ is the matrix representation of T with respect to a basis of $\mathbb{R}^n$.

9.3.4. Theorem (Linear change of variable formula): *Let* $T : \mathbb{R}^n \longrightarrow$ $\mathbb{R}^n$ *be a nonsingular linear transformation. Then* $\forall\ f \in L_1(\mathbb{R}^n), (f \circ T) \in$ $L_1(\mathbb{R}^n)$ *and*

$$\int f(y)d\lambda(y) = |\det T| \int (f \circ T)(y)\,d\lambda(y)$$

Proof: For $f = \chi_E, E \in \mathcal{L}_{\mathbb{R}^n}$, the required equality follows from theorem 7.4.6 and exercise 7.5.3. The proof for the general case is an application of the 'simple function technique' and is left as an exercise. ∎

9.3.5. Exercise:

(i) Let S be a vector subspace of $\mathbb{R}^n$ such that S has dimension less than n. Show that $S \in \mathcal{B}_{\mathbb{R}^n}$ and $\lambda(S) = 0$.

(ii) Show that the Lebesgue measure λ on $\mathbb{R}^n$ is invariant under orthogonal linear transformations.

It is natural to try to extend theorem 9.3.4 to cases when T is not necessarily linear. We shall show that a change of variable formula is possible for transformations which can be approximated locally by linear transformations. Before proceeding further, we ask the reader to recall the contents of appendix G.

9.3.6. Lemma: *Let* $T : V \longrightarrow W$ *be a* C^1*-mapping, where* V *and* W *are open subsets of* $\mathbb{R}^n$. *Let* $E \subset V$ *be such that* $\lambda(E) = 0$. *Then* $T(E) \in \mathcal{L}_{\mathbb{R}^n}$ *and* $\lambda(T(E)) = 0$.

Proof: Let $E \subseteq V$ be such that $\lambda(E) = 0$. Since T is differentiable at every $y \in V$, given $\epsilon > 0$ we can choose $\delta > 0$ such that $\forall\ x \in V$ with $|x - y| < \delta$,

$$\frac{|T(y) - T(x) - T'(x)(x - y)|}{|x - y|} < \epsilon.$$

Thus

$$|T(y) - T(x)|\ <\ (\|T'(x)\| + \epsilon)|x - y|.$$

Let

$$M(x, \epsilon) := \|T'(x)\| + \epsilon.$$

Let $m \in \mathbb{N}$ be such that $m \geq M(x, \epsilon)$, and let $p \in \mathbb{N}$ be such that $1/p < \delta$. Then

$$|T(y) - T(x)| < m|x - y|, \quad \forall\ y \in B(x, 1/p).$$

Thus we have $E = \bigcup_{m,p} E_{m,p}$, where for each $m, p \in \mathbb{N}$,

$$E_{m,p} := \{x \in E \mid |T(y) - T(x)| < m|x - y|\ \forall\ y \in B(x, 1/p)\}.$$

Since $\lambda(E) = 0$, clearly $\lambda(E_{m,p}) = 0\ \forall\ m$ and p. To prove the required claim, it is enough to show that $T(E_{m,p}) \in \mathcal{L}_{\mathbb{R}^n}$ and $\lambda(T(E_{m,p})) = 0\ \forall\ m$ and p. Since $\lambda(E_{m,p}) = 0$, given $\epsilon > 0$ we can find (by exercise 7.5.2) open balls $\{B(x_i, r_i)\}_{i \geq 1}$ such that $0 < r_i < 1/p\ \forall\ i$ and

$$E_{m,p} \subseteq \bigcup_{i=1}^{\infty} B(x_i, r_i)\ \text{ with }\ \sum_{i=1}^{\infty} \lambda B(x_i, r_i) < \epsilon.$$

For $x \in E_{m,p}$, if $x \in B(x_i, r_i)$, then $|x - x_i| < r_i < 1/p$ and hence

$$|T(x) - T(x_i)|\ <\ m|x - x_i|\ <\ mr_i.$$

Thus $T(x) \in B(T(x_i), mr_i)$. Hence

$$T(E_{m,p})\ \subseteq\ \bigcup_{i=1}^{\infty} B(T(x_i), mr_i).$$

Now using exercise 7.5.7 along with the translation invariance of λ, we have

$$\sum_{i=1}^{\infty} \lambda(B(T(x_i), mr_i))\ =\ \sum_{i=1}^{\infty} m^n \lambda(B(T(x_i), r_i))$$

$$=\ \sum_{i=1}^{\infty} m^n \lambda(B(x_i, r_i)) = m^n \epsilon.$$

Hence $\overset{*}{\lambda}(T(E_{m,p})) = 0$. Thus $T(E_{m,p}) \in \mathcal{L}_{\mathbb{R}^n}$ and $\lambda(T(E_{m,p})) = 0$, proving the claim. ∎

9.3.7. Corollary: *Let* $T : V \longrightarrow W$ *be as in lemma 9.3.6. Further, assume that* T *is also a homeomorphism. Then* $T(E) \in \mathcal{B}_{\mathbb{R}^n}$ *iff* $E \in \mathcal{B}_{\mathbb{R}^n}$, *and* $T(E) \in \mathcal{L}_{\mathbb{R}^n}$ *iff* $E \in \mathcal{L}_{\mathbb{R}^n}$.

Proof: Let

$$\mathcal{S} := \{A \subseteq W \mid T^{-1}(A) \in \mathcal{B}_{\mathbb{R}^n} \cap V\}.$$

Clearly, $\mathcal{S}$ is a σ-algebra of subsets of W, and, T being continuous, $\mathcal{S}$ includes open subsets of W. Hence S includes $\mathcal{B}_{\mathbb{R}^n} \cap W$. Now suppose that for $E \subseteq V$ we have $T(E) \in \mathcal{B}_{\mathbb{R}^n} \cap W$. Then $E = T^{-1}(T(E))$, and hence $E \in \mathcal{B}_{\mathbb{R}^n} \cap V$. The above arguments applied to T^{-1} in place of T will show that $E \in \mathcal{B}_{\mathbb{R}^n} \cap V$ implies $T(E) \in \mathcal{B}_{\mathbb{R}^n} \cap W$. Next, let $E \in \mathcal{L}_{\mathbb{R}^n}$. Since λ is σ-finite, we can write

$$E = \bigcup_{m=1}^{\infty} E_m, \text{ where each } E_m \in \mathcal{L}_{\mathbb{R}^n} \text{ and } \lambda(E_m) < +\infty.$$

To show that $T(E) \in \mathcal{L}_{\mathbb{R}^n}$, it is enough to show that $T(E_m) \in \mathcal{L}_{\mathbb{R}^n}$ for every m. Since $\lambda(E_m) < +\infty$, using exercises 7.4.2 and 7.5.3 we can choose a Borel set $B \subseteq V$ such that

$$E_m \subseteq B \text{ and } \lambda(B \setminus E_m) = 0.$$

Then $\overset{*}{\lambda}(T(B \setminus E_n)) = 0$, by lemma 9.3.6, and hence $T(B \setminus E_n) \in \mathcal{L}_{\mathbb{R}^n}$. Since

$$T(E_m) = T(B) \cup T(B \setminus E_m)$$

and $T(B) \in \mathcal{B}_{\mathbb{R}^n}$, by the earlier part, we have $T(E_m) \in \mathcal{L}_{\mathbb{R}^n}$. The reverse implication follows from the above arguments applied to T^{-1}. ∎

9.3.8. Theorem: *Let V, W be open subsets of $\mathbb{R}^n$ with $\lambda(W) < +\infty$, and let $T : V \longrightarrow W$ be a bijective C^1-map. Let $T_i, 1 \le i \le n$, be the coordinate maps of T such that*

$$J_T(x) := \det \left[\frac{\partial T_i}{\partial x_j}(x) \right] \ne 0 \ \forall \ x \in \mathbb{R}^n.$$

Let $\mu(E) := \lambda(T(E)) \ \forall \ E \in \mathcal{B}_{\mathbb{R}^n}$. Then μ is a finite measure on $\mathcal{B}_{\mathbb{R}^n}$, and

$$(D\mu)(x) = |J_T(x)| \ \forall \ x \in V.$$

Proof: First note that μ is a finite measure, and hence $(D\mu)(x)$ exists for a.e. x, by theorem 9.2.4. We shall show that $(D\mu)(x)$ in fact exists $\forall \ x \in V$. Also, $J_T(x) \ne 0 \ \forall \ x$ implies by the inverse function theorem (appendix G) that T is a homeomorphism. Let $dT(x)$ be the differential of T at x.

Case (i): Assume that $0 \in V, T(0) = 0$ and $(dT)(0) = Id$, the identity transformation. We shall show that $(D\mu)(0) = 1 = |J_T(0)|$.

Let $1 > \epsilon > 0$ be fixed. By the differentiability of T at 0, $\exists \ \delta > 0$ such that

$$|T(x) - x| < \epsilon|x| \quad \forall \ 0 < |x| < \delta.$$

Thus for $|x| < r$,

$$|T(x)| < \epsilon|x| + |x| < (1 + \epsilon)r, \text{ i.e., } T(B(0, r)) \subseteq B(0, (1 + \epsilon)r).$$

We claim that $B_1 := B(0, (1 - \epsilon)r) \subseteq T(B(0, r))$. To see this, note that

$$B_1 = (B_1 \setminus T(B(0, r))) \cup (B_1 \cap T(B(0, r))).$$

Since $0 \in B_1 \cap T(B(0, r))$ and $T(B(0, r))$ is open, $B_1 \cap T(B(0, r))$ is a nonempty open set. On the other hand, if $x \in V$ with $|x| = r$, then

$$r = |x| \le |x - T(x)| + |T(x)| < \epsilon|x| + |T(x)| = r\epsilon + |T((x)|.$$

Thus $|T(x)| > (1 - \epsilon)r$, i.e., no boundary point of $B(0, r)$ is mapped into B_1. Hence

$$B_1 \setminus T(B(0, r)) = B_1 \setminus T(\overline{B(0, r)}).$$

Once again, T being continuous, $T(\overline{B(0, r)})$ is compact and hence $B_1 \setminus T(B(0, r))$ is also open. Thus B_1 is a disjoint union of two open sets. Since B_1 is a connected set, one of them should be empty. As $B_1 \cap T(B(0, r)) \ne \emptyset$, we have $B_1 = B_1 \cap T(B(0, r))$ and hence $B_1 \subseteq T(B(0, r))$. Thus $\forall\ r < \delta$,

$$B(0, (1 - \epsilon)r) \subseteq T(B(0, r)) \subseteq B(0, (1 + \epsilon)r).$$

Hence

$$\frac{\lambda(B(0, (1 - \epsilon)r))}{\lambda(B(0, r))} \le \frac{\lambda(T(B(0, r)))}{\lambda(B(0, r))} \le \frac{\lambda(B(0, (1 + \epsilon)r))}{\lambda(B(0, r))},$$

i.e.,

$$(1 - \epsilon)^n \le \frac{\lambda(T(B(0, r)))}{\lambda(B(0, r))} \le (1 + \epsilon)^n.$$

Since this holds $\forall\ r < \delta$ and $0 < \epsilon < 1$, we have

$$\lim_{r \to 0} \frac{\lambda(T(B(0, r)))}{\lambda(B(0, r))} = 1,$$

i.e.,

$$(D\mu)(0) = 1 = |J_T(0)|.$$

Case (ii): Assume that $0 \in V$, $T(0) = 0$ and $A := (dT)(0)$ is a nonsingular transformation. We shall show that $(D\mu)(0) = |J_T(0)|$.

Consider $S(x) := A^{-1}(T(x)), x \in V$. Then S is also a C^1-homeomorphism and $(dS)(0) = Id$. Thus, by case (i),

$$(D\nu)(0) = 1, \text{ where } \nu(E) := \lambda(S(E)), E \in \mathcal{B}_{\mathbb{R}^n}.$$

Since $\nu(E) = |\det A^{-1}|\lambda(T(E)) = |\det A^{-1}|\mu(E)$, we have

$$(D\mu)(0) = |\det A|(D\nu)(0) = |\det A| = |J_T(0)|.$$

Case (iii): Assume that $0 \in V$, $T(0) = 0$ and $A := (dT)(0)$ is singular. We shall show that $(D\mu)(0) = 0 = |J_T(0)|$.

Note that $A(\mathbb{R}^n)$ is a vector subspace of $\mathbb{R}^n$ of dimension less than n and hence $\lambda(A(\mathbb{R}^n)) = 0$, by exercise 9.3.5(i). Let $\eta > 0$ be given. Choose $\delta > 0$ such that

$$|T(x) - A(x)| \; < \; \eta|x|, \; \forall \; 0 < |x| < \delta.$$

Thus for $r < \delta$, if $|x| < r$ then $|T(x) - A(x)| < \eta r$. Hence

$$\begin{aligned} T(B(0,r)) & \subseteq & \{y \in \mathbb{R}^n | \; |y - A(x)| < \eta r \; \forall \; |x| < r\} \\ & = & \{rz \in \mathbb{R}^n | \; |z - A(x)| < \eta \; \forall \; |x| < 1\}. \end{aligned}$$

Let

$$E_\eta := \{z \in \mathbb{R}^n \; | \; |z - A(x)| < \eta \; \forall \; |x| < 1\}.$$

Then $\lambda(T(B(0,r))) \leq r^n \lambda(E_\eta)$. Since the sets E_η decrease to $A(B(0,1))$ as $\eta \to 0$, given $\epsilon > 0$ we can choose $\eta > 0$ such that $\lambda(E_\eta) < \epsilon$ (recall that $\lambda(A(\mathbb{R}^n)) = 0$). For this η and $\; \forall \; 0 < r < \delta$, we have

$$\lambda(T(B(0,r))) \; \leq \; r\epsilon.$$

Thus

$$\frac{\lambda(T(B(0,r)))}{\lambda(B(0,r))} \; \leq \; \frac{r^n \epsilon}{\lambda(B(0,r))} \; = \; C\epsilon,$$

where $C := \dfrac{r^n}{\lambda(B(0,r))}$ is a constant independent of r. Thus

$$(D\mu)(0) \; = \; \lim_{r \to 0} \frac{\mu(B(0,r))}{\lambda(B(0,r))} \; = \; 0 \; = \; |J_T(0)|.$$

Case (iv): Let $x \in V$ be fixed. We shall show that $(D\mu)(x) = |J_T(x)|$. Define, for $y \in \widetilde{V} := (V - x)$,

$$S(y) := T(y + x) - T(x).$$

Then S is also a C^1-homeomorphism with $0 \in \widetilde{V}$ and $S(0) = 0$. Since

$$S(B(0,r)) = \{T(y + x) - T(x) | y \in B(0,r)\} = \{T(z) - T(x) | z \in B(x,r)\},$$

we have

$$\lambda(S(B(0,r))) = \lambda(T(B(x,1) + T(x))) = \lambda T((B(x,r))).$$

Hence by cases (i) and (iii),

$$(D\mu)(x) = |J_S(0)| = |J_T(x)|. \; \blacksquare$$

9.3.9. Theorem (Nonlinear change of variable formula): *Let* $T :$ $V \longrightarrow W$ *be a bijective* C^1-*mapping from an open subset* V *of* $\mathbb{R}^n$ *onto an open subset* W *of* $\mathbb{R}^n$ *such that* $J_T(x) \neq 0 \; \forall \; x \in V$. *Then the following hold:*

(i) *If $E \subseteq V$ is such that $E \in \mathcal{L}_{\mathbb{R}^n}$, then $T(E) \in \mathcal{L}_{\mathbb{R}^n}$ and*

$$\lambda(T(E)) = \int_E |J_T(x)| \, d\lambda(x).$$

(ii) *If $f \in L_1(W)$, then $(f \circ T)|J_T| \in L_1(V)$ and*

$$\int_W f(x) d\lambda(x) = \int_V (f \circ T)(x) \, |J_T(x)| \, d\lambda(x).$$

Proof: Since $J_T(x) \neq 0 \quad \forall \ x \in V$, by the inverse function theorem, T is a homeomorphism, and by corollary 9.3.7, $T(E) \in \mathcal{L}_{\mathbb{R}^n} \ \forall \ E \in \mathcal{L}_{\mathbb{R}^n}$. Let

$$W_m = W \cap \{x \in \mathbb{R}^n | \ |x| < m\}, m \geq 1.$$

Then each W_m is an open set with $\lambda(W_m) < +\infty$. For each $m \geq 1$, define

$$\mu_m(E) := \lambda(T(E) \cap W_m), \quad E \in \mathcal{L}_{\mathbb{R}^n}.$$

Then μ_m is a well-defined finite measure. By lemma 9.3.6 it follows that $\mu_m \ll \lambda$. Thus by the Radon-Nikodym theorem (9.1.15) and theorem 9.2.4, we have $\forall \ E \in \mathcal{L}_{\mathbb{R}^n}$,

$$\mu_m(E) = \int_E (D\mu_m)(x) \, d\lambda(x). \tag{9.18}$$

Note that $\mu_m(E) = 0$ if $E \cap T^{-1}(W_m) = \emptyset$. Also, for $x \in V$ such that $T(x) \in W_m$, we have $T(B(x,r)) \subseteq W_m$ for all sufficiently small $r > 0$ (since T is continuous). Thus, for all sufficiently small r,

$$\mu_m(T(B(x,r))) = \lambda(T(B(x,r))). \tag{9.19}$$

If we consider the restricted map $T : T^{-1}(W_m) \longrightarrow W_m$ and apply theorem 9.3.8, we have, for every $x \in T^{-1}(W_m)$,

$$\lim_{r \to 0} \frac{\lambda(T(B(x,r)))}{\lambda(B(x,r))} = |J_T(x)|. \tag{9.20}$$

From (9.18), (9.19) and (9.20) it follows that

$$\lambda(T(E) \cap W_m) = \int_{T^{-1}(W_m)} \chi_E(x) \, |J_T(x)| \, d\lambda(x).$$

Now letting $m \to \infty$ and using theorem 3.6.3 and the monotone convergence theorem, we have $\forall \ E \in \mathcal{L}_{\mathbb{R}^n}$,

$$\lambda(T(E) \cap W) = \int_V \chi_E(x) \, |J_T(x)| \, d\lambda(x).$$

In particular, if $E \subseteq V$ and $E \in \mathcal{L}_{\mathbb{R}^n}$, then

$$\lambda(T(E)) = \int_E |J_T(x)| \, d\lambda(x).$$

This proves (i).

For (ii), we prove that the required claim holds for $f = \chi_E, E \in \mathcal{L}_{\mathbb{R}^n} \cap W$; the rest, being an application of the 'simple function technique', is left as an exercise. So, let $E \in \mathcal{L}_{\mathbb{R}^n} \cap W$. Then $E = A \cup N$, where $A \subseteq W$ is a Borel set and $\lambda(N) = 0$. Since T is continuous, $T^{-1}(A) \in B_{\mathbb{R}^n} \subseteq \mathcal{L}_{\mathbb{R}^n}$, and hence, by part (i),

$$
\begin{aligned}
\lambda(A) &= \lambda(T(T^{-1}(A))) \\
&= \int_{T^{-1}(A)} |J_T(x)| \, d\lambda(x) \\
&= \int_V (\chi_A \circ T)(x) \, |J_T(x)| \, d\lambda(x).
\end{aligned} \tag{9.21}
$$

Since $\lambda(N) = 0$, we can choose a Borel set B such that $N \subseteq B$ and $\lambda(B) = 0$. Then

$$
0 = \int_V (\chi_B \circ T)(x) \mid J_T(x)| \, d\lambda(x).
$$

The integrand being a nonnegative function, we get $(\chi_B \circ T)(x) \, |J_T(x)| = 0$ for a.e. $x(\lambda)$. Hence $(\chi_N \circ T)(x) \, |J_T(x)| = 0$ for a.e. $x(\lambda)$. Thus

$$
\int_V (\chi_N \circ T)(x) \, |J_T(x)| \, d\lambda(x) = 0 = \lambda(N \setminus A). \tag{9.22}
$$

From (9.21) and (9.22), we have

$$
\lambda(E) = \lambda(A) + \lambda(N \setminus A) = \int_V (\chi_E \circ T)(x) \, |J_T(x)| \, d\lambda(x). \quad \blacksquare
$$

9.3.10. Corollary. *Let $X, Y \in \mathcal{L}_{\mathbb{R}^n}$ and let $T : X \longrightarrow Y$ be a map such that the following hold:*

(i) *There exist open sets $V \subseteq X$ and $W \subseteq Y$ such that*

$$
\lambda(X \setminus V) = \lambda(Y \setminus W) = 0.
$$

(ii) *$T : V \longrightarrow W$ is a one-one, C^1-mapping such that*

$$
J_T(x) \neq 0 \ \forall \ x \in V.
$$

Then $\forall \ f \in L_1(Y)$, the function $(f \circ T) \, |J_T(x)| \in L_1(X)$, being defined arbitrarily on $X \setminus V$, and

$$
\int_Y f(y) d\lambda(y) = \int_X (f \circ T)(x) \, |J_T(x)| \, d\lambda(x).
$$

Proof: This follows from theorem 9.3.9. $\blacksquare$

9.3.11. Example (Polar coordinate transformation): Let

$$
V := \{(r, \theta) \in \mathbb{R}^2 \mid r > 0, \, 0 < \theta < 2\pi\} \ \text{ and } \ W := \mathbb{R}^2 \setminus \{(x, 0) \mid x \geq 0\}.
$$

Clearly, V and W are open subsets of $\mathbb{R}^2$, and $T : V \longrightarrow W$, defined by

$$T(r, \theta) := (r \cos \theta, r \sin \theta),$$

is a one-to-one mapping. T is called the **polar coordinate** transformation. It is easy to check that T is a C^1-mapping and

$$|J_T(x)| = r \ \forall \ x \in V.$$

Let

$$X = \{(r, \theta) \in \mathbb{R}^2 \mid r \geq 0, \ 0 \leq \theta \leq 2\pi\}.$$

Since

$$X \setminus V = \{(r, 0) \mid r \geq 0\} \cup \{(r, 2\pi) \mid r \geq 0\} \cup \{(0, \theta) \mid 0 \leq \theta \leq 2\pi\},$$

it is easy to check that $T(X) = \mathbb{R}^2$ and $\lambda(X \setminus V) = 0$, λ being the Lebesgue measure on $\mathbb{R}^2$. Thus for any $f \in L_1(X)$, by corollary 9.3.10 and Fubini's theorem,

$$\int_{\mathbb{R}^2} f(y) d\lambda(y) = \int_X (f \circ T)(x) |J_T(x)| \, d\lambda(x)$$

$$= \int_0^\infty \int_0^{2\pi} (f \circ T)(r, \theta) \, r \, d\lambda(r) \, d\lambda(\theta).$$

9.3.12. Exercise: Let

$$C_\alpha := \{(x, y) \in \mathbb{R}^2 \mid x \geq 0, y \geq 0 \ \text{and} \ x^2 + y^2 \leq \alpha^2\}$$

and

$$S_\alpha := \{(x, y) \in \mathbb{R}^2 \mid 0 \leq x \leq \alpha, 0 \leq y \leq \alpha\}.$$

Then the following hold:

(i) Using example 9.3.11 and Fubini's theorem, respectively, show that

$$\int_{C_\alpha} e^{-(x^2+y^2)} d\lambda(x, y) = \frac{\pi}{4}(1 - e^{-\alpha^2}),$$

and

$$\int_{S_\alpha} e^{-(x^2+y^2)} d\lambda(x, y) = \left(\int_0^\alpha e^{-x^2} dx \right)^2.$$

(ii) Using the inequality

$$\int_{C_\alpha} e^{-(x^2+y^2)} d\lambda(x, y) \leq \int_{S_\alpha} e^{-(x^2+y^2)} d\lambda(x, y) \leq \int_{C_\beta} e^{-(x^2+y^2)} d\lambda(x, y),$$

where $\alpha = \sqrt{2}\alpha$, deduce that

$$\int_0^\infty e^{-x^2} dx = \frac{\sqrt{\pi}}{2}.$$

(For a more general form of this exercise, see exercise 9.3.15.)

9.3.13. Example: As another application of the change of variable formulas, let us compute $V_n(a)$, the volume (i.e., the Lebesgue measure) of the ball

$$B(0, a) := \{ \boldsymbol{x} \in \mathbb{R}^n \mid |\boldsymbol{x}| < a \}$$

for $a \in \mathbb{R}, a > 0$ and $n \geq 3$. Let λ_n denote the Lebesgue measure on $\mathbb{R}^n$ and λ the Lebesgue measure on $\mathbb{R}$. First note that, using the linear change of variable formula (theorem 9.3.4) for the linear transformation $T(\boldsymbol{x}) = a\boldsymbol{x}, \boldsymbol{x} \in \mathbb{R}^n$, we have

$$V_n(a) = |\det T| \, V_n(1) = a^n V_n(1).$$

Thus to compute $V_n(a)$, it is enough to compute $V_n(1)$. Let us denote a general point of $\mathbb{R}^{n-2}$ ($n \geq 3$) by $\boldsymbol{w}$. Then using Fubini's theorem, we have

$$
\begin{aligned}
V_n(1) &= \int_{\mathbb{R}^n} \chi_{V_n(1)}(\boldsymbol{x}) \, d\lambda_n(\boldsymbol{x}) \\
&= \int_{\mathbb{R}^2} \int_{\mathbb{R}^{n-2}} \chi_{V_n(1)}(\boldsymbol{w}, x, y) \, d\lambda_{n-2}(\boldsymbol{w}) \, d\lambda(x) \, d\lambda(y) \\
&= \int_{\mathbb{R}^2} \int_{\mathbb{R}^{n-2}} \chi_{V_{n-2}(1-(x^2+y^2)^{1/2})}(\boldsymbol{w}) \, d\lambda_{n-1}(\boldsymbol{w}) \, d\lambda(x) \, d\lambda(y) \\
&= \int_{\mathbb{R}^2} (V_{n-2}(1 - (x^2 + y^2)^{1/2})) \, d\lambda(x) \, d\lambda(y) \\
&= \int_{\mathbb{R}^2} (1 - (x^2 + y^2))^{(n-2)/2} V_{n-2}(1) \, d\lambda(x) \, d\lambda(y) \\
&= V_{n-2}(1) \int_0^{2\pi} \int_0^1 (1 - r^2)^{(n-2)/2} \, r \, dr \, d\theta \\
&= 2\pi V_{n-2}(1)/n.
\end{aligned}
$$

Thus if n is even, say $n = 2k$, then

$$V_n(1) = \frac{(2\pi)^{n/2}}{n(n-2)\cdots 4.2} = \frac{\pi^k}{k!}.$$

If n is odd, say $n = 2k - 1$, then

$$V_n(1) = \frac{2(2\pi)^{\frac{n-1}{2}}}{n(n-2)\cdots 3.1} = \frac{2^{2k}\pi^{k-1}k!}{2k!}.$$

9.3.14. Exercise: Let $a > 0$ and

$$S_n(a) := \left\{ \boldsymbol{x} \in \mathbb{R}^n \,\middle|\, \sum_{i=1}^n |\boldsymbol{x}| \leq a \right\}.$$

Show that

(i) $\lambda_n(S_n(a)) = a^n \lambda_n(S_n(1))$.

(ii) $\lambda_n(S_n(1)) = 2/n \lambda_n(S_{n-1}(1))$, $\forall\ n \geq 2$.

(iii) $\lambda(S_n(a)) = 2^n a^n / n$.

9.3.15. Exercise: Let A be any positive definite $n \times n$ matrix (i.e., $A = T^t T$ for some nonsingular matrix), and let $\boldsymbol{m} \in \mathbb{R}^n$ be fixed. Show that

$$\int_{\mathbb{R}^n} \exp\{-1/2[(\boldsymbol{x} - \boldsymbol{m})^t A^{-1} (\boldsymbol{x} - \boldsymbol{m})]\} d\lambda_n(\boldsymbol{x}) = |\det A|^{1/2} (\sqrt{2\pi})^n.$$

(Here each $\boldsymbol{x} \in \mathbb{R}^n$ is written as an $n \times 1$ column vector, and t denotes the transpose of a matrix.)

9.3.16. Exercise: Let $\boldsymbol{v}^1, \boldsymbol{v}^2, \ldots, \boldsymbol{v}^n$ be n-vectors in $\mathbb{R}^n$. Let

$$P := \left\{ \sum_{j=1}^{n} t_j \boldsymbol{v}^j \,\middle|\, 0 \le t_j \le 1, 1 \le j \le n \right\},$$

called the **parallelogram** determined by the vectors $\boldsymbol{v}^1, \ldots, \boldsymbol{v}^n$. Show that

$$\lambda_n(P) = |\det T|,$$

where T is the matrix with v^j as the jth column.

9.3.17. Exercise (Integration of radial functions): Let $\phi : [0, \infty) \longrightarrow \mathbb{R}$ be any nonnegative real valued measurable function. Show that $\forall \; n \ge 3$,

$$\int_{\mathbb{R}^n} \phi(|\boldsymbol{x}|) d\lambda_n(\boldsymbol{x}) = nV_n(1) \int_0^\infty \phi(r) r^{n-1} dr$$

as follows:

(i) Let $T : \mathbb{R}^n \longrightarrow [0, \infty)$ be defined by $T(\boldsymbol{x}) := |\boldsymbol{x}|$. Show that T is measurable. Use theorem 9.3.1 to write

$$\int_{\mathbb{R}^n} \phi(|\boldsymbol{x}|) d\lambda_n(\boldsymbol{x}) = \int_0^\infty \phi(r) d(\lambda_n T^{-1})(r).$$

(ii) Using Fubini's theorem and example 9.3.13, show that $\forall \; a \in (0, \infty)$

$$(\lambda_n T^{-1})[0, a) = nV_n(a) = nV_n(1) \int_0^a r^{n-1} dr.$$

Deduce from this that

$$\int_0^\infty \phi(r) d(\lambda_n T^{-1})(r) = nV_n(1) \int_0^\infty \phi(r) r^{n-1} dr.$$

(We proved this for $n = 2$ in theorem 7.4.10, using the simple function technique. The same technique can be used to prove this exercise also.)

9.3.18. Exercise: Compute $J_T(\boldsymbol{x}), \boldsymbol{x} \in \mathbb{R}^3$, for the following transformations:

(i) Let
$$V := \{(r,\theta,z) \in \mathbb{R}^3 \mid r > 0,\ 0 < \theta < 2\pi,\ -\infty < z < +\infty\}$$
and
$$W := \mathbb{R}^n \setminus \{(x,0,0) \mid x \geq 0\}.$$
The transformation $T : V \longrightarrow W$ is defined by
$$T(r,\theta,z) := (r\cos\theta, r\sin\theta, z).$$

T is known as the **cylindrical coordinates transformation** and (r,θ,z) are called the **cylindrical coordinates** of a point in V.

(ii) Let
$$V := \{(\rho,\theta,\phi) \mid \rho > 0, 0 < \theta < 2\pi, 0 < \phi < \pi\}$$
and
$$W := \mathbb{R}^3 \setminus (\{(x,0,0) \mid x \geq 0\} \cup \{(0,0,z) \mid z \in \mathbb{R}\}).$$
The transformation $T : V \longrightarrow W$ is defined by
$$T(\rho,\theta,\phi) := (\rho\cos\theta\sin\phi, \rho\sin\theta\sin\phi, \rho\cos\phi).$$

T is called the **spherical coordinates transformation** and (ρ,θ,ϕ) are called the **spherical coordinates** of a point in V.

Chapter 10

Signed measures and complex measures

The aim of this chapter is to discuss the properties of set functions which are countably additive but are not necessarily nonnegative or even real-valued. Such set functions arise naturally. For example, if we consider a linear combination of finite measures, it need not be a measure, i.e., it need not be nonnegative (of course, it will be countably additive). Another way in which such set functions can arise is when we integrate an integrable function: for $f \in L_1(X, \mathcal{S}, \mu)$

$$\nu(E) := \int_E f d\mu, \ E \in \mathcal{S}.$$

We shall study such set functions in the next section.

10.1. Signed measures

10.1.1. Definition: Let $(X, \mathcal{S})$ be a measurable space. A set function $\mu : \mathcal{S} \longrightarrow \mathbb{R}^*$ is called a **signed measure** if it has the following properties:

(i) $\mu(\emptyset) = 0$.

(ii) μ takes at most one of the values $+\infty$ or $-\infty$.

(iii) Whenever $\{E_n\}_{n \geq 1}$ is a sequence of pairwise disjoint sets in $\mathcal{S}$ with $E := \bigcup_{n=1}^{\infty} E_n$, then

$$\mu(E) = \sum_{n=1}^{\infty} \mu(E_n),$$

where the equality holds in the sense that every rearrangement of the series $\sum_{n=1}^{\infty} \mu(E_n)$ converges to $\mu(E)$ if $|\mu(E)| < +\infty$, and diverges properly to

$\mu(E)$ otherwise. Note that the series $\sum_{n=1}^{\infty} \mu(E_n)$ is absolutely convergent whenever $|\mu(E)| < \infty$.

A signed measure μ on $(X, \mathcal{S})$ is said to be **finite** if $|\mu(X)| < +\infty$, and **σ-finite** if there exist sets $A_n \in X, n = 1, 2, \dots$, such that $X = \bigcup_{n=1}^{\infty} A_n$ and $|\mu(A_n)| < +\infty$ for every n.

10.1.2. Example: Let μ_1, μ_2 be measures on $(X, \mathcal{S})$ such that at least one of them is finite. Define $\forall \ E \in \mathcal{S}$,

$$\nu(E) := \mu_1(E) - \mu_2(E).$$

Then ν is signed measure on $\mathcal{S}$. Clearly $\nu(\emptyset) = 0$. Let $E = \bigcup_{n=1}^{\infty} E_n$,, where the E_n's are pairwise disjoint elements of $\mathcal{S}$. Then $\mu_i(E) = \sum_{n=1}^{\infty} \mu_i(E_n)$, $i = 1, 2$. Suppose $\mu_1(A) < +\infty \ \forall \ A \in \mathcal{S}$. If $\mu_2(E) < +\infty$ also, then the series $\sum_{n=1}^{\infty} (\mu_1(E_n) - \mu_2(E_n))$ is absolutely convergent to $\mu_1(E) - \mu_2(E)$. Hence

$$\nu(E) = \mu_1(E) - \mu_2(E) \ = \ \sum_{n=1}^{\infty} \mu_1(E_n) - \sum_{n=1}^{\infty} \mu_2(E_n)$$

$$= \ \sum_{n=1}^{\infty} (\mu_1(E_n) - \mu_2(E_n))$$

$$= \ \sum_{n=1}^{\infty} \nu(E_n).$$

In case $\mu_2(E) = +\infty$ or $-\infty$, clearly the series $\sum_{n=1}^{\infty} (\mu_1(E_n) - \mu_2(E_n))$ is divergent to $-\mu_2(E) = \mu_1(E) - \mu_2(E)$. Thus ν is a signed measure. If both μ_1 and μ_2 are finite measures, then

$$|\nu(X)| \leq |\mu_1(X)| + |\mu_2(X)| < +\infty,$$

i.e., ν is a finite signed measure. Similarly, if both μ_1 and μ_2 are σ-finite, then ν will also be σ-finite. ∎

We shall show that the method described in example 10.1.2 is the only way of constructing signed measures (see theorem 10.1.12). Before we do that, we give some properties of signed measures which are similar to those of measures.

10.1.3. Proposition: *Let μ be a signed measure on $(X, \mathcal{S})$. Then the following hold:*

(i) *If $A, B \in \mathcal{S}$ and $A \cap B = \emptyset$, then $\mu(A \cup B) = \mu(A) + \mu(B)$.*

(ii) *If $A \in \mathcal{S}$ with $|\mu(A)| < \infty$ and $B \in \mathcal{S}$ with $B \subseteq A$, then $|\mu(B)| < +\infty$ and $\mu(A \setminus B) = \mu(A) - \mu(B)$.*

(iii) *μ is finite iff $|\mu(A)| < +\infty \ \forall \ A \in \mathcal{S}$.*

Proof: The proof of (i) is obvious. To prove (ii), let $A \in \mathcal{S}$ and $|\mu(A)| < \infty$. If $B \in \mathcal{S}$ and $B \subseteq A$, then $A = (A \setminus B) \cup B$, and we have

$$\mu(A) = \mu(A \setminus B) + \mu(B).$$

Since $|\mu(A)| < +\infty$ and μ can take at most one of the values $+\infty$ or $-\infty$, we get $|\mu(A \setminus B)| < +\infty$ and $|\mu(B)| < \infty$. Further,

$$\mu(A \setminus B) = \mu(A) - \mu(B).$$

(iii) Follows from (ii). ∎

10.1.4. Proposition: *Let μ be a signed measure on $(X, \mathcal{S})$ and $\{E_n\}_{n \geq 1}$ be a sequence in $\mathcal{S}$. Then the following hold:*

(i) *If $E_n \subseteq E_{n+1}$ for every $n \geq 1$, and $E := \bigcup_{n=1}^{\infty} E_n$, then*

$$\mu(E) = \lim_{n \to \infty} \mu(E_n).$$

(ii) *If $E_{n+1} \subseteq E_n$ for every $n \geq 1$ and $|\mu(E_n)| < +\infty$ for some n, then for $E := \bigcap_{n=1}^{\infty} E_n$,*

$$\mu(E) = \lim_{n \to \infty} \mu(E_n).$$

Proof: Proceed as in theorem 3.6.3, keeping in mind proposition 10.1.3. We leave the details as an exercise. ∎

10.1.5. Definition: Let μ be a signed measure on $(X, \mathcal{S})$. A set $A \in \mathcal{S}$ is called a **positive set** for μ if

$$\mu(E) \geq 0, \ \forall \ E \subseteq A, E \in \mathcal{S}.$$

Similarly, a set $A \in \mathcal{S}$ is called a **negative set** for μ if

$$\mu(E) \leq 0, \ \forall \ E \subseteq A, E \in \mathcal{S}.$$

A set $A \in \mathcal{S}$ which is both a positive and a negative set for μ is called a **μ-null set.**

In order to show that example 10.1.2 is the only method of constructing signed measures, we first try to find the largest set $A \in \mathcal{S}$ which is positive for μ. Of course, $\emptyset$ is both a positive and a negative set for any signed measure μ. One can consider the union of all possible positive sets for μ in order to get the largest positive set. Two problems arise. First of all we cannot ensure this union will be in the σ-algebra $\mathcal{S}$. Next, an arbitrary union of positive sets need not be a positive set. Also, it is natural to ask the question: do there exist sets of positive μ-measure which are also positive sets for μ? The answers are provided by the next lemma.

10.1.6. Lemma: *Let μ be a signed measure on $\mathcal{S}$. Then the following hold:*

   (i) *If A is a positive set for μ and $B \subseteq A, B \in \mathcal{S}$, then B is also a positive set for μ.*

   (ii) *If $\{A_n\}_{n \geq 1}$ is a sequence of positive sets for μ, then $\bigcup_{n=1}^{\infty} A_n$ is also a positive set for μ.*

   (iii) *If $E \in \mathcal{S}$ and $0 < \mu(E) < +\infty$, then there exists a set $A \subseteq E, A \in \mathcal{S}$, such that A is a positive set for μ and $\mu(A) > 0$.*

Proof: The proof of (i) is obvious.

   (ii) Let $\{A_n\}_{n \geq 1}$ be a sequence of sets which are positive for μ, and let $A := \bigcup_{n=1}^{\infty} A_n$. Let

$$B_1 := A_1 \quad \text{and} \quad B_n = A_n \setminus \left(\bigcup_{k=1}^{n-1} A_k \right), \text{ for } n \geq 2.$$

Then the sets $B_n, n = 1, 2, \ldots$, are pairwise disjoint and $A = \bigcup_{n=1}^{\infty} B_n$. Let $E \in \mathcal{S}$ with $E \subseteq A$. Then $E = \bigcup_{n=1}^{\infty} (B_n \cap E)$. Since $B_n \cap E \subseteq A_n$ and A_n is a positive set for μ, $\mu(B_n \cap E) > 0$ for every n. Thus

$$\mu(E) = \sum_{n=1}^{\infty} \mu(B_n \cap E) \geq 0.$$

Hence A is a positive set for μ.

   (iii) Let $E \in \mathcal{S}$ and $0 < \mu(E) < +\infty$. Either E itself is a positive set for μ, or it contains sets of negative measure. In the earlier case we are through. In the later case, let η_1 be the smallest positive integer such that there exists a set $E_1 \subseteq E$ with $E_1 \in \mathcal{S}$ and $\mu(E_1) < -1/\eta_1$. Note that $\mu(E \setminus E_1) < \infty$. Thus we can apply the above argument to $E \setminus E_1$. Proceeding inductively, either we will be through after some finite number of steps, or we will have a sequence $\{\eta_k\}_{k \geq 1}$ of positive integers and sets $E_k \in \mathcal{S}, k \geq 1$, with the properties that $\forall k \geq 1$,

$$E_k \subseteq E \setminus \left(\bigcup_{j=1}^{k-1} E_j \right)$$

and η_k is the smallest positive integer such that $\mu(E_k) < -1/\eta_k$. Put

$$A := E \setminus \left(\bigcup_{n=1}^{\infty} E_k \right).$$

Then $E = A \cup (\bigcup_{k=1}^{\infty} E_k)$ and these sets are pairwise disjoint. Thus

$$\mu(E) = \mu(A) + \sum_{k=1}^{\infty} \mu(E_k).$$

Since $\mu(E) < +\infty$, the series on the right hand side of the above equality is absolutely convergent. Hence $\sum_{k=1}^{\infty} 1/n_k$ is convergent, and we have $\eta_k \to \infty$ as $k \to \infty$. Also, since $\mu(E_k) \le 0 \ \forall \ k$ and $\mu(E) > 0$, we have $\mu(A) > 0$. To complete the proof, we show that A is a positive set. Let $B \subseteq A$ with $B \in \mathcal{S}$, and let $\epsilon > 0$ be given. Choose η_k such that $1/(\eta_k - 1) < \epsilon$. Since $\forall \ B \subseteq E \setminus (\bigcup_{j=1}^{k} E_j)$ with $B \in \mathcal{S}$ we have $\mu(B) \ge -1/(\eta_k - 1)$ (by the defining property of the η_k's). In particular, $\forall \ B \subseteq A \subseteq E \setminus (\bigcup_{j=1}^{k} E_j)$ with $B \in \mathcal{S}$, we have

$$\mu(B) \ge -1/(\eta_k - 1) > -\epsilon.$$

Since $\epsilon > 0$ is arbitrary, $\mu(B) \ge 0$. ∎

10.1.7. Exercise: Let $\{A_n\}_{n \ge 1}$ be a sequence of negative (null) sets for μ. Show that $\bigcup_{n=1}^{\infty} A_n$ is also a negative (null) set for μ.

10.1.8. Theorem (Hahn decomposition): *Let μ be a signed measure on $(X, \mathcal{S})$. Then there exist sets $A, B \in \mathcal{S}$ such that the following hold:*

(i) *$X = A \cup B$ and $A \cap B = \emptyset$.*

(ii) *A is a positive set for μ and B is a negative set for μ.*

Proof: Since μ takes at most one of the values $+\infty$ or $-\infty$, we may assume without loss of generality that $-\infty \le \mu(E) < +\infty \ \forall \ E \in \mathcal{S}$ (for otherwise we can consider $-\mu$). Our idea of the proof is to construct a set A which is a positive set for μ, for which $\mu(A)$ is largest and is such that $B := X \setminus A$ is a negative set for μ. Let

$$\beta := \sup\{\mu(E) \mid E \text{ is a positive set for } \mu\}.$$

Clearly $\beta \ge 0$, since $\emptyset$ is a positive set. Let $\{E_k\}_{k \ge 1}$ be a sequence of sets which are positive for μ and such that

$$\beta = \lim_{k \to \infty} \mu(E_k).$$

Let $A := \bigcup_{k=1}^{\infty} E_k$. By lemma 10.1.6, A is a positive set for μ and hence $\mu(A) \le \beta$. Also, $A \setminus E_k \subseteq A$ implies that $\mu(A \setminus E_k) \ge 0 \ \forall \ k$. Thus $\forall \ k$,

$$\mu(A) = \mu(E_k) + \mu(A \setminus E_k) \ge \mu(E_k).$$

This implies that $\mu(A) \ge \lim_{k \to \infty} \mu(E_k) = \beta$. Thus $\mu(A) = \beta$ and, by our assumption that the value $+\infty$ is not taken by μ, we have $\beta < +\infty$. Let $B = X \setminus A$. To show that B is a negative set for μ, let $E \subseteq B$ and $E \in \mathcal{S}$. If $\mu(E) > 0$ then $0 < \mu(E) < \beta < +\infty$ and, by lemma 10.1.6, there exists a set $F \in \mathcal{S}, F \subseteq E$, such that $\mu(F) > 0$ and F is a positive set for μ. But then $F \cup A$ is also a positive set and

$$\beta > \mu(F \cup A) = \mu(F) + \mu(A) > \mu(F) + \beta.$$

This implies that $\mu(F) = 0$, a contradiction. Hence $\forall\ E \in \mathcal{S}$ with $E \subseteq B$ we have $\mu(E) \leq 0$, i.e., B is a negative set for μ. ∎

10.1.9. Definition: Let μ be a signed measure on $(X, \mathcal{S})$. A pair of sets $A, B \in \mathcal{S}$ is called a **Hahn decomposition** of X with respect to μ if $X = A \cup B$ with $A \cap B = \emptyset$, where A is a positive set for μ and B is a negative set for μ.

Theorem 10.1.8 shows that a Hahn decomposition of X always exists. However, a Hahn decomposition need not be unique. This follows from the next exercise.

•10.1.10. Exercise: Let μ be a signed measure on $(X, \mathcal{S})$ and let A, B be a Hahn decomposition of X with respect to μ. Let $N \in \mathcal{S}$ be such that $\mu(N) = 0$. Show that $(A \setminus N), B \cup N$ is also a Hahn decomposition of X. Further, if A_1, B_1 and A_2, B_2 are two Hahn decompositions of X with respect to μ, then $\mu(A_1 \triangle A_2) = \mu(B_1 \triangle B_2) = 0$, and $\forall\ E \in \mathcal{S}$, $\mu(E \cap A_1) = \mu(E \cap A_2)$, $\mu(E \cap B_1) = \mu(E \cap B_2)$.

10.1.11. Exercise: Let $(X, \mathcal{S}, \mu)$ be a measure space and $f \in L_1^r(X, \mathcal{S}, \mu)$. Let

$$\nu(E) := \int_E f d\mu, \quad E \in \mathcal{S}.$$

Find a Hahn decomposition of X with respect to ν.

Finally, we prove that every signed measure is the difference of two measures.

10.1.12. Theorem (Jordan decomposition): *Let μ be a signed measure on $(X, \mathcal{S})$. Then there exist measures μ^+ and μ^- on $(X, \mathcal{S})$ with the following properties:*

(i) *$\mu = \mu^+ - \mu^-$ and at least one of the measures μ^+ and μ^- is finite.*

(ii) *$\mu^+ \perp \mu^-$, i.e., there exist disjoint sets $A, B \in \mathcal{S}$ such that $\mu^+(B) = \mu^-(A) = 0$ and $A \cup B = X$.*

(iii) *If $\mu = \nu - \eta$, where ν and η are measures with at least one of them being finite and $\nu \perp \eta$, then $\mu^+ = \nu$ or η and μ^- equals the other. In other words, the decomposition of μ as a difference of two singular measures is unique.*

Proof: Let $X = A \cup B$ be a Hahn decomposition of X with respect to μ, where A is a positive set for μ and B is a negative set for μ. Define μ^+ and

μ^- on $\mathcal{S}$ as follows:

$$\mu^+(E) := \mu(A \cap E) \quad \text{and} \quad \mu^-(E) := \mu(B \cap E), \quad E \in \mathcal{S}.$$

Clearly, μ^+ and μ^- are measures on $\mathcal{S}$ with $\mu = \mu^+ - \mu^-$, and at least one of μ^+ and μ^- is finite, since μ takes at most one of the values $+\infty$ or $-\infty$. That $\mu^+ \perp \mu^-$ is obvious. Finally, let $\mu = \nu - \eta$, where ν and η are measures with $\nu \perp \eta$, and say ν is finite. Then μ never takes the value $+\infty$ and hence μ^+ is also finite. Let $C, D \in \mathcal{S}$ be such that $\nu(C) = \eta(D) = 0$ with $C \cap D = \emptyset$ and $C \cup D = X$. Clearly C is a positive set for μ and D is a negative set for μ. Thus C, D is also a Hahn decomposition of X with respect to μ. Hence by exercise 10.1.10 we have $\forall\ E \in \mathcal{S}$,

$$\mu^+(E) = \mu(E \cap A) = \mu(E \cap C) = \nu(E)$$

and

$$\mu^-(E) = \mu(E \cap B) = \mu(E \cap D) = \eta(E). \quad \blacksquare$$

10.1.13. Definition: Let μ be a signed measure on $(X, \mathcal{S})$. The measures μ^+ and μ^-, as given by theorem 10.1.12, are called the **upper** and **lower variations** (or **positive part** and **negative part**) of μ, respectively. The measure $|\mu| := \mu^+ + \mu^-$ is called the **total variation** of μ.

10.1.14. Exercise: Let $(X, \mathcal{S}, \mu)$ be a measure space and $f \in L_1^r(X, \mathcal{S}, \mu)$. Let

$$\nu(E) := \int_E f d\mu, \quad E \in \mathcal{S}.$$

Show that $\forall\ E \in \mathcal{S}$,

$$\nu^+(E) = \int_E f^+ d\mu, \ \nu^-(E) = \int_E f^- d\mu \quad \text{and} \quad |\nu|(E) = \int_E |f| d\mu.$$

•**10.1.15. Exercise:** Let μ be a signed measure on $(X, \mathcal{S})$. Show that the following statements are equivalent:

  (i) μ is finite (σ-finite).

  (ii) μ^+, μ^- are both finite (σ-finite).

  (iii) $|\mu|$ is finite (σ-finite).

•**10.1.16. Exercise:** Let μ be a signed measure on $(X, \mathcal{S})$. Show that

$$|\mu(E)| \le |\mu|(E) \ \forall\ E \in \mathcal{S}$$

and $|\mu|$ is the smallest measure on $\mathcal{S}$ with this property, i.e., if ν is any other measure on $\mathcal{S}$ such that $|\mu(E)| \le |\nu|(E) \ \forall\ E \in \mathcal{S}$, then $|\mu|(E) \le \nu(E) \ \forall\ E \in \mathcal{S}$.

The next theorem gives an alternate description of the measures μ^+, μ^- and $|\mu|$. For $E \in \mathcal{S}$, we say $\{E_1, E_2, \ldots, E_n\}$ is a **measurable partition** of E if $E_1, E_2, \ldots, E_n$ are pairwise disjoint and $E = \bigcup_{i=1}^{n} E_i$.

10.1.17. Theorem: *Let μ be a signed measure on $(X, \mathcal{S})$. Then $\forall \ E \in \mathcal{S}$, the following hold:*

(i) $\mu^+(E) = \sup\{\mu(F) \mid F \subseteq E, F \in \mathcal{S}\}$.

(ii) $\mu^-(E) = \sup\{-\mu(F) \mid F \subseteq E, F \in \mathcal{S}\}$.

(iii)

$$|\mu|(E) = \sup\left\{\sum_{i=1}^{n} |\mu(F_i)| \,\middle|\, \{E_1, \ldots, E_n\} \text{ is a measurable partition of } E\right\}.$$

Proof: (i) Let A, B be a Hahn decomposition of X with respect to μ. For $E \in \mathcal{S}$, clearly

$$\mu^+(E) = \mu(E \cap A) \leq \sup\{\mu(F) \mid F \subseteq E, F \in \mathcal{S}\}. \qquad (10.1)$$

Since B is a negative set for μ, if $F \subseteq E$ with $F \in \mathcal{S}$, then

$$\mu(F) = \mu(F \cap A) + \mu(F \cap B) \leq \mu(F \cap A) = \mu^+(F) \leq \mu^+(E).$$

Hence

$$\sup\{\mu(F) \mid F \subseteq E, F \in B\} \leq \mu^+(E). \qquad (10.2)$$

Thus (i) follows from (10.1) and (10.2). Also, observing that $\mu^- = (-\mu)^+$, (ii) follows from (i).

Finally, to prove (iii), let $E \in \mathcal{S}$ be fixed and let α denote the right side of the equality in (iii). Then for any finite collection $\{F_1, \ldots, F_n\}$ of sets from $\mathcal{S}$ with $E = \bigcup_{i=1}^{n} F_i$ and $F_i \cap F_j = \emptyset$ for $i \neq j$, we have

$$\begin{aligned}
\sum_{i=1}^{n} |\mu(F_i)| &= \sum_{i=1}^{n} |\mu^+(F_i) - \mu^-(F_i)| \\
&\leq \sum_{i=1}^{n} |\mu^+(F_i)| + \sum_{i=1}^{n} |\mu^-(F_i)| \\
&= \sum_{i=1}^{n} |\mu|(F_i) \\
&= |\mu|(E).
\end{aligned}$$

Thus $\alpha \leq |\mu|(E)$. On the other hand, if we consider the collection $\{E \cap A, E \cap B\}$, then

$$\alpha \geq |\mu(E \cap A)| + |\mu(E \cap B)| = \mu^+(E) + \mu^-(E) = |\mu|(E).$$

Hence $\alpha = |\mu|(E)$. This proves (iii). ∎

10.1.18. Exercise: Let $(\mathbb{R}, \mathcal{L}_\mathbb{R}, \lambda)$ be Lebesgue measure space and let

$$\nu(E) := \int_E x e^{-x^2} d\lambda(x), \quad E \in \mathcal{L}_\mathbb{R}.$$

Show that ν is a signed measure with $(-\infty, 0)$ as a positive set and $(0, \infty)$ as a negative set for ν. Find all positive, negative and null sets for ν. Also find μ^+, μ^- and $|\mu|$.

10.1.19. Exercise: Let $\{a_n\}_{n \geq 1}$ be a sequence of real numbers. Define μ on $(\mathbb{N}, \mathcal{P}(\mathbb{N}))$ by

$$\mu(E) := \sum_{n \in E} a_n.$$

Show that μ is a signed measure iff $\sum_n a_n$ is absolutely convergent. Find a Hahn decomposition of μ and show that it is unique if $a_n \neq 0 \ \forall \ n$.

10.2. Radon-Nikodym theorem for signed measures

In section 9.1, we characterized the measures which arise via integration. For example, theorem 9.1.15 said that for σ-finite measures μ and ν we have $\nu \ll \mu$ iff there exists a nonnegative measurable function f such that

$$\nu(E) := \int_E f d\mu \quad \forall \ E \in \mathcal{S}.$$

The proof of this theorem as given in section 9.1 required some special properties of $L_2(X, \mathcal{S}, \mu)$. We give another proof here which is based on the Hahn decomposition theorem. First, let us consider a finite measure μ on a measurable space $(X, \mathcal{S})$, and let f be any nonnegative measurable function on $(X, \mathcal{S})$. Let

$$\nu(E) = \int_E f d\mu, \quad E \in \mathcal{S}.$$

If $\nu(E) \neq 0$ for some E, then clearly $\exists n \in \mathbb{N}$ such that

$$\nu\{x \in E \mid 1/2^n \leq f(x) < 1/2^{n-1}\} > 0.$$

Let

$$E_n := \{x \in E \mid 1/2^{n-1} \leq f(x) < 1/2^n\}.$$

Then, $\forall \ A \in \mathcal{S}$ with $A \subseteq E_n$,

$$\nu(A) = \int_A f d\mu \geq \mu(A)/2^n.$$

Thus, for $\epsilon = 1/2^n$,

$$\nu(A) - \epsilon \mu(A) \geq 0, \ \forall \ A \subseteq E_n \text{ and } \nu(E_n) > 0.$$

We show that the above conclusion holds in general also when $\nu \ll \mu$.

10.2.1. Lemma: *Let μ, ν be finite measures on $(X, \mathcal{S})$ such that $\nu \neq 0$ and $\nu \ll \mu$. Then there exist a set $E \in \mathcal{S}$ with $\nu(E) > 0$ and an $\epsilon > 0$ such that $\nu(F) \geq \epsilon\mu(F) \ \forall \ F \subseteq E, F \in \mathcal{S}$.*

Proof: For every integer $n \geq 1$, consider the signed measure $(\nu - \mu/n)$. Our aim is to show that there exists some n such that $(\nu - \mu/n)$ has a positive set of positive measure. For this, consider a Hahn decomposition A_n, B_n of X with respect to $\nu - \mu/n$. Then $\ \forall \ n$,

$$(\nu - \mu/n)(B_n) \ \leq \ 0 \ \text{ and } \ (\nu - \mu/n)(A_n) \geq 0.$$

Let $A := \bigcup_{n=1}^{\infty} A_n$ and $B := \bigcap_{n=1}^{\infty} B_n$. Then $\ \forall \ n$,

$$\nu(B) \ \leq \ \nu(B_n) \ \leq \ \mu(B_n)/n \ \leq \ \mu(X)/n.$$

Hence $\nu(B) = 0$. Since $X = A \cup B$, we get $\nu(A) = \nu(X) > 0$. Thus $\nu(A_{n_0}) > 0$ for some n_0. Also, A_{n_0} is a positive set for $(\nu - \mu/n_0)$. Choosing $\epsilon = 1/n_0$ completes the proof. ■

Next we prove the Radon-Nikodym theorem for finite measures.

10.2.2. Theorem (Radon-Nikodym theorem for finite measures): *Let μ, ν be finite measures on $(X, \mathcal{S})$ and $\nu \ll \mu$. Then there exists a non-negative $f \in L_1^r(X, \mathcal{S}, \mu)$ such that $\ \forall \ E \in \mathcal{S}$,*

$$\nu(E) = \int_E f d\mu.$$

Further, if g is any other function such that

$$\nu(E) = \int_E g d\mu, \forall \, E \in \mathcal{S},$$

then $f(x) = g(x)$ for a.e. $x(\mu)$.

Proof: The idea of the proof is as follows. Consider the set S of all non-negative measurable functions g on X such that

$$\int_E g d\mu \ \leq \ \nu(E) \ \text{ for all } \ E \in \mathcal{S}.$$

We shall show that the 'largest' function in S is the required f. For this, first we note that $S \neq \emptyset$. For example $g = \epsilon\chi_E \in S$, where ϵ and E are as given by lemma 10.2.1. Let

$$\alpha := \sup\left\{ \int g d\mu \mid g \in S \right\}.$$

Clearly $0 < \alpha < \infty$. Let $g_n \in S$, $n = 1, 2, \ldots$, be such that

$$\alpha = \lim_{n \to \infty} \int g_n d\mu.$$

Put

$$f(x) := \sup_{n \geq 1} g_n(x), \ x \in X.$$

We shall prove that f is the required function. Note that for $g, h \in S$,

$$(g \vee h)(x) := \max\{g(x), h(x)\}, \ x \in X,$$

is also in S. To see this, let $E \in \mathcal{S}$ be fixed and $E_1 = \{x \in E \mid g(x) \geq h(x)\}$. Then

$$
\begin{aligned}
\int_E (g \vee h) d\mu &= \int_{E_1} (g \vee h) d\mu + \int_{E \setminus E_1} (g \vee h) d\mu \\
&\leq \int_{E_1} g d\mu + \int_{E \setminus E_1} h d\mu \\
&\leq \nu(E_1) + \nu(E \setminus E_1) \\
&= \nu(E). \tag{10.3}
\end{aligned}
$$

Thus $g \vee h \in S$. Let

$$h_n := g_1 \vee g_2 \vee \ldots \vee g_n \in S \ \forall \ n.$$

Then $\{h_n\}_{n \geq 1}$ increases to f, and, by the monotone convergence theorem and (10.3), $\forall \ E \in \mathcal{S}$

$$\int_E f d\mu = \lim_{n \to \infty} \int_E h_n d\mu \leq \nu(E). \tag{10.4}$$

Hence

$$f \in S \ \text{and} \ \int f d\mu \leq \alpha.$$

Since $g_n \leq f \ \forall \, n$,

$$\alpha = \lim_{n \to \infty} \int g_n d\mu \leq \int f d\mu.$$

Thus $\alpha = \int f d\mu$. To show that equality holds in (10.4) for all E, consider

$$\eta(E) := \nu(E) - \int_E f d\mu, \quad E \in \mathcal{S}.$$

Then η is a finite measure and $\eta \ll \mu$. If $\eta \equiv 0$, we are through. If not, i.e., $\eta \not\equiv 0$, $\exists \ \epsilon > 0$ and a set $E_0 \in \mathcal{S}$ such that $\mu(E_0) > 0$ and E_0 is a positive set for $\eta - \epsilon\mu$ (by lemma 10.2.1). Thus $\forall \ E \subseteq E_0$ and $E \in \mathcal{S}$,

$$\nu(E) - \int_E f d\mu - \epsilon\mu(E) > 0,$$

i.e.,

$$\nu(E) \geq \int_E (f + \epsilon) d\mu.$$

Thus $\forall\ E \in \mathcal{S}$,

$$
\begin{aligned}
\nu(E) &= \nu(E \cap E_0) + \nu(E \cap E_0^c) \\
&\geq \int_{E \cap E_0} (f + \epsilon) d\mu + \int_{E \cap E_0^c} 1 \, d\mu \\
&= \int_{E \cap E_0} (f + \epsilon \chi_{E_0}) d\mu + \int_{E \cap E_0^c} (f + \epsilon \chi_{E_0}) d\mu \\
&= \int_E (f + \epsilon \chi_{E_0}) d\mu.
\end{aligned}
$$

Hence $(f + \epsilon \chi_{E_0}) \in S$. On the other hand,

$$
\int (f + \epsilon \chi_{E_0}) d\mu = \int f d\mu + \epsilon \mu(E_0) = \alpha + \epsilon \mu(E_0) > \alpha,
$$

which is a contradiction. Hence $\eta \equiv 0$, i.e.,

$$
\nu(E) = \int_E f d\mu \text{ for every } E \in \mathcal{S}.
$$

The uniqueness of f follows from exercise 8.1.8. ∎

10.2.3. Exercise: Extend theorem 10.2.2 when μ, ν are σ-finite measures.

Our next aim is to extend theorem 10.2.2 to signed measures. Recall that for $f \in L_1^r(X, \mathcal{S}, \mu)$, if we define

$$
\nu(E) := \int_E f d\mu, \quad E \in \mathcal{S},
$$

then ν is a finite signed measure on $(X, \mathcal{S})$ and has the special property that $\nu(E) = 0$ whenever $\mu(E) = 0$. In fact, if f is a real-valued measurable function on f and has the property that either $f^+ \in L_1^r(X, \mathcal{S}, \mu)$ or $f^- \in L_1^r(X, \mathcal{S}, \mu)$, then

$$
\nu(E) := \int_E f^+ d\mu - \int_E f^- d\mu, \quad E \in \mathcal{S},
$$

is a well-defined signed measure on $(X, \mathcal{S})$ having the property that $\nu(E) = 0$ whenever $\mu(E) = 0$. This motivates our next definition.

10.2.4. Definition: Let $(X, \mathcal{S}, \mu)$ be a measure space. A signed measure ν on $(X, \mathcal{S})$ is said to be **absolutely continuous** with respect to μ if $\nu(E) = 0$ whenever $\mu(E) = 0$. We write this as $\nu \ll \mu$.

An equivalent definition of absolute continuity for signed measure in terms of its variation measures is given by the following proposition.

10.2.5. Proposition: *Let $(X, \mathcal{S}, \mu)$ be a measure space and ν be a signed measure on $(X, \mathcal{S})$. Then the following statements are equivalent:*

(i) $\nu \ll \mu$.

(ii) $\nu^+ \ll \mu$ *and* $\nu^- \ll \mu$.

(iii) $|\nu| \ll \mu$.

Proof: (i) $\Rightarrow$ (ii) Let $A, B \in \mathcal{S}$ be a Hahn decomposition of X with respect to ν. Let $\mu(E) = 0$. Thus

$$\mu(A \cap E) = \mu(B \cap E) = 0,$$

and, by the the given hypothesis, we have

$$\nu(E \cap A) = 0 = \nu(E \cap B) = 0.$$

Thus

$$\nu^+(E) = \nu(A \cap E) = 0 \quad \text{and} \quad \nu^-(E) = -\nu(B \cap E) = 0.$$

Hence $\nu^+ \ll \mu$ and $\nu^- \ll \mu$.

The implication (ii) $\Rightarrow$ (iii) is obvious, as $|\nu| = \nu^+ + \nu^-$.

To prove (iii) $\Rightarrow$ (i), let $\mu(E) = 0$. Then by the given hypothesis,

$$|\mu|(E) = \nu^+(E) + \nu^-(E) = 0$$

and hence $\nu^+(E) = 0 = \nu^-(E) = 0$, i.e., $\nu(E) = 0$. ∎

Jordan's decomposition theorem together with proposition 10.2.5 gives us the following extension of the Radon-Nikodym theorem for signed measures:

10.2.6. Theorem (Radon-Nikodym): *Let $(X, \mathcal{S}, \mu)$ be a σ-finite measure space and let ν be a σ-finite signed measure on $(X, \mathcal{S})$ such that $\nu \ll \mu$. Then there exists a real-valued measurable function f such that either $f^+ \in L_1^r(\mu)$ or $f^- \in L_1^r(\mu)$ and*

$$\nu(E) = \int_E f \, d\mu := \int_E f^+ \, d\mu - \int_E f^- \, d\mu, \ \forall \ E \in \mathcal{S}.$$

Further, the function f is unique in the sense that if there exists some other measurable function g such that

$$\nu(E) = \int_E g \, d\mu \ \forall \ E \in \mathcal{S},$$

then $f(x) = g(x)$ for a.e. (μ).

This unique f is denoted by $\dfrac{d\nu}{d\mu}(x)$ and is called the **Radon-Nikodym derivative** of ν with respect to μ.

Proof: By exercise 10.1.15, both the measures ν^+ and ν^- are σ-finite. Thus, by proposition 10.2.5, $\nu^+ \ll \mu$ and $\nu^- \ll \mu$. Now an application of the Radon-Nikodym theorem for σ-finite measures (exercise 10.2.3) applied to ν^+ and ν^- completes the proof. ■

10.2.7. Exercise: Show that f, as given by theorem 10.2.2, will be in $L_1^r(X, \mathcal{S}, \mu)$ iff ν is a finite signed measure.

10.2.8. Exercise: Let μ be a σ-finite measure and ν be a σ-finite signed measure on $(X, \mathcal{S})$ such that $\nu \ll \mu$. Show that

$$\frac{d\nu}{d\mu}(x) = \frac{d\nu^+}{d\mu}(x) - \frac{d\nu^-}{d\mu}(x) \text{ for a.e. } x(\mu).$$

Next we define the integrability of functions with respect to signed measures and use it to extend theorem 10.2.6 to the case when both μ and ν are signed measure (see theorem 10.2.14).

10.2.9. Definition: Let $(X, \mathcal{S})$ be a measurable space and let μ be a signed measure on $(X, \mathcal{S})$.

(i) For a nonnegative real valued measurable function f on X we write

$$\int f d\mu := \int f d\mu^+ - \int f d\mu^-,$$

whenever either $f \in L_1^r(X, \mathcal{S}, \mu^+)$ or $f \in L_1^r(X, \mathcal{S}, \mu^-)$. In case f belongs to both of them, we say f is **integrable** with respect to the signed measure μ.

(ii) If f is a real-valued measurable function on f such that either f^+ is integrable with respect to μ or f^- is integrable with respect to μ, we write

$$\int f d\mu := \int f^+ d\mu - \int f^- d\mu.$$

We say f is **integrable** with respect to μ if both f^+ and f^- are integrable with respect to μ.

We denote by $L_1^r(X, \mathcal{S}, \mu)$ the space of real-valued μ-integrable functions on X which are integrable with respect to μ.

10.2.10. Proposition: *Let μ be a signed measure on $(X, \mathcal{S})$. Then the following statements are equivalent:*

(i) $f \in L_1^r(X, \mathcal{S}, \mu)$.

(ii) $f \in L_1^r(X, \mathcal{S}, \mu^+) \cap L_1^r(X, \mathcal{S}, \mu^-)$.

(iii) $f \in L_1^r(X, \mathcal{S}, |\mu|)$.

Proof: The implications (i) $\Leftrightarrow$ (ii) are just a restatement of the definition. The implications (ii) $\Leftrightarrow$ (iii) follow from the fact that

$$\int f d\mu = \int f d\mu^+ + \int f d\mu^-$$

for every measurable function f, whenever either side exists. ∎

10.2.11. Exercise: Let $f \in L_1(X, \mathcal{S}, \mu), \mu$ a signed measure. Show that

$$\left| \int f d\mu \right| \leq \left| \int |f| \, d\mu \right| \leq \int |f| \, d|\mu|.$$

The notion of absolute continuity of a signed measure with respect to another signed measure can be defined as follows.

10.2.12. Definition: Let μ, ν be signed measure on $(X, \mathcal{S})$. We say ν is **absolutely continuous** with respect to μ if $|\mu|(E) = 0$ implies $\nu(E) = 0$. We write this as $\nu \ll \mu$.

10.2.13. Remark: Note that for signed measured ν and μ, $\nu \ll \mu$ is not defined by requiring $\nu(E) = 0$ whenever $\mu(E) = 0$ for $E \in \mathcal{S}$. See exercises 10.2.17 and 10.2.18.

10.2.14. Theorem: *Let μ, ν be σ-finite signed measures on $(X, \mathcal{S})$ such that $\nu \ll \mu$. Then there is a real-valued measurable function f on X such that $\forall \ E \in \mathcal{S}$,*

$$\nu(E) = \int_E f d\mu.$$

Further, f is unique in the sense that if g is any other real measurable function on X with

$$\nu(E) = \int_E g d\mu, \ \forall E \in \mathcal{S},$$

then $f(x) = g(x)$ for a.e. $x(|\mu|)$.

Proof: Let A, B be a Hahn decomposition of X with respect to μ. Then $\forall \ E \in \mathcal{S}$,

$$\mu^+(E) = \mu(A \cap E) \text{ and } \mu^-(E) = -\mu(B \cap E).$$

For $E \subseteq A$, $\mu(E) = \mu^+(E) + \mu^-(E) = |\mu|(E)$. Thus $\mu^+(E) = 0 = |\mu|(E) = 0$ implies that $\nu(E) = 0$. Hence $\nu \ll \mu^+$ on $(A, \mathcal{S} \cap A)$. Since both ν and μ^+ are σ-finite, an application of theorem 10.2.6 gives a measurable function f_A on A such that $\forall \ E \in A \cap \mathcal{S}$,

$$\nu(E) = \int_E f_A \, d\mu^+.$$

Similarly, we will have a measurable function f_B on B such that $\forall\ E \in B \cap \mathcal{S}$,

$$\nu(E) = \int_E f_B \, d\mu^-.$$

Define $f_A = 0$ on B and $f_B = 0$ on A. Then $f := f_A + f_B$ is a measurable function on X and, $\forall\ E \in \mathcal{S}$,

$$
\begin{aligned}
\nu(A) &= \nu(E \cap A) + \nu(E \cap B) \\
&= \int_{E \cap A} f_A \, d\mu^+ + \int_{E \cap B} f_B \, d\mu^- \\
&= \int_E f \, d\mu^+ + \int_E f \, d\mu^- = \int_E f \, d\mu.
\end{aligned}
$$

The uniqueness of f follows from the fact that $f_A(x)$ is unique for a.e. $x(\mu^+)$, and the fact that $f_B(x)$ is unique for a.e. $x(\mu^-)$, and the fact that $\mu^+ \ll |\mu|$, $\mu^- \ll |\mu|$, together with exercise 9.1.7. ∎

10.2.15. Exercise: Let μ and ν be σ-finite measures on $(X, \mathcal{S})$ such that $\mu - \nu$ is also a measure. If $\nu \ll \mu - \nu$, show that $\nu \ll \mu$ and

$$\mu\left(\left\{x \in X \,\middle|\, \frac{d\nu}{d\mu}(x) = 1\right\}\right) = 0.$$

10.2.16. Exercise: Let μ be a σ-finite signed measure. Since $\mu^+ \ll \mu$ and $\mu^+ \ll |\mu|$, we have measurable functions f and g such that

$$\int_E f \, d\mu = \int_E g \, d|\mu|, \quad \forall\ E \in \mathcal{S}.$$

What is the relation between f and g?

10.2.17. Exercise: Let μ be a signed measure on $(X, \mathcal{S})$ and f a real-valued measurable function on $(X, \mathcal{S})$ such that $\forall\ E \in \mathcal{S}, \nu(E) = \int_E f \, d\mu$ is defined. Does $\mu(E) = 0$ imply $\nu(E) = 0$? For example, consider the Lebesgue measurable space $(\mathbb{R}, \mathcal{L})$. Let

$$\mu(E) := \int_E x \, d\lambda(x), \ E \in \mathcal{L}, \ \text{and} \ f(x) = e^{-x}.$$

Can you conclude that $\nu(E) = 0$ if $|\mu|(E) = 0$?

10.2.18. Exercise: Let μ_1 and μ_2 be defined on $([0, 1], \mathcal{L} \cap [0, 1])$ by

$$\mu_1(E) := 2\lambda(E \cap [0, 1/2]) - \lambda(E) \ \text{and} \ \mu_2(E) := \int_E x \, d\lambda(x),$$

where λ is the Lebesgue measure restricted to $\mathcal{L} \cap [0, 1]$. Show that $\mu_2 \ll \mu_1$, but $\mu_1(E) = 0$ need not imply $\mu_2(E) = 0$.

10.2.19. Proposition: *Let ν_1, ν_2, μ be σ-finite signed measures such that $\nu_1 + \nu_2$ is also a σ-finite signed measure on $(X, \mathcal{S})$.*

(i) *If $\nu_1 \ll \mu$ and $\nu_2 \ll \mu$, then $(\nu_1 + \nu_2) \ll \mu$ and for a.e. $x(\mu)$*

$$\frac{d(\nu_1 + \nu_2)}{d\mu}(x) = \frac{d\nu_1}{d\mu}(x) + \frac{d\nu_2}{d\mu}(x).$$

(ii) *If $\nu_1 \ll \mu$, then*

$$\left| \frac{d\nu_1}{d\mu}(x) \right| = \frac{d|\nu_1|}{d|\mu|}(x) \ \text{ for a.e. } x(\mu).$$

Proof: (i) We first assume that μ is a measure. Let $\nu_i = \nu_i^+ - \nu_i^-, i = 1, 2,$ be the Jordan decomposition of ν_i. Since $\nu_i^+ \ll \mu$ and $\nu_i^- \ll \mu$, by exercise 9.1.21,

$$\frac{d(\nu_1^+ + \nu_2^+)}{d\mu}(x) = \frac{d\nu_1^+}{d\mu}(x) + \frac{d\nu_2^+}{d\mu}(x) \quad \text{for a.e. } x(\mu),$$

and

$$\frac{d(\nu_1^- + d\nu_2^-)}{d\mu}(x) = \frac{d\nu_1^-}{d\mu}(x) + \frac{d\nu_2^-}{d\mu}(x) \quad \text{for a.e. } x(\mu).$$

Since $\nu_1 + \nu_2$ is a signed measure, using the above equalities and exercise 10.2.8, we have, for $E \in \mathcal{S}$ with $|(\nu_1 + \nu_2)(E)| < +\infty$,

$$
\begin{aligned}
(\nu_1 + \nu_2)(E) &= (\nu_1^+ + \nu_2^+)(E) - (\nu_1^- + \nu_2^-)(E) \\
&= \int_E \frac{d(\nu_1^+ + \nu_2^+)}{d\mu} d\mu - \int_E \frac{d(\nu_1^- + \nu_2^-)}{d\mu} d\mu \\
&= \int_E \left(\frac{d\nu_1^+}{d\mu} - \frac{d\nu_1^-}{d\mu} \right) d\mu + \int_E \left(\frac{d\nu_2^+}{d\mu} - \frac{d\nu_2^-}{d\mu} \right) d\mu \\
&= \int_E \left(\frac{d\nu_1}{d\mu} + \frac{d\nu_2}{d\mu} \right) d\mu.
\end{aligned}
$$

Since ν_1 and ν_2 are σ-finite, this equality extends to every $E \in \mathcal{S}$. Now, from the uniqueness of the Radon-Nikodym derivative, we have

$$\frac{d(\nu_1 + \nu_2)}{d\mu}(x) = \frac{d\nu_1}{d\mu}(x) + \frac{d\nu_2}{d\mu}(x) \quad \text{for a.e. } x(\mu).$$

In the general case when μ is a signed measure, let $A, B \in \mathcal{S}$ be a Hahn decomposition of X with respect to μ. Consider the restrictions of ν_1, ν_2 and μ to A and B respectively and apply the earlier case to get, $\forall \ E \in \mathcal{S}$,

$$(\nu_1 + \nu_2)(E \cap A) = \int_{E \cap A} \left(\frac{d\nu_1}{d\mu^+} + \frac{d\nu_2}{d\mu} \right)(x) d\mu^+ \qquad (10.5)$$

and

$$(\nu_1 + \nu_2)(E \cap B) = \int_{E \cap B} \left(\frac{d\nu_1}{d\mu^-} + \frac{d\nu_2}{d\mu} \right)(x) d\mu^-. \qquad (10.6)$$

From the uniqueness of the Radon-Nikodym derivative, it follows that

$$\frac{d\nu_i}{d\mu^+}(x) = \frac{d\nu_i}{d\mu}(x) \text{ for a.e. } (\mu)x \in A$$

and

$$\frac{d\nu_i}{d\mu^-}(x) = \frac{d\nu_i}{d\mu}(x) \text{ for a.e. } (\mu)x \in B.$$

In view of this, the required result follows from (10.5) and (10.6). This proves (i).

(ii) First consider μ to be a σ-finite measure such that $\nu_1 \ll \mu$. Then $\forall\ E \in \mathcal{S}$.

$$\nu(E) = \int_E \frac{d\nu}{d\mu}(x)d\mu(x) \text{ and } |\nu|(E) = \int_E \frac{d|\nu|}{d\mu}(x)d\mu(x).$$

Let A, B be a Hahn decomposition of X with respect to ν, then

$$\nu^+(E) = \mu(E) = |\mu|(E), \ \forall\ E \subseteq A$$

and

$$\nu^-(E) = -\mu(E) = |\mu|(E), \ \forall\ E \subseteq B.$$

Thus

$$\frac{d\nu}{d\mu}(x) = \frac{d|\nu|}{d\mu}(x) \text{ for a.e. } (\mu)x \in A$$

and

$$\frac{d\nu}{d\mu}(x) = \frac{d|\nu|}{d\mu}(x) \text{ for a.e. } (\mu)x \in B.$$

Hence

$$\frac{d\nu}{d\mu}(x) = \frac{d|\nu|}{d\mu}(x) \text{ for a.e. } x(\mu).$$

In the general case, we can consider a Hahn decomposition C, D of X with respect to μ and apply the above case to the restrictions of ν and μ to C and D respectively. ∎

10.2.20. Exercise: Let μ, ν be σ-finite signed measures on $(X, \mathcal{S})$ such that $\nu \ll \mu$ and $\mu \ll \nu$. Show that $\frac{d\mu}{d\nu}(x) \neq 0$ for a.e. $x(\mu)$ and

$$\frac{d\nu}{d\mu}(x) = \left(\frac{d\mu}{d\nu}(x)\right)^{-1} \text{ for a.e. } x(\mu).$$

10.2.21. Theorem: *Let $\mathcal{M}_b(X, \mathcal{S})$ denote the set of all finite signed measures on $(X, \mathcal{S})$. For $\mu, \nu \in \mathcal{M}_b(X, \mathcal{S})$ and $\alpha \in \mathbb{R}$, let $\forall\ E \in \mathcal{S}$*

$$(\mu + \nu)(E) := \mu(E) + \nu(E) \quad and \quad (\alpha\mu)(E) := \alpha(\mu(E)).$$

Then $\mathcal{M}_b(X, \mathcal{S})$ *becomes a vector space over* $\mathbb{R}$ *under these operations. Further, for* $\mu \in \mathcal{M}_b(X, \mathcal{S})$, *let*

$$\|\mu\| := |\mu(X)|.$$

Then $\|\mu\|$ *is a norm on* $\mathcal{M}_b(X, \mathcal{S})$, *and the latter is a Banach space under this norm.*

Proof: That $\mathcal{M}_b(X, \mathcal{S})$ is a vector space under the above operations of addition and scalar multiplication is obvious. That $\|\mu\|$ is indeed a norm is also easy to check. We show that $\mathcal{M}_b(X, \mathcal{S})$ is a Banach space under this norm. Let $\{\mu_n\}_{n \geq 1}$ be a Cauchy sequence in $\mathcal{M}_b(X, \mathcal{S})$, i.e.,

$$\lim_{n \to \infty} \|\mu_n - \mu_m\| \to 0 \ \text{ as } \ n, m \to \infty.$$

Since $\forall \ E \in \mathcal{S}$,

$$
\begin{aligned}
|\mu_n(E) - \mu_m(E)| &\leq \ |\mu_n - \mu_m|(E) \\
&\leq \ |\mu_n - \mu_m|(X) \\
&= \ \|\mu_n - \mu_m\|,
\end{aligned}
\tag{10.7}
$$

$\{\mu_n(E)\}_{n \geq 1}$ is a Cauchy sequence of real numbers. Let

$$\mu(E) := \lim_{n \to \infty} \mu_n(E), \quad E \in \mathcal{S}.$$

We can claim that $\mu \in \mathcal{M}_b(X, \mathcal{S})$ and $\lim_{n \to \infty} \|\mu_n - \mu\| = 0$. For this, clearly $\mu(\emptyset) = 0$. Let $E = \bigcup_{n=1}^{\infty} E_n$ be a disjoint union of elements of $\mathcal{S}$. We shall show that $\mu(E) = \sum_{n=1}^{\infty} \mu(E_n)$. Note that $\forall \ k$ and $\forall \ n$,

$$
\Big| \mu(E) - \sum_{j=1}^{k} \mu(E_j) \Big| \ \leq \ |\mu(E) - \mu_n(E)| + \Big| \mu_n(E) - \sum_{j=1}^{k} \mu_n(E_j) \Big|
$$

$$
+ \Big| \sum_{j=1}^{k} \mu_n(E_j) - \sum_{j=1}^{k} \mu(E_j) \Big|.
\tag{10.8}
$$

Let $\epsilon > 0$ be given. We choose k_0 such that

$$\|\mu_n - \mu_m\| \leq \epsilon, \ \forall \ n, m \geq k_0.$$

Then for $m, n \geq k_0$, using (10.7), we have

$$|\mu_n(E) - \mu_m(E)| \leq \epsilon.
\tag{10.9}$$

Also $\forall\ m,n \geq k_0,$

$$\left| \sum_{j=1}^{k}[\mu_n(E_j) - \mu_m(E_j)] \right| \ \leq\ \sum_{j=1}^{k}|\mu_n(E_j) - \mu_m(E_j)|$$

$$\leq\ \sum_{j=1}^{k}|\mu_n - \mu_m|(E_j)$$

$$=\ |\mu_n - \mu_m|(E)$$

$$\leq\ \|\mu_n - \mu_m\| \leq \epsilon.$$

Thus, letting $m \to \infty$, we get $\forall\ n \geq k_0$

$$\left| \sum_{j=1}^{k}[\mu_n(E_j) - \mu(E_j)] \right| \ \leq\ \epsilon. \tag{10.10}$$

Finally, since $\mu_n(E) = \sum_{j=1}^{k}\mu_n(E_j)$ for all fixed $n \geq k_0$, we can choose k_1 such that $\forall\ k \geq k_1$

$$\left| \mu_n(E) - \sum_{j=1}^{k}\mu_n(E_j) \right| \ \leq\ \epsilon. \tag{10.11}$$

Thus for $k \geq k_1$, using (10.8), (10.9), (10.10) and (10.11), we have

$$\left| \mu(E) - \sum_{j=1}^{k}\mu(E_j) \right| \ \leq\ 3\epsilon.$$

This proves that $\mu(E) = \sum_{j=1}^{\infty}\mu(E_j)$, and hence μ is a signed measure. Since

$$|\mu(E)| \ =\ \lim_{n \to \infty}|\mu_n(X)| \ <\ +\infty,$$

$\mu \in \mathcal{M}_b(X,\mathcal{S})$. Finally we show that $\|\mu_n - \mu\| \to 0$ as $n \to \infty$. Note that from (10.9) we have, $\forall\ n,m \geq k_0$ and $E \in \mathcal{S}$,

$$|\mu_n(E) - \mu_m(E)| \ \leq\ \epsilon.$$

Letting $m \to \infty$, we get $\forall\ n \geq k$,

$$|\mu_n(E) - \mu(E)| \ \leq\ \epsilon \ \text{ for every } E \in \mathcal{S}.$$

Combining this with theorem 10.1.17, we get

$$(\mu_n - \mu)^+(X) \ =\ \sup\{(\mu_n - \mu)(F) \,|\, E \in \mathcal{S}\} \ \leq\ \epsilon.$$

Similarly, $(\mu_n - \mu)^-(X) \leq \epsilon$. Hence $\forall\ n \geq k$,

$$\|\mu_n - \mu\| \ =\ |\mu_n - \mu|(X) \ =\ (\mu_n - \mu)^+(X) + (\mu - \mu)^+(X) \ \leq\ 2\epsilon.$$

Thus,

$$\lim_{n \to \infty}\|\mu_n - \mu\| = 0.$$

This completes the proof. ∎

10.2.22. Exercise: For $\mu, \nu \in \mathcal{M}_b(X, \mathcal{S})$, we say ν is **smaller** than μ, and write this as $\nu \leq \mu$, if $\nu(A) \leq \mu(A) \ \forall \ A \in \mathcal{S}$. Prove the following:

(i) Show that $\forall \ \mu, \nu \in \mathcal{M}_b(X, \mathcal{S})$, there exists $\eta \in \mathcal{M}_b(X, \mathcal{S})$ such that $\eta \geq \mu$, $\eta \geq \nu$ and $\eta \leq \delta$ whenever $\delta \in \mathcal{M}_b(X, \mathcal{S})$ with $\delta \geq \mu$ and $\delta \geq \nu$. In a sense η is the smallest of all the signed measures which are bigger than both μ and ν. This η is denoted by $\mu \vee \nu$.
(Hint: $\mu \vee \nu = (\mu + \nu - |\mu - \nu|)/2$.)

(ii) Show that $\forall \ \mu, \nu \in \mathcal{M}_b(X, \mathcal{S})$ there exists a finite signed measure, denoted by $\mu \wedge \nu$, which is smaller than both μ and ν and is larger than any signed measure which is smaller than μ and ν both.

10.2.23. Note: The order relation $\leq$ defined in exercise 10.2.22 respects the algebraic operations on $\mathcal{M}_b(X, \mathcal{S})$, i.e., for ν, μ and $\eta \in \mathcal{M}_b(X, \mathcal{S})$, if $\nu \leq \mu$, then $\nu + \eta \leq \mu + \eta$ and $\alpha\nu \leq \alpha\mu \ \forall \ \alpha \geq 0, \alpha \in \mathcal{S}$. Also for $\mu, \nu \in \mu$, $\sup\{\mu, \nu\} := \mu \vee \nu$ and $\inf\{\mu, \nu\} := \mu \wedge \nu$ exist. $\mathcal{M}_b(X, \mathcal{S})$ is an example of a **Banach lattice**.

10.3. Complex measures

Let $(X, \mathcal{S})$ be a measurable space and μ, ν be two finite signed measured on $(X, \mathcal{S})$. Consider $\eta : \mathcal{S} \longrightarrow \mathbb{C}$ defined by

$$\eta(E) := \mu(E) + i\nu(E), \quad E \in \mathcal{S}.$$

Clearly $\eta(\emptyset) = 0$. Let $\{E_n\}_{n \geq 1}$ be a sequence of pairwise disjoint sets in $\mathcal{S}$ and let $E := \bigcup_{n=1}^{\infty} E_n$. Then the series $\sum_{n=1}^{\infty} (\mu(E_n) + i\nu(E_n))$ is absolutely convergent, and it converges to $\mu(E) + i\nu(E)$. Hence $\sum_{n=1}^{\infty} \eta(E_n)$ is independent of any rearrangement of the series, and we may write

$$\eta(E) = \sum_{n=1}^{\infty} \eta(E_n).$$

Thus η is a countably additive complex-valued set function on $(X, \mathcal{S})$.

10.3.1. Definition: Let $(X, \mathcal{S})$ be a measure space. A set function $\nu : \mathcal{S} \longrightarrow \mathbb{C}$ is called a **complex measure** on $(X, \mathcal{S})$ if the following are satisfied:

(i) $\mu(\emptyset) = 0$.

(ii) μ is countably additive in the following sense: if $E := \bigcup_{n=1}^{\infty} E_n$, where the E_n's are pairwise disjoint sets from $\mathcal{S}$, then $\sum_{n=1}^{\infty} \mu(E_n)$ is absolutely convergent and converges to $\mu(E)$. We write this as

$$\mu(E) = \sum_{n=1}^{\infty} \mu(E_n).$$

10.3.2. Example: Clearly, every finite signed measure can be treated as a complex measure. The set function $\eta = \mu + i\nu$, where μ, ν are finite signed measures, is a complex measure. Another way of constructing complex measures is to consider a complex-valued integrable function f on $(X, \mathcal{S}, \mu)$ and define

$$\nu(E) := \int_E f d\mu, \quad E \in \mathcal{S}.$$

Then ν is a complex measure. In fact, the equality

$$\nu(E) = \int_E \mathrm{Re}\,(f) d\mu + i \int_E \mathrm{Im}\,(f) d\mu, E \in \mathcal{S},$$

shows that this example is the same as the earlier one. However, this complex measure ν has the property that if $\mu(E) = 0$ for some $E \in \mathcal{S}$, then clearly $\nu(E) = 0$ as a complex number. This motivates the next definition.

10.3.3. Definition: Let $(X, \mathcal{S}, \mu)$ be a measure space and ν a complex measure on $\mathcal{S}$. We say ν is **absolutely continuous** with respect to μ if $\nu(E) = 0$ for all $E \in \mathcal{S}$ for which $\mu(E) = 0$. We write this as $\nu \ll \mu$.

The question we would like to answer is the following: does the Radon-Nikodym theorem hold when ν is a complex measure and $\nu \ll \mu, \mu$ being a σ-finite measure? The answer is yes. Before we prove this, we make the following observations.

10.3.4. Proposition: *Let ν be a complex measure on $(X, \mathcal{S})$. Then there exist finite measures $\nu_1, \nu_2, \nu_3,\ \nu_4$ on $(X, \mathcal{S})$ such that $\nu_1 \perp \nu_2,\ \nu_3 \perp \nu_4$ and $\forall\ E \in \mathcal{S}$,*

$$\nu(E) = \nu_1(E) - \nu_2(E) + i\nu_3(E) - i\nu_4(E).$$

Proof: For every $E \in \mathcal{S}$, consider

$$(\mathrm{Re}\,(\nu))(E) := \ \text{Real part of } \nu(E)$$

and

$$(\mathrm{Im}\,(\nu))(E) := \ \text{Imaginary part of } \nu(E).$$

Then $(\mathrm{Re}\,(\nu))$ and $(\mathrm{Im}\,(\nu))$ are finite signed measures on $(X, \mathcal{S})$. Put $\nu_1 := (\mathrm{Re}\,(\nu))^+, \nu_2 := (\mathrm{Re}\,(\nu))^-, \nu_3 := (\mathrm{Im}\,\nu)^+$ and $\nu_4 := (\mathrm{Im}\,(\nu))^-$. ∎

10.3.5. Definition: Let ν be a complex measure on $(X, \mathcal{S})$. A complex-valued measurable function g on X is said to be ν-**integrable** if $g \in L_1^r(X, \mathcal{S}, \nu_i)\ \forall\ 1 \leq i \leq 4$, and in that case we write

$$\int g d\nu := \int g d\nu_1 - \int g d\nu_2 + i \int g d\nu_3 - i \int g d\nu_4.$$

10.3.6. **Theorem (Radon-Nikodym theorem for complex measures):** *Let* $(X, \mathcal{S}, \mu)$ *be a* σ-*finite measure space and let* ν *be a complex measure on* $\mathcal{S}$ *such that* $\nu \ll \mu$. *Then there exists a complex-valued function* $f \in L_1(X, \mathcal{S}, \mu)$ *such that*

$$\int g d\nu = \int f g d\mu$$

for all $g \in \bigcap_{i=1}^{4} L_1^r(X, \mathcal{S}, \nu_i)$, *where the* $\nu_i, 1 \le i \le 4$, *are as given by proposition 10.3.4.*

Proof: Consider $\nu_1, \nu_2, \nu_3, \nu_4$ as given by proposition 10.3.4. Then $\nu_i \ll \mu \ \forall \ i = 1, 2, 3, 4$. Thus by the Radon-Nikodym theorem (exercise 10.2.3), $\exists \ f_i \in L_1^r(X, \mathcal{S}, \mu)$ such that

$$\nu_i(E) = \int_E f_i d\mu, \quad \forall \ E \in \mathcal{S}. \tag{10.12}$$

Let $f := f_1 - f_2 + i f_3 - i f_4$. Then f is a complex-valued measurable function, $f \in L_1(X, \mathcal{S}, \mu)$ and

$$\nu(E) = \int_E f d\mu, \quad \forall \ E \in \mathcal{S}.$$

Next, using (10.12) and the simple function technique, it is easy to show that

$$\int g d\nu_i = \int f_i g d\mu, \tag{10.13}$$

whenever $g \in L_1^r(X, \mathcal{S}, \nu_i)$. Let $g \in \bigcap_{i=1}^{4} L_1^r(X, \mathcal{S}, \nu_i)$. Then (10.13) holds for such a g and each $i = 1, 2, 3, 4$. We have

$$
\begin{aligned}
\int g d\nu &= \int g d\nu_1 - \int g d\nu_2 + i \int g d\nu_3 - i \int g d\nu_4. \\
&= \int g(f_1 - f_2 + i f_3 - i f_4) d\mu \\
&= \int g f d\mu. \ \blacksquare
\end{aligned}
$$

Recall that in case ν is real-valued, i.e., when ν is a finite signed measure, we showed that

$$L_1^r(X, \mathcal{S}, \nu^+) \cap L_1^r(X, \mathcal{S}, \nu^-) = L_1^r(X, \mathcal{S}, |\nu|).$$

To prove a similar result for complex measures, we take a hint from theorem 10.1.17. and make the following definition.

10.3.7. Definition: Let ν be a complex measure on $(X, \mathcal{S})$. For $E \in \mathcal{S}$, define

$$|\nu|(E) = \sup \left\{ \sum_{i=1}^{n} |\nu(E_i)| \,\middle|\, \{E_1, \ldots, E_n\} \text{ is a measurable partition of } E \right\}.$$

The set function $|\nu|$ is called the **total variation** of ν.

10.3.8. Theorem: *Let ν be a complex measure on $(X, \mathcal{S})$. Let $\nu_i, 1 \leq i \leq 4$, be the finite measures given by proposition 10.3.4. Then the following hold:*

(i) $|\nu|(E) \leq \sum_{i=1}^{4} \nu_i(E), \quad \forall\ E \in \mathcal{S}.$

(ii) $|\nu|$ *is a finite measure on* $(X, \mathcal{S})$.

(iii) $|\nu(E)| \leq |\nu|(X), \quad \forall\ E \in \mathcal{S}.$

(iv) $\nu_i(E) \leq |\nu|(E), \quad \forall\ E \in \mathcal{S}.$

(v) $L_1(X, \mathcal{S}, |\nu|) = \bigcap_{i=1}^{4} L_1(X, \mathcal{S}, \nu_i).$

(vi) *For any measure μ on $(X, \mathcal{S}), \nu \ll \mu$ iff $\nu_k \ll \mu$ iff $|\nu| \ll \mu$.*

Proof: The proof of (i) is easy. To prove (ii), first note that, $|\nu|(\emptyset) = 0$. To prove the countable additivity of $|\nu|$, let $A = \bigcup_{j=1}^{\infty} A_j$. where $A_j \in \mathcal{S}\ \forall\ j$ and $A_i \cap A_j = \emptyset$ for $i \neq j$. Let $\alpha < |\nu|(A)$, where $\alpha \in \mathbb{R}$ is arbitrary. Let $E_1, E_2, \ldots, E_n \in \mathcal{S}$ be such that $E_i \cap E_j = \emptyset$ for $i \neq j, A = \bigcup_{j=1}^{n} E_j$ and $\alpha < \sum_{j=1}^{n} |\nu(E_j)|$. Then

$$\alpha \ < \ \sum_{j=1}^{n} \sum_{k=1}^{\infty} |\nu(E_j \cap A_k)| \ = \ \sum_{k=1}^{\infty} \sum_{j=1}^{n} |\nu(E_j \cap A_k)| \ \leq \ \sum_{k=1}^{\infty} |\nu|(A_k).$$

Since $\alpha < |\nu|(A)$ is arbitrary, we have

$$|\nu|(A) \ \leq \ \sum_{k=1}^{\infty} |\nu|(A_k). \tag{10.14}$$

To prove the reverse inequality, we may assume without loss of generality that $|\nu|(A) < +\infty$. It is easy to see that $|\nu|(E) \leq |\nu|(F)$ whenever $E \subseteq F$. Thus $|\nu|(A_j) < +\infty\ \forall\ j$. Let $\epsilon > 0$ be given. Choose $\ \forall\ j$, sets $E_k^j \in \mathcal{S}, 1 \leq k \leq k_j$, such that $E_k^j \cap E_\ell^j = \emptyset$ for $k \neq \ell, A_j = \bigcup_{k=1}^{k_j} E_k^j$ and

$$|\nu|(A_j) - \epsilon/2^j \ \leq \ \sum_{j=1}^{k_j} |\nu(E_k^j)|.$$

Then $\forall\ m$,

$$\sum_{j=1}^{m}|\nu|(A_j)\ \leq\ \sum_{j=1}^{m}\epsilon/2^j+\sum_{j=1}^{m}\sum_{k=1}^{kj}|\nu(E_k^j)|$$

$$<\ \epsilon+\sum_{j=1}^{m}\sum_{k=1}^{kj}|\nu(E_n^j)|+|\nu(\bigcup_{j=m+1}^{\infty}A_j)|$$

$$<\ \epsilon+|\nu|(A).$$

Since this holds $\forall\ m$ and $\epsilon>0$, we have

$$\sum_{j=1}^{\infty}|\nu|(A_j)\ \leq\ |\nu|(A). \tag{10.15}$$

Equations (10.14) and (10.15) prove that $|\nu|$ is a measure. Since

$$|\nu|(X)\ \leq\ \sum_{i=1}^{4}\nu_i(X)\ <\ +\infty$$

(by (i)), $|\nu|$ is a finite measure. This proves (ii).

To prove (iii), let $E\in\mathcal{S}$ be fixed. Then $X=E\cup E^c$ and hence

$$|\nu(E)|\ \leq\ |\nu(E)|+|\nu(E^c)|\ \leq\ |\nu|(X).$$

To prove (iv), let A_1,B_1 be a Hahn decomposition of X with respect to $\mathrm{Re}\,(\nu)$. Then $\forall\ E\in\mathcal{S}$,

$$\begin{aligned}\nu_1(E)\ &:=\ (\mathrm{Re}\,(\nu))^+(E)\\ &=\ (\mathrm{Re}\,(\nu))(E\cap A_1)\\ &=\ |(\mathrm{Re}\,(\nu))(E\cap A_1)|\\ &\leq\ |\nu(E\cap A_1)|\\ &\leq\ |\nu(E\cap A_1)|+|\nu(E\cap B_1)|\\ &\leq\ |\nu|(E).\end{aligned}$$

Similarly,

$$\begin{aligned}\nu_2(E)\ &:=\ (\mathrm{Re}\,(\nu))^-(E)\\ &=\ |(\mathrm{Re}\,(\nu))(E\cap B_1)|\\ &\leq\ |\nu(E\cap B_1)|+|\nu(E\cap A_1)|\\ &\leq\ |\nu|(E).\end{aligned}$$

That $\nu_3(E)$ and $\nu_4(E)$ are both less than $|\nu|(E)$ can be proved similarly, using a Hahn decomposition of X.

To prove (v), let us first consider f, a nonnegative simple measurable function on $(X, \mathcal{S})$. Let

$$f = \sum_{j=1}^{m} \alpha_j \chi_{E_j}.$$

Then, using (i), we have

$$
\begin{aligned}
\int f \, d|\nu| &= \sum_{j=1}^{m} \alpha_j |\nu|(E_j) \\
&\le \sum_{j=1}^{m} \alpha_j \left(\sum_{k=1}^{4} \nu_k(E_j) \right) = \sum_{k=1}^{4} \left(\int f \, d\nu_k \right). \quad (10.16)
\end{aligned}
$$

Also, using (iv), $\forall \ k = 1, 2, 3, 4$, we have

$$
\begin{aligned}
\int f \, d\nu_k &= \sum_{j=1}^{m} \alpha_j \nu_k(E_j) \\
&\le \sum_{j=1}^{m} \alpha_j |\nu|(E_j) = \int f \, d|\nu|. \quad (10.17)
\end{aligned}
$$

From (10.16) and (10.17), the claim of (v) follows when f is a nonnegative simple function. Also note that a function f on X is defined a.e. $(|\nu|)$ iff f is defined a.e. $(\nu_k), k = 1, 2, 3, 4$. Let f be any nonnegative measurable function and let $\{s_n\}_{n \ge 1}$ be a sequence of nonnegative simple measurable functions on X increasing to $|f|$ a.e. $|\nu|$. Application of the monotone convergence theorem to equations (10.16) and (10.17) above, with f replaced by s_n, gives

$$\int |f| \, d|\nu| \le \sum_{k=1}^{n} \left(\int |f| \, d\nu_k \right) \quad \text{and} \quad \int |f| \, d\nu_k \le \int |f| \, d|\nu|.$$

Thus

$$f \in L_1(X, \mathcal{S}, |\nu|) \ \text{iff} \ f \in \bigcap_{k=1}^{4} L_1(X, \mathcal{S}, \nu_k).$$

This proves (v).

Finally, if μ is a measure and $\mu \ll \nu$, then $\mu(E) = 0$ implies $\nu(E) = 0$. In particular, for $E \in \mathcal{S}$ fixed with $\mu(E) = 0$, we have $\mu(F) = 0$ for every set $F \subseteq E, F \in \mathcal{S}$. Thus $\nu(F) = 0 \ \forall \ F \subseteq E$, and it follows that $|\nu|(E) = 0$. Hence $\nu \ll \mu$ implies $|\nu| \ll \mu$. Also it follows from (iv) that $\nu_k \ll |\nu| \ \forall \ k = 1, 2, 3, 4$. Thus $\nu_k \ll \mu \ \forall \ k$. Finally, if $\ \forall \ k, \nu_k \ll \mu$, then, noting that $\nu = \nu_1 - \nu_2 + i\nu_3 - i\nu_4$, it follows that $\nu \ll \mu$. This prove (vi). $\blacksquare$

10.3.9. Exercise: Consider $\mathcal{M}(X,\mathcal{S})$, the set of all complex measures on $(X,\mathcal{S})$. Define the operations of addition, scalar multiplication and norm on $\mathcal{M}(X,\mathcal{S})$ as follows: for $\mu,\nu \in \mathcal{M}(X,\mathcal{S})$ and $\alpha \in \mathbb{C}$,

(i) $(\mu + \nu)(E) := \mu(E) + \nu(E)$, $E \in \mathcal{S}$.

(ii) $(\alpha\mu)(E) := \alpha\mu(E)$, $E \in \mathcal{S}$.

(iii) $\|\mu\| := |\mu|(X)$.

Show that $\mathcal{M}(X,\mathcal{S})$ is a Banach space with these operations.

10.3.10. Remark: In view of theorem 10.3.8(v), theorem 10.3.6 can be stated as follows: Let μ be a σ-finite measure and ν a complex measure on $(X,\mathcal{S})$ such that $\nu \ll \mu$. Then $\exists\ f \in L_1(X,\mathcal{S},\mu)$ such that

$$\int g d\nu = \int f g d\mu, \quad \forall\ g \in L_1(X,\mathcal{S},|\nu|).$$

10.3.11. Proposition: *Let* $(X,\mathcal{S},\mu)$ *be a* σ*-finite measure space and let* $f \in L_1(X,\mathcal{S},\mu)$ *be a complex-valued function. Let*

$$\nu(E) := \int_E f d\mu, \quad E \in \mathcal{S}.$$

Then ν *is a complex measure and,* $\forall\ E \in \mathcal{S}$,

$$|\nu|(E) = \int_E |f| d\mu.$$

In particular,

$$\|\nu\| = |\nu|(X) = \int |f| d\mu = \|f\|_1.$$

Proof: Let $E \in \mathcal{S}$ be fixed. Then for any measurable partition $\{F_1,\dots,F_n\}$ of E,

$$\sum_{j=1}^n |\nu(F_j)| = \sum_{j=1}^n \left| \int_{F_j} f d\mu \right| \le \int_E |f| d\mu.$$

Hence

$$|\nu|(E) \le \int_E |f| d\mu. \qquad (10.18)$$

To prove the reverse inequality, let $\{s_n\}_{n\ge 1}$ be a sequence of nonnegative simple functions such that $|s_n| \le 1\ \forall\ n$ and s_n increases to χ_E. Define for

$x \in X$,

$$g_n(x) := \begin{cases} s_n(x)\left(\dfrac{\overline{f(x)}}{|f(x)|}\right) & \text{if} \quad f(x) \neq 0, \\ \\ 0 & \text{if} \quad f(x) = 0, \end{cases}$$

where $\overline{f(x)}$ denotes the complex conjugate of $f(x)$. Then $\{g_n f\}_{n\geq 1}$ converges to $\chi_E |f|$ and $|g_n f| \leq |f| \in L_1(X, \mathcal{S}, \mu)$. Thus by Lebesgue's dominated convergence theorem, we get

$$\int_E |f| d\mu = \lim_{n\to\infty} \int f g_n d\mu. \tag{10.19}$$

Also, s_n being a simple function, let $s_n = \sum_{j=1}^m \alpha_j \chi_{E_j}$, where $\{E_1, \dots, E_m\}$ is a measurable partition of X. Since $s_n \leq \chi_E, s_n(x) = 0$ for every $x \in X \setminus E$ and $0 \leq \alpha_j \leq 1 \; \forall \; j$. Thus

$$\left| \int f g_n d\mu \right| = \left| \int_E f g_n d\mu \right|$$
$$= \left| \sum_{j=1}^m \alpha_j \int_{E\cap E_j} f d\mu \right|$$
$$\leq \sum_{j=1}^m \left| \int_{E\cap E_j} f d\mu \right|$$
$$= \sum_{j=1}^m |\mu(E \cap E_j)|$$
$$\leq |\mu|(E). \tag{10.20}$$

From (10.18), (10.19) and (10.20), we get

$$|\mu|(E) = \int_E |f| d\mu.$$

In particular, with $E = X$, we get $\|\mu\| = \|f\|$. ∎

10.3.12. Corollary (Polar representation): *Let μ be a complex measure on $(X, \mathcal{S})$. Then there exists a measurable function f such that $|f(x)| = 1$ for all $x \in X$, and, $\forall E \in \mathcal{S}$,*

$$\mu(E) = \int_E f d|\mu|.$$

Proof: Clearly $\mu \ll |\mu|$. Let f be the function, as given by remark 10.3.10, such that $\forall \; E \in \mathcal{S}$

$$\mu(E) = \int_E f d|\mu|.$$

Let
$$A := \{x \in X \mid |f(x)| < 1\} \quad \text{and} \quad B := \{x \in X \mid |f(x)| > 1\}.$$
Then by proposition 10.3.11, we get
$$\int_A (1 - |f|) d|\mu| = |\mu|(A) - \int_A |f| d|\mu| = 0.$$
This implies that $|\mu|(A) = 0$. Similarly, the equality
$$\int_B (|f| - 1) d|\mu| = \int_B |f| d|\mu| - |\mu|(B) = 0$$
implies that $|\mu|(B) = 0$. Hence
$$|f(x)| = 1 \text{ for a.e. } (|\mu|) \ x \in X.$$
We can redefine f to be such that $|f(x)| = 1 \ \forall \ x \in X$ and still have, $\forall \ E \in \mathcal{S}$,
$$\mu(E) = \int_E f d|\mu|. \quad \blacksquare$$

10.3.13.   Exercise (Hahn decomposition for finite signed measures): Let μ be a finite signed measure on $(X, \mathcal{S})$. Show that there exist disjoint sets $A, B \in \mathcal{S}$ with the following properties:

(i) $A \cup B = X$.

(ii) $\mu(E) > 0 \ \forall \ E \in \mathcal{S}, E \subseteq A$.

(iii) $\mu(E) < 0 \ \forall \ E \in \mathcal{S}, E \subseteq B$.

(Hint: Use corollary 10.3.12 and $A := \{x \in X \mid f(x) = 1\}$, $B := \{x \in X \mid f(x) = -1\}$.)

10.4. Bounded linear functionals on $L_p^r(X, \mathcal{S}, \mu)$

Let $(X, \mathcal{S}, \mu)$ be a σ-finite measure space. Recall that for $1 \leq p < \infty$, the space $L_p^r(X, \mathcal{S}, \mu)$, as defined in section 8.4, is the space of all real-valued measurable functions on $(X, \mathcal{S})$ such that $\int |f|^p d\mu < +\infty$. The space $L_p^r(X, \mathcal{S}, \mu)$ is a vector space over $\mathbb{R}$, and if we identify functions which agree a.e. (μ), then, for $f \in L_p^r(X, \mathcal{S}, \mu)$,
$$\|f\|_p := \left(\int |f|^p d\mu \right)^{1/p}$$
defines a norm on $L_p^r(X, \mathcal{S}, \mu)$ under which $L_p^r(X, \mathcal{S}, \mu)$ is complete. Let $1 < p < \infty$. By Hölder's inequality, for $f \in L_p^r(X, \mathcal{S}, \mu)$ and $g \in L_q^r(X, \mathcal{S}, \mu)$, where $1/p + 1/q = 1$, we have $fg \in L_1^r(X, \mathcal{S}, \mu)$ and
$$\int |fg| d\mu \leq \|f\|_p \|g\|_q.$$

Let the map $T : L_p^r(X, \mathcal{S}, \mu) \longrightarrow \mathbb{R}$ be defined by

$$T(f) = \int fg d\mu.$$

Then T is a well-defined linear map and

$$|T(f)| \leq \|g\|_q \|f\|_p, \ \forall \ f \in L_p^r(X, \mathcal{S}, \mu).$$

In the case $p = 1$ and $g \in L_\infty^r(X, \mathcal{S}, \mu)$, let

$$T(f) := \int fg d\mu, \quad f \in L_1^r(X, \mathcal{S}, \mu).$$

Once again, T is a linear map from $L_1^r(X, \mathcal{S}, \mu)$ into $\mathbb{R}$, and

$$|T(f)| \leq \|g\|_\infty \|f\|_1, \quad \forall \ f \in L_1^r(X, \mathcal{S}, \mu).$$

For $1 \leq p < \infty$, let q be such that $1/p + 1/q = 1$ when $1 < p < \infty$ and $q = \infty$ when $p = 1$. We call q the **conjugate of** p. The conclusion of the above discussion can be stated as follows:

10.4.1. Proposition: *Let $1 \leq p < \infty$ and $g \in L_q^r(X, \mathcal{S}, \mu)$, where q is the conjugate of p. Then $T : L_p^r(X, \mathcal{S}, \mu) \longrightarrow \mathbb{R}$ defined by*

$$T(f) := \int fg d\mu, \quad f \in L_p^r(X, \mathcal{S}, \mu),$$

is a linear map and

$$|T(f)| \leq \|g\|_q \|f\|_p, \quad \forall \ f \in L_p^r(X, \mathcal{S}, \mu).$$

Further,

$$\sup_{\|f\|_p = 1} |T(f)| = \|g\|_q.$$

Proof: Clearly, T is linear and

$$\sup_{\|f\|_p = 1} |T(f)| \leq \|g\|_q. \tag{10.21}$$

We may assume, without loss of generality, that $\|g\|_q \neq 0$. If $1 < p < \infty$, put

$$f_0 := |g|^{q-1} \|g\|_q^{-q/p}.$$

Then

$$|f_0|^p = |g|^{p(q-1)} \|g\|_q^{-q} = |g|^q \|g\|_q^{-q}.$$

Thus

$$\|f_0\|_p^p = \left(\int |g|^q d\mu \right) \|g\|_q^{-q} = 1.$$

Further,

$$T(f_0) = \left(\int |g|^q d\mu \right) \left(\|g\|_q^{-q/p} \right) = \|g\|_q^{q(1-\frac{1}{p})} = \|g\|_q.$$

Thus

$$\sup_{\|f\|_p=1} |T(f)| \geq \|g\|_q. \tag{10.22}$$

From (10.21) and (10.22), it follows that

$$\sup_{\|f\|_p=1} |T(f)| = \|g\|_q, \quad \text{if } 1 < p < \infty.$$

In the case $p = 1$, let ϵ be any real number such that $0 < \epsilon < \|g\|_\infty$. Then it follows from the definition of $\|g\|_\infty$ that

$$\mu(\{x \in X \mid |g(x)| > \|g\|_\infty - \epsilon\}) > 0.$$

Let

$$E := \{x \in X \mid |g(x)| > \|g\|_\infty - \epsilon\}.$$

Since μ is σ-finite, we can assume without loss of generality that $0 < \mu(E) < \infty$. Define $\forall \, x \in X$,

$$f_0(x) := \left(\frac{\alpha(x)}{\mu(E)} \right) \chi_E(x),$$

where $\alpha(x) = 1$ if $g(x) \geq 0$ and $\alpha(x) = -1$ if $g(x) < 0$. Then $\|f_0\|_1 = 1$ and

$$T(f_0) = \frac{1}{\mu(E)} \int_E |g(x)| d\mu(x) \geq \|g\|_\infty - \epsilon.$$

Since this holds $\forall \, \epsilon > 0$, we have

$$T(f_0) \geq \|g\|_\infty. \tag{10.23}$$

From (10.21) and (10.23), we get

$$\sup_{\|f\|_1=1} |T(f)| = \|g\|_\infty. \quad \blacksquare$$

The aim of the rest of the section is to show that every linear map $T : L_p^r(X, \mathcal{S}, \mu) \longrightarrow \mathbb{R}$ which satisfies the condition $|T(f)| \leq M\|f\|_p$ for some $M \geq 0$ and for every $f \in L_p^r(X, \mathcal{S}, \mu)$ is of the form $T(f) = \int fg d\mu$ for some $g \in L_q^r(X, \mathcal{S}, \mu)$. The proof is an application of the Radon-Nikodym theorem. (Note that we have already proved this result independently for $p = 2$ in theorem 8.9.20 and used it in theorem 9.1.15 to deduce a proof of the Radon-Nikodym theorem. An independent proof of the Radon-Nikodym theorem was also given in theorem 10.2.2 and exercise 10.2.3.) Before we prove this, we observe the following.

10.4.2. Proposition: *Let* $T : L_p^r(X, \mathcal{S}, \mu) \longrightarrow \mathbb{R}, 1 \leq p \leq \infty$, *be any linear map. Then the following statements are equivalent (and if any one of them is satisfied, we call T a* **bounded linear functional** *on* $L_p^r(X, \mathcal{B}, \mu)$).

(i)   *There exists a constant $M \geq 0$ such that*

$$|T(f)| \leq M \, \|f\|_p \ \forall \ f \in L_p^r(X, \mathcal{S}, \mu).$$

(ii) *T is a continuous map.*

If T satisfies either (i) or (ii), then

$$\|T\| := \sup_{\|f\|_p = 1} |T(f)|$$

exists and

$$\|T(f)\| \leq \|T\| \|f\|_p, \ \forall \ f \in L_p^r(\mu).$$

Further,

$$\|T\| = \inf \{ M \mid |T(f)| \leq M \|f\|_p \ \forall \ f \in L_p^r(X, \mathcal{S}, \mu) \}.$$

The nonnegative number $\|T\|$ is called the **norm** of the linear map T.

Proof: The implication (i) $\Rightarrow$ (ii) is obvious. Conversely, suppose T is continuous but (i) does not hold. Then $\forall \ n, \ \exists \ f_n \in L_p^r(X, \mathcal{S}, \mu)$ such that

$$|T(f_n)| > n \|f_n\|_p.$$

Since T is linear, $T(f) = 0$ if $f(x) = 0$ for a.e. $x(\mu)$. Thus $\|f_n\| \neq 0 \ \forall \ n$ and

$$\left| T \left(\frac{f_n}{n \|f_n\|} \right) \right| > 1.$$

Let

$$g_n := \frac{f_n}{n \|f_n\|_p}.$$

Then $g_n \in L_p^r(X, \mathcal{S}, \mu)$ and $\|g_n\|_p = 1/n \to 0$ as $n \to \infty$. But $|T(g_n)| > 1 \ \forall \ n$, which contradicts the continuity of T. Hence (ii) $\Rightarrow$ (i) also.

Next, let either (i) or (ii) hold, and let

$$K := \inf \{ M \mid |T(f)| \leq M \|f\|_p, \ \forall \ f \in L_p^r(X, \mathcal{S}, \mu) \}.$$

Clearly, by the definition of K,

$$\|T(f)\| \leq K \|f\|_p, \ \forall \ f \in L_p^r(X, \mathcal{B}, \mu).$$

Also, since (i) holds, $\exists \ M$ such that

$$|T(f)| \leq M, \ \forall \ f \in L_p^r(X, \mathcal{S}, \mu) \text{ with } \|f\|_p = 1.$$

Hence

$$\|T\| := \sup_{\|f\|_p = 1} |T(f)|$$

exists. Further, $\forall\ f \in L_1^r(X, \mathcal{S}, \mu)$ with $\|f\|_p \neq 0$, since $\left\|\dfrac{f}{\|f\|_p}\right\|_p = 1$,

$$\left|T\!\left(\frac{f}{\|f\|_p}\right)\right| \leq \|T\|, \quad \text{i.e.,}\quad |T(f)| \leq \|T\|\|f\|_p.$$

Hence $\|T\| \geq K$. On the other hand,

$$\|T(f)\| \leq K\|f\|_p, \quad \forall\ f \in L_p^r(X, \mathcal{S}, \mu),$$

implies that $\|T\| \leq K$. Thus $\|T\| = K$. $\blacksquare$

10.4.3. Theorem (Riesz representation): *Let* $(X, \mathcal{S}, \mu)$ *be a σ-finite, complete measure space and let $1 \leq p < \infty$. Let $T : L_p^r(X, \mathcal{S}, \mu) \longrightarrow \mathbb{R}$ be a continuous linear map. Then there exists a unique $g \in L_q^r(X, \mathcal{S}, \mu)$, where q is the conjugate of p, such that*

$$T(f) = \int fg\,d\mu, \quad \forall\ f \in L_p^r(X, \mathcal{S}, \mu),$$

and $\quad \|T\| = \|g\|_q$.

Proof: The idea of the proof is as follows. Suppose there exists some $g \in L_q^r(X, \mathcal{S}, \mu)$ with

$$T(f) = \int fg\,d\mu, \quad \forall\ f \in L_p^r(X, \mathcal{S}, \mu).$$

If $\mu(X) < +\infty$, then we should have

$$\nu(E) := T(\chi_E) = \int_E g\,d\mu, \quad \forall\ E \in \mathcal{S}.$$

This suggests an application of the Radon-Nikodym theorem for ν to locate g. Thus we shall prove the required claim when $\mu(X) < +\infty$ by proving the following steps:

Step 1. Consider

$$\nu(E) := T(\chi_E), \ E \in \mathcal{S}.$$

Then ν is a well-defined finite signed measure, and $\nu \ll \mu$.

Step 2. The Radon-Nikodym derivative $\dfrac{d\mu}{d\nu}(x) := g(x) \in L_q(X, \mathcal{S}, \mu)$.

Step 3. The map T is given by

$$T(f) = \int fg\,d\mu, \quad \forall\ f \in L_p.$$

These steps will prove the claim in the case when $\mu(X) < +\infty$. Finally, we shall extend the claim when μ is σ-finite. We prove these steps one by one.

That ν is well-defined, follows from the fact that for $E \in \mathcal{S}$ we have $\chi_E \in L_p^r$ (since $\mu(X) < +\infty$). Clearly

$$\nu(\emptyset) = 0 \text{ and } |\nu(X)| = |T(1)| < \infty.$$

The finite additivity of ν follows from the fact that T is linear. To prove the countable additivity of μ, let $E = \bigcup_{n=1}^\infty E_n$ be a union of pairwise disjoint sets from $\mathcal{S}$. Let $A_n := \bigcup_{k=1}^n E_k$. Then $\{\chi_{A_n}\}_{n\geq 1}$ increases to χ_E and, by the dominated convergence theorem, we have

$$\lim_{n\to\infty} \int |\chi_{A_n} - \chi_E|^p d\mu = 0. \tag{10.24}$$

Also,

$$|T(\chi_E - \chi_{A_n})| \leq M \|\chi_E - \chi_{A_n}\|_p.$$

Thus using (10.24) we have

$$\lim_{n\to\infty} |T(\chi_E - \chi_{A_n})| = 0.$$

Using the fact that T is linear, the above gives

$$\nu(E) = T(\chi_E) = \lim_{n\to\infty} T(\chi_{A_n}). \tag{10.25}$$

Since $\chi_{A_n} = \sum_{k=1}^n \chi_{E_k}$, from (10.25) we have

$$\begin{aligned} \nu(E) &= \lim_{n\to\infty} \sum_{k=1}^n T(\chi_{E_k}) \\ &= \lim_{n\to\infty} \sum_{k=1}^n \nu(E_k) \\ &= \sum_{k=1}^\infty \nu(E_k). \end{aligned}$$

Hence ν is a well-defined signed measure on $(X, \mathcal{S})$. Suppose, $\mu(E) = 0$. Then $\|\chi_E\|_p = 0$ and hence

$$|T(\chi_E)| \leq M \|\chi_E\|_p = 0.$$

Thus $|\nu(E)| = 0$. Hence $\nu \ll \mu$, proving step 1.

To prove step 2, let

$$g(x) := \frac{d\mu}{d\mu}(x) \text{ for a.e. } x(\mu).$$

Note that g is real-valued and

$$T(\chi_E) = \int_E g d\mu, \ \forall \ E \in \mathcal{S}.$$

Thus, using the linearity of T and of the integral, we have

$$T(s) = \int s \, g \, d\mu, \qquad (10.26)$$

for every nonnegative simple measurable function s on $(X, \mathcal{S})$. We show that this implies the required claim of step 2, i.e., $g \in L_q(\mu)$. Assume first that $1 < p < \infty$. Choose a sequence $\{\phi_n\}_{n \geq 1}$ of nonnegative simple measurable functions increasing to $|g|^q$. Let

$$A := \{x \in \mid g(x) \geq 0\} \quad \text{and} \quad B := \{x \in X \mid g(x) < 0\}.$$

Define

$$S_n(x) := (\chi_A - \chi_B)(\phi_n(x))^{1/p}, \quad x \in X.$$

Then $\{S_n\}_{n \geq 1}$ is a sequence of simple measurable functions, and

$$\|S_n\|_p = \left(\int \phi_n(x) d\mu(x) \right)^{1/p}.$$

Further, since

$$g(x)S_n(x) = |g(x)|(\phi_n(x))^{1/p} \quad \text{and} \quad (\phi_n(x))^{1/q} \leq |g(x)|,$$

we have

$$g(x)S_n(x) \geq (\phi_n(x))^{1/p+1/q} = \phi_n(x).$$

Hence

$$0 \leq \int \phi_n(x) d\mu(x) \leq \int S_n(x)g(x)d\mu(x) \leq T(S_n).$$

Thus

$$\int \phi_n(x) d\mu(x) \ \leq \ |T(S_n)|$$
$$\leq \ \|T\|\|S_n\|_P$$
$$= \ \|T\| \left(\int \phi_n d\mu \right)^{1/p},$$

i.e.,

$$\left(\int \phi_n d\mu \right)^{1-1/p} \leq \|T\|.$$

Thus

$$\int \phi_n d\mu \ \leq \ \|T\|^q.$$

Since this holds $\forall \ n$, by the monotone convergence theorem, we have

$$\int |g|^q d\mu \ \leq \ \|T\|^q.$$

This proves that $g \in L_q^r(\mu)$ and $\|g\|_q \le \|T\|$ in the case $1 < p < \infty$. For the case $p = 1$, since $\forall\ E \in \mathcal{S}$,

$$T(\chi_E) = \int_E g d\mu,$$

we have

$$\left| \int_E g d\mu \right| \le |T(\chi_E)| \le \|T\| \mu(E).$$

Thus it follows from theorem 8.1.9 that

$$|g(x)| \le \|T\| \quad \text{for a.e. } x(\mu).$$

Hence $g \in L_\infty^r(X, \mathcal{S}, \mu)$ and $\|g\|_\infty \le \|T\|$. Thus $\forall\ 1 \le p < \infty$, the function $g \in L_q^r(X, \mathcal{S}, \mu)$ with $\|g\|_q \le \|T\|$. This proves the claim of step 2.

To prove step 3, first note that from (10.26) we have, for every simple measurable function s,

$$T(s) = \int s g d\mu.$$

Using theorem 8.6.1, given $f \in L_p(X, \mathcal{S}, \mu)$ we choose a sequence $\{s_n\}_{n \ge 1}$ of simple functions in $L_p^r(X, \mathcal{S}, \mu)$ such that $\lim\limits_{n \to \infty} \|f - s_n\|_p = 0$. Then, by the continuity of T, $T(f) = \lim\limits_{n \to \infty} T(s_n)$. Also, using Hölder's inequality, in case $1 < p < \infty$, we have

$$\left| \int f g d\mu - \int s_n g d\mu \right| \le \int |f - s_n| |g| d\mu \le \|f - s_n\|_p \|g\|_p.$$

In case $p = 1$, clearly

$$\left| \int f g d\mu - \int s_n g d\mu \right| \le \int |f - s_n| |g| d\mu \le \|f - s_n\|_1 \|g\|_\infty.$$

Thus in either case we will have

$$\lim_{n \to \infty} \int s_n g d\mu = \int f g d\mu.$$

Hence $\forall\ f \in L_p^r(X, \mathcal{S}, \mu)$,

$$T(f) = \lim_{n \to \infty} T(s_n) = \lim_{n \to \infty} \int s_n g d\mu = \int f g \, d\mu.$$

Further, from proposition 10.4.1, we have $\|T\| = \|g\|_q$. To prove the uniqueness of g, let there exist some $g_1 \in L_p^r(\mu)$ such that

$$\int f g \, d\mu = \int f g_1 d\mu.$$

Then $g - g_1 \in L_q^r(X, \mathcal{S}, \mu)$ and

$$(T_{g-g_1})(f) := \int f g d\mu - \int f g_1 d\mu = 0, \ \forall\ f \in L_p^r(\mu).$$

Thus

$$0 = \| T_{g-g_1} \| = \| g - g_1 \|_q,$$

i.e., $g = g_1$. This completes the proof in the case $\mu(X) < +\infty$.

To prove the theorem when μ is σ-finite, let $\{X_n\}_{n \geq 1}$ be an increasing sequence of sets in $\mathcal{S}$ such that $\bigcup_{n=1}^{\infty} X_n = X$ and $\mu(X_n) < +\infty$ for every n. Consider the continuous linear map $T_n : L^r_p(X_n, \mathcal{S} \cap X_n, \mu) \longrightarrow \mathbb{R}$, defined by

$$T_n(f) = T(f), \ \forall \ f \in L^r_p(X_n, X_n \cap \mathcal{S}, \mu),$$

where each f is treated as a function on X, with $f \equiv 0$ on X_n^c. Then by the earlier case, there is a function $g_n \in L^r_q(X_n, X_n \cap \mathcal{S}, \mu)$ such that $\forall \ f \in L^r_p(X, \mathcal{S}, \mu)$,

$$T(\chi_{X_n} f) = \int_{X_n} f g_n \, d\mu.$$

If we treat g_n as an element of $L^r_p(X, \mathcal{S}, \mu)$, with $g_n \equiv 0$ on X_n^c, then

$$\| g_n \|_q \leq \| T \|.$$

Since $\{X_n\}_{n \geq 1}$ is an increasing sequence and every g_n is uniquely determined (except for a set of μ-measure zero), we may assume that $g_{n+1}(x) = g_n(x)$ for $x \in X_n$ for every n. Define g on X by

$$g(x) := g_n(x), \quad \text{if } x \in X_n.$$

Then g is a well-defined measurable function on $(X, \mathcal{S})$, and the sequence $\{|g_n(x)|\}_{n \geq 1}$ increases to $|g_n|$, $\forall \ x \in X$. Hence , by the monotone convergence theorem and continuity of T, we have, in case $1 < p < \infty$,

$$\int |g|^q \, d\mu = \lim_{n \to \infty} \int |g_n|^q d\mu \leq \| T \|^q.$$

Thus $g \in L^r_q(X, \mathcal{S}, \mu)$ when $1 < p < \infty$. If $p = 1$, clearly $\| g_n \|_\infty \leq \| T \| \ \forall \ n$, and this implies that $g \in L^r_\infty(X, \mathcal{S}, \mu)$ with $\| g \|_\infty \leq \| T \|$.

Finally, for $f \in L^r_p(X, \mathcal{S}, \mu)$, since $\chi_{X_n} f \to f$ and $|\chi_{X_n} f| \leq f$, by the dominated convergence theorem $\chi_{X_n} f \to f$ in $L^r_p(X, \mathcal{S}, \mu)$. Also, $\chi_{X_n} fg \to fg$ and $|\chi_{X_n} fg| \leq |fg| \in L^r_p(X, \mathcal{S}, \mu)$. Thus, again by the dominated convergence theorem $\forall \ f \in L^r_p(X, \mathcal{S}, \mu)$,

$$\int fg d\mu = \lim_{n \to \infty} \int_{X_n} fg d\mu = \lim_{n \to \infty} \int_{X_n} f g_n d\mu = \lim_{n \to \infty} T(\chi_{X_n} f) = T(f).$$

The claim that $\| T \| = \| g \|_q$ now follows from theorem 10.4.3. ∎

10.4.4. Remarks:

(i) The claim of proposition 10.4.1 for the case $1 < p < \infty$ holds even when μ is not σ-finite (analyze the proof carefully).

(ii) When $1 < p < \infty$, theorem 10.4.3 can be extended to cases when μ is not necessarily σ-finite. We show that there exists a set $W \in \mathcal{S}$ such that μ restricted to W is σ-finite and T restricted to W^c is the zero map. For this, let $E \in \mathcal{S}$ with μ being σ-finite on E. Let g_E denote the unique element of $L_q^r(E, E \cap \mathcal{S}, \mu)$ such that $\forall\ f \in L_p^r(X, \mathcal{S}, \mu)$

$$T(\chi_E f) = \int_E f g_E \, d\mu.$$

If we define $g_E = 0$ outside E, then $g_E \in L_q^r(X, \mathcal{S}, \mu)$. Also if $A \subseteq E$, then it follows from the uniqueness of g_E that $g_A = g_E$ a.e. (μ) on A. For every $E \in \mathcal{S}$ such that μ is σ-finite on E, let

$$\nu(E) := \int |g_E|^q d\mu.$$

Then $\forall\ A \subseteq E$ with $A \in \mathcal{S}$,

$$\nu(A) = \int |g_A|^q d\mu \leq \int |g_E|^q d\mu,$$

since

$$\int |g_E|^q \, d\mu = \| g_E \|_q^q = \| T_E \|^q,$$

where T_E is the restriction of T to $L_p^r(E, E \cap \mathcal{S}, \mu)$, we have $\|T_E\| < \|T\|$. Hence the set

$$S := \{\nu(E) \mid E \in \mathcal{S},\ \mu \text{ being } \sigma\text{-finite on } E\}$$

is bounded above. Note that S is a nonempty set. Let $\alpha := \sup S$, and let $\{E_n\}_{n \geq 1}$ be a sequence of sets from $\mathcal{S}$ such that μ is σ-finite on each E_n with

$$\lim_{n \to \infty} \nu(E_n) = \alpha.$$

Let

$$W := \bigcup_{n=1}^{\infty} E_n.$$

Then μ is σ-finite on W. Further, since

$$\nu(E_n) \leq \nu(W) \leq \alpha\ \forall\ n,$$

we have $\alpha = \nu(W)$. Let $f \in L_p^r(X, \mathcal{S}, \mu)$. Then the set

$$A := \{x \in X \mid |f(x)| \neq 0\} \in \mathcal{S}.$$

Further, μ is σ-finite on A, because $A = \bigcup_{k=1}^{\infty} A_n$, where $A_n = \{x \in X \mid n < |f(x)| \leq n+1\}$ and $\mu(A_n) < +\infty\ \forall\ n$. Thus μ is σ-finite on $A \cup W$ also, and

$$\nu(A \cup W) \leq \alpha = \nu(W).$$

As $\nu(W) \leq \nu(A \cup W)$, we have $\nu(W) = \nu(A \cup W)$, i.e.,

$$\int |g_{A \cup W}|^q d\mu = \int |g_W|^q d\mu.$$

Thus $g_{A \cup W}(x) = 0$ for a.e. x on $A \setminus W$. Since $g_A(x) = g_{A \cup W}(x)$ for a.e. $(\mu)x \in A$, we have $g_A(x) = 0$ for a.e. $(\mu)x \in A \setminus W$. Thus

$$T(f\chi_{W^c}) = T(f\chi_{A \cap W^c}) = \int_{A \cap W^c} fg_A d\mu = 0.$$

Hence T restricted to W^c is the zero map. In fact, if we define $g(x) := g_W(x)$ on W, and equal to 0 elsewhere, then for $f \in L_p^r(X, \mathcal{S}, \mu)$

$$T(f) = T(f\chi_W) = \int fg_W d\mu = \int f g\, d\mu.$$

Clearly, $g \in L_q^r(X, \mathcal{S}, \mu)$, and, as before, $\|g\|_q = \|T\|$.

(iii) When $p = 1$, the condition that μ is σ-finite in theorem 10.4.3 is necessary. For example, let $X = [0, 1]$, $\mathcal{S} = \{A \subset X \mid A \text{ or } A^c \text{ is countable}\}$ and μ the counting measure on $\mathcal{S}$. Then $f \in L_1(X, \mathcal{S}, \mu)$ iff f vanishes on all but countably many points $a_1, a_2, \ldots$ in X with $\sum_{i=1}^{\infty} |f(a_i)| < +\infty$. Consider the linear map $T : L_1(X, \mathcal{S}, \mu) \longrightarrow \mathbb{R}$, defined by

$$T(f) := \sum_{x \in [0,1]} xf(x).$$

Since

$$|T(f)| \leq \sum_{x \in [0,1]} |f(x)| = \|f\|_1,$$

T is a continuous linear functional on $L_1(X, \mathcal{S}, \mu)$. Clearly, if $T(f) = \int fg d\mu$ for some $g \in L_\infty(X, \mathcal{S}, \mu)$, then we should have $g(x) = x \;\; \forall \;\; x$. But the function $g(x) = x$ is not a measurable function on $(X, \mathcal{S})$.

(iv) For $p = 1$, theorem 10.4.3 can be extended for a class of measure spaces which are more general than the space of σ-finite measures. These are called decomposable measure spaces. For this, we refer the reader to Hewitt and Stromberg [18].

(v) Theorem 10.4.3 remains valid for $L_p(X, \mathcal{S}, \mu)$, the class of complex-valued measurable function on X such that $\int |f|^p d\mu < +\infty$. For this, one can consider $(\text{Re}\, T)(f) := \text{Re}\,(T(f))$ and $(\text{Im}\, T)(f) := \text{Im}\,(T(f))$ and apply theorem 10.4.3.

Extended real numbers

A.1. Extended real numbers

Let $\mathbb{R}$ denote the set of all real numbers and let

$$\mathbb{R}^* := \mathbb{R} \cup \{+\infty\} \cup \{-\infty\},$$

where $+\infty$ and $-\infty$ are two symbols read as **plus infinity** and **minus infinity**. We extend the algebraic operations and the order relation of $\mathbb{R}$ to $\mathbb{R}^*$ as follows:

1. For every $x \in \mathbb{R}$, $-\infty < x < +\infty$.

2. For every $x \in \mathbb{R}$,

$$(-\infty) + x = -\infty \quad \text{and} \quad (+\infty) + x = +\infty;$$
$$(+\infty) + (+\infty) = +\infty \quad \text{and} \quad (-\infty) + (-\infty) = -\infty.$$

3. For every $x \in \mathbb{R}$,

$$\left. \begin{array}{l} x(+\infty) = (+\infty)x = +\infty \\ x(-\infty) = (-\infty)x = -\infty \end{array} \right\} \quad \text{if } x > 0,$$

$$\left. \begin{array}{l} x(+\infty) = (+\infty)x = -\infty \\ x(-\infty) = (-\infty)x = +\infty \end{array} \right\} \quad \text{if } x < 0.$$

Further,

$$(+\infty)0 = (-\infty)0 = 0, \ (\pm\infty)(+\infty) = (\pm\infty) \ \text{and} \ (\pm\infty)(-\infty) = (\mp\infty).$$

Note that the relations $-\infty + (+\infty)$ and $(+\infty) + (-\infty)$ are not defined.

The set $\mathbb{R}^*$, also denoted as $[-\infty, +\infty]$, with the above properties is called the set of **extended real numbers**. The symbol $+\infty$ is also denoted by ∞, when no confusion arises.

A.2. $\sup(A)$ and $\inf(A)$

For a nonempty set $A \subseteq \mathbb{R}^*$, we write $\sup(A) := +\infty$ if $A \cap \mathbb{R}$ is not bounded above, and $\inf(A) := -\infty$ if $A \cap \mathbb{R}$ is not bounded below. Thus

- $\sup(A)$ *and* $\inf(A)$ *always exist for every nonempty subset A of* $\mathbb{R}^*$.

A.3. Limits of sequences in $\mathbb{R}^*$

For $\{x_n\}_{n \geq 1}$ any monotonically increasing sequence in $\mathbb{R}^*$ which is not bounded above, we say $\{x_n\}_{n \geq 1}$ is **convergent to** $+\infty$ and write

$$\lim_{n \to \infty} x_n = +\infty.$$

Similarly, if $\{x_n\}_{n \geq 1}$ is a monotonically decreasing sequence which is not bounded below, we say $\{x_n\}_{n \geq 1}$ is **convergent to** $-\infty$ and write

$$\lim_{n \to \infty} x_n = -\infty.$$

Hence

- *every monotone sequence in $\mathbb{R}^*$ is convergent.*

Thus for any sequence $\{x_n\}_{n \geq 1}$ in $\mathbb{R}^*$, the sequences $\{\sup_{k \geq j} x_k\}_{j \geq 1}$ and $\{\inf_{k \geq j} x_k\}_{j \geq 1}$ always converge. We write

$$\limsup_{n \to \infty} x_n := \lim_{j \to \infty} (\sup_{k \geq j} x_k)$$

and

$$\liminf_{n \to \infty} x_n := \lim_{j \to \infty} (\inf_{k \geq j} x_k).$$

$\lim_{n \to \infty} \sup x_n$ is called the **limit superior** of the sequence $\{x_n\}_{n \geq 1}$ and $\liminf_{n \to \infty} x_n$ is called the **limit inferior** of the sequence $\{x_n\}_{n \geq 1}$. Note that

$$\liminf_{n \to \infty} x_n \leq \limsup_{n \to \infty} x_n.$$

We say a sequence $\{x_n\}_{n \geq 1}$ is **convergent** to $x \in \mathbb{R}^*$ if $\liminf_{n \to \infty} x_n = \limsup_{n \to \infty} x_n =: x$, say. In that case we write $\lim_{n \to \infty} x_n := x$.

A.4. Series in $\mathbb{R}^*$

Let $\{x_k\}_{k \geq 1}$ be a sequence in $\mathbb{R}^*$ such that for every $n \in \mathbb{N}$, $s_n := \sum_{k=1}^n x_k$ is well-defined. We say that the series $\sum_{k=1}^\infty x_k$ is **convergent** to x if $\{s_n\}_{n \geq 1}$ is convergent. We write this as $x = \sum_{k=1}^\infty x_k$, x being called the **sum of**

the series $\sum_{k=1}^{\infty} x_k$. For example, if each $x_k \geq 0$, then the series $\sum_{k=1}^{\infty} x_k$ is always convergent.

Let $\{x_k\}_{k \geq 1}$ be a sequence in $\mathbb{R}^*$, $x_n \geq 0$ for every n. Let $\sigma : \mathbb{N} \to \mathbb{N}$ be any bijective map. Then the series $\sum_{k=1}^{\infty} x_{\sigma(k)}$ is called an **arrangement** of the series $\sum_{k=1}^{\infty} x_k$.

- *For every rearrangement σ, the series $\sum_{k=1}^{\infty} x_{\sigma(k)}$ and $\sum_{k=1}^{\infty} x_k$ converge to the same sum.*

Clearly, both the series are convergent in $\mathbb{R}^*$. Let $\alpha := \sum_{k=1}^{\infty} x_k$ and $\beta := \sum_{k=1}^{\infty} x_{\sigma(k)}$. To prove $\alpha = \beta$, in view of the symmetry, it is enough to prove that $\beta \leq \alpha$. Now

$$\beta = \sum_{k=1}^{n} x_{\sigma(k)} \leq \sum_{k=1}^{m} x_k \leq \sum_{k=1}^{\infty} x_k = \alpha,$$

where in the the middle term $m := \max\{\sigma(1), \cdots, \sigma(k)\}$. Hence $\beta \leq \alpha$, proving the required claim.

Similar arguments apply to $\{x_{n,m}\}_{n,m \geq 1}$, any double-indexed sequence of nonnegative elements of $\mathbb{R}^*$. For every fixed n, the series $\sum_{m=1}^{\infty} x_{n,m}$ is convergent in $\mathbb{R}^*$. Let $y_n := \sum_{m=1}^{\infty} x_{n,m}$. Further, $\sum_{n=1}^{\infty} y_n$ is also convergent in $\mathbb{R}^*$. Let $y := \sum_{n=1}^{\infty} y_n$. We can also define for all fixed m, $z_m := \sum_{n=1}^{\infty} x_{n,m}$, and $z := \sum_{m=1}^{\infty} z_m$ in $\mathbb{R}^*$. We show that both these processes lead to the same sum, i.e., $y = z$, which is written as

$$\sum_{m=1}^{\infty} \left(\sum_{n=1}^{\infty} x_{n,m} \right) = \sum_{n=1}^{\infty} \left(\sum_{m=1}^{\infty} x_{n,m} \right).$$

To see this, we note that $\forall \, r, s \in \mathbb{N}$,

$$\sum_{n=1}^{r} \sum_{m=1}^{s} x_{n,m} \leq \sum_{m=1}^{s} \sum_{n=1}^{\infty} x_{n,m} \leq \sum_{m=1}^{\infty} \sum_{n=1}^{\infty} x_{n,m}.$$

Hence

$$y := \sum_{n=1}^{\infty} \sum_{m=1}^{\infty} x_{n,m} \leq \sum_{m=1}^{\infty} \sum_{n=1}^{\infty} x_{n,m} =: z.$$

The reverse inequality follows from symmetry.

A similar result holds for rearrangement of double-indexed series of nonnegative terms in $\mathbb{R}^*$:

- *Let $\sigma : \mathbb{N} \to \mathbb{N} \times \mathbb{N}$ be any bijective map, and let $\{x_{n,m}\}_{n \geq 1, m \geq 1}$ be a double-indexed sequence of nonnegative elements of $\mathbb{R}^*$. Then*

$$\sum_{r=1}^{\infty} x_{\sigma(r)} = \sum_{n=1}^{\infty} \sum_{m=0}^{\infty} x_{n,m} = \sum_{m=1}^{\infty} \sum_{n=1}^{\infty} x_{n,m}.$$

Axiom of choice

Let A, B be two sets. One defines $A \times B$, the **Cartesian product** of A and B, to be the empty set if either A or B or both are empty, and to be the set of all ordered pairs (a, b), $a \in A$, $b \in B$, when both A and B are nonempty. Similarly, for a finite family of nonempty sets $A_1, \ldots, A_n$, we define their Cartesian product to be the set

$$A_1 \times \cdots \times A_n := \{(x_1, x_2, \ldots x_n) \mid x_i \in A_i, i = 1, 2, \ldots, n\}.$$

Obviously, $A_1 \times \cdots \times A_n$ is a nonempty set. We can think of $A_1 \times \cdots \times A_n$ as the set of all functions $f : \{1, 2, \ldots, n\} \longrightarrow \bigcup_{i=1}^{n} A_i$ with $f(i) = x_i \in A_i$ for each i. One can copy this to define the Cartesian product of any arbitrary family of sets, say $\{A_\alpha\}_{\alpha \in I}$, to be the set

$$\prod_{\alpha \in I} A_\alpha := \left\{ f : I \to \bigcup_{\alpha \in I} A_\alpha \,\middle|\, f(\alpha) \in A_\alpha, \, \forall \, \alpha \in I \right\}.$$

However, there is no surety that the set $\prod_{\alpha \in I} A_\alpha$ is nonempty, i.e., we do not know that there always exists at least one function $f : I \to \bigcup_{\alpha \in I} A_\alpha$ such that $f(\alpha) \in A_\alpha \ \forall \ \alpha \in I$, although intuitively it seems obvious that such a function should always exist. However, this cannot be proved with the usual axioms of set theory. (For a short introduction to axiomatic set theory, see Rana [30]. For detailed account of axiomatic set theory, the axiom of choice, and its history, see Halmos [15] and Fraenkel [12]). The way out of the above dilemma is to treat this an axiom itself, called the **axiom of choice**:

- *If $\{A_\alpha\}_{\alpha \in I}$ is a nonempty family of sets such that each A_α is nonempty, then there exists a function $f : I \longrightarrow \bigcup_{\alpha \in I} A_\alpha$ such that $f(\alpha) \in A_\alpha \ \forall \ \alpha \in I$.*

Such a function is called a **choice function**.

The axiom of choice has many equivalent formulations; a useful one is the following:

- *If $\{A_\alpha \mid \alpha \in I\}$ is a nonempty family of pairwise disjoint sets such that $A_\alpha \neq \emptyset$ for every $\alpha \in I$, then there exists a set $E \subseteq \bigcup_{\alpha \in I} A_\alpha$ such that $E \cap A_\alpha$ consists of precisely one element for each $\alpha \in I$.*

The axiom of choice finds applications in many diverse branches of mathematics. (We have used it in section 4.6 to construct nonmeasurable subsets of $\mathbb{R}$.)

Continuum hypothesis

Let X and Y be two sets. We say X and Y are **equipotent** iff there exists a bijection between them. We write this as $X \approx Y$. In a sense, equipotent sets have same 'number' of elements.

We say a set A is **finite** if $A \approx \{1, 2, \ldots, n\}$ for some $n \in \mathbb{N}$, and we say A is **countable** if $A \approx \mathbb{N}$, the set of natural numbers. A set which is not countable is called **uncountable.** For example, $\mathbb{N}, \mathbb{Z}, \mathbb{Q}$ are all countable sets while $\mathbb{R}$ is uncountable. (For a detailed discussion, see Rana [30].)

The statement $X \approx Y$ means X and Y have the same 'number of elements', and can be made precise as follows (see Halmos [15] for details). Let $\mathcal{C}$ be a collection of sets such that any two members of $\mathcal{C}$ are equipotent to each other. Then one can assign a symbol, called its **cardinal number**, to each $A \in \mathcal{C}$, denoted by $\text{card}(A)$. Thus

$$\text{card}(A) = \text{card}(B) \quad \text{iff} \quad A \approx B.$$

The cardinal number of a set A is also called the **cardinality** of A. For example, for any set A which is equipotent to $\{1, 2, \ldots, n\}$, we write $\text{card}(A) = n$. For any set $A \approx \mathbb{N}$, we write $\text{card}(A) = \aleph_0$, called **aleph-nought**. For any set $A \approx \mathbb{R}$, we write $\text{card}(A) = \mathfrak{c}$, called **cardinality of the continuum**. For finite sets, it is easy to see that if $\text{card}(A) = n$, then $\text{card}\,(\mathcal{P}(A)) = 2^n$, where $\mathcal{P}(A)$ is the set of all subsets of A. We define, for any nonempty set X,

$$\text{card}(\mathcal{P}(X)) := 2^{\text{card}(X)}.$$

For example,

$$\text{card}(\mathcal{P}(\mathbb{N})) := 2^{\aleph_0} \quad \text{and} \quad \text{card}(\mathcal{P}(\mathbb{R})) := 2^{\mathfrak{c}}.$$

For a finite set A, we know that

$$\text{card}(\mathcal{P}(A)) = 2^{\text{card}(A)} > \text{card}(A).$$

Can the same be said about arbitrary sets which are not necessarily finite? For two sets A and B, we say $\text{card}(A) \preceq \text{card}(B)$ if there exists a one-one map from A into B. We write $\text{card}(A) < \text{card}(B)$ if $\text{card}(A) \preceq \text{card}(B)$ but $\text{card}(A) \neq \text{card}(B)$. Now we ask the question:

- *Is* $\text{card}(A) < \text{card}(\mathcal{P}(A))$ *for any nonempty set A?*

The answer is in the affirmative and is due to George Cantor (see Rana [30] for a proof). It can be shown that $2^{\aleph_0} = \mathfrak{c}$, i.e., $\mathcal{P}(\mathbb{N}) \approx \mathbb{R}$. Thus we have the following:

$$0 < 1 < 2 < \cdots < n < \cdots < \aleph_0 < 2^{\aleph_0} = \mathfrak{c} < 2^{\mathfrak{c}} < 2^{2^{\mathfrak{c}}} < \cdots .$$

This raises the following natural question:

- *Does there exist a cardinal number α such that $\aleph_0 < \alpha < 2^{\aleph_0} = \mathfrak{c}$?*

That is, does there exist a set $A \subset \mathbb{R}$ such that $A \not\approx \mathbb{R}$ and $\mathbb{N} \subset A$ but $A \not\approx \mathbb{N}$? The answer to this question is not known. The statement that the answer to the above question is in the negative is called the **continuum hypothesis:**

- *There does not exist any cardinal number between $\aleph_0$ and $2^{\aleph_0} = \mathfrak{c}$.*

An equivalent formulation of this is the following:

- *The set $\mathbb{R}$ can be well-ordered in such a way that each element of $\mathbb{R}$ is preceded by only countably many elements.*

We used this in section 3.4, to prove Ulam's theorem. It is known that the continuum hypothesis is independent of the Zermelo-Fraenkel axioms of set theory.

Urysohn's lemma

In theorem 8.6.2, we needed the following result:

- *Let K be a compact subset of $\mathbb{R}^n$ and U an open subset of $\mathbb{R}^n$ with $K \subset U$. Then there exists a continuous function $g : \mathbb{R}^n \longrightarrow [0,1]$ such that $g(x) = 1 \; \forall x \in K$ and $g(x) = 0 \; \forall \, x \notin U$.*

This follows from the following result, known as **Urysohn's lemma**:

D.1. Theorem: *Let (X, d) be any metric space and A, B be closed subsets of X such that $A \cap B = \emptyset$. Then there exists a continuous function $g : X \longrightarrow [0,1]$ such that $g(x) = 1 \; \forall \, x \in A$ and $g(x) = 0 \; \forall \, x \in B$.*

Proof: For any nonempty set $Y \subseteq X$, and $x \in X$, let

$$d(x, Y) := \inf\{d(x, y) \mid y \in Y\}.$$

Then it is easy to see that for every $x, z \in X$

$$|\, d(x, Y) - d(z, Y)\,| \;\leq\; d(x, z).$$

Thus $x \longmapsto d(x, Y)$ is a uniformly continuous function. Further, if Y is a closed set, then $d(x, Y) = 0$ iff $x \in Y$.

Now, given disjoint closed sets A and B, define $\forall \, x \in X$,

$$g(x) := \frac{d(x, B)}{d(x, A) + d(x, B)}.$$

Clearly g is a continuous function with the required properties. ∎

D.2. Corollary: *Let A be a closed subset of X and U an open subset of X such that $A \subseteq U$. Then there exists a continuous function $g : X \longrightarrow [0,1]$ such that $g(x) = 1 \; \forall \; x \in A$ and $g(x) = 0 \; \forall \; x \notin U$.*

Proof: This follows from theorem D.1 with $B = U^c$. ∎

D.3. Corollary: *Let (X, d) be a metric space and $x, y \in X, x \neq y$. Then there exists a continuous function $g : X \to [0,1]$ such that $g(x) \neq g(y)$.*

Proof: This follows from theorem D.1 with $A = \{x\}, B = \{y\}$. ∎

The second corollary has a great significance. It ensures that metric spaces have a rich supply of real-valued continuous functions: any two distinct points can be separated by a real-valued continuous function. Urysohn's lemma can be extended to some topological spaces. For details see Hewitt and Stromberg [18], Munkres [26].

Singular value decomposition of a matrix

We consider matrices with real entries only. For an $m \times n$ matrix $A = [a_{ij}]$, its transpose is the $n \times m$ matrix $[b_{ij}] := A^t$, where $b_{ij} = a_{ji}$, for $1 \leq i \leq n$ and for $1 \leq j \leq m$. We write the elements of $\mathbb{R}^n$ as $1 \times n$ matrices.

E.1. Theorem: *Let A be an $m \times n$ real matrix of rank r. Then there exist matrices P, Q and D with the following properties:*

(i) *P is an $m \times r$ matrix with $P^t P = Id$.*

(ii) *Q is an $n \times r$ matrix with $Q^t Q = Id$.*

(iii) *D is an $r \times r$ diagonal matrix with nonzero real entries.*

(iv) *$A = PDQ^t$.*

The representation $A = PDQ^t$ is called the **singular value decomposition** of A.

Proof: Consider the $m \times m$ real matrix $B := AA^t$. Since B is symmetric, all its eigenvalues are real. In fact, it is easy to see that all the eigenvalues of B are nonnegative and there exists a complete set of orthonormal eigenvectors of B. Since $\text{rank}(B) = \text{rank}(A)$, B has r positive eigenvalues, say $\lambda_1, \dots, \lambda_r$. Let $x_1, \dots, x_r, \dots, x_m \in \mathbb{R}^m$ be the complete set of orthonormal eigenvectors of B, x_i being the eigenvector corresponding to the eigenvalue

$\lambda_i, 1 \leq i \leq r$. Then

$$AA^t x_i^t = \begin{cases} \lambda_i x_i^t & \text{if } 1 \leq i \leq r, \\ \\ 0^t & \text{if } r+1 \leq i \leq m. \end{cases}$$

Thus for $r+1 \leq i \leq m$,

$$x_i AA^t x_i^t = 0, \quad \text{i.e., } |x_i A|^2 = 0, \quad \text{i.e., } x_i A = 0.$$

Let

$$y_i := \frac{x_i A}{\sqrt{\lambda_i}}, \quad 1 \leq i \leq r.$$

Clearly $y_1, \ldots, y_r$ are orthonormal vectors in $\mathbb{R}^n$. Let P be the $m \times r$ matrix whose column vectors are $x_1^t, \ldots, x_r^t$, and let Q be the $n \times r$ matrix whose column vectors are $y_1^t, \ldots, y_r^t$. Then

$$
\begin{aligned}
A &= IA \\
&= (x_1^t x_1 + \cdots + x_m^t x_m)A \\
&= x_1^t x_1 A + \cdots + x_r^t x_r A \\
&= x_1^t(\sqrt{\lambda_1} y_1) + \cdots + x_r^t(\sqrt{\lambda_r} y_r) \\
&= PDQ^t,
\end{aligned}
$$

where D is the $r \times r$ diagonal matrix with entries $\sqrt{\lambda_1}, \ldots, \sqrt{\lambda_r}$. ∎

E.2. Corollary: *Let A be an $n \times n$ real nonsingular matrix. Then there exist $n \times n$ orthogonal matrices P_1 and P_2 and an $n \times n$ diagonal matrix D having positive entries such that $A = P_1 D P_2$.*

Proof: Take $P_1 = P$ and $P_2 = Q^t$, where P, Q are the matrices as given by theorem E.1. ∎

E.3. Note: The positive real numbers $\sqrt{\lambda_1}, \ldots, \sqrt{\lambda_r}$, obtained in the proof of theorem E.1 are called the **singular values** of the matrix A.

Functions of bounded variation

F.1. Definition: Let $f : [a,b] \longrightarrow \mathbb{R}$, and let $P := \{a = x_0 < x_1 < \ldots < x_n = b\}$ be a partition of $[a,b]$. Let

$$V_a^b(P,f) := \sum_{k=1}^{n} |f(x_k) - f(x_{k-1})|.$$

We call $V_a^b(P,f)$ the **variation** on f over $[a,b]$ with respect to the partition P. Let

$$V_a^b(f) := \sup\{V_a^b(P,f) \mid P \text{ a partition of } [a,b]\}.$$

The extended real number $V_a^b(f)$ is called the **total variation** of f over $[a,b]$. The function f is said to be of **bounded variation** if $V_a^b(f) < +\infty$.

F.2. Example: Suppose $f : [a,b] \longrightarrow \mathbb{R}$ is a monotonically increasing or monotonically decreasing function. Then for every partition P of $[a,b]$,

$$V_a^b(P,f) = |f(b) - f(a)|.$$

Hence

$$V_a^b(f) = |f(b) - f(a)| < +\infty.$$

Thus every monotone function is of bounded variation.

F.3. Proposition: *For functions f and g on $[a,b]$, the following hold:*

(i) *If f is of bounded variation, then f is a bounded function.*

(ii) *If f and g are of bounded variation, then so are the functions f +*
g, f − g, fg and αf for every α ∈ ℝ.

Proof: Exercise. ∎

F.4. Proposition: *Let f : [a, b] ⟶ ℝ be of bounded variation. For*
x, y ∈ [a, b] with x ≤ y, let $V_x^y(f)$ denote the variation of f in the interval
[x, y] if x < y, and $V_x^y(f) = 0$ if x = y. Then the following hold:

(i) $V_a^c(f) + V_c^b(f) = V_a^b(f)$, ∀ a ≤ c ≤ b.

(ii) $V_a^x(f), x \in [a, b]$, *is an increasing function.*

(iii) $|f(y) - f(x)| \leq V_a^y(f) - V_a^x(f)$, ∀ a ≤ x ≤ y ≤ b.

(iv) *The function $V_a^x(f) - f(x), a \leq x \leq b$, is an increasing function.*

Proof: (i) It is easy to see that for every partition P of $[a, b]$,

$$V_a^b(f, P) \leq V_a^c(f) + V_c^b(f).$$

Hence $V_a^b(f) \leq V_a^c(f) + V_c^b(f)$. To prove the reverse inequality, let $\epsilon > 0$ be
given. Choose partitions P_1 and P_2 of $[a, c]$ and $[c, b]$, respectively, such that

$$V_a^c(f) - \epsilon/2 < V_a^c(P_1, f) \text{ and } V_c^b(f) - \epsilon/2 < V_c^b(P_2, f).$$

Let $P := P_1 \cup P_2$. Then P is a partition of $[a, b]$, and

$$V_a^c(f) + V_c^b(f) - \epsilon < V_a^c(P_1, f) + V_c^b(P_2, f) = V_a^b(P, f) \leq V_a^b(f).$$

Since $\epsilon > 0$ is arbitrary, we get the required reverse inequality.

(ii) Since $V_a^x(f) \geq 0$ ∀ $x \in [a, b]$, it follows from (i) that $V_a^x(f)$ is an
increasing function of x.

(iii) Let P be any partition of $[a, x]$. Then $P_1 := P \cup \{y\}$ is a partition
of $[a, b]$, and

$$V_a^y(f) \geq V_a^y(P_1, f) = V_a^x(P, f) + |f(y) - f(x)|.$$

Since this holds for every partition P of $[a, x]$, we get

$$V_a^y(f) \geq V_a^x(f) + |f(y) - f(x)|.$$

This proves (iii).

(iv) Let $a \leq x < y \leq b$. Then it follows from (iii) that

$$f(y) - f(x) \leq |f(y) - f(x)| \leq V_a^y(f) - V_a^x(f).$$

Thus

$$(V_a^y(f) - f(y)) - (V_a^x(f) - f(x)) \geq 0.$$

This proves (iv). ∎

F.5. Theorem (Jordan): *Let f : [a, b] ⟶ ℝ. Then f is of bounded*
variation iff f is the difference of two monotonically increasing functions.

Proof: If $f = g - h$, where g and h are monotonically increasing functions, then it follows from example F.2 and proposition F.3 that f is of bounded variation. Conversely, let f be of bounded variation. Let $g(x) := V_a^x(f)$ and $h(x) := V_a^x(f) - f(x)$. Then g and h are monotonically increasing, by proposition F.4, and $f = g - h$. ∎

F.6. Exercise:

(i) Let $f : [a, b] \longrightarrow \mathbb{R}$ be a differentiable function such that its derivative f' is a bounded function. Show that f has bounded variation.

(Hint: Use Lagrange's mean value theorem.)

(ii) Let $f : [0, 1] \longrightarrow \mathbb{R}$ be defined by

$$f(x) := \begin{cases} x^2 \sin \dfrac{\pi}{x} & \text{if } x \neq 0, \\ 0 & \text{if } x = 0. \end{cases}$$

Show that f is a continuous function of bounded variation.

(iii) Let $f : [0, 1] \longrightarrow \mathbb{R}$ be defined by

$$f(x) := \begin{cases} x \sin \dfrac{\pi}{x} & \text{if } x \neq 0, \\ 0 & \text{if } x = 0. \end{cases}$$

Show that f is uniformly continuous but is not of bounded variation.

Differentiable transformations

For $x \in \mathbb{R}^n, x := (x_1, \dots, x_n)$, let $|x| := (\sum_{i=1}^{n} x_i^2)^{1/2}$. For $a \in \mathbb{R}^n$ and $r > 0$, let $B(a, r) := \{x \in \mathbb{R}^n \mid |x - a| < r\}$. We denote by $\{e^1, e^2, \dots, e^n\}$ the standard basis of $\mathbb{R}^n$.

G.1. Definition: Let $U \subseteq \mathbb{R}^n$ be an open set and $T : U \longrightarrow \mathbb{R}^m$ be a mapping. We say that T is **differentiable** at $a \in U$ if there exists a linear mapping $A : \mathbb{R}^n \longrightarrow \mathbb{R}^m$ such that

$$\lim_{h \to 0} \left| \frac{T(a+h) - T(a) - A(h)}{h} \right| = 0.$$

Equivalently, for each $\epsilon > 0$ there exists $\delta > 0$ such that $B(a, \delta) \subseteq U$ and $\forall \ y \in B(a, \delta)$,

$$| \ T(x) - T(a) + A(x - a) \ | \ \leq \ \epsilon |x - a|.$$

Whenever such an A exists, it is unique and is denoted by $dT(a)$, called the **differential** of T at a. We say that T is a **differentiable mapping** on U if T is differentiable at every point $a \in U$.

For $T : U \longrightarrow \mathbb{R}^m$, let $T(x) = (T_1(x), T_2(x), \dots, T_m(x))$. Then the functions $T_i, 1 \leq i \leq m$, are called the **coordinate functions** of T, and we write this as $T = (T_1, \dots, T_m)$. Each T_i is a map from $U \longrightarrow \mathbb{R}$. We denote by $(D_j T_i)(x), 1 \leq j \leq n$, the jth partial derivative of T_i at x, whenever it exists.

G.2.   Theorem: *Let $T : U \subseteq \mathbb{R}^n \longrightarrow \mathbb{R}^m$ be differentiable at $a \in U$. Then T is continuous at a and all the partial derivatives $(D_j T_i)(a)$ exist, $1 \leq i, j \leq n$, with $D_j T_i(a)$ being the ith coordinate of $(dT(a))(e^j)$.*

Proof: By definition, given $\epsilon > 0$ there exists $\delta > 0$ such that $\forall\ x \in B(a, \delta) \subseteq U$,

$$| T(x) - T(a) - dT(a)(x - a) | \leq \epsilon |x - a|.$$

Thus

$$| T(x) - T(a) | \leq | dT(a)(x - a) | + \epsilon |x - a|. \tag{G.1}$$

Let $dT(a)$ have the matrix $[a_{ij}]$ with respect to some bases on $\mathbb{R}^n$ and $\mathbb{R}^m$. Then for $x = (x_1, \dots, x_n), a = (a_1, \dots, a_n)$,

$$| dT(a)(x - a) | = \left(\sum_{k=1}^{n} \left(\sum_{j=1}^{n} a_{kj} (x_j - a_j) \right)^2 \right)^{1/2}.$$

By the Cauchy-Schwarz inequality,

$$\left| \sum_{j=1}^{n} a_{kj} (x_j - a_j) \right| \leq \left(\sum_{j=1}^{n} |a_{kj}|^2 \right)^{1/2} \left(\sum_{j=1}^{n} (x_j - a_j)^2 \right)^{1/2}.$$

Hence

$$| dT(a)(x - a) | \leq \left(\sum_{k=1}^{n} \sum_{j=1}^{n} |a_{kj}|^2 \right)^{1/2} \left(\sum_{j=1}^{n} (x_j - a_i)^2 \right)^{1/2}.$$

Let us write

$$\|dT(a)\| := \left(\sum_{k=1}^{n} \sum_{j=1}^{n} |a_{kj}|^2 \right)^{1/2}.$$

Then

$$| dT(a)(x - a) | \leq \|dT(a)\|\, |x - a|. \tag{G.2}$$

From (G.1) and (G.2), we have

$$| T(x) - T(a) | \leq (\epsilon + \|dT(a)\|) |x - a|,$$

which clearly implies the continuity of T at a. Next we show that $(D_j T_i)(a)$ exists for every i, j. Let $A_i(e^j)$ denote the ith coordinate of $(dT(a))(e^j)$, for every $1 \leq j \leq n$ and $1 \leq i \leq m$. Then $\forall\ h \in \mathbb{R}, h \neq 0$,

$$\left| \frac{T_i(a + he^j) - T_i(a) - hA_i(e^j)}{h} \right| \leq \left| \frac{T(a + he^j) - T(a) - dT(a)(he^j)}{h} \right|.$$

This is because, for $x = (x_1, \dots, x_n) \in \mathbb{R}^n$ we have $|x_i| < |x|, 1 \leq i \leq n$. It follows from the above inequality and the differentiability of T at a that the partial derivative $(D_j T_i)(a)$ exists and is the ith coordinate of $(dT(a))(e^j)$.

∎

G.3. Theorem: *Let U be an open subset of $\mathbb{R}^n$ and $T : U \longrightarrow \mathbb{R}^m$ be a mapping with coordinate functions $T_1, \ldots, T_m$. Then the following hold:*

(i) *T is differentiable at $a \in U$ iff each $T_i : U \longrightarrow \mathbb{R}$ is differentiable at a. Further, in that case the ith row of the matrix of $(dT)(a)$ is the matrix vector of $(dT_i)(a)$.*

(ii) *If all the $m \times n$ partial derivatives $(D_j T_i)(a)$ exist $\forall \ a \in U$ and are continuous (in that case, we say that T is a C^1-**mapping** on U), then T is differentiable.*

Proof: (i) Let T be differentiable at $a \in U$ and T_i be its ith component. Let A_i denote the ith coordinate map of the linear map $(dT)(a)$. Then for $h \in \mathbb{R}^n, h \neq 0$,

$$\left| \frac{T_i(a+h) - T_i(a) - A_i(h)}{h} \right| \leq \left| \frac{T(a+h) - T(a) - dT(a)(h)}{h} \right|.$$

Hence T_i is differentiable at a with $(dT_i)(a)$ the ith coordinate map of $(dT)(a)$. Thus the ith row in the matrix of $(dT)(a)$ is the $1 \times n$ matrix of $(dT_i)(a)$.

Conversely, suppose each T_i is differentiable at a. Consider the linear map A whose i^{th} coordinate function is $(dT_i)(a)$. Then

$$| T(a+h) - T(a) - A(h) |$$

$$= \left(\sum_{i=1}^n | T_i(a+h) - T_i(a) - (dT_i)(a)(h) |^2 \right)^{1/2}$$

$$\leq \sum_{i=1}^n | T_i(a+h) - T_i(a) - (dT_i)(a)(h) |.$$

From this it follows that T is differentiable at a and $(dT)(a)$ has i^{th} coordinate map $(dT_i)(a)$. This proves (i).

(ii) To show that T is differentiable, it is enough to show that each T_i is differentiable. Thus we may assume without loss of generality that $m = 1$. We are given that $(D_j T)(a)$ exists $\forall \ a \in U, 1 \leq j \leq n$, and is a continuous function. We shall show that T is differentiable. In view of theorem G.2, the natural candidate for $(dT)(a)$ is given by

$$(dT)(a)(x) := \sum_{j=1}^n (D_j T)(a) x_j, \ x = (x_1, \ldots, x_n) \in U.$$

We show that $(dT)(a)$ is indeed as defined above. We prove it by induction on n. For $n = 1$, it is obvious. So assume this for $n - 1$. To prove it for n, for $x = (x_1, \ldots, x_n) \in \mathbb{R}^n$ let $\pi(x) := (x_1, \ldots, x_{n-1})$. Note that $\pi(x + y) = \pi(x) + \pi(y)$ and the set $\pi(U) = \{y \in \mathbb{R}^{n-1} | y = \pi(x) \text{ for some } x \in U\}$ is an open subset of $\mathbb{R}^{n-1}$. Now, for any $a = (a_1, \ldots, a_n) \in U$ and $h = (h_1, \ldots, h_n) \in \mathbb{R}^n$ such that $a + h \in U$, we have

$$T(a + h) - T(a) - \sum_{j=1}^{n}(D_j T)(a)h_j$$

$$= T(\pi(a + h), a_n + h_n) - T(\pi(a + h), a_n) - (D_n T)(a)h_n$$

$$+ T(\pi(a + h), a_n) - T(\pi(a), a_n) - \sum_{j=1}^{n-1}(D_j T)(a)h_j. \quad \text{(G.3)}$$

Consider the function $\tilde{T} : \pi(U) \longrightarrow \mathbb{R}$ defined by

$$\tilde{T}(t) := T(t, a_n), \quad t \in \pi(U).$$

It is easy to check that the $(D_j \tilde{T})(t)$ exist for all $1 \leq j \leq n - 1$. In fact, $(D_j \tilde{T})(t) = (D_j T)(t, a_n)$, and hence $\tilde{T}$ has all partial derivatives in $\pi(U)$, and they are continuous. Thus, by the induction hypothesis, $\tilde{T}$ is differentiable at every $t \in \pi(U)$. In particular, $\tilde{T}$ is differentiable at $\pi(a)$, and by theorem G.2 we have

$$(d\tilde{T})(\pi(a))(t) = \sum_{j=1}^{n-1}(D_j T)(a)t_j,$$

for any $t = (t_1, \ldots, t_{n-1}) \in \mathbb{R}^{n-1}$. Thus given $\epsilon > 0$, we can choose $0 < \delta' < \epsilon$ such that for all $s \in \mathbb{R}^{n-1}$ with $|s| < \delta' < 1$ we have $(\pi(a) + s) \in U$ and

$$\left| \tilde{T}(\pi(a) + s) - \tilde{T}(\pi(a)) - \sum_{j=1}^{n-1}(D_j T)(a)s_j \right| \leq \epsilon|s|/2. \quad \text{(G.4)}$$

Next, by the continuity of $(D_n T)(a)$, we can choose $\delta > 0$ such that $0 < \delta < \delta'$ and $\forall \ x \in \mathbb{R}^n$ with $|x - a| < \delta$, we have $x \in U$ and

$$\left| (D_n T)(x) - (D_n T)(a) \right| < \epsilon/2. \quad \text{(G.5)}$$

Now, fix $h := (h_1, \ldots, h_n) \in \mathbb{R}^n$ with $|h| < \delta$. Then $|\pi(h)| < \delta'$, and by the mean-value theorem for one variable, we have $0 < \theta < 1$ such that

$$T(\pi(a + h), a_n + h_n) - T(\pi(a + h), a_n) = h_n(D_n T)(\pi(a + h), a + \theta h_n).$$

Then

$$\left| (\pi(a + h), a_n + \theta h_n) - a \right| < \left| (\pi(h), \theta h_n) \right| < |h| < \delta. \quad \text{(G.6)}$$

Thus, using (G.5) and (G.6), we get

$$T(\pi(a + h), a_n + h_n) - T(\pi(a + h), a_n) - (D_n T)(a)h_n \ | < \ \epsilon|h_n|/2. \quad \text{(G.7)}$$

Combining (G.3), (G.4) and (G.7), we have, $\forall \; |h| < \delta$,

$$\left| \; T(a+h) - T(a) - \sum_{j=1}^{n}(D_jT)(a)h_j \; \right| \; \leq \; \epsilon|\pi(h)|/2 + \epsilon|h_n|/2 \; \leq \; \epsilon.$$

Hence T is differentiable at a. ∎

G.4. Definition: Let U be an open subset of $\mathbb{R}^n$ and $T : U \longrightarrow \mathbb{R}^n$ be differentiable at $a \in U$. Let the matrix of $(dT)(a)$ with respect to a basis of $\mathbb{R}^n$ be denoted by $[(dT)(a)]$, i.e., the ij^{th} element of $[(dT)(a)]$ is $(D_jT_i)(a)$, where T_i is the ith coordinate function of T. The **Jacobian** of T at a is defined to be the determinant of the matrix $[(dT)(a)]$ and is denoted by $J_T(a)$. Note that if T is a C^1-mapping on U, then $J_T(a)$ is a continuous function on U.

G.5. Theorem (Inverse function): *Let U be an open subset of $\mathbb{R}^n$ and $T : U \longrightarrow \mathbb{R}^n$ be a C^1-mapping. Suppose that $J_T(a) \neq 0 \; \forall \; a \in U$. Then for every $a \in U$, there exists an open neighborhood V of a with $V \subseteq U$ such that*

(i) *T is one-one on V.*

(ii) *$T(V)$ is in an open neighborhood of $T(a)$.*

(iii) *$T^{-1} : T(V) \longrightarrow V$ is a C^1-mapping and*

$$(dT^{-1})(y) = ((dT)(T^{-1}(y)))^{-1}, \quad \forall \; y \in V.$$

Proof (S. Kumaresan): Since T is a C^1-map, by theorem G.3, T is differentiable on U. Let $a \in U$ be fixed arbitrarily. Without loss of generality, we may assume that $(dT)(a) = Id$, the identity transformation on $\mathbb{R}^n$, for otherwise, we can consider the transformation $S := ((dT)(a))^{-1}T$. Since in the matrix representation of $(dT)(x)$, the ij^{th} entry is $(D_jT_i)(x)$, it is easy to show that $\forall \; t \in \mathbb{R}^n$,

$$|(dT)(x)(t)| \; \leq \; \left(\sum_{i=1}^{n}\sum_{j=1}^{n}|D_jT_i(x)|^2 \right)^{1/2} |t|.$$

Let

$$\|(dT)(x)\| := \left(\sum_{i=1}^{n}\sum_{j=1}^{n}|D_jT_i(x)|^2 \right)^{1/2}.$$

Then $\forall \, t \in \mathbb{R}^n$,

$$| \; (dT)(x)(t) \; | \; \leq \; \|dT(x)\| \, |t|.$$

Since each $(D_jT_i)(x)$ is continuous, it follows that $x \longmapsto \|(dT)(x)\|$ is also a continuous map. Thus we can choose $\delta > 0$ such that for every $x \in B(a, \delta)$

$$\|(dT)(x) - (dT)(a)\| < 1/2. \tag{G.8}$$

Next, let $x_1, x_2 \in B(a, \delta)$. Then by the mean-value theorem for vector-valued functions, we have some $0 < \theta < 1$ such that

$$| \, T(x_1) - T(x_2) - dT(a)(x_1 - x_2) \, |$$
$$\leq | \, (dT)(x_1 + \theta(x_2 - x_1))(x_1 - x_2) - (dT)(a)(x_1 - x_2) \, |$$
$$\leq \left(\sup_{0 < \theta < 1} \|(dT)x_1 + \theta(x_2 - x_1) - (dT)(a)\| \right) |x_2 - x_1|. \quad \text{(G.9)}$$

Since for every $0 < \theta < 1$,

$$x_1 + \theta(x_2 - x_1) - a = (1 - \theta)(x_1 - a) + \theta(x_2 - a),$$

we have

$$|x_1 + \theta(x_2 - x_1) - a| \; \leq \; (1 - \theta)|x_1 - a| + \theta|x_2 - a| \; \leq \; \delta.$$

Hence using (G.8) we have for every $0 < \theta < 1$,

$$| \, (dT)(x_1 + \theta(x_2 - x_1)) - (dT)(a) \, | \; \leq \; 1/2. \quad \text{(G.10)}$$

From (G.9) and (G.10) it follows that for every $x_1, x_2 \in B(a, \delta)$,

$$| \, T(x_1) - T(x_2) - (dT(a))(x_1 - x_2) \, | \; \leq \; |x_1 - x_2|/2. \quad \text{(G.11)}$$

Since $(dT)(a) = Id$, from (G.11) it follows that T is one-one on $B(a, \delta)$. This proves (i).

We show next that there exists $\delta_1 > 0$ such that $B(T(a), \delta_1) \subseteq T(B(a, \delta))$. For this, let $\delta_1 > 0$ be arbitrary and let $y \in B(T(a), \delta_1)$. We construct a sequence $\{x_k\}_{k \geq 1}$ recursively as follows. Take $x_0 = a$ and for $k \geq 1$ let

$$x_k := x_{k-1} + y - T(x_{k-1}).$$

Clearly, $x_0 \in B(x_0, \delta)$. Assume $x_0, x_1, \ldots, x_{n-1} \in B(x_0, \delta)$. Since

$$x_k - x_{k-1} = x_{k-1} - x_{k-2} - (T(x_{k-1}) - T(x_{k-2})),$$

by (G.11) we have

$$|x_k - x_{k-1}| \; \leq \; |x_{k-1} - x_{k-2}|/2 \; \leq \; |x_1 - x_0|/2^{k-1} \; < \; \delta_1/2^{k-1}.$$

Thus if we choose $\delta_1 = \delta/2$, then

$$|x_k - x_0| \; \leq \; \left(\sum_{j=1}^{k} (1/2)^{j-1} \right) |x_1 - x_0| \; < \; \delta.$$

Thus $\{x_k\}_{k\geq 1}$ is a Cauchy sequence in $\mathbb{R}^n$ and hence is convergent. Let $x := \lim_{k\to\infty} x_k$. Then

$$
\begin{aligned}
|x - x_0| &= \lim_{n\to\infty} |x_n - x_0| \\
&\leq \lim_{n\to\infty} \sum_{k=1}^{n} |x_k - x_{k-1}| \\
&\leq \lim_{n\to\infty} \sum_{k=1}^{n} 2^{-k}\delta \; < \; \delta.
\end{aligned}
$$

Hence $x \in B(a,\delta)$, and clearly

$$
x = \lim_{k\to\infty} x_k = \lim_{k\to\infty} (x_{k-1} + y - T(x_{k-1})) = x + y - T(x).
$$

Thus $T(x) = y$. This proves that

$$
B(T(a), \delta/2) \subseteq T(B(a,\delta)).
$$

Let $V := B(a,\delta)$ and $y \in T(B(a,\delta))$. Let $x \in B(a,\delta)$ be such that $T(x) = y$, and let $\eta > 0$ be such that $B(x,\eta) \subseteq B(a,\delta)$. Then

$$
B(y, \eta/2) \subseteq T(B(x,\eta)) \subseteq T(B(a,\delta)).
$$

Hence y is an interior point of $T(B(a,\delta))$. Thus $T(V)$ is an open neighborhood of $T(a)$. This proves (ii).

To prove (iii), let $y \in B(T(a), \delta/2)$ and let $x := T^{-1}(y), x \in B(a,\delta)$. Let k be such that $y + k \in B(T(a), \delta)$, and let $x + h \in B(a,\delta)$ be such that $T(x+h) = y + k$. Then by the differentiability of T at x,

$$
k = T(x+h) - y = T(x+h) - T(x) = (dT)(x)(h) + o(|h|), \qquad \text{(G.12)}
$$

where $o(|h|)/|h| \to 0$ as $|h| \to 0$. Also, using (G.11) we have

$$
|k - h| = |T(x+h) - T(x) - h| \leq |h|/2.
$$

Hence $|h| \leq 3|k|/2$. Using this and (G.12), we get

$$
T^{-1}(y + k) - T^{-1}(y) = h = ((dT)(x))^{-1}(k) + o(|k|)
$$

where $o(|k|)/|k| \to 0$ as $|k| \to 0$. Thus T^{-1} is differentiable at y and $(dT^{-1})(y) = ((dT)(x))^{-1}$. This proves (iii).

Further, since for every y

$$
(dT(T^{-1}(y))) \circ ((dT^{-1})(y)) = Id,
$$

it follows that for every $1 \leq i, j \leq n$,

$$
\sum_{j=1}^{m} (D_j T_i)(T^{-1}(y))(D_k T_j^{-1})(y) = \delta_{ij}. \qquad \text{(G.13)}
$$

Note that T^{-1} is continuous on $T(B(a,\delta))$ and each $D_j T_i$ is continuous on $B(a,\delta)$. Equation (G.13), by Cramer's rule, expresses each $(D_j(T_i^{-1})(y))$ as the quotient of continuous functions (the denominator being nonzero) and hence is a continuous function. Thus T^{-1} is also a C^1-map. ∎

G.6. Theorem: *Let U be an open subset of $\mathbb{R}^n$ and $T : U \longrightarrow W \subseteq \mathbb{R}^n$ be a one-one C^1-mapping. Further, let $J_T(x) \neq 0 \ \forall \ x \in U$. Then the following statements hold:*

  (i) *W is an open set.*

  (ii) *$T^{-1} : W \longrightarrow U$ is a C^1-mapping.*

  (iii) *$T^{-1} : W \longrightarrow U$ is a homeomorphism.*

Proof: Let $x \in W$ and $T(x) = y$, for $y \in U$. Since U is open, we can find $\delta > 0$ such that $B(a, \delta) \subseteq U$. Then, as shown in theorem G.5,

$$B(y, \delta/2) \subseteq T(B(a, \delta)) \subseteq W.$$

Hence W is also open. Since T is a C^1-mapping and $J_T(x) \neq 0 \ \forall \ x \in U$, by the inverse function theorem, T^{-1} is also a C^1-mapping. In particular, T^{-1} is also continuous. ∎

References

[1] Aliprantis, C.D. and Burkinshaw, O. *Principles of Real Analysis* (3rd Edition). Academic Press, Inc. New York, 1998.

[2] Apostol, T.M. *Mathematical Analysis.* Narosa Publishing House, New Delhi (India), 1995.

[3] Bartle, Robert G. *A Modern Theory of Integration,* Graduate Studies in Mathemaics, Volume 32, American Mathematicsl Society,Providence, RI, 2001.

[4] Bhatia, Rajendra *Fourier Series.* Hindustan Book Agency, New Delhi (India), 1993.

[5] Billingsley, Patrick *Probability and Measure.* 3rd Edition, John Wiley and Sons, New York, 1995.

[6] Bourbaki, N. *Intégration, Chap. V.* Actualités Sci. Indust. 1244. Hermann, Paris, 1956.

[7] Carslaw, H.S. *Introduction to the Theory of Fourier's Series and Integrals.* Dover Publications, New York, 1952.

[8] Carathéodory, C. *Vorlesungen über Reelle Funktionen.* Leipzig, Teubner, and Berlin, 1918.

[9]   Carathéodory, C. *Algebraic Theory of Measure and Integration.* Chelse Publishing Company, New York, 1963 (Originally published in 1956).

[10] Daniell, P.J. *A general form of integral.* Ann. of Math. (2)19 (1919), 279-294.

[11] DePree, Jonn D. and Swartz, Charles W, *Introduction to Analysis,* John Wiley & Sons Inc., New York, 1988

[12] Fraenkel, A. A.*Abstract Set Theory*, Fourth Edition, North-Holland, Amsterdam, 1976.

[13] Friedman, A. *Foundations of Modern Analysis.* Holt, Rinehart and Winston, Inc., New York, 1970.

[14] Halmos, P.R. *Measure Theory.* Van Nostrand, Princeton, 1950.

[15] Halmos, P.R. *Naive Set Theory.* Van Nostrand, Princeton, 1960.

[16] Hawkins, T.G. *Lebesgue's Theory of Integration: Its Origins and Development.* Chalsea, New York, 1979.

[17] Hewitt, E. and Ross, K.A. *Abstract Harmonic Analysis, Vol.I.* Springer-Verlag, Heidelberg, 1963.

[18] Hewitt, E. and Stromberg, K. *Real and Abstract Analysis.* Springer-Verlag, Heidelberg, 1969.

[19] Kakutani, S. and Oxtoby, J.C. *A non-separable translation invariant extension of the Lebesgue measure space.* Ann.of Math. (2) 52 (1950), 580-590.

[20] Kline, M. *Mathematical Thoughts from Ancient to Modern Times.* Oxford University Press, Oxford, 1972.

[21] Kolmogorov, A.N. *Foundations of Probability Theory.* Chelsea Publishing Company, New York, 1950.

[22] Körner, T.W. *Fourier Analysis.* Cambridge University Press, London, 1989.

[23] Lebesgue, H. *Integrale, longueur, aire.* Ann. Math. Pura. Appl. (3) 7 (1902), 231-259.

[24] Luxemburg, W.A.J. *Arzela's dominated convergence theorem for the Riemann integral.* Amer. Math. Monthly 78 (1971), 970-979.

[25] McLeod, Robert M., *The Generalized Riemann Integral,* Carus Monograph, No.20, Mathemaical Associaiton of America, Washington, 1980.

[26] Munkres, James E. *Topology,* 2nd Edition, Prentice Hall, Englewood Cliffs, NJ, 1999.

[27] Natanson, I.P. *Theory of Functions of a Real Variable.* Frederick Ungar Publishing Co., New York, 1941/1955.

[28] Parthasarathy, K.R. *Introduction to Probability and Measure.* Macmillan Company of India Ltd., Delhi, 1977.

[29] Parthasarathy, K. R. *Probablity Measures on Metric Spaces,* Academic Press, New York, 1967.

[30] Rana, Inder K. *From Numbers to Analysis,* World Scientific Press, Singapore, 1998.

[31] Riesz, F. *Sur quelques points de la théorie des fonctions sommables.* Comp. Rend. Acad. Sci. Paris 154 (1912), 641-643.

[32] Riesz, F. *Sur l'intégrale de Lebesgue.* Acta Math. 42 (1920), 191-205.

[33] Riesz, F. and Sz.-Nagy, B. *Functional Analysis.* Fredrick Ungar Publishing Co., New York, 1955.

[34] Royden, H.L. *Real Analysis* (3rd Edition). Macmillan, New York, 1963.

[35] Saks, S. *Theory of the Integral.* Monografje Matematyczne Vol. 7, Warszawa, 1937.

[36] Serrin, J. and Varberg, D.E. *A general chain-rule for derivatives and the change of variable formula for the Lebesgue integral.* Amer. Math. Monthly 76 (1962), 514-520.

[37] Solovay, R. *A model of set theory in which every set of reals is Lebesgue measurable.* Ann. of Math. (2) 92 (1970), 1-56.

[38] Srivastava, S. M. *Borel Sets*, Springer-Verlag, Heidelberg, 1998.

[39] Stone, M.H. *Notes on integration, I-IV.* Proc. Natl. Acad. Sci. U.S. 34 (1948), 336-342, 447-455, 483-490; 35 (1949), 50-58.

[40] Titchmarch, E.C. *The Theory of Functions.* Oxford University Press, Oxford, 1939 (revised 1952).

[41] Ulam, S.M. *Zur Masstheorie in der allgemeinen Mengenlehre.* Fund. Math. 16 (1930), 141-150.

[42] Zygmund, A. *Trigonometric Series*, 2 Vols. Cambridge University Press, London, 1959.

Index

Index of notations

$S(P, f)$: Riemann sum of f with respect to P,   17
$\mathcal{R}[a, b]$: Set of Riemann integrable functions on $[a, b]$,   18
$\omega(f, J)$: Oscillation of f in the interval J,   20
$\omega(f, x)$: Oscillation of f at x,   20
χ_A : Characteristic function of the set A,   30

Chapter 2

$\mathbb{L}_0$: Collection of simple functions on $\mathbb{R}$,   48

Chapter 3

$\mathcal{F}(I)$: The algebra generated by intervals,   52
$\tilde{\mathcal{I}}$: The collection of left-open, right-closed intervals,   55
$\mathcal{P}(X)$: Power set of X; the collection of all subsets of X,   55
$\mathcal{C} \cap E$: Subsets of E which are elements of $\mathcal{C}$,   56
$f^{-1}(E)$: The set $\{x | f(x) \in E\}$,   57
$\mathcal{F}(\mathcal{C})$: The algebra generated by $\mathcal{C}$,   57
μ_F : Set function induced by the function F,   62
μ^* : Outer measure induced by μ,   71
$\mathcal{S}^*$: Collection of μ^*-measurable sets,   76
$\mathcal{S}(\mathcal{C})$: Sigma-algebra (σ-algebra) generated by $\mathcal{C}$,   81
$\mathcal{B}_X$: The σ-algebra of Borel subsets of a topological space X,   82
$\mathcal{B}_\mathbb{R}$: The σ-algebra of Borel subsets of $\mathbb{R}$ 82
$\mathcal{I}_r$: Open intervals with rational end points,   82
$\mathcal{I}_d$: Subintervals of $[0, 1]$ with dyadic end points,   82
$\mathcal{M}(\mathcal{C})$: Monotone class generated by $\mathcal{C}$,   86
$\mathcal{L}_F$: The σ-algebra of μ_F^*-measurable sets,   88
μ_F : Lebesgue-Stieltjes measure induced by F,   89
$(X, \mathcal{S})$: Measurable space,   92
$(X, \mathcal{S}, \mu)$: Measure space,   92
$(X, \overline{\mathcal{S}}, \overline{\mu})$: The completion of a measure space $(X, \mathcal{S}, \mu)$,   92

Chapter 4

λ^* : Lebesgue outer measure,   95
$\mathcal{L}$: σ-algebra of Lebesgue measurable subsets of $\mathbb{R}$,   95
λ : The Lebesgue measure on $\mathbb{R}$,   95
$\mathcal{I}_0$: The collection of all open intervals in $\mathbb{R}$,   96
diameter(E) : The diameter of a subset E of $\mathbb{R}$,   96
$f'(x)$: The derivative of f at x,   96
$A + x$: The set $\{y + x | y \in A\}$,   101
xE : The set $\{xy | y \in E\}$,   103
$\mathfrak{c}$: Cardinality of the continuum,   110

Chapter 6

$V_a^b(f)$	:	Variation of f over the interval $[a,b]$, 176
$\displaystyle\liminf_{h\downarrow c}\Phi(x)$	:	Lower right limit of Φ at c, 180
$\displaystyle\limsup_{h\downarrow c}\Phi(x)$	:	Upper right limit of Φ at c, 180
$\displaystyle\liminf_{h\uparrow c}\Phi(x)$	:	Lower left limit of Φ at c, 180
$\displaystyle\limsup_{h\uparrow c}\Phi(x)$	:	Upper left limit of Φ at c, 180
$(D_+f)(c)$	:	Lower right derivative of f at c, 180
$(D^+f)(c)$	:	Upper right derivative of f at c, 180
$(D_-f)(c)$	:	Lower left derivative of f at c, 180
$(D^-f)(c)$	:	Upper left derivative of f at c, 180
$V_{-\infty}^{+\infty}(F)$	:	Variation of F on $\mathbb{R}$, 198

Chapter 7

$\mathcal{A}\otimes\mathcal{B}$	:	Product of the σ-algebra $\mathcal{A}$ with $\mathcal{B}$, 211
$\mathcal{B}_{\mathbb{R}^2}$	:	The σ-algebra of Borel subsets of $\mathbb{R}^2$, 211
$(X\times Y,\mathcal{A}\otimes\mathcal{B},\mu\times\nu)$	:	The product measure space, 213
E_x	:	Section of E at x, 215
E^y	:	Section of E at y, 215
$\mathcal{L}_{\mathbb{R}^2}$	:	Lebesgue measurable subsets of $\mathbb{R}^2$, 229
$\lambda_{\mathbb{R}^2}$	:	Lebesgue measure on $\mathbb{R}^2$, 229
$\tilde{\mathcal{I}}^2$	:	The set $\{I\times J|I,J\in\tilde{\mathcal{I}}\}$, 229
$\det T$	:	Determinant of T, 232

$$\left(\prod_{i=1}^{n}X_i,\bigotimes_{i=1}^{n}\mathcal{A}_i,\prod_{i=1}^{n}\mu_i\right) : \text{Product of a finite number}$$
$$\text{of measure spaces,}\quad 237$$

$\mathcal{L}_{\mathbb{R}^n}$	:	Lebesgue measurable subsets of $\mathbb{R}^n$, 239
$\lambda_{\mathbb{R}^n}$	:	Lebesgue measure on $\mathbb{R}^n$, 239
$\mathcal{B}_{\mathbb{R}^n}$	:	The σ-algebra of Borel subsets of $\mathbb{R}^n$, 239
$B(\mathbf{x},r)$	:	The open ball in $\mathbb{R}^n$ with center at $\mathbf{x}$ and radius r, 240

Chapter 8

$\mathbb{C}$: Field of complex numbers, 243
$\mathrm{Re}\,(f)$: Real part of a complex-valued function f, 243
$\mathrm{Im}\,(f)$: Imaginary part of a complex-valued function f, 244
$L_1^r(X, \mathcal{S}, \mu)$: Real-valued μ-integrable functions, 244
$L_1(X, \mathcal{S}, \mu)$: Complex-valued μ-integrable functions, 244
$f_n \xrightarrow{p} f$: f_n converges to f pointwise, 248
$f_n \xrightarrow{\text{a.e.}} f$: f_n converges to f almost everywhere, 248
$f_n \xrightarrow{\text{u}} f$: f_n converges to f uniformly, 248
$f_n \xrightarrow{\text{a.u.}} f$: f_n converges to f almost uniformly, 250
$f_n \xrightarrow{m} f$: f_n converges to f in measure, 255
$\mathcal{M}(X)$: The set of all measurable functions on X, 260

$\left.\begin{array}{l} L_p(X, \mathcal{S}, \mu) \\ L_p(\mu) \end{array}\right\}$: The space of pth-power integrable functions of f, 262

$\|f\|_p$: p^{th} norm of f, 262
f_h : The function $f_h(x) := f(x + h) \;\forall\, x$, 281
$f * g$: Convolution of f with g, 283
$L_1^{loc}(\mathbb{R}^n)$: Space of locally integrable functions on $\mathbb{R}^n$, 286
$C^\infty(U)$: The set of infinitely differentiable functions on U, 287
$C_c^\infty(U)$: The set $\{f \in C^\infty(U) \mid \mathrm{supp}(f) \text{ is compact}\}$, 287
$\overline{B(0,1)}$: Closure of the ball $B(0,1)$, 287
$L_\infty(X, \mathcal{S}, \mu)$: Space of essentially bounded functions, 291
$\|f\|_\infty$: Essential supremum of f, 292
$C_0(\mathbb{R}^n)$: The set of continuous functions on $\mathbb{R}^n$ vanishing at infinity, 295
$L_2(X, \mathcal{S}, \mu)$: Space of square integrable functions, 296
$\|f\|_2$: L_2-norm of f, 296
$\langle f, g \rangle$: Inner product of $f, g \in L_2$, 296
$S^\perp$: The set $\{f \in L_2(X, \mathcal{S}, \mu) \mid \langle f, g \rangle = 0 \;\forall\, g \in S\}$, 298

Chapter 9

$\nu \ll \mu$: ν is absolutely continuous with respect to μ, 311
$(\mathbb{R}, \mathcal{B}_F, \mu_F)$: Completion of the measure space $(\mathbb{R}, \mathcal{B}_\mathbb{R}, \mu_F)$, 314
$\mu \perp \nu$: μ is singular with respect to ν, 319
$\dfrac{d\nu}{d\mu}(x)$: Radon-Nikodym derivative of ν with respect to μ, 320
$(D\mu)(x)$: Derivative of μ at x, 324
$(\overline{D}\mu)(x)$: Upper derivative of μ at x, 327
$(\underline{D}\mu)(x)$: Lower derivative of μ at x, 327

μT^{-1}	:	The measure induced by T, 332
$J_T(x)$	:	Jacobian of T at x, 336

Chapter 10

μ^+	:	Upper variation of a signed measure μ, 351
μ^-	:	Lower variation of a signed measure μ, 351
$|\mu|$	:	Total variation of a signed measure μ, 351
$\nu \ll \mu$	:	Absolute continuity of a signed measure ν with respect to a measure μ, 356
$\displaystyle\int f d\mu$	:	Integral of f with respect to a signed measure μ, 358
$\nu \ll \mu$	:	ν absolutely continuous with respect to a signed measure μ, 359
$\mathcal{M}_b(X,\mathcal{S})$	:	Space of all finite signed measures on $(X,\mathcal{S})$, 362
$\|\mu\|$	:	Norm of a signed measure μ, 363
$\nu \le \mu$	:	ν is smaller than μ, 365
$\mu \vee \nu$	:	Maximum of μ and ν, 365
$\mu \wedge \nu$	:	Minimum of μ and ν, 365
$\nu \ll \mu$	:	Absolute continuity of a complex measure ν with respect to a measure μ, 366
$|\nu|$	:	Total variation of a complex measure ν, 368
$\mathcal{M}(X,\mathcal{S})$	:	Space of all complex measures on $(X,\mathcal{S})$, 371
$\|\mu\|$	:	Norm of a complex measure μ, 371
$\|T\|$	:	Norm of a bounded linear functional, 376

Appendices

$X \approx Y$	:	X equipotent to Y, 391
$\mathrm{card}(A)$	:	Cardinality, cardinal number of A, 391
$\aleph_0$	:	Cardinality of $\mathbb{N}$, 391
$\mathfrak{c}$	:	Cardinality of the continuum, 391
$2^{\mathrm{card}(X)}$	:	Cardinality of the power set of X, 391
A^t	:	Transpose of a matrix, 395
$V_a^b(P,f)$	:	Variation of f over $[a,b]$ with respect to a partition P, 397
$V_a^b(f)$	:	Variation of f over $[a,b]$, 397
$(dT)(a)$	:	Differential of a differentiable mapping T, 401
$(D_j T_i)(x)$	:	j^{th} partial derivative of T_i at x, 401
$J_T(x)$	:	Jacobian of T at x, 405

Titles in This Series

TITLES IN THIS SERIES